I CROSSED THE LINE

THE LIAM DUNNE STORY

with Damian Lawlor

Sliabh Bán Productions
P.O. Box No. 6369,
Fortfield, Dublin 6W.

Softback ISBN 0-9545829-2-6
Hardback ISBN 0-9545829-3-4

A CIP record of this book is available from the British Library.

Photography: Ray MacManus, Brendan Moran, Sportsfile
Additional photographs: Daily Telegraph, Syl Ivors
Layout and design: Mary Guinan, Temple of Design
Printed in Ireland by Future Print

Special thanks to Pat Duffy in Readymix for all his help and support.

ACKNOWLEDGEMENTS
(Liam Dunne)

Once my mind was made up to go ahead with this book, I decided to be straight down the line all the way. This is just the way I see things, it doesn't have to be right or wrong. I hope it's a good GAA book but I also hope it's a lot more than that.

There are many people I want to thank. My sisters Gráinne, Siobhán, Fiona and Ailish. My brothers, Kieran, Tomás and Seán. Through all the bad times we have stayed very close together, something that has been special to me. We were lucky to grow up together and have the craic, which is not a problem for the Dunnes.

To Tom, Willie, Mick and Jimmy and the Oulart-The-Ballagh boys of 1994 who made history by winning the club's first county title. To Liam, Rory, Seamus and the Wexford boys of 1996 – we got to the top of the world together lads and it was an honour to share the voyage with you. I want to say a special thanks to Andy and Patsy Roche, two people that played a big part in my life.

When times were bad and I sometimes felt there was no way out, my good friend Brendan O'Connor was always there. So too were Sport and Foxten. Liam Griffin was the same; a man who never put me wrong in life.

Three great hurling men rowed in behind me for this venture. John Doyle of the Cleary-Doyle Group was one of the main men who set up the Wexford Supporters Group, a great help to hurling and football in the county over the years.

Wexford Park would not be what it is today only for the work of Pat Neville, even if the man himself would not want to take the credit for any of it.

Anthony Darcy has been a friend of mine for a long time. He comes from Tinahely but has always held Wexford close to his heart. We had a few good days on the golf course together, although Anthony seems to spend a lot of his time in the bunkers.

Brian Carthy was the man who put the idea for a book in my head and his company, Sliabh Bán Productions Ltd, were a pleasure to deal with. Thanks Brian for your honesty, time and professionalism. It was a pleasure to work with you.

Mary Guinan put in some hard work and showed great patience in designing the book. I enjoyed your company, Mary, thanks for all your help.

Many hours were spent writing this book in the company of Damian Lawlor. I had never met or spoke to him before but over the months we were together working on this venture in Oulart and the Ashdown Park Hotel in Gorey, a friendship was made.

I feel now as if I have known Damian all my life. Having read the book it's only now that I realise how many ups and downs and twists and turns I have faced in my life. Damian put them together in a fantastic fashion. Thank you for your time and dedication. I have a new friend for life.

To the people of Wexford. All I ever wanted was to do my best for you. Thanks for all the support over the years.

ACKNOWLEDGEMENTS
(DAMIAN LAWLOR)

Life gets easier when you surround yourself with decent, genuine people. And I'm extremely lucky in that regard.

At the start, this was an exciting, daunting project to undertake but it quickly became more than just an assignment. After months of research I started writing in May. By June I was on a mission: To bring Liam Dunne's story to life and do it justice.

I had admired his hurling skills for several years from the terraces and reported on his many controversies from the press box but somehow, we had never met before February 2004. Suffice to say that we are great friends now. Thanks Liam, Eithne, Billy and Aoife for everything and to Liam's mother, Eileen who is a great character.

My hope is that the book will do Liam's life and career justice, his story is one of the most fascinating, honest and enthralling in the GAA. With the endless support and belief of those close to me and with the strength of the story, we now have his tale chronicled forever.

I want to thank those people now. Since we first met, my girlfriend Ruth has encouraged me to the last, she is very supportive and I am lucky to have her in my life.

My colleague and friend Jackie Hennessy is one of the most positive people you could ever meet and she helped me immensely, not only by sub-editing the book but by being a great pal as well.

Richard Gallagher is also one of the most respected sub-editors in Irish journalism. I now know why. Thanks to you and Evelyn for all your help, confidence and advice along the way.

Christy O'Connor is a top GAA writer, a mine of hurling information and a rock solid man. This is one of the few occasions that a Tipp man could possibly join forces with a Clare man! I appreciate everything Christy.

Cian Murphy has been a colleague and friend for the past six years. I learned a lot from his first book with Mike McNamara and he was never short of a word or two of support on this journey. Garry Doyle, my old mate and sparring partner, is also a man you would want in your corner.

Kieran Shannon was always there. 'Shak' helped start me off with the *Star* newspaper almost six years ago and was the first person I told about the book.

Jackie Cahill and Paul Collins were on the other end of the phone all year long. We threw ideas around and helped each other get by in a busy GAA season.

Brian Carthy is a man apart. He would stand on his head for you and at times he did just that. I never looked on him as a publisher, always a friend.

Seán Boylan is an amazing person. His herbal remedies tasted worse than sour milk but they got me through the busiest year of my life. Liam Griffin is of the same ilk and was a huge help. Alan Aherne was most gracious with his time all year.

Sportsfile's Ray McManus and Brendan Moran provided the inspiration for the book's front cover; Mary Guinan from the Temple of Design did fantastic work on the lay-out; while Sharon Murphy and Maire Scully were invaluable in promoting and marketing the book.

I haven't seen much of the lads in Kilruane lately but friends stay friends. Cheers for all the crack over the years, Shane, Chalky, Cronan, Mark, Sleepy and the rest of the lads.

I want to record my thanks to the *Star* newspaper editor Ger Colleran, MD Paul Cooke and sports editor Eoin Brannigan for giving me a chance in this business.

The final word goes to my family. My father, John and mother, Mary are both top class people who have put others first throughout their lives. I'm proud of them. Thanks for everything. I hope that success follows my brothers, Seán and David and sister Colette wherever they go.

I dedicate my part in this book to my late grandmother, Margaret Glennon, Cloughjordan and Kilruane.

Much has happened in my 16 year hurling career and more still in my life which vanishes under your eyes. One minute you are centre stage in Croke Park, a purple and gold shirt on your back and the next it's all over. But life still goes on. I made mistakes and plenty of them during my years in hurling but above all I enjoyed my time. I hope you enjoy reading about it.

As I flick back over the years, there are constant reminders of those who have helped me. My greatest supporter in life has been my mother, Eileen, never too far from my mind whether playing in Croke Park or just doing my daily work. With her down-to-earth attitude to life, I gratefully acknowledge her role in any success I have had on and off the field. Thanks mother.

My wife, Eithne, has carried the burden of a lot of my downfalls over the last few years. She always stays in the background but now it's time to take some of the limelight. Eithne is a brilliant partner and a great mother to Billy and Aoife, two fantastic little people that are the shining lights in our lives.

Dad passed away in July 2004. It was a great pity that he never got to see the new house at Kyle Cross and to get a chance to read my book but deep down he never left Oulart. And our hearts.

I had been consumed by my first addiction, football. And as soon as that was taken away from me, I just knew what would happen. It was as if I had no choice
Tony Adams, *Addicted*, 1999

– CHAPTER ONE –
Down and dirty

Kilmuckridge, Wexford, November 1, 2002, 2 am

It's a story that needs to be told.

I want to give you a look beyond the tunnel, an insight into what 16 turbulent years as an intercounty hurler were like, how you can isolate those close to you and instead build a life to revolve around sport. The game has thrown everything at me, good, bad and ugly. Most of it has been my own doing too. But not all of it. It's time to get some stuff off my chest.

At first it was an obsession to win something for Wexford, who had not lifted a cup of any sort since 1968. When I first started out, one of my team-mates, George O'Connor, had played in 16 major finals and lost 15 of them. That was what we were up against. Wexford were perennial losers and I grew to be one as well.

When I look back on it, we had so much talent but used to shit ourselves at the thoughts of winning a trophy. It took me eight years to help shed the tag and when I finally did it was like a walk on air. I drank to toast our All-Ireland win in 1996, drank some more when I won my third All Star that Christmas and went on the beer all over again the following year when we retained our Leinster title. Then I broke my leg and this time decided to drink to ease the boredom. It was brilliant, I could take alcohol for almost any reason. Like when I was at home like a spare tool in crutches and out of the game for 16 months or like when, six years later, I became the first intercounty player to be sent off in three successive championships. Any excuse for the booze.

Many stories are often built around the theme of success but you don't always read tales of the price of it or the pitfalls involved. The most powerful part of my tale lies in what happened after the summer of 1996 when the backslapping died down, the cheers faded and the streets emptied. Maybe that's what makes it different.

I have tried to be straight down the line about everything that went on. Most GAA fans think of me as a dirty little bastard that broke fingers for a living. Christ, I was out of line on several occasions but I don't think I was the criminal they made me out to be, not when you see some of the stuff that goes on at the moment, lads spitting at opponents and hitting each other on the head.

I was never like that. As a 5ft 8in squirt who was usually deployed at either centre or wing back, I was much smaller than guys I marked and sometimes a good bit slower; so I played on the edge to survive. Mothers winced when they saw me mark little Johnny for fear I would take his hand off but they didn't realise that at the same time I was dreading being taken to the cleaners by their sons.

It's hard to stay at the top, or anywhere near it. I'm playing against young lads whose fathers I found a handful about 16 years ago. One roasting will signal the end. I'm on the team since 1988 and I would love to call it a day but quite simply, I can't go out like this, not after a five-month slump on the beer, not after getting the red card for the third summer in a row.

I want to walk away with a bit of class, with my reputation intact, but it won't be easy because over the years controversy dogged me the way verbal bloopers follow George Bush and tribunals haunt politicians. It's time for a clean slate; give it one more go and get the bad stuff off my chest as well. So here goes.

I have been a boil on the arse of the GAA for the past few years and have not been much better for my family to deal with. But how could anyone else like me when I almost hated myself? You don't become a heavy drinker if you are at ease with yourself. But I did.

My name is Liam Dunne and I am 35. I'm still in love with hurling, even though the only thing left is to fail a drugs test. And as sure as Jesus, I'll overdose on a cough bottle next or take two Lemsips and the Irish Sports Council will come and test me. Then I'll have the clean sweep. Hurling was always my first addiction and once that looked like going down the tubes, I turned to my second hobby, drink.

It's my own fault that after almost 16 years of intercounty hurling, I still have a point to prove. It's the last thing I need at my age. Jesus, I should be sitting down with my slippers on, looking back at the scrapbooks and telling my young lad, Billy, about the good times. Instead, I have to run myself into the ground for one more season just so I can retire with a bit of dignity. And for someone who was once described as the best hurler in the country, that's a long fall.

It's never healthy to be addicted to anything, I suppose, not even sport. And I finally lost control of the wheel and went into freefall when I hit Martin Comerford on the shoulder in the 2002 Leinster final. It wasn't Martin's fault, it was mine, and so I walked the line yet again. The same happened in 2000 and 2001 and I was the first player to get red cards in three consecutive years. Not quite the piece of history I was looking for. I turned to booze for a few months then, forgot about everything else in my life and went haywire for a while. They say that alcohol is like love. The first kiss is magic, the second is intimate and the third is routine.

It just became a habit and you join me at the start of November, the first night in five months I haven't taken a drink. I know my body clock well enough. We have ticked together for over three decades and it tells me something is missing. It's crying out for what it has lived on for almost half a year, the taste of Bulmers or Heineken.

A look at the alarm clock tells me it's 2 am. I must be off my head. The normal Joe Soap might go down for a quick cup of tea or hot milk so I decide to give that a shot, only it's not tea I want.

I draw the duvet back softly, conscious not to wake my wife, Eithne. She has it hard enough as it is, looking after our two little children, Billy and Aoife, and needs her rest.

I move toward the fridge and I'm not going to say no. On a frosty night, this is a warm and friendly greeting, as cosy as I am going to get. Opening the door, I reach in and take out a couple of cans of Heineken.

Something inside says 'Stop! Cop on and leave it back!' But my head is boss right now so I slug back the first one and move out of the kitchen, passing the mirror in the living-room. A mirror, it's as good a place as any to go soul-searching because there is no place to hide and sure enough I'm exposed.

Jesus, is that really me? I look like shit. A sad bastard who thinks he has the weight of the world on his shoulders. Roy Keane looks in the mirror every morning so he can see the truth; he cannot tolerate fooling himself. But I am fine with the self-delusion. I turn away and head for the couch. A few beers won't kill me.

I ask the same question every morning of myself: 'Have I got something to offer Manchester United?' At this moment in time the answer, always, is yes.
Roy Keane, July 25, 2004

– CHAPTER TWO –
Look back in anger

As I sit down with the Heineken in my hand, the reminder that I used to be someone sits on the mantlepiece: the first All Star award I won, 12 years ago.

Two more followed, in 1993 and 1996. Life was good then; my career was even better. They say these awards separate you from the rest, that an All Star possesses something extra, boundaries that few others can find. Go out and play your game, everything else will look after itself. But I am no hero now.

While I used to push my body to extraordinary limits as an athlete, running up mountains for stamina and down them for speed, I have already failed the first small test on my comeback by not staying off the drink for even one night.

I'm not quite a frumpy, middle-aged man but I'm well out of shape. Casper boasts a better colour. A few weeks ago my skin started to sag. Frown lines and ageing lines. All my own fault.

I first slipped down the slope in 2000 when I was sent off against Offaly. It was my first time getting the line for Wexford but it happened again the year after, and the year after that again. Mud stuck and soon I became known in the game as a poisonous little hoor. Liam Dunne: back page news for all the wrong reasons.

If you know the GAA and understand hurling, then you may get where I'm coming from. If you don't know the game, you might struggle to comprehend why a grown man chose to go on the beer and neglect his family just because of problems on the sportsfield.

And sure, it's only a sport. But it's a parochial one and a national one. It gives you a chance to make your name or leave a mark on life, a chance that would not be there otherwise. So I gave hurling life status and as I got older, pushed my wife and kids to the side so I could feed my habit.

At first, the love wasn't reciprocated. When I was a young lad, managers and selectors said I was too small to make it. Others ignored me because of where I came from and what school I went to. But I think I proved them wrong.

My brother Tomás had to deal with the same sort of treatment. He was one of the best players in the county but had to wait seven years between his first and second game with the Wexford senior team. Eventually he proved them wrong too.

I held my place on the Wexford senior team for 16 years and played 126 intercounty games as well as countless tournament and challenge matches.

Respect was something I valued, but three red cards over all of those games and that respect wasn't long disappearing. You do the maths, though. One red card every 42 games. Jesus, I'm no Osama Bin Laden.

Sitting here nursing a can of beer in the winter of 2002, I know I could have one more year with Wexford but must be extra careful because a referee will send me off if I even look like doing something dirty, no questions asked.

Pick a game of hurling, any game. Say it's Wexford against Offaly. If Brian Whelahan pulls a stroke like I did, he won't be sent off. He wouldn't do it anyway but I'm just saying that's the way it is with me now; if I step an inch over the line I'm gone. Disciplinary officials from a hurling hotbed like Cavan or somewhere will gladly throw the book at me too, if they can stay awake long enough during the hearings.

Since the first red card, managers have encouraged their teams to go down injured when I'm around. It's some craic. If I pull, they hit the deck. I've seen lads rolling around in agony and then once play moves on, I ask them if they're okay and they're fine. Some lads will try anything to get an edge.

I don't mind supporters having a go either; they pay their money and are entitled to scream what they like in my direction. But I do mind what they say in front of my mother and wife. I'm not getting paid for hurling for the county. If I was they could say whatever they wished.

The TV pundits are getting a good few bob, though. I've taken a right old lash from them in recent years; it's their job. A few of them reckon I'm finished and while they could be right, I'm not going to listen to someone like Pete Finnerty from the *Sunday Game* telling me where I stand. I'm not listening to a waffler like him giving the country his opinion.

Finnerty was my captain on the 1991 All Star trip to Toronto and I never met a guy with a bigger head or a finer opinion of himself. Everything revolved around Peter the Great out there. It was 'me this' and 'me that'. We all had to listen to what he won and what he should have won over the years and although I was only a greenhorn starting out and should have been in awe, five minutes was enough in his company.

Now I have to listen to him having the craic at my expense on TV and I wonder why, if he was such an expert, he never did any wonders for Galway after he hung up his sliotar but instead is happy to sit back in a studio armchair, laughing and joking at the likes of me. Whatever about Finnerty, the rest of them can hardly all be wrong, I suppose.

The John Troy clash was my first red card for Wexford. I did clip him but although I promise you I got the ball first, he went down on the ground, screaming like a baby.

My next walk to the line was an absolute joke for all concerned, when we played Tipperary in the 2001 All-Ireland semi-final replay. Their wing forward Brian O'Meara missed out on his last chance of appearing in an All-Ireland final and that was down to me as well because I started it. There were public campaigns waged to try and get Brian freed for the final and rightly so; I couldn't believe we had been sent off in the first place.

It was handbags at paces; you would see more aggression in a convent. No other hurler would have walked for that incident bar Liam Dunne. But because there were two of us involved, Brian had to go as well.

The last red mist arrived just a few months ago, July 2002, and has had the worst effect on me of the lot. I was accused of splitting Martin Comerford's head in the last few minutes of the Leinster final against Kilkenny, despite the fact my hurley only made contact with his shoulder. I did hit him a silly blow and the referee had little choice but to send me off. And yet, while it was senseless, it was not as vicious as people made out. Some members of the Kilkenny backroom staff told him to stay down, make it look bad.

'Don't get up Martin, don't get up, keep the head down, he'll get the line.'

It was only Martin's first year. He's a grand chap but was new to the scene, so of course he was going to follow orders, do what he was told. But there's more. After that game, people started to harp back to the 1996 All-Ireland final when Limerick blamed me for breaking Gary Kirby's fingers early in the match and putting their danger-man and free-taker out of the game. That outstanding charge enjoyed a new lease of life when Gary appeared on a TG4 documentary and had a right old go, questioning my attitude and suggesting I had it all pre-planned.

Jesus, you don't approach an All-Ireland final in that frame of mind. I didn't go out to do him. I actually held him scoreless and got man of the match in that final. The Wexford defence didn't give a free away in the entire second half so he could hardly have been a match-winner from placed balls.

While we both contested a dropping ball early in the game and we did make contact, he pulled the same time as I did and the ball broke loose. Moments later he pointed a huge free; there was no talk of a broken finger then.

His body language however was not that of a hurler in an All-Ireland final. I think he knew as the game wore on that Limerick were about to lose their second final in three years.

But I was a handy scapegoat in defeat.

So there you have it. After 16 years of top-class hurling, this is what I have come to, a bitter man with time almost up.

Those in the Kirby, Troy, O'Meara and Comerford camps may believe they were right, but though I have always played the game hard I have played it fair.

Put your hand up and I will pull if the ball is there to be won. I will try and win the clash but I won't compromise the situation by trying to avoid your hands or fingers in the process.

From time to time, I will also tap a lad in the chest or the ribs just to see how he reacts, to see if he wants to be on the field or not. Call it childish but most hurlers do it all the time. Look at the Clare hurlers when they take the field. They are like men possessed. They will do anything to put you off your game. It's not just them; there are loads of lads out there who are no angels but I'm the clown that's known for it and gets caught.

'Don't put your hand up around that lad, he'll take your fingers off.'

'Pity to see him finishing his career like that, he used to be good.'

'Remember 1993 and 1996, he played some stuff.'

Nice tags to be labelled with for the rest of your life. No mention of the All Stars, the All-Ireland, the two Leinster medals, the two Railway Cups and the three county titles with Oulart-The-Ballagh.

At first I thought the drink would help me get through the close season. I was never a stranger to it, enjoyed the session as much as the rest, but this time the depression and alcohol have blended into a lethal cocktail. Silly, isn't it? But what the hell? We live in a drink culture anyway. No-one will notice.

And they didn't. But while I kept my habit quiet enough, I soon started to feel the same after 10 pints as I used to after five or six.

More worrying was the fact I did not need the company to go for a few pints. I was as happy on my own as I was with friends. I would talk to Mick the Shilling if I had to but could just as easily slink into a corner by myself.

And it wasn't just one pub that I would go to; there were a few handpicked all over the county and if they opened late, well it was good enough for me.

The couch, however, became my most dangerous refuge. Going to the pub and drinking is one thing but this was a lot more sinister. I dread to think what Liam Griffin, my old manager and friend, would say if he could see me. Or what my former team-mates would think, guys who used to respect me and sometimes look my way for a bit of guidance. They would be sympathetic, I'm sure, but I never needed pity before; I was one of their leaders.

After another two cans, I rose from the couch, walked to the mantelpiece, and spotted my All-Ireland medal. I remembered the day well. How I would have loved to bottle that feeling in September 96! But Griffin knew the pitfalls of victory. He called the entire panel into a room the morning after that win over Limerick and seriously dampened the mood by warning that one of us, one of the men who won Wexford's first All-Ireland title since 1968, would become an alcoholic.

'Some member of this group will be in trouble,' he said, in deadly earnest, and his words really caught us.

Half of the team were already contemplating where to go drinking for the rest of the week. The other half were arranging the social schedule as far as Christmas.

But he was not finished: 'And enjoy this moment because after today you will never be together as a squad or a group again.'

Jesus, take back our medals altogether, will you.

I can tell you now that he was right on the second count. We were never together as a group again, which seems unbelievable for a party of 30 men who almost lived with each other for a year.

And on the first count, was he right? Was I 'the one' he was talking about?

I will be straight. I don't know what the actual definition of an alcoholic is or how close I am to being one. But right now, in November 2002, I am fairly close.

I think I can stop drinking but I'm not sure if I want to. It's kind of confusing. Sometimes I think I can get on top of the problem at the drop of a hat and just stay in but when I ended up on a tear until 7 am a couple of days ago, I wasn't so sure.

My memories of most of that night are vague but I recall fumbling in my pocket, gathering some loose change for the taxi fare and handing it to the driver. Luckily, he chose not to ask what I was doing out at that time on a midweek night.

As I arrived in home, the wake-up call I had been desperately looking for hit me smack in the face. Thank God for it. My two little children were in the hall, five-year-old Billy and little Aoife, who is only three. They said nothing but their innocent stares were like a thousand piercing daggers.

'What was Daddy doing out all night? Where was he?' their eyes seemed to ask.

Feeling lower than I had ever done, I rubbed their heads and tucked them into bed.

Eithne said nothing when I got to our room. I quickly fell asleep and eventually woke up at 11.30 am to the realisation there was no-one in the house, which suited me.

I didn't really want to talk to anyone. I knew I had been an absolute prick to live with but it was finally time to do something about it.

I made a cup of tea, sat down and thought about how I could drag myself out of this mess. Some people have no-one to turn to but I was lucky in this regard. The solution was pretty obvious.

After sipping my tea, I picked up the phone. Liam Griffin, the man who got me my first sales job without even knowing me, would have the answer because he always did.

Griffin had got that job because, as he said, while he didn't know me, he believed in me.

'Liam, it's me,' I said. 'I need to talk to you for 10 minutes. Friday will do fine. See you then.'

This guy knows me inside out. He had made me captain of Wexford for the first time. He reversed the decision a few weeks later but he did it for the county and the team and it was his call. We had become close friends and I felt I could tell him anything, which was just as well because things had gone way too far. I had crossed the line.

Tomorrow, it was time to go back.

Liam Dunne was no Mother Teresa. But he was not the Hannibal Lector that people make him out to be either.
Liam Griffin, former Wexford manager, March 2004

– CHAPTER THREE –
The three-in-a-row

I take the blame for my downfall squarely on the chin but every stream has a source and you can trace the start of my troubles back to 2000.

After three years of stalling, it was supposed to be the year Wexford hurling got back on a high again.

The county board formed a committee to find a new manager in the wake of the departure of Rory Kinsella, and we were excited about the new man and what he could bring to the job, how he could shape or mould us back into Championship contenders.

Rory had been brilliant to the team. He was a players' man to the last and showed huge loyalty by playing me even though I was not fully right after breaking my ankle and losing almost 18 months of hurling.

Anyway, this committee shortened their list down to two candidates: Pat Herbert from Limerick and Joachim Kelly, the former Offaly hurler.

Unfortunately, at the end of the day expense became an issue and the county board opted for Joachim because they thought they could save a few pounds in mileage.

I am full sure that when Joachim took over he meant to do his best for us and it's possible someone from a different province would have worked better but not a guy from a county who were among our fiercest rivals.

Frankly, it's not an era I remember with great fondness. We reverted to the state of chaos in which we had been back in 1995.

The Wexford Supporters Club ensured Joachim was looked after like all intercounty managers these days. He was supplied with a Citroen car that had 'JJ Byrne's Garage' plastered all over the side so he had no complaints.

He was a decent bloke but not a good manager. For example, we could get away with murder and lads just did what they wanted. Before the Championship, we were supposed to have given up the beer but one player had to be pulled out of the Centenary Rooms not long before a big game after telling us the week before he was giving up the booze like the rest of the squad.

The end result was that we approached the Offaly match, our first game in Leinster that year, in poorer shape than any team I'd been involved with. The League campaign was poor and the week before that first Championship match, Joachim and his selectors, Brendan O'Connor and Mick Butler, brought us down to New Ross for a Chinese with the aim of bonding as a team.

Some of the boys were used only to bacon and cabbage and had hardly ever seen fried rice or noodles so they ate all around them. A few days later, when the burping and farting finally left our systems, we were sent out to play Offaly at Croke Park.

It's an awful thing to say but I took to the field that day suspecting we were going to get a right hiding, and after five minutes my worst suspicions were confirmed. We had no answer for Offaly, who came out at 100 miles per hour. Usually, after 10 or 15 minutes, a guy can start to get his second wind but it never came that day.

With 10 minutes gone I could feel the pressure, and as a ball came down from the sky, I pulled wildly on Paudie Mulhare and hit him on the back of the head. I didn't mean it but I should have got the line. Paudie put his hand to his head: 'Jesus Christ, Liam, what did you do that for?'

'Paudie,' I replied, going over and tapping him on the chest, 'whether you believe me or not, I didn't mean to hit you on the back of the head.'

Referee Willie Barrett gave me a yellow card and there were no further problems between the two of us for the rest of the game. No, the only difficulties were in the Wexford dressing-room, where lads knew in their hearts and souls we were a beaten team.

I tried to lift it in the second half. 'Fuck it, Declan, just pull on the next ball,' I roared to Declan Ruth, who was finding big Gary Hanniffy almost impossible to manage. Again, Willie shot me a look, clearly not too happy with my attitude.

Next thing, Offaly brought on John Troy as a sub. There had been a history between us going back to 1994 when he pulled wildly on me and nearly took my head off, and 1996 when, still bearing a grudge, I did the same to him.

As bad as I felt on the pitch, huffing and puffing, he looked much worse. He was coming back from a hand injury, and a blind man could see he was seriously overweight.

Soon, the ball bounced toward our goal and I went to flick it away. I got the ball but also caught Troy on the hand and down he went like a bag of spuds, roaring on the ground.

Willie Barrett was 40 yards away but I could already see him going for his pocket and knew I was gone.

'Willie,' I pleaded, 'when you watch this on TV tonight, you'll realise the mistake you made.'

Hardly able to hear me above the howls of pain coming from Troy, he said nothing but gave me a second yellow and then a red card. For the first time in my intercounty career, which started all the way back in 1988, I had been sent off.

The Offaly crowd cheered and Troy got up straightaway, a miraculous recovery. As I walked off the pitch, the abuse became more vocal and insulting. I was told later that the Kilkenny manager, Brian Cody, who was in the stand, went over to my 'friends' and told them to sit down, which they quickly did. It wasn't to be Cody's last time standing up for me and that's something strange for a lad from Wexford to say about a Kilkenny man.

In the dressing-room, I cursed Troy but I was the fool now. I sat in the dressing-room thinking of my mother and how hurt she would be, never mind my team-mates after our hammering, 3-15 to 1-8. I also thought of Liam Griffin and what he would say to me, how I had let the side down after everything he drilled into us in 1996.

Larry O'Gorman, the best hurler I ever played with and one of the greatest characters as well, was someone I soldiered with during most of my career but had been dropped by Joachim. Rather than watch the rest of the game unfold, he joined me in the dressing-room.

'It's bad out there and it's getting worse,' Larry moaned, and when you see The Brother, as he is known, in a bad mood, you know things cannot be good.

We were drubbed by 13 points and after the game, Joachim came over and told me not to make any rash decisions. He was talking about me walking away from the game but I had no intention of retiring and, as it turned out, I was back hurling a week after the Troy incident.

I went straight back playing with Oulart-The-Ballagh and soon began to look forward to 2001, a chance to get back on track. I felt there was little chance Joachim would stay on as manager. His selectors, Brendan O'Connor and Mick Butler, tried to arrange a meeting with him to find out what his plans were and eventually they met halfway between Wexford and Offaly. Joachim told them he hadn't his mind made up. A few days later, they learned that Kelly was not staying on, but as far as I know they never heard it from the man himself.

We were hardly filled with hope, then, when word circulated that another committee was being set up to find another new manager, but this time they did better. Tony Dempsey, now a Fianna Fáil TD, took over and brought Ger Cushe, one of my main friends and a former team-mate, and Davy Morris in as selectors.

Early in their reign I, as one of the elder berries of the bunch, was asked to make a speech. I begged the squad to pull in the one direction. We had been fighting everyone, it seemed, since Rory Kinsella left, but with Tony we had a real players' man and there were just no excuses left.

That year, though Kilkenny smashed us 2-19 to 0-12 in the Leinster final, we reached an All-Ireland semi-final with Tipperary. They looked to have us well beaten in Croke Park but we showed remarkable spirit to claw our way back with three incredible goals in the second half, two from Larry O'Gorman, who wound the clock back with a sensational display. In the end Tipp were the ones hanging on for their lives. But with 45 seconds left and Tipp on the rack, referee Pat O'Connor blew his whistle and declared a draw: Wexford 3-10, Tipperary 1-16. We had prepared well but maybe deep down we knew we had lost our chance of reaching another All-Ireland final.

Still, Liam Griffin was in the back-room at this stage and one of my old sparring partners, Martin Storey, had been called back into the panel after his retirement and so we felt there was a decent chance of causing another shock.

Pat Horan was the man in the middle for the replay, which was staged in a downpour at Croke Park, and it wasn't long before he lost all control of the game.

In one corner Rory Mallon and Eoin Kelly were taking lumps out of one another, while down at the other end Mitch Jordan and Tomás Costello had also started flaking each other. I looked across the pitch, where Darren Stamp was delivering on his earlier promise to smack Tipp's wing forward Mark O'Leary, who we had found a handful in the drawn game, when he scored four points from play.

At this stage, I poked my marker, Brian O'Meara, a few digs to see how he would react. Now Brian had never hit a man in his life but all the same I reckoned I'd see how he would handle it.

I tipped the end of the hurl into his ribs and straightaway he tapped me back with the bos of his hurl. It's macho stuff but it happens in hurling games all the time. I walked backwards but hit him another little tip whereupon he turned around, drove his hurl up where it really hurts and left me winded.

But I wouldn't let it go and so I drove the hurl into his ribs again. This went on and on until we had hit each other a fourth time and the linesman Pat Aherne had his flag up. It was silly stuff and I presumed all we were going to get was a dressing down and maybe a booking.

How wrong I was! By now Horan had lost what little control he'd started with, his face was bright red and you could see he was under serious pressure. Before the game, his umpires had arrived late, which hadn't helped, but it seemed rows had broken out in every area of the field and he was all at sea; the occasion was too big for him. He sought Pat Aherne's advice and the linesman pointed out the two players he'd seen digging each other. I went over to Horan: 'Jesus Pat, it's not that bad.' But he was about to lose the rag and the next thing he produced the red card and flashed it at both of us. I could not believe what was happening. Brian O'Meara looked at me in disgust.

'Look what you're after doing now,' he said.

'Ah Jesus,' I replied.

As I walked off the pitch for the second year in a row, I felt as low as I had ever done. The crowd didn't really jeer this time; they were pretty much concentrating on another row being waged down the other end of the field between Mitch and Tomás.

I put my head down in despair and trotted along to the sideline with my hurl in my hand. I looked up briefly to see Jordan arriving alongside me. He too had been sent off.

In the dressing-room, I was disconsolate. Tom Dempsey, another close friend and former team-mate, came down from the TV studios to console me. Tony Dempsey brought the team into the warm-up room. Alone, I put on my tracksuit as he tried to rouse them one last time.

'Lads, we can still do this,' he roared. And then he went around to the lads one by one. He came to Mitch Jordan.

'Mitch. I want you to get in front of your man for the second half. Get in front and win that ball for us. What do you say to that?'

'Jaysus, Tony, I was sent off 10 minutes ago.'

That put the apple in Tony's throat and ended his speech fairly quickly.

Things had happened so fast. Very few had seen Mitch get the line and I nearly cracked a smile when I saw Tony's face, but quickly remembering my own troubles I just dropped the head again. The lads went out on the field and tried their best but we never had a hope and were well beaten, 3-12 to 0-10.

After the game, I walked out of Croke Park a broken man. I can only imagine how Brian felt, but I couldn't believe we had been sent off. The first people I saw were my wife and two kids and it was a huge relief, to be honest. Little Aoife was only two then and all she wanted was to get up in Daddy's arms; she didn't care about hurling. Here I was, leaving Croke Park as a man, after playing a man's game, and going back into my private life, where a little girl is waiting just to be picked up and hugged. She was so innocent but I was delighted with the hug; to tell the truth, there weren't too many others who wanted one from me.

A few days later, Mitch and I were called to a Games Administration Committee disciplinary meeting in Dublin. Séamus Howlin, the Wexford chairman at the time, collected us and on the way told me I would get a month's suspension but warned Mitch he would get three.

We approached Jack White's pub and decided there was little or no point going to Dublin if that was the case, so we asked Séamus to let us off there but he refused and reminded us that we still had a chance of getting Brian O'Meara off the hook so he could play in the All-Ireland final against Galway.

We stayed going but it was the biggest waste of a night and the worst decision I ever made, going to HQ that night. Pat Horan had sent his report into Croke Park on the evening of the replay and not even Nelson Mandela, Bono and John Hume together could have changed it.

We met Brian O'Meara, Nicky English and Tipp secretary Michael O'Brien up there and, players being players, Mitch and I went up to chat to Brian. The Dublin football manager at the time, Tommy Carr, came out of the room. He had been in hot water for his verbal roasting of referee Michael Curley but didn't seem too troubled by his experience inside the corridors of power.

'Cheer up, lads, it could be worse,' he quipped. But Brian O'Meara didn't seem too confident as he went in first to explain the situation. Mitch went in next and finally I was called before the committee.

I have never seen such a crowd in my life.. There were definitely two who were half asleep and another who had his hand under his ear to prop his chin up and looked like he was dozing off as well. Another guy from Cavan or somewhere, a great hurling man I'd say, was also on his way for 40 winks and wasn't even listening to what I was saying. All we were short of was Waldorf and Statler, the two boys on the balcony from the *Muppet Show*.

'If you saw what happened in the Kilkenny-Galway semi-final the day after our match, you will understand that Brian O'Meara and I were harshly treated,' I insisted. 'The stuff that went on between those two teams at the start of the game was X-rated. There were some awful tackles and hits that were let go. And if Brian is to miss an All-Ireland final over something silly like what we were involved in, there is something seriously wrong with the GAA.'

Yawns all round. They didn't even look up. I knew it was a waste of time and it was no surprise to me when O'Meara's ban was upheld along with my own for striking with the hurley. I was very upset that Brian missed the final and it overshadowed everything in the run-up to the game against Galway. *The Star* newspaper ran a 'Save Brian O'Meara' campaign and the whole country was talking about it. But let's just say I was not getting as much sympathy as Brian and rightly so, I suppose.

I was portrayed as the bad boy but I really felt that if Brian had got off with the suspension I should have as well. I thought the GAA and Horan had made a huge mistake in the first place but there was no-one else called to account except O'Meara and I and it sickened me. You only have to take the 2003 All-Ireland football final as an example, when Armagh's Diarmaid Marsden got sent off. The Tyrone guy Philip Jordan went running straight into him and referee Brian White put the Armagh corner forward off. It was a horrendous decision and I sat in front of the TV screaming at the injustice of it. And then, later in the year, they handed out a Vodafone All Star Referees award to White, another joke of a decision.

But while the sending-off really upset Brian, it had an adverse effect on me too. All of a sudden, I was being demonised and it wasn't long before an earlier incident, the Gary Kirby one, was dragged up as proof of my criminal tendencies.

If the GAA was a wild-west town, my face would have been on 'Wanted' posters on every saloon bar and every dusty street. It even got to the stage where letters were arriving in the post, lovely pieces of prose and poetry accusing me of being a dirty little bastard, good for nothing only mayhem.

Back home, I got plenty of support, but even still, the lads, my friends, were only half joking when they asked me if I was going to do the decent thing and call it a day. I didn't mind the ribbing but other things were starting to worry me. There was never much abuse from players or opponents on the field but my private life took the brunt of it instead. I now had a reputation; the name Liam Dunne was being mentioned for all the wrong reasons.

When I went off on holidays to Lanzarote with the Wexford team, my mind was still a little uneasy. I couldn't help thinking of the hurt my mother and wife must have felt, Griffin too, when I got the line, people who had done more for me than anyone else. When my brother Seán enquired if I had considered going for three red cards in a row, I just laughed and told him to watch his back at training but not for one moment did I dream it would come true.

In the 2002 Championship, we ended up playing Kilkenny in the Leinster final and although they were dominant in every hurling showdown in the province since about 1997, Wexford trained to win this game and really believed we would. Griffin popped in and out of the camp and was a huge help. Tony, Ger and Davy had also worked well with us and I was in no doubt we would beat them and cause a shock.

Big John Hoyne came over to mark me and didn't hold back. Our exchanges reminded me of the shuddering tussles his predecessor and my old friend John Power and I used to enjoy. With five minutes to go, Wexford were right in there, only a point down.

Declan Ruth had held their danger-man, Henry Shefflin, exceptionally well but all over the field, Wexford men had done their job and there was never more than two points in it. With time almost up, I looked at Hoyne and asked: 'Have ye not got enough Leinster medals?'

He tipped me with the hurley in the chest and replied: 'It's not Leinster medals we want at all.'

He was not being arrogant; they had more provincial medals than they knew what to do with and another one would be no big deal, but there was no way they were going to let us have a title either.

With just a point in it, their manager, Brian Cody, switched Martin Comerford out to mark me and almost immediately, James McGarry floated a puck-out down on top of the two of us. I stayed where I was and pulled. Martin Comerford moved forward and I hit him on the back of the shoulder. It was a stupid blow, especially when I knew I was already a marked man with referees. He went down and the medics came racing onto the field like it was a lifesaving operation and started to pour water on his head. What about his shoulder? Where I actually hit him.

I had pulled 10 times harder on John Hoyne and nothing had happened. But now Henry Shefflin came running at me and a few of the Wexford lads made a go for him. There were a few right shots exchanged. I stood there and braced myself for what was to come. That's when some Kilkenny man urged Comerford to stay on the deck. As I said, it was his first Championship so of course he was going to stay down but I felt like hitting the guy who had told him to do so. That made my blood boil.

By now Ger Harrington, the referee, had little choice. 'You're off,' he said calmly, as he flashed the red card.

'Ah, fucking hell!' I whispered, the wind taken out of my sails. I wanted the ground to open up and take me there and then. I was mortified, disgusted, devastated, embarrassed and crushed. At the same time, I was mystified as to why I had pulled on Comerford like that in the first place and raging with the fuss his camp had made over it. I like Martin, he's a good lad, but there he was holding his head and yet I had only made contact with his shoulder. Of course I knew what I was doing when I pulled on him and I knew the referee, who had a great game in fairness, didn't have much choice given the circumstances. But this was the worst I had ever felt on a field, worse than when I had broken my leg or lost the 1997 All-Ireland semi-final.

I walked off the pitch. Tony Dempsey called me over and although I looked at him, I just went straight by him and into the dressing-room for my third early shower in as many years. Fittingly, the water was cold this time.

On the way into the dressing-room, I met the same steward I had met after being sent off after the incident with Brian O'Meara the year before. He told me to sit down and have a cup of water. I told him he wouldn't be seeing me here again, peeled off my gear and headed for the shower, absolutely dazed at what had just happened. I turned the water on and, as I said, it was freezing but I stepped straight under it, felt nothing. As the drips poured down on me, I really felt like ending it all there and then, which is stupid because it's only a game. Wexford could have scored a winning goal outside but I wouldn't have noticed.

As it turned out, we lost by two points, 0-19 to 0-17, and almost immediately, our goalkeeper, Damien Fitzhenry, came into the dressing-room, saw me and came over to where I was sitting. Throwing a comforting arm around me, Fitzy said: 'I don't know what to say to you.'

I didn't know what to say either. All the usual faces flashed through my mind. Eithne, my mother, my aunt Ann: they were all up in the stand again. Groundhog Day. We had all been here before but this was the worst.

After that game, I did something I never usually did and travelled home with the team. In my mind, this was my last journey with the Wexford senior hurling squad and I was going back home with them. Before we hopped on the bus, I met Eithne and she was in a far worse state than me. All the lads in the family crowded around and sympathised but I couldn't shake the empty feeling inside. This was just humiliating. All down the years, I had my toughest battles against Kilkenny and had saved my best hurling for those games but now they were laughing at me. I looked around at the lads on the bus. Many of them were just in the squad for the first time and I knew they would have many good days ahead of them, but for me it was the end, and no harm either.

I went home and drowned my sorrows with a mixture of vodka, Baileys and Heineken. It was no time to be thinking straight.

The day after that game, the realisation that I would be gone for two months hit me. The GAC would ban me for 'ungentlemanly conduct', which warranted a four-week suspension, but because it was my second dismissal within a year, it was automatically doubled.

I knew I had to get away from town, so Eithne, the kids and I decided to head off to Dungarvan for a couple of days. But we soon found there was no getting away from it there either. I met Dan Shanahan, Fergal Hartley and Paul Flynn, all Waterford hurlers, and they were talking about the whole affair again. My head dropped even lower.

Word had it that Griffin was furious with me so I avoided him, and also stayed away from my mother's house, until the week after the Leinster final. Mam had held onto all the papers and, reading them, I found little solace or comfort in any, except for a few words of comfort from Brian Cody, who argued that I was unlucky to have walked.

A couple of days later, I travelled to Portlaoise to see Wexford get cleaned out by Clare in the qualifiers. That defeat ended our campaign.

Afterwards, I brought my young lad, Billy, into our dressing-room to see the lads, thinking it would be his last chance to meet his heroes. As we walked out, Clare's Colin Lynch came over and shook hands with Billy and me. Lynch had been the original bad boy of the GAA in 1998, when the Association seemed to be hunting for his blood. This was a guy who had the entire country on his back after the 1998 Munster final with Waterford, when he was subjected to a witch-hunt after pulling hard right from the throw-in.

Colin didn't say much to me but what he did say struck a chord: 'Don't let them get to you, Liam.'

It was a small gesture and I appreciated it, but in a sense it came too late. By now I scarcely had the stomach for anything and was feeling worse with each passing day. I didn't want to do anything, had little interest in work and never wanted to see a hurling field or play a match again.

On the Tuesday after the Clare defeat, one of my friends, Ray Keogh, asked me to go and see his Dad, Christy, who was sick. Christy had handed me my first ever Wexford senior jersey and was a man I had an awful lot of time for so I told Ray, who was also on the squad for years, there was no problem.

We went to see him in a nursing home the following day and I brought my Leinster final jersey with me.

'What's that?' Ray enquired.

'It's the last jersey I will wear for Wexford and your Dad gave me my first so I want him to have it,' I replied.

'Well, if that's your last jersey, I'll frame it,' Ray said.

We went up to the nursing home and poor Christy was looking frail. Lying back in his chair, he opened his eyes and saw me.

'Are you having a hard time of it, Liam?' he asked.

'I am, Christy,' I sighed. 'Some lads won't even look at me.'

'Well,' he whispered, 'when a lad won't even look at you, that's the biggest sort of a bollix you can get. At least if a lad looks at you and faces you, there's something in him.'

They were words I didn't forget. We went back to Ray's house and Christy passed away on the Friday of that week. I went to the removal that night and they put my Wexford jersey on his coffin.

After that, hurling was the last thing on my mind, and in fact there was little or nothing occupying any space in my head. I went on an excursion of alcohol. Officially, the binge started on July 13 and I drank every night until the first weekend in November. If there was beer in a glass, I had to get it down and on to the next one.

It continued right until the morning that I saw my two little kids on the doorstep and arranged that meeting with Griffin.

That Friday could not come quick enough; I wanted to pour all this out to the man that I would give up everything for, the man who got me my first job when he hardly even knew me.

Thankfully, the day came and, Griffin being Griffin, the 10 minutes he promised turned into three and a half hours.

'You look terrible,' was his opening greeting, and I spent the next hour telling him just why. For once, I did most of the talking and spelt it out.

I told him about the binge and how the sending-off against

Kilkenny had almost destroyed me. He said it was easy to see how bad I felt because I had no shape and just looked terrible.

'I can see by your physical condition that you have let yourself go,' he said, straight out. 'Your wife and family are suffering but there is a way out. If you are prepared to start work now, I think you can dig yourself out of this hole.

'Stop drinking now and start training. You have one more year to offer Wexford and salvage everything. One more year, but only if you start now,' he warned.

Feeling relieved, I went home and thought about what he had said. I decided to do as he had advised and try to dig myself out of the hole. It was like a weight off my mind so what did I do? I went straight to the pub and had a right few pints. It was a dreadful thing to do. But I didn't go out on Saturday night. For only the second time in nearly six months, I stayed in.

It was no surprise, though, that I couldn't sleep and I hankered for a taste of alcohol in the middle of the night so I got up and went down to the kitchen. This time, I ignored the fridge and instead drank cups of tea. At 6.40 am, I got up a third time and again turned a blind eye to the temptations that lay inside the fridge. Instead, I looked in the mirror and forced myself to see a different person.

'There's only one way to dig myself out of this fucking mess,' I said, teeth gritted. I put on a pair of togs and socks. Over the togs, I put on tracksuit bottoms and threw on a T-shirt. Over the T-shirt went a black plastic bag, a jersey and a tracksuit top. That was the heavy stuff but there were a couple of final touches: a wet suit and cap.

We lived two minutes from Morriscastle beach and at 7 am on November 3, 2002, my bender officially stopped. The wind howled mercilessly as I jogged down to the beach. It was an unfriendly place and I got no sympathy whatsoever from Mother Nature as I was blown along in the pitch dark, half afraid someone was running up behind me. Way back, there was one light, a lone lamppost that shone like a beacon beyond on the roadway that I kept looking to for reassurance. My first run only lasted a few minutes but I stopped, walked on and ran again. Once more, my legs gave way but I continued running after another few minutes.

I stayed at the beach for an hour and came home with my gear absolutely drowned. Later that day, at 4 pm, I was down there again and that night I scored another big plus by staying home for the second night in a row.

On Monday morning, I was down at Morriscastle beach at 7 am once more and again that evening. When I returned home, I went looking for my diary, looked up that day's date and in large, clear print wrote:

> *My goal for 2003 is to be the Wexford Hurler of the Year.*
> *Honour and Respect. Liam Dunne, November 5, 2002.*

Two little words that meant so much: honour and respect. It was a long time since I had either and it would require something extraordinary to get them back. Maybe I never would.

*I can get up in the morning and look myself in the mirror
and my family can look at me too and that's all that matters.*
Lance Armstrong, US cyclist

– CHAPTER FOUR –
The wonder years

Someone once told me life wasn't about the size of the dog in the fight, more the size of the fight in the dog. It was good advice.

All through my childhood, I was quiet and easygoing but deep down I was a fiery little hoor and not to be messed with. In sport, I seemed to be smaller than most other lads my age and it took me a long time to find my feet but when I did, I quickly learned to compensate for those two or three missing inches and found out there were other ways to make do.

I arrived into the world, destination Gorey, on June 12 1968 after giving Mam a relatively trouble-free birth. Five siblings had come before me, so there were no trumpet blasts or anything like that. The Dunnes had seen it all before, you see, so apart from a few strange heads of black hair looking into the cot at me when I came home, I am told it was soon back to your stations. We grew up in that sort of an unfazed environment.

And it was just as well because there were eight of us in our family. I had two sisters on each side of me and three brothers older so it was a fight for your own corner.

Home was Kyle Cross, a cottage at Kyle-Oulart in the Oulart-The-Ballagh parish, about 12 miles from Gorey. Over the years, there were three or four extensions added to the house. I got a chance to buy the house at 34 years of age, decided to make a new start and sat munching a choc-ice on the wall as builder John Kennedy and his men bulldozed it to make way for the next generation, my own lot.

We were close enough as a family without being painful or over the top about it. While we would look out for one another, there was a nice age difference from the oldest to the youngest so we all had different agendas. At the end of the day, we can still look each other in the face and do one another a favour. Isn't that what it's all about?

It wasn't always simple, though. By the time that my father, Tom, had finally left home in the early 1990s, I had kind of grown up without him being around. All in all, we turned out okay but it was tough.

An engineer with Irishenco, Dad was based in Dublin in my early years and that still allowed him to hurl for the parish until the call to go to London came and then he was even farther away. The nearest job Dad got to Oulart when I was a kid was in Rosslare. After that it could be Cork, Turlough Hill, Limerick or Britain, where he was based up to the time of his death in July 2004.

When he ended up working in St Helena, off the coast of Africa, it was really the end of his close involvement with the family and we knew things were not going to change when he started missing birthdays and holidays.

I do remember my father making hurleys for me when I was too small for any of the normal sizes. I also know he brought us to matches when we were kids and he was the one who started us hurling, but that's about it, they are the memories.

He took a decision to work away and gradually made the choice to stay away. He was gone for most of my life afterwards although he did come home for my wedding in 1996. He rang me from Dublin Airport the following morning and we chatted for a few minutes. He said he had to go to catch his flight and I never suspected I would see and speak to him only once after that.

That was early in July 2004, when I went to see him in a Southampton hospital, where he was terminally ill with leukaemia. The rest of my brothers and sisters had been over to see him weeks beforehand; I said I would go when I was ready.

But you can never be ready for something like that and when I finally got it together and visited him, it was difficult. We chatted for a while and I would say that both of us found it hard to deal with; there were plenty of questions I wanted to ask him, like why did he have to lose touch and why didn't he come home a bit more. I wanted to point out how tough it was growing up with no father around and how hard it was for my mother and the rest of them. But what was the point?

He was very sick and didn't need the hassle. Instead, we talked about how things were in Oulart and we talked about Wexford hurling, two things we would always have in common.

At the end, we shook hands and I knew that was the last time I would see my father. His absence didn't stop me thinking about him over the years but thoughts can go only so far.

My mother, Eileen, however, has always been there. She was and still is Ground Control for the eight of us. When she was a child, her own family moved from Wexford to Cork and back again when her Dad, Patrick, was made Garda sergeant in Oulart village. Mam loved GAA as well. She played camogie in Cork with Grenagh and when Oulart started a club in 1984, she always stayed involved. She met my Dad in the village years back; they got married and we soon started to arrive on the scene. Her brother, Seán Woulfe, used to spend his summers between Wexford and Cork, where he hurled with all sorts of clubs, illegally, I might add. Seán was a strong swimmer but at just 24 he was swept off a pier with two friends and while they survived, he didn't. They found his body seven days later.

Another of my mother's brothers, Borgie, a good hurler, also suffered a tragic death. His home went on fire one Easter weekend and while he and his wife got out, he heard his children screaming and went back into the house. Borgie never came back out and only two of the children, Damien and Willie, made it out.

A few years later, when Willie grew up, he went out on his motorbike one Saturday evening to get a bag of chips and was killed. That's tough in anyone's language.

There were happier times, however. It was like *The Waltons* at times in Kyle-Oulart; four boys used to sleep in one room and the girls in another but there were no sweet goodnight calls from one to the other as we dozed off. You were more likely if you were yapping to get a shoe in the face to send you to sleep.

I don't really remember many of my early days but I suppose that in itself suggests we were happy enough. I do recall that later, when things moved on a bit, two of us transferred into another room, which was an absolute luxury.

As for the rest of the place, well the only heating we had in that house was the summertime. We had a great big oil cooker alright but there was never a whole lot of oil put in it and little wonder that we looked forward to spring, summer and the warm weather so much. Although Dad had a good number, there were that many of us he would have needed a job in rocket science or brain surgery to keep it all going.

We had plenty of hobbies and stuff to keep us active. Our interests were well varied but they mainly centred on sports and music; we were always hitting a sliotar or playing some instrument or other.

Kieran, the eldest, played underage hurling until he was forced to pack it in because of poor eyesight. That's what he told us anyway. From what I recall, he was no Christy Ring. He used to play in goal and there are just some things that even glasses cannot help you with. He went on to qualify as a secondary school teacher but could not get a job in his chosen field back then and turned to the South Eastern Health Board, where he still works.

Tomás works as a roofer and has always been the 'chancer' of the family. That lad had a go at everything and got blamed for most of what went wrong anywhere within a 10-mile radius of the house. He was a great hurler who played senior for Wexford on and off for 10 seasons until 1994 but didn't get half the credit he deserved.

Over the following years as I hit the town, I would encounter selectors and county board officials who slated Tomás for his wildness. I would agree it was scandalous behaviour even though I was probably a much bigger culprit.

Tomás always got caught but he has always been a success at what he put his hand to.

Seán works for Munster Joinery, who are based in Ballydesmond, Co Cork. Growing up, he tried all types of sport from squash to table tennis and was good at most of them. Later on, he won junior football and hurling All-Ireland titles with the county. Although he was the fastest thing on two legs at the time, he used to play in goal, which I always felt was such a waste.

My multitalented sister Siobhán was the first superstar in the Dunne family. She had two Gaelic football All Star awards by the time she was 24 and also played for Wexford in an All-Ireland camogie final, which they lost.

My mother always reminds us that Siobhán was the first All Star in the family and she's right. Siobhán was a great player and was always on the go. After winning the two awards, she went to Dublin for international soccer trials.

We had a great laugh all the way up along over our little sibling rivalry, and I got huge pleasure years later, the morning after my third All Star, ringing her to gloat that my days of trailing in her shadow were over. Siobhán works as a horticulturist now.

Fiona was another graduate of the Dunne sports academy; she had little choice but to play. Like our youngest sister, Ailish, she played camogie for most of her youth. She now runs O'Brien's pub in Killenagh. Gráinne, a devoted housewife these days, was the only one of the family not to compete and instead opted for music when we were kids. My mother maintained she was the only one with sense but she also succumbed to the hurling bug and married Pat Dooley who won an All-Ireland 'B' medal with Kildare.

There was always a lot of competition when we were kids because no matter what one member of the family achieved, there was always another to do something better a few days later. When I won my first All Star, a local reporter, David Medcalf, came to the house, but not to talk to me at all; he wanted to grill my mother on the sporting achievements of the family in general.

'Eileen's famous sporting family have done it all,' his article read and, one by one, it detailed the honours we had collected. Mam was fairly proud when she saw that hitting the newsagents.

There is no doubt that knowing the lads at home were just as good as me in their chosen fields kept me on my toes but while we were always into something competitive, there was a fairly relaxed feeling about my early days in Oulart.

As with many families, there were times during my childhood when our family or one of the neighbours needed a dig-out and certain people were always quick to offer the helping hand. Fintan Cooney was one such Good Samaritan.

Times were hard enough around our area because the economy was often in tatters but we were lucky we had this man. He was the ultimate believer in community spirit, owned a bit of land, a pub and a grocery shop. To say Fintan Cooney was good to the Dunnes, and many others in Oulart, would be an understatement. I'd say a lot of locals might not have got through the hard times only for him. He thought nothing of putting his hand into his own pocket and asked nothing in return.

A former chairman of Oulart-The-Ballagh GAA club, he died after a heart attack and was buried on the day we beat Offaly in the 1997 Leinster semi-final. I ran out first on the bench for the team picture that afternoon and offered up a few seconds' private thought for him. At the funeral the following day, Fintan's wife, Clare, who is also my godmother, singled me out to thank me for scoring a goal to his memory.

Now, I don't really know if he did guide the ball into the net for me – it probably owed more to a mistake by the goalkeeper, David Hughes – but I thought of Fintan when I hit the back of the net from a 65-metre free and remembered him after the game again. He was great to us, my mother especially. Some people come straight into your mind when you cast it back. Fintan Cooney was one of them.

At various stages, the eight of us streamed into Oulart National School, where the principal, Michael Bracken, performed an incision on my first day by separating me from my minder, Kieran, who was in fifth class. Michael carried me down to junior infants as the tears streamed out of my eyes. I did not want to be there.

'What's your name?' he asked.

'Liam Dunne,' I stammered.

'Are you Kieran's brother?'

'Yes.'

'Well, listen to him and not to Tomás and you'll be okay.' Despite the fact he was a lovely man, I was afraid of Michael for the rest of my time at Oulart NS. I suppose from day one I knew that school and I were never going to be close friends.

It was there, however, that I began to realise there was a lot of history in the parish. And Irish history doesn't boast many finer moments than the 1798 rebellion. You talk about battles but one of the few we won in that era was at Oulart Hill, where rebels led by Fr John Murphy, Edward Roche and Morgan Byrne defeated the North Cork Militia. It was a great win for the United Irishmen, though they lost nearly every other skirmish.

And I have more than education to thank school for. The friends I made there: Bartle Sinnott, Bartle Redmond, Martin Dempsey, Henry Cleary and Gay Cooney are still my best. I tasted my first drop of alcohol with those lads, they laughed at my first car, I got involved in my first scrap trying to stand up for them while they ran away, and we've ended up bailing each other out ever since.

They were the wonder years. The village never seemed too small for us by the way. Oulart has developed now but back then it had the usual layout: church, school, shop, monument to 1798 and, not surprisingly, two pubs, Cooney's and the Sportsman's Inn. That was it, straightforward and simple, but it had everything I wanted.

Top of the list was hurling and when I was eight and about three foot tall, I played my first game for Oulart-The-Ballagh under-10s. We came up against Shelmaliers/Castlebridge and because of my size I was tucked into corner forward, where I prayed to the Man Above I wouldn't get hit. Two things I remember about that game: we got bottles of 7-up afterwards and Anthony Stamp was our captain. Anthony would later die in a freak accident in what turned out to be one of the worst years in the parish's history, 1987.

But in the actual game, I can't even remember hitting a ball. They had put me out of the way but with Dad over the team, there was no chance I would be substituted. That sort of nepotism still exists in Wexford to this day and it gets under my skin. If my chance in management ever comes, we'll see what can be done about it.

So an undistinguished debut but Dad kept making little hurleys for me because I was shorter than others and needed a special stick. I remember getting my very first hurley from a local man called Frank Randall, who had been making them for years. Of course, the one Frank gave me was way too big so my father spliced it for me, basically trimmed the handle of the hurley down and put a little v into it.

Over the next few years, I was coming thick and fast to Dad asking for sticks to be shortened until I caught him on a bad night and he told me to go down to the shed and do it myself. Innocent as I was, I started on my good hurleys, wielding the jigsaw and glue in the shed like a seasoned professional, or so I fancied, but of course making shit of all my sticks.

By the time I got the hang of the whole routine, I was left with a fair few duds.

Still, I kept practising hard and often with them. I also started watching games on TV. For some reason, I really latched onto the Galway team of 1979 and 1980. When they played, I was glued to the box watching classy players like Iggy Clarke, Seán Silke and the

Connolly brothers in action.

My memories of watching Wexford in the late 1970s are vague. For me it was all Galway and my main man, Cork's Jimmy Barry Murphy. Looking back at my scrapbooks from 1977, it's interesting to see that I drew a picture of the Liam MacCarthy Cup on the last page of my first ever collection. I suppose every young lad in hurling territory does it at some stage but it's good to see the ambition was there from day one.

My aspirations in the classroom, however, took longer to develop. The only reason I began to find school tolerable in the first place was because we were guaranteed game time between 2 and 3 o'clock. I would hurl my heart out during the day and pray it wouldn't rain so I could play an under-12 game that night. I never won very much at underage level and that was usually because we came up against town teams like Enniscorthy, who were a lot stronger. And while that was disheartening, the notion of stopping never occurred to me.

Eventually, things took a turn for the better: when I was in fourth class, Breda Jacob joined the school as a teacher. She was married to the legendary Wexford hurler Mick, and together with Joe Hyland and Liam Keogh, she took over our under-10 team.

Breda, whose sons Rory and Mick are on the current Wexford senior team, was my first proper hurling coach and she brought me to a different level by simply holding skills competitions and teaching the class to jab-lift, roll-lift, solo, hand-pass and tackle. If some lad got 20 roll-lifts in a competition, I would be green with envy and would speed home to train that night and make sure I got 21 the next day.

Around 1980, Mick Jacob senior took a special interest in me and asked me to go up to the local field and hit back the sliotar as he practised his free-taking. This was the big time now. I was Mick's Mini-Me and delighted to be, thank you very much. Although I was only 13 at the time, the truth is I idolised the man and was thrilled to be asked to bang a few balls with him.

We used to go to Mass every Sunday but my reasons for attending were far from religious. Mick would always go to first Mass and I wouldn't even look at the priest. Instead, I would wait for Communion and try to walk past him while he went to the altar, just hoping for some sort of acknowledgement from him. Some went to pray to God but I was sitting only two seats away from the real one and didn't need prayers.

It was a dream to even hit the balls back. Fair enough, I was under massive pressure to get the ball back to the 70-yard line, where he was lofting them over. I was like Sonic the Hedgehog, buzzing all over the place, driving balls out to him with all my might, running back to collect them and striking another one out the field.

Mick would say a few words when he sensed I was flagging and it was like putting petrol in a car because I would just lift my game one more time to keep clearing the balls out the field for as long as I could. Another local hero of mine was Ned Buggy. I used to idolise him.

I tried to copy his style of free-taking, where he had the left hand off the hurl and put it back on again just as he was about to strike, but I could never do it and soon abandoned my efforts. Ned won an All Star in 1979 and presented me with the only real medal I won at underage, the 1981 Rackard Cup, and I was chuffed.

We later went on to play handball together and I actually marked him in a hurling match later again, when he pulled a foot over the ball and pulverised me with a smack. I looked at him in disbelief. Imagine Ned Buggy hitting me! Still, it was great to play against him.

Maybe hanging with the heroes started to pay off. At 13, I was brought into county under-14 trials as a corner forward and they left me in the panel until the Leinster final, when I was dropped.

The managers, Pat Murphy and Bill Hayden, never actually told me I was chopped but I was so small and miserable they probably forgot. Instead, they asked me to carry the hurls for the final and I told them to get stuffed, that I wanted to go to the stands and watch Wexford, who were in three finals that day. We lost all of them, something I was to get fairly used to in the years to come.

I wasn't really that upset about getting the heave-ho. To tell you the truth, I was afraid of a good few lads that we came up against around then and as a small corner forward I was getting a lot of smacks and wasn't too brave about it either.

There was some compensation for me when the club went on to win the Wexford under-14 Féile na nGael competition. In the All-Ireland series, we were hammered by Galway and, interestingly, only three of that team went on to play senior for Oulart-The-Ballagh. The following year, I made the county under-14 team again and was brought on after 10 minutes of the Leinster final against Kilkenny, and once more we were thrashed.

But while hurling was a night-and-day job, there was more on my mind as well. I had also been playing a lot of soccer at the time and had been going very well for nearby Kilmuckridge Vocational School, where I studied, or at least attended, after national school.

At 14, I was playing about four years above my level and my efforts started to catch the attention of a few local scouts. To tell the truth, I was big into it and absolutely loved playing in the middle of the field, the department where one of my future heroes, Roy Keane, was to make his name.

There was a fair danger that hurling could have gone by the wayside, especially when I came home from school one day to discover that big news awaited me.

I was just 14 years of age and already my sporting career was coming to its first crossroads. It would be the first of many difficult junctions along the way.

All animals are equal but some are more equal than others.
George Orwell, Animal Farm

– CHAPTER FIVE –
The wizard of OZY

As a kid, my main ambition was to play hurling for Wexford but I was also willing to see how far I could take my soccer career. The idea appealed to me mainly because it looked like my hurling ambitions had stalled, especially after my graduation from Oulart NS to Kilmuckridge Vocational School, which was not one bit fashionable in the GAA world. You really had to be attending St Peter's to break into intercounty hurling at that stage.

That sort of shit was rife in Wexford at the time but thank God, we have moved on, though not fully. We still have selectors trying to get their own favourites on teams, despite the fact they are plainly not good enough.

Back then, Oulart was not a fashionable club and the likes of Tomás and I would lose out to some other lad who was on the county team because his father knew someone. The prejudice was a lot worse back then than it is now so it was no bad thing to throw myself into soccer as it was the main game at Kilmuckridge VS anyway.

I played each day as hurling went on the back burner for a while and my friend Pat Rossitter and I developed into decent players. We were two of the main figures in the team that won the Wexford Schools Cup in 1981 and I really enjoyed my central-midfield role.

One evening early in that same season, word filtered through to the school that I was picked for Ireland under-15 trials. This was a big surprise because firstly it had never crossed my mind and secondly I was underage again the following year, 1982, when a trial was much more likely. But Pat got the call as well and we travelled to Dublin to play the Waterford Youth team, who were about three years above our fighting weight.

I got a right land when I walked into the AUL sports complex, because it seemed we had the Ritz for changing-rooms, a five-star job. There was gear laid out and folded for me and not a ditch in sight to tog out in. Everyone had his own designated area and we were introduced to two of the team's 'star' players; one was on Luton Town's books and the other had just signed with Leeds United. They definitely had a bit of time for themselves alright but it seems no-one else did because the pair of them never got anywhere in the end.

I could have got used to that way of life. I remember my mouth was still wide open as I tried to figure how to sneak home the trendy playing gear in front of me. Our teacher, Michael Enright, brought us up to the capital for the trials but his influence wasn't enough to see us onto the first 11 and so we were handed substitutes' jerseys.

Still, that was fine. Better to come in and make the impression. And we looked on in amusement as our team-mates got the runaround from these gigantic poles from Waterford, some of them sporting the beginnings of a dodgy moustache on their upper lips.

At half time, though, the grins were wiped from our faces when Pat and I were plucked from the comfort zone and thrown into midfield. We got stuck in and held our own, and looking back, I thought the game went well for both of us.

We were instructed to go back to our clubs and wait for word from the FAI. The prospect of making a career across the water had never occupied my mind but I was ready to give it a shot if the call arrived. In the end, I didn't have to worry. The advice from the Irish management was to keep the game up but I hadn't made the cut this time. Never mind, I did keep soccer going with the school and my two teams, The Ballagh FC and St Joseph's, and we went on to win a lot of trophies, but by the time the next year's trials came along, I already had my hands stuck in another pie, handball, and had lost most of my interest in the beautiful game.

Where I got time for school in between my sporting pursuits I don't know but the fact that I was never one for the books was no great surprise to Mam and when my 1983 Group Cert exams came around she held out little hope for me.

Nevertheless, I slowly took to the books. When I would go into a room to swot, my family presumed I was just reading comics in between a text book. They had about as much faith in me as Michael Moore has in George Bush.

Still, when the results came, I surprised them all with six honours, two passes and just one fail, not the seven or so predicted for me by my loving family.

For the record, here are my 1983 Group Cert results. Irish NG (I had decided at that stage one language was enough for me); Woodwork B; English C; Maths C; Geography C; History C; Mechanical Drawing C; Metalwork C; Science B.

Now, I was hardly Dr Liam Dunne PhD yet and even after these fine results I still couldn't see a career in Trinity or UCD beckoning. But by no means was I ready to leave school either even though, at the time, it was the done thing to push off after the Inter Cert. Instead, I was keen to give it a good old go for another year and maybe then wave goodbye to the education system.

For days my mother remained in a state of mild and pleasant shock over my results but I knew I had sacrificed a bit of hurling and soccer to study and was aware that if I put more work in I could keep going in school. For example, I knew as much about science at the start of second year as I did of the Irish language but had applied myself to it during the second and third terms and actually ended up liking it. So I pondered my short-term future and, to pass the long summer away, got a job with Andy Roche in Blackwater, only a few miles down the road. I was 15, had a Group Cert behind me and was only waiting for the voice to break before finally gaining my membership card to the Men's Club.

Andy ran a joinery business and I thought I could give him a hand, but after my first day I'm sure he thought otherwise. The first task I was handed was to put two panes of glass into a window, a job that would usually take maybe 20 minutes. Andy left me on my own and told me to head back to the workshop when I was finished.

That was in the morning. When he returned later that evening, I was still scratching my head. It took me most of the day to install them.

'I thought you were able to make your own hurleys, Liam,' Andy scowled.

'I am Andy, but I never claimed to be able to put glass in a window.'

A look of despair spread across his face and I'd say he wondered what he had let himself in for. Little wonder, then, that I was confined to the workshop for the rest of the summer, which I actually loved. After a while, I even got the hang of the job.

Shortly before the end of that summer, my brother Kieran qualified from UCC as a secondary schoolteacher. But even though he had worked very hard to get the results he just could not get a job. It made me think that if someone like him couldn't land a full-time position, what hope had I? I decided to leave school.

In the end, it was no tough choice. I had never fully intended doing the Leaving Cert anyway, so Andy and I agreed terms and he paid me my first permanent wage packet: a princely 35 punts per week. It was a lot for me and much more than Kieran got in his first job. In fact, I had to subsidise him with a few loans despite the fact he was eight years older.

The job was fairly relaxed and you could talk hurling, which suited me. Andy's Dad, Jim, had been on the 1940 Wexford junior team that won the Leinster final, the county's first big win in 30 years, so there was no getting away from the game in work.

It helped even more that two of my best mates, Martin Dempsey and Bartle Sinnott, also took time out of school after they had struggled with the Group Cert. It took their parents that much longer

than my Mam to realise the boys were wasting their time with
academic pursuits.

I had a bit of sense by now and was saving a few quid, and as my
hurling career still hadn't taken off, I devoted most of my spare time to
handball. There was something about handball I liked; it was not hugely
popular but it was fast and tricky and suited someone my size.

I won a bronze medal at the Community Games in Mosney in
1981 and kept it up. Of course the fact I was a teenager meant once I
found a new passion, every other sport and interest went out the
window. I went on to win under-14 singles and doubles, with Pat
Rossitter, at the Wexford Championships. By the time I was 17, I was
winning under-21 titles and significantly adding to my trophy cabinet all
the time. The local newspapers said many of my wins were inevitable
but, in fairness, while I was good at the game, there was a very small
pool of players around the circuit and that didn't help my progress. But
Nicky O'Toole drove me the length and breadth of the country to help
improve me all the same.

I continued the game at a pretty high standard for as long as I
could and in my last year at under-18 played Peter McAuley from
Louth, who had won numerous world titles. Everyone in the game saw
it as a huge test and while he beat me 21-17, 21-4, it was great to be
even in the same alley as someone of that quality.

Although my love of handball never waned, matches were
increasingly hard to come by as there was just no-one to play. And so I
rarely played once I hit 18, which was a shame, but in hindsight I can at
least say handball later helped my hand-to-eye co-ordination for
hurling. While I was sorry to eventually call it a day, the lack of
handball competition allowed me to devote more time to my new
vices: women and nightlife. At 16 I started 'tipping around', as the lads
at home would say.

It was now that I sampled my first drink, when I strolled down the
village to Linda's Nightclub a boy and staggered home thinking I was a

man. I ordered a large bottle of Harp. The lads, Martin Dempsey and Bartle Sinnott, were nearby so I had to make it look good but it was tough because the bottle was almost bigger than myself.

One pint later and I really was twisted, the floor coming up to meet me, but I just kept a stupid grin on my face, snuck into the corner and hoped the dizziness would go away.

As a further demonstration of my new-found manhood, I also invested around this time in a lovely set of wheels. Well, it was lovely if you were a big girl's blouse or a 78-year-old granny. For some bizarre reason, my first purchase was a bright yellow Ford Fiesta, price 2,500 punts, with the licence plate OZY 678. If a lad ever wanted to remain discreet in Oulart, he had no chance driving this screaming-yellow heap of junk around the place and looking like Big Bird.

It cost me another £700 to insure it, but having being brought up very independent, I wanted my own car and this rotten yellow machine was what I ended up with.

My first crash duly came in the OZY. Luckily it wasn't fatal, and the following morning, as I had little recollection of the night before, I found it strange to see so many briars tangled up in the wipers and hanging out the window.

There were times, I honestly think, when that car drove itself home. It was like Herbie from the movies, or so we liked to think.

Like Herbie, when he was angry, OZY had a habit of getting his own back on you. One night, trembling with hope, I brought some girl out of a disco and we headed to the car. Trying to act cool, I went to open the door, whereupon the handle snapped off. I strolled around to the passenger side; that handle snapped as well. But like any red-blooded young lad about to get lucky, I wasn't going to give up so I crawled into the boot and up through the car, eventually unlocking it and opening it for the two of us. I can now tell you that it wasn't worth all the effort.

Apart from doing ourselves harm, we never really caused much grief to others during our teenage years, though I clearly remember our first real serious altercation.

Most teenagers get into hassles with bikers at a late-night disco or outside a chipper, but we stooped to an all-time low when we were run out of an old folks' party.

After a trip down to the local nightclub, Linda's, we decided there wasn't much happening, but one of the lads got a tip-off that there was a party in nearby Curracloe. It was a wind-up, though. Our mole neglected to say it was a senior citizens' function. Undeterred, we went in and donned the party hats and started blowing all sorts of whistles and singing with the grannies. We thought it was some crack but one chap really took exception to our presence and even though a local man, Larry Donohue, stood up for us, we were told to clear off.

With a few pints down me, I left and hopped into a car that still looked bright yellow even in the pitch dark. I had my party hat on and was about to drive home with the lads when I turned on the radio and quickly copped that my car didn't actually have one.

'We might as well clean out what's in it,' Bartle Sinnott laughed, sticking a few golf balls and tapes in his pocket.

'Might as well, now that we're here,' I agreed. We fleeced the car before withdrawing and eventually finding OZY.

Days later, we met Larry again and he looked upset. I asked him was there anything wrong and he said he was raging because his car had been broken into and his stereo and other belongings had been stolen. My face dropped.

We had mistakenly and drunkenly gone into his car but all we took were golf balls and tapes of The Drifters. Someone had come along and fleeced the car after us.

'Jesus, Larry,' I sympathised, 'some people would take the eye out of the back of your head.' And I made my excuses and left.

Between the messing, I kept my hurling going and was called up to the county under-16 team in 1984 but was once more dropped as they went on to win the Leinster blitz.

A year later, I was in no doubt that I would make the minor panel when the time came to go to trials. So I played away with the club and tried to prepare for what was to come. I need not have bothered; word got back to me that I wasn't hurling well enough to merit even a trial.

At that stage I was playing at centre back, having told the club selectors I was finished in the forwards, and when I later saw some of the lads who had made the squad, I was just disgusted.

In fact, I still feel raw about not making that team. Some of the players were absolutely putrid and I've never heard tell of a lot of them since, yet I was deemed not good enough to even get a chance. The real reason, of course, was that I was not a student at St Peter's College. Had I been studying there, my chances of making the Wexford minor team were so much better. But I had been at Kilmuckridge VS and proud of it and my own club would not have been the most fashionable either so I had to bite my tongue and wait for the season to drift by. Let no-one tell you we are all equals in Wexford because this who-you-are shit still goes on here today. Some are more equal than others.

At least motivation was not in short supply for my last year as a minor, and in the 1986 Leinster Championship I was finally selected to play on the team and lined out at right-half forward against Carlow. We beat them well, I played fine and we had another good win over Laois in the semi-final.

Lying in wait for us in the final, however, were Offaly. They annihilated us. It hadn't helped that our management opted to make 13 changes from the semi-final but in truth, Daithí Regan, Michael Duignan, Declan Pilkington and company simply destroyed us. And right through the next eight years or so, they were well on top of us.

That day, though, I played my own game: sidesteps, swerves, ball control, running up and down the field, striking off both sides, and what I didn't score that day, I set up for the rest of the team.

As I walked off the field, crushed and disheartened, Fr Butler approached me.

'Young Dunne,' he said, as he clasped his two hands on my shoulders, 'you're going to have many days back in Croke Park, many days.'

I looked at him, silently asking forgiveness for thinking this holy man was talking nonsense. But maybe I began to believe a few weeks later when I was called up to the county under-21 team. Imagine, I couldn't make the minor team a year before and now here I was on the under-21 team. Someone else can try to figure it out.

Anyway, the under-21s met Offaly again, this time in the Leinster final, and we drew. I was brought on as a sub for the replay, which we won. But I looked on from the bench as we beat Derry in the All-Ireland semi-final before Galway won the Championship with the likes of Joe Cooney and Gerry McInerney.

People think I had a great old time of it but that was the sum of my career up to minor level: a Rackard Cup medal; a Féile medal and a sub's place on the county under-21 team that won the Leinster title; 18 county handball and three Wexford soccer championships.

That's pretty miserable in my language, but even then I didn't realise the extent of the famine that lay ahead.

But to tell the truth, after what happened to the village of Oulart in 1987, winning trophies was about the last thing we were concerned with.

Life is what happens to you when you're busy making other plans.
John Lennon

– CHAPTER SIX –
Tragedy visits Oulart

There is a moment in everyone's childhood or teenage years when innocence is swiped away and replaced with a harsh slap of reality. The people of Oulart-The-Ballagh got much more than a slap of it in 1987; we got a full-force blow in the face.

There is nothing like a death of someone you know well to knock the stuffing out of you, but when you are young and it happens twice, well, it just leaves you on your knees. When I turned on the radio early on March 2, 2004, and heard on the news that the Tyrone footballer Cormac McAnallen had died the night before, I was dumbfounded. The first thing that came into my head was what a lovely chap he was and how in the name of Jesus could this have happened. It's sometimes a cliché when people pass away, but Cormac really was top-class, an honest and friendly guy. I had the pleasure of knowing him. We sat together at the 2003 All Stars and although he seemed a quiet lad at first, he soon chatted away and we had a great conversation, mainly because he was such an interesting bloke.

At one stage, Cormac said I must have been sick of the All Stars and asked me how many functions I had been at. He was genuinely surprised to hear it was actually my first since 1997.

His death just left a trail of disbelief around the country and I never saw so many from different corners of Ireland express their sympathy. I suppose Tyrone people will never get over it, especially after one of his former team-mates, Paul McGirr, had also passed away during an Ulster minor football clash in 1997.

Like a lot of the Oulart people, I felt our tragic memories were rammed home again when I heard of Cormac's death; 1987 is a year seldom mentioned around these parts but it's never too far from our minds either.

After strolling through my teenage years without too many worries or cares, I had just started to concentrate on breaking into the club senior team. Anthony Stamp and Richard Ormond, two guys slightly older than me, were also busy making a name for themselves. Anthony was only about 21 and was part of the team that had just beaten our arch-rivals Buffers Alley in a tournament game. To us, it felt like the All-Ireland final because you didn't get the satisfaction of beating those lads too often.

But shortly after, word ran through the village like wildfire of Anthony's death in an accident near The Ballagh. We really didn't know how to take it.

I didn't anyway. It shook everyone in the village. We're a close lot and while you might have one or two families not talking to each other, there would be a strong sense of unity.

But seeing grown men hurt and looking at how long it took people to get back on their feet left us all vulnerable for a long time afterwards. For once, hurling just seemed like a meaningless little hobby, no more than that. Country people are great at rallying behind a family in times of need and that was exactly what happened as people supported the Stamp family. Locals undertook all sorts of acts of kindness that would genuinely leave you in admiration of them.

They say time is the best healer of all and maybe it is and maybe it isn't. But just as things were starting to get back to normal for the rest of the village, we heard more tragic news, this time of Richard Ormond's sudden death.

Once more, the area was grief-stricken. Two young men with it all in front of them had been taken from their families. No-one had expected it and no-one around knew what to say.

In a way, Richard's death was worse because the whole county sympathised with us now and the outpouring of grief was even bigger than when Anthony had died.

Richard was only 22 and made me captain of a team for the first time at under-10 level. He was driving a juggernaut and it jackknifed about two miles outside Gorey, at a spot only 500 yards from where my uncle Billy was killed.

Like Cormac McAnallen, Richard was the role model of the village and you could tell that by looking at the sleeves on his scout's badge; he was so decorated there was barely any more room left on them. You had to achieve many different things to earn a badge but Richard had dozens of them and was a real leader. With Anthony, he had played on the team that won the 1985 under-21 Championship. Both of them were set for good, solid senior careers and yet, here they were, taken away from us in their prime.

How do you react? The first instinct was to turn their deaths into a cause and try to win the club Championship in their memory. Playing for your county is supposed to be an honour but when Christy Keogh selected me at wing back on the Wexford under-21 team that year, I cared little for it after what had happened to us in the village. Most of the lads on the Oulart-The-Ballagh senior team felt the same. The tragedies had brought us closer and we made a pledge to try and win the club Championship for the two lads. But in hindsight, a trophy seemed so insignificant at the end of it all. Maybe such passionate resolutions, like 'winning it for the lads' are inevitable after a sudden death but in a way I feel it's not a healthy exercise; nor was it a good idea to be showing us, before games, the jerseys the two lads used to wear.

I think we were shown them once too often because while we went out that year and trained ourselves into the ground, we came a cropper in the county semi-final. I lost the cool in that game and was sent off for the first time – I wish it had been the last – in my career.

Cloughbawn were the opponents on the day. They had the game won but my direct marker, John Fleming, was absolutely sewing it into me. He kept tipping me on the top of the head, pulling my helmet down and taunting me.

'You're only a little chap, Dunne. Go home.'

It wasn't a lad having a bit of banter; there was needle and what sounded like a bit of malice in his taunts. I managed to ignore him but made a silent vow that John Fleming would get what was owed to him some day.

But despite my self-control toward Fleming, I was sent off for an altercation with another of their players, Tom Byrne, and for that I got six months. Although I was intending to attend the county Games Administration Committee hearing, I was told beforehand that even if I brought Mother Teresa as a character witness it would be to no avail, so I gave it a miss.

It was the end to a horrible year but I suppose there was some compensation seven years later when I went on to win the club's first senior county title with Anthony Stamp's brother, Declan, and Richard Ormond's brother James. And I suppose my mood lightened a little when I was called into the Wexford senior panel for the first time and just smiled when I thought of the trouble I had making the minor team just a couple of years previous.

While I had been out enjoying myself on the town as a young man, I was also putting more into hurling than many other lads in the county at that time and it felt brilliant to get the call-up, but at the same time it was a big surprise. It took me so long to get out of the traps but I had always felt there was prejudice against my club. The fact Tomás had never played minor for the county was seen as an absolute scandal in the village at the time, but as I say, to make the team it was often a case of who you knew.

My friend and clubmate Martin Storey hadn't played minor for Wexford either so I entertained no great hopes of getting any sort of a senior call-up after my past experiences with the county. But I got the nod. First though, I had to wait for my six-month club ban to end. Meanwhile, the Wexford manager, Christy Keogh, was forever asking me when I was free to play. I was only 19 but was playing some stuff and the management wanted me quickly on board. Because I couldn't play League games, they arranged challenge matches against Waterford so they could take a look at me for when the suspension did end.

My first taste of intercounty hurling was fiery. Welcoming me to the intercounty stage, Decies midfielder Shane Ahearne told me it was 'the only fucking time' I'd wear the county colours. Nice one, Shane. I played against him twice in a few weeks though and held my own. I knew there was a lot more to come if I got the chance. Christy's other selectors, by the way, were Robbie Jacob, Tom Mooney, Bernie Rathford and Hopper McGrath.

I did fine in the two challenge games and was duly handed my League debut at wing back against Tipperary in 1988. Over the next few weeks, I kept my head down and tried to make no silly mistakes and it was absolute fantasy land when I learned I was picked for our senior Championship match against Laois a few weeks later.

There was little or no fuss at home at the news of my Championship debut. My mother had in a sense seen it all before and anyway she had no car at the time so she found it hard to get to games; she didn't even make it to my debut in the end.

Dad was away as usual and the brothers weren't that interested, to be honest. And as for the girls, well they had their own things going on and they hardly batted an eyelid either. But it was a dream come true for me and naturally I was dead nervous; I never slept a wink in the lead-up to that game.

There was little or no advice for me from my peers; it was a case of 'look after your own patch' and I didn't really feel comfortable asking my new team-mates for tips because, well to be truthful, they weren't exactly the most welcoming bunch.

There are certain guys I went on to win an All-Ireland senior medal with that wouldn't even look me in the face or give me a word or two when I first joined the squad. As my own career developed, I always remembered that ignorance and would try to have a quiet chat with a new guy coming into the squad.

Anyway, I didn't get the red carpet, but that didn't affect me as much as it backfired on some of those lads who ignored me; they were dropped within a year or two.

Along came my big moment, the day I had waited for since I was a kid, when I drew pictures of the Liam MacCarthy Cup and kept cuttings of Mick Jacob, Jimmy Barry Murphy, the Connollys and Noel Skehan in scrapbooks. Around the village, people had kept the build-up at a low key and no-one treated me any differently. That all helped but still, minutes before the game I was a nervous wreck, going to the toilet every five minutes. I sat in the cubicle and wished my father was there to see me. I felt angry and sad at the same time that he wasn't.

Along with John Conran, who guided Wexford to the 2004 Leinster title, I was picked at midfield. He was coming to an end and I was starting out; maybe both of us had a point to prove.

Eventually, the game got underway. All was going well until Pat Critchley, who was selected at corner forward, dropped back as a third midfielder for Laois, and while it was a tactic that was hardly ever used back then, it worked wonders for our rivals and had the opposite effect on us. We didn't know how to handle the situation and they ran rings around us at the start. As I was the young gun, it was the easy call to put the blame on me and, sure enough, five minutes before the break, I was moved to wing forward. I knew what was coming at half-time and barely looked up as they told me I was being taken off.

Wexford went on to win that game but I was very disappointed myself. A few days later, I picked up a copy of the *Irish Independent* to learn that Martin Quigley had been recalled for the Kilkenny match and there was no L Dunne either in the starting team or on the subs' bench.

'Here we go again,' I thought.

When people asked me about being dropped, I shrugged my

shoulders as though I couldn't give a toss either way, but in truth I was devastated. I couldn't believe I had been taken right off the panel.

Then fate intervened. Larry O'Gorman broke a bone in his hand days before the semi-final and when I came back from playing pitch-and-putt, I got a call from Bro John Cahill, who did all the dirty work for the management team by telling players they were dropped. Bro Cahill asked me to return to the squad and I agreed. Even though I wouldn't see a sniff of action that day, I was handed Larry O's number seven jersey for the occasion.

We beat Kilkenny, but once more I was axed from the panel for the Leinster final with Offaly. They asked me to carry the hurls for that game but I looked on from the stands with my father, who had come home for the game, and my mother while we got beaten by the Faithful County, 3-12 to 1-14.

The barren times continued with the club and the county under-21s, and when the 1989 senior season started, Martin Storey and I were left out in the cold while other guys from my club were brought into the panel. Although we get on fine now, I held my own clubman and Wexford selector Robbie Jacob responsible for my omission; I felt he should have known what I was capable of. Storey felt likewise.

In the end, I was hurling so well for Oulart they just had to call me back in, and that's not being big-headed. My face didn't fit Wexford hurling at the time but I was determined to slot in somewhere.

The relationship between Liam Dunne and Wexford hurling was brittle. I was in and out, musical chairs. Six weeks before they met Kilkenny, I was drafted in again but with no League games behind me and no signs of any chance to prove myself, I had the feeling I would be surplus to requirements soon after.

No shock then when I read in the paper a week ahead of the Kilkenny match I had yet again been scratched from the official squad. They didn't even have the guts to tell me I was gone; let a newspaper do the job instead.

There was nothing more I wanted than to hurl for Wexford but I didn't even bother having words with the management, and they never even gave me a ticket for that game. I was by now built up with fury but just decided to prove them wrong, though admittedly I thought I had been doing that all along.

I'm not going to harp on about results and personal performances; I don't want my story to be like that. But just to see how off the ball the senior selectors were, take a look at my displays in the 1988 under-21 Championship. I scored 0-12 from wing back against Laois, about half of which were from frees. In the same competition a year later, I got the same against Carlow before Kilkenny took us in the next round. I had been voted Man of the Match in the 1989 under-21 Wexford final, but once more we lost to Buffers Alley.

My days of underage hurling were now over and here I was, finally in the real world but, for all my huffing and puffing, with zilch to show for it. It wasn't a great return for almost 15 years of competitive sport but although I held no personal animosity towards Christy Keogh, who at least wanted me in the camp, there was one motivation in relation to the rest of the Wexford management, and that was to prove them wrong. Top of the list was my own clubman Robbie Jacob. For a long time I didn't see eye to eye with him. Those selectors got the boot anyway after the loss to Kilkenny and by the time Martin Quigley, Dave Bernie and Jimmy Furlong took over for the 1989/1990 League, it was a foregone conclusion that not only would I be in the panel but I would be on the team as well.

In the lead-up to the new season, I gave everything I had at club level and was a certainty to make the Wexford team. We had been beaten in yet another county final by Buffers Alley; it was our fourth defeat at the final hurdle and we had yet to reach the Holy Grail. But out of the campaign I got a call-up.

A few other guys joined the squad as well but like dominoes they were dropped one by one. This time, when the official list of 25 was drawn up, I was still in.

Finally, I felt comfortable in the same group as the likes of George and John O'Connor, Billy Byrne, Martin Storey, Eamon Cleary and Tom Dempsey and didn't look to the sideline after making one mistake, fearing a substitution.

Guys were a bit nicer to me when they saw me making progress, which I suppose shows how fickle is human nature, and I played most of the League vying for a wing-back slot with Larry O'Gorman, Seánie Flood and John O'Connor.

It was all the same to me who I was up against for the position because I was going to make it regardless; my mind was made up. Behind the scenes, Dave Bernie was another with plenty on his mind. Deep down, he knew we were light years behind other counties so he brought a more professional approach with him, which resulted in the Wexford Supporters Club being founded, under the guidance of John Doyle. Dave contacted the successful racehorse trainer Jim Bolger and got him involved, and through his contacts, the 'Club' expanded. We were much better looked after once that was established and had tracksuits, proper gear and all the basics we wouldn't have enjoyed in the past.

I enjoyed playing in the League games and really felt like we were at something when we reached the 'home final' against Kilkenny, who won well, 3-12 to 1-10, leaving us facing Laois in the Championship. We were not in the best shape after losing the League, but whatever we had was enough to easily get us past the poor bastards, who we always seemed to meet and beat in those years.

There is no doubt, in hindsight, that we went into the Dublin game taking them for granted and we were duly caught on the hop in one of the worst ever results for our county. They beat us 2-16 to 1-17 and we were left on the scrapheap. Call it sour grapes if you like, but Pat Delaney of Laois, not the best referee I have ever seen, was in charge of that game and he seemed oblivious to the fact they wanted to take our centre forward, Martin Storey, out of the game as soon as possible.

Now Dublin had a decent team, with the likes of Brian McMahon (their second All Star), Shay Boland, MJ Ryan and John Twomey, but their manager, Lar Foley, had them wound up like psychopaths and hurling was not top of their agenda.

Early on, Storey nearly had his nose taken off by their resident hard-man, Tommy McKeown, and as the game developed, we got the feeling we were sitting ducks. At the end, I felt as bad as I had ever done on a hurling field, slumped deep in the doldrums. Being part of the team almost seemed an embarrassment, which was hard to take.

I will never forget the dressing-room afterwards; it was like Beirut in the bad times. Lads were black and blue and had lumps taken out of them. It's all very well to say we learned from that game and they never beat us after that but what a backlash there was at home. The local press went nuts and rightly so.

It had been a dire year. The League final defeat had been one thing. Although I had done well marking DJ Carey, we had lost the game after all, and then the Dubs mugged us. The club scene was a total washout as well and we blew like a timid breeze out of the Wexford Championship.

At this stage, we were too used to accepting defeat with both the club and county. We were underachievers with no tangible hope of shedding that tag. It was small consolation that I was one of the few to come out of it all with a bit of reputation intact. You don't celebrate getting the right numbers for the Lotto if you haven't bought a ticket. But it had been my first year getting a fair crack at the whip and that was the only reason I got away without much criticism.

The likes of John Conran called for club teams in Wexford to be less 'physical' and concentrate on the skills of the game. He urged the county board not to respond to supporter pressure but to keep faith in management.

Another man involved with the underage scene at the time, Liam Griffin, said the root of Wexford's problems was at national-school level, where children were no longer hurling. Griffin maintained the county was in a crisis and he was right. So you can imagine my amazement when I heard I had received an All Star nomination for the season just gone by. We had been beaten by Dublin in the first round of the Championship and yet I was on the short list. I didn't know how in the name of God I was there.

Little did I realise that the next few weeks would see my career turned on its head for good and that a lad from a small, country village, who had struggled to make the county team for so long, was going to become big business. I certainly wasn't prepared for what was about to happen.

Youth will come here and beat on my door and force its way in.
Henrik Ibsen

– CHAPTER SEVEN –
The silver lining

From being a small-town hero with an underachieving club and a county going nowhere, I suddenly stood out from all the rest. It's amazing what two little words can do for you. All Star. It has a nice ring to it and even though I was never one to sing from the rooftops about my own game, this was a fair achievement, considering we had done nothing as a county.

I don't think I changed after the award. I mean after two years and just two and a half Championship games, I still couldn't fathom how I had even got a nomination for the 1990 short-list in the first place. Wexford hadn't seen fit to hand me a regular place on the panel in the previous three seasons, for God's sake, so how could this happen?

But the journalists picked the team and they obviously saw something worthwhile so along with Kieran McGuckian from Cork and Galway's Gerry McInerney I was nominated for the left half-back position, while my old buddy Tom Dempsey was in with a chance of a place on the full-forward line.

The two of us headed up from Wexford to the All Star banquet in the Burlington Hotel, not having a clue what to expect. Whatever about Tom, this was all new to me anyway.

We were told to gather in a room, where I ordered a pint of Guinness. When I went to pay for it, the barman told me it was a free bar. This development seemed to me almost as good as the All Star nomination itself. I could get used to this way of life and the attention that went with it.

A few reporters gathered around but apart from Tom O'Riordan, to whom I had spoken a few times, I hadn't had many dealings with journalists from the national papers and knew very few of them.

In fairness, I had gained a decent profile out of that year's National League but can say in all honesty I felt I had no chance of winning an All Star. Cork won the Championship so surely they would dominate the list.

After losing the League, they faced Tipperary in the Munster final, whose manager, Babs Keating, still claims he was taken out of context when he stated that 'Donkeys don't win Derbys.' They don't, but as sure as there won't be snow at Christmas, Babs's comments backfired on him and Cork went all the way.

Back at the Burlington, we were finally called together for the naming of the team of 1990. The tension was worse than in the dressing-room before a Leinster final. I remember getting a shake in my leg as the MC announced another new player had been selected: Liam Dunne from Wexford had made the left-half-back slot his own.

Not for the first time, but for an entirely new reason, I nearly choked on my pint of Guinness and almost felt queasy. Surely this couldn't be right.

But Cork's Tomás Mulcahy, one of the game's superstars, came over straightaway and congratulated me. I wasn't on magic mushrooms after all – I had actually won an All Star.

'Congrats, Liam! It's well deserved,' he said, grasping my hand.

'Erm, thanks, Tomás. Well done yourself!' I replied, still dazed.

'I didn't actually get one,' he laughed.

After that, the first thing I did was look for Dempsey and I didn't have to try too hard to find him. We spent the night together and you couldn't ask for better company. I toasted the journalists and had a great laugh with Johnny Leahy from Tipperary. It was my first time getting to know him and I found him to be great company, but we didn't do each other any good because it was well into the early hours when we called it a day.

Leahy was one of the game's characters. He was loved, hated and misunderstood all at once but what a genius he was on the field! Of course he might have been a bit of a pup, but most of us are at some stage.

The next morning, I was the last hurler down to get my picture taken for the official All Star 1990 poster. Without doubt, I'm the sickest-looking GAA player you'll ever see in one of those pictures. My eyes are so far back in my head that I look more like a rock star than an All Star.

Paul Curran, the Dublin footballer, was the only player who turned up after me but at least he had some bit of colour left in his cheeks. I was white as a sheet.

As I hit the road for home, the realisation struck me that things would never be the same again. I tried to make it seem like no big deal but deep inside I was burning a fire of pride. On arriving back in Oulart, I deliberately played the whole thing down, even putting my All Star out of sight in a plastic bag, but Mam and Dad were waiting at the door for me and you could see they were proud.

With Dad gone away so much, it was rare to see the two of them together. I suppose that made it even lovelier to find them waiting at the door and I won't forget it. It was one of the moments I will treasure, a chance to show the old man what I had achieved; after all, he put me on the road in the first place.

The All Star was soon extracted from me and given pride of place in the Dunne residence, on top of the TV. There had been little fuss around home when I made my Wexford debut but all of a sudden it was Mardi Gras in Oulart. And this was also a real big thing for Mam.

The local press made a fuss. They came to interview Mam and compare the achievements of Siobhán and I. Of course my multitalented sister kept reminding me she had twice as many All Stars as myself, so my bragging rights were severely dented at home.

I tried to keep out of the limelight that evening and repaired instead to the quiet and friendly confines of Fintan Cooney's pub, where no man's reputation is safe, no matter who he is.

The man himself was waiting for me inside with a bottle of champagne. Not for me, thanks, I told him, I'd rather have a pint of Guinness.

The ever-faithful Tom Dempsey took his life in his hands by coming down to the village and joining me. Buffers Alley men were usually about as welcome in Oulart as Ian Paisley at a Celtic match but Tom got away with it that night.

The celebrations continued well into the night and for several days, until it was crystal clear to me that my days of just being an ordinary fellow were over. I was suddenly recognised a lot more and was asked by several clubs to make presentations.

This is how a lad can get sucked in by drink. It's the first step towards losing the run of yourself. Hurlers generally don't refuse invites to these functions because they know they will be slated if they do. The problem is it's not long before people are buying you pints and more pints. Soon the trap is sprung.

People mean well but if you turn down an invite, word spreads rapidly and you get a bad reputation, especially if the request is to present medals to kids. But when you do turn up, you are under pressure to stay until the end of the night and drink the pints they put before you. As I said, it can become an alarming way of life.

When one club learns you are on the circuit, expect at least five other calls; you can imagine the scene. Wexford have the best fans in the land but they were starved of success and finding an All Star among them was the closest thing they had to a bit of glory. I didn't mind obliging clubs and I didn't mind having a few pints along the way, but others might feel uncomfortable in that role.

One evening Duffry Rovers requested I come down and present medals to their juvenile team and I told them there would be no problem. I handed over the goods to their team captain, Damien Fitzhenry, and two years later he was playing behind me in the Wexford goal. That shows you what can happen in the game in a short space of time – not that I needed any reminders, having struggled to even make the county squad in 1988 and 1989.

The celebrity lifestyle continued with an interview with South East Radio, which for me at the time was like the BBC World Service, apart from the accents. All the national journalists seemed to have my number by now and I didn't mind chatting away with them, which is all part and parcel of the GAA.

There is no point in saying otherwise, the All Star really changed people's perception of me. It opened doors wherever I went and in many ways made up for being stuck in the doldrums so long.

The real bonus was our trip to Toronto late that year, where the 1990 hurling and football All-Ireland champions went out to play the new All Star teams. I had barely been past Tinahely but here I was heading to Canada.

Tom Dempsey made the trip too and we flew from Dublin to Shannon to collect the Munster lads.

Apart from the Cork guys, who just refused to mix with us, there was good interaction on that trip. I also remember looking on in awe of the Kerry footballer Jack O'Shea and thinking of how much this guy had won in the game.

Offaly's Johnny Pilkington and Brian Whelahan were both there as well, as was their goalkeeper Jim Troy, who roomed with me. Dempsey was next door with Noel Sheehy.

Dempsey was the chief entertainer on that trip. He set the fire alarm off one night and within seconds big Jack O'Shea was sprinting down the corridor towards the exit door in his boxer shorts. I was strolling up the corridor with a sliotar in my hand and, fully aware the alarm was a hoax, stopped Jacko in mid-sprint and asked him to sign the ball. Semi-naked, but obliging as ever, he scrawled his name and then tore on out the door.

The trip was great. I had been to Scotland in 1988 with the Ireland under-21s but this was the big time. Most of us got on well, though the Cork lads, as I said, didn't want to know about the rest of the entourage. They spent most of their time in a bar called The Cellar so one evening Dempsey and I went down there to see what was so great about the place. We were quite ready to mix with them but they more or less ignored us, so we left.

The match itself was very competitive. I remember Tomás Mulcahy and Declan Carr having serious words with each other during the exhibition game. There were some heavy shots taken between the two. Teddy McCarthy was all the rage back then and there was a big fuss over which All Star team he would play for. Teddy won All-Ireland medals in both codes with Cork that season but as it turned out he was actually sent off in the football exhibition so he couldn't play the hurling anyway.

The trip was a real eye-opener. You found yourself mixing with the likes of Nicky English, a genuine superstar, and it was easy to take the eye off the ball and start thinking this will always be the way. But being a hero is about one of the shortest-lived professions around.

Despite the All Star, my ambitions were only starting. I felt there was still a point to prove in Wexford so when we got back to business in February of 91 I knew I was up there to be shot down.

We got to the League final that year and lost again, this time by 2-6 to 0-10 against Offaly. We had beaten Kilkenny after a semi-final replay and fell at the final hurdle again. It was sickening to lose two finals in a row because, no matter what way it's perceived now, the League was big business back then.

Along the way, we met our Dublin friends again and though the most recent encounter had been saucy, this was a game like nothing I have ever played in. It was a bloodbath from start to finish. Lar Foley probably thought he would get away with the tactics he had inflicted on us the year before, but there was no chance. 'Remember 1990,' was our war cry.

Minutes into the game, John O'Connor nearly lost an eye when one of the Dublin players pulled high on a ball. The eye injury was so bad certain newspapers apologised for printing a photograph of it the next day.

After that, without being too macho, it was stand and deliver from us. We beat them by two points and this time they were the ones that arrived butchered into the dressing-rooms at the finish.

If such a game took place now, six lads could easily have gone to jail for offences and I'm deadly serious. Besides almost taking the eye out of John O they had also targeted Martin Storey, who was battered all over. If you had a queasy stomach out there you were in trouble.

But the win meant nothing when we eventually lost the final and there was now an underlying fear in the team – we seemed to lose every final we played right down to the Oireachtas and the Walsh Cup.

I remember one of our first losses to Offaly some years before in the Walsh Cup. They were all back in the pub as if no game had taken place at all; the cup meant nothing to them. Wexford would have loved to win it, though, but like the rest it went by the wayside.

Things didn't get much better for the Championship that year either and the underachievers tag was stuck firmly on us. It was Groundhog Day again, we beat Laois in the first round of the Leinster campaign and then faced Kilkenny, which fuelled my personal firefight with John Power, their rugged but classic centre forward.

Power and I delivered some heavy blows in that game and there was a mark on my leg for three weeks afterwards. I actually hated him over our first few encounters but gradually grew to admire him for what he is and would now consider him a real gentleman off the field and a fine hurler on it.

John always played me well. He was never going to do much scoring but he was always creating, and years later he was still making the likes of DJ look good. For this game, however, his creative streak was nullified because we just spent the hour flaking each other, which I

I CROSSED THE LINE

could live with. Over the years we might have let go a few fecks here and there, but there was no real mouthing between us.

We should have won the game and although we led at the break from an Eamon Sinnott goal, they won by 2-9 to 0-13. It was typical Kilkenny.

Of course, every serious hurling fan will remember that as the match where DJ took his famous steps on the way to clinching a crucial goal. The result hung on a knife edge until that incident changed the game. DJ came tearing after a high ball. Kilkenny's Liam McCarthy nudged me in the back and out of the way and the ball almost merged with DJ like a hand to a glove.

Photos show five of us chasing after him and by my reckoning he took eight steps with the ball and then hit it. People still discuss it and some claim he took many more but in my book he was only three steps over the legal limit, and sure what is that in the GAA?

Fair play to him, I suppose, if he'd taken 20 steps on the day he'd have got away with it. I still maintain that our keeper, Ted Morrissey, should have saved it anyway. It certainly was stoppable. Ted should have been ready for it. DJ had no option but to go for goal because they needed it and it wasn't the hardest shot to stop.

Still, everyone had to shoulder the blame. I mean, we badly needed scores at the other end too but there was no chance because we had two players who couldn't play there, John O'Connor in one corner and John Conran in the other.

They couldn't hold their places out the field but were shoved into the corner and so we never looked like hauling it back and lost by just two points. Another hard-luck story.

Disgusted, I shook hands with Power and I said: 'See you again, sonny.' And that was it, we were out.

I never recovered from the defeat that year. I barely hit a ball for my club and it really took the sting out of my game. Larry O'Gorman scored 2-4 off me in the Wexford Championship soon after for Faythe

Harriers, although he claims it was more like 3-11. Something was wrong with our club too; I recall us scoring 4-12 in one Championship game and still losing.

Still, everyone expected I would pick up my second All Star at the end of that year and I was foolish enough to listen to them. Things hadn't gone well but I had done pretty well in the season. To be truthful, I had hurled 10 times better in 91 than I had the year before and had coped well with John Power so I bought into the publicity and actually believed I would make the All Stars. Silly me.

There were 13 Munster men picked. DJ Carey and Michael Walsh were the only two from anywhere else. The years were ticking away and the clock shows no mercy.

But I just looked to 1992 and was heartened when it began full of promise. Tomás, at 30, was the new prodigal son of Wexford and had regained his place in the county squad after seven years out in the cold. He held his place with George O'Connor for the season. But where had he been for seven years?

He had always hurled well for Oulart-The-Ballagh and had been ignored, probably because he had a huge reputation for doing what hurlers shouldn't be doing and that was going out on the tear. I reckon if you are good enough for the job and are willing to go training that should be enough. But Tomás wasn't a politician, you see. We are back to the old chestnut of who you know and where you come from.

Anyway, my other brother Seán had just won his second All-Ireland medal, in junior football this time, and Siobhán had just won two camogie medals with Wexford, so overall it was a good time for the family.

April arrived with an air of hope and optimism. I like that month; the slate is clean, winter is over and it's the time when you can sense the hard work starting to pay off, and in those days it signalled the start of the real business in the GAA world.

The club played a tournament game to kick the season off and

unlike now when club players normally just turn up for the
Championship, the county players had to show their faces.

We played St Martin's on this occasion and near the end of the
game I felt something snap. I took off my boot and, just to illustrate the
highly scientific approach to sports injuries we had back then, I went
over to a tap and poured cold water on it before heading for the pub. I
found it too sore to move so I sat down, handed people money to buy
me a pint and later went home to bed.

The next morning it had swollen like a balloon and turned yellow
and blue, not unlike the Wexford colours. Our club chairman, Joe
O'Shaughnessy, brought me to see Dr Pat O'Neill in Dublin and I
underwent surgery by Dr Ray Moran, brother of the former soccer
international Kevin. Five pins and a plate were put in and I was told to
take 12 weeks off. Lovely.

I was strictly confined to Beaumount Hospital, where the nurses
had a great laugh at my expense, or more specifically, at the expense of
the dodgy bunch coming to visit me.

The nurses were mostly from Dublin and found it hugely
entertaining to see these rough country lads with their inscrutable
accents arriving in groups of six and seven. Some of the old reliables, the
two Bartles, Tom Sinnott, Mike O'Dowd and Martin Dempsey, visited
me for the sole purpose of eating everything I had in the locker.
One night, it was pretty late when the boys arrived and munched all my
provisions apart from a box of Maltesers, which I refused to let go. They
suggested an escape down to the local pub for a pint and, bored off my
tree, I agreed, threw on a tracksuit and headed off to the Beaumount
House, where we slaked our thirst.

Now two days after a serious operation, a pub is the last place you
should be, but I just had to get out. Two security guards stopped us on
the way back into the hospital and threatened to report me for a breach
of hospital regulations. To make matters worse, one of the lads, Mike
O'Dowd, had part of a hurley stuck in his shin bone, which had
become so badly infected he could barely walk, and when the security

guard saw both of us limping, he thought we were taking the piss.

We managed to defuse the standoff by telling him how desperate I had been for a pint and explaining that Mick had half a camán lodged in his leg. The guard just sat there scratching his head but in the end let us through, and Mick even succeeded in getting that bit of a hurl seen to.

Cyril Farrell from Galway had taken over the county team and although the League was dismal, he had a few weeks to work with us and brought Wexford to a Leinster final.

Cyril had introduced a lot of hurling into the set-up and he knew what he was at. He started getting lads to train at 7.30 in the morning and got a good response. I missed out on the lads beating Laois and Dublin and sat in the dressing-rooms, deeply frustrated, as we got past the first-round and semi-final games. So I was more than delighted when we qualified to meet the Cats again in the final, because by the time that game came around I was fit enough to come into contention.

Cyril and Martin Quigley called the shots equally and it was decided not to start me, which I was okay with. We got hammered 3-16 to 2-9 in the final and while I was brought on for Diarmuid McDonald in the second half, I didn't enjoy a moment of it. McDonald was doing fine on John Power at centre back but he was young and the selectors took the easy option of calling him ashore.

The truth is that we were beaten in a lot of sectors that day and, unfortunately, that was the end of Cyril. Like Michael O'Grady in 1987, he wasn't given enough time at all.

Afterwards, I tried to stand back and analyse what was going wrong. In five years of intercounty hurling, I had played the equivalent of only five Championship games: 1988, a half hour versus Laois; 1989, dropped; 1990, one game, versus Dublin; 1991, two games, versus Laois and Kilkenny; 1992, a half hour versus Kilkenny. That was only three full games, not good enough for a 24-year-old with aspirations to go to the top.

I CROSSED THE LINE

Aware that my career was not going to go back in time, I put everything I had into my club for the rest of the year and we reached the county final. Robbie Jacob was our manager at the time and after beating Cloughbawn in the semi-final, we had two weeks off before the big one.

Robbie trained us four nights in the first week and three in the second. I told him we had done way too much but he told me where to get off and when we went out against Buffers Alley once more in the final we couldn't walk. They cleaned us off the field and we didn't even manage a score from play. We had left everything on the training pitch and lost our fifth county final. At the time, Buffers Alley sewed it into us.

We were a club, a county going nowhere. And for once, we were damn sure of reaching our destination.

Players wanted to get the jersey but they had no real commitment to it.
They blamed referees, drinking, pitches and anything else they could think of.
It all came down to self-belief
Ger Loughnane, Raising the Banner, 2001

– CHAPTER EIGHT –
Doing the Hucklebuck

No other team or county has ever celebrated failure quite like Wexford. We are glorious in victory and even more splendid in defeat.

Look back at the Clare teams that Ger Loughnane guided to All-Ireland titles in 1995 and 1997 – everyone loved them at the start but they were the most hated team in the land by the time they won their second title. But all through the years, Wexford have remained a firm favourite; many would see us as their second team and will get behind us when their own side gets knocked out.

'Poor old Wexford, sure they'll give it a lash anyway.'

Even though the boys won a Leinster title in 2004, it remains the mentality. But it's no wonder because flick back through the annals and you will see that we became so used to losing we just accepted it.

I will never forget 1993 for two reasons: I played some of the best hurling of my career and we got to League and Leinster finals and lost both of them. Despite the fact we were beaten in two finals, Wexford people still saw the year as a success. God help them, they were so starved of success, it probably was.

Under Christy Keogh, we went unbeaten in the League and beat Limerick to reach the final, breaking in new players like Damien Fitzhenry, Eamon Scallan and Larry Murphy.

At last, it looked like we were moving up a gear but we had been here before. This was our third League final in four years and we had yet to win one and it would be tough against a Cork side with gala names like Teddy McCarthy, Tomás Mulcahy, Jim Cashman, Denis Walsh, Ger Cunningham and Kevin Hennessy.

Unlike now, the League was big business back then and we would have loved to win it for the fans. I will never forget those days in Thurles, running out in front of crowds of nearly 30,000 and the whole of Wexford looking for that elusive slice of success.

I suppose the real find of the season was Fitzhenry. Just two years before, I presented him with medals at the Duffry Rovers presentation night but here he was now making his name in the Wexford goal, an example to everyone. Fitzy came from a huge sporting family of 10 boys and five girls but soon made his own name.

Before the first game, my brother Tomás got a well-deserved start when Dave Guiney, late for the game, had a minor crash and that let Tomás into the team and I was thrilled; he should have been there anyway.

Although there were six years between Tomás and me, that season would bring us much closer and it probably had the same effect on the rest of the family. My mother was in her element now and really enjoyed that year, although my father was still in the Isle of Wight and Luton and only got home every two months or so then.

We enlisted the help of all my cousins from Cork, the Woulfes, with whom we used to play out our own Cork-Wexford sagas all those years ago. They came down to see the final, wearing the red but not begrudging Tomás or I a bit of success at the same time.

The first encounter was close throughout and at the end, Martin Storey was tripped by John Hartnett. The referee, Willie Barrett, awarded a free and we missed a golden chance to win it when John O'Connor drove it wide with only 45 seconds left.

It ended 2-11 apiece but I really enjoyed the game and played some good stuff. The newspapers said I was the finest hurler in the country at that stage and while I wasn't too sure about that I did feel really comfortable in Thurles.

Delighted with ourselves after drawing with the likes of Brian Corcoran, who was fast becoming a legend, Tomás Mulcahy, Kevin Hennessy, Teddy McCarthy and Jim Cashman, we went back to Hayes's Hotel after the game to a reception hosted by Royal Liver, sponsors of the competition. There, you could see the contrast; the Cork lads sat down drinking minerals while the Wexford lads absolutely hopped off the free beer. You could already tell who the winners would be.

Our lot set a fine example by slugging off a few bottles of wine but at the other side the Cork manager, Canon Michael O'Brien, had his troops well in order – they were on 7-Up.

One evening before the replay Christy Keogh went through the team, player by player, to discuss tactics and encourage us by identifying weaknesses in the opposition. He was animated as he went around the dressing room.

'Niall McDonald, you will be on Ger Manley. Stop him from getting to the ball first and the job is done.

'George O'Connor, you'll be on Seánie O'Leary. You're quicker than him so use your pace and he will be helpless.

'Tom Dempsey, go straight for goals and no messing – take your scores.'

He then turned to Eamon Scallan and placed his hand on the shoulder of our new corner forward.

'Eamon, you're on Brian Corcoran on Sunday. God help you, son!'

What could you do but laugh? Brian was the Young Hurler of the Year in 1992 and truly one of the best I have ever seen but Eamon didn't exactly need to be told that two men wouldn't have stopped Corcoran back then.

The replay arrived and we gathered in Thurles again. I felt we were relaxed enough to do the job, land the League title and get ready for the Championship, and the rest of the lads were even more confident.

I remember Larry O'Gorman sitting in the dressing-room, singing and humming away to himself. Every so often he would throw in a whistle. He was singing that bloody awful Eurovision entry *Why Me?* by Linda Martin.

I started taking the piss out of him. Let's face it, the song isn't exactly a classic. But Larry's logic was simple: 'I'm marking Teddy McCarthy today. He's down in the Cork dressing-room dreading the prospect of marking Larry O and he is thinking to himself, "Why me?"'

What could you say to that?

After five minutes, Teddy had three points scored off him. Larry O was then moved to wing back and then up to centre forward out of the way.

'Why Larry?' we wondered. That was 'The Brother' for you. We called him that because he used it to salute everyone else. He was some hurler and a real character as well. His one-liners became legendary over the years, and the Wexford camp would have been a much quieter place without him.

While Larry struggled that day I could hardly have gone any better and though I started off marking Tomás Mulcahy in each game, I ended up on six or seven different lads before they eventually brought up Corcoran from corner back to say hello.

Brian was an absolute class act then, and we really did feel for poor old Eamon Scallan, who had to try and mark him at his peak. Though I'm surprised, by the way, that Brian came out of retirement for Cork in 2004 – he had a lot to lose in terms of reputation. The gamble, however, clearly paid off.

Anyway, John O'Connor was in the thick of it again for the replay when he mishit a late 70-metre free that would have given us the game and again we drew; we got 1-8 while Cork nabbed 0-11.
We scored a goal in each half of extra time, which should have been enough to see us through but Cathal Casey hit balls over from all angles and Jim Cashman got a dramatic equaliser before John O had that chance with the free.

John O didn't know it then but he would later more than make up for those two misses in a much more important game.

Once more, extra time failed to separate us and Jim Cashman pointed for them in the last seconds to leave us locked at 3-9 to 0-18. They were an arrogant old team, Cork, and you couldn't fault them for that – success breeds that sort of an attitude – but we were slowly getting some respect from them.

The League was a huge competition back then and not surprisingly, those games dominated the media, who lapped up the excitement of it all. Once more, good old Wexford were championed as the underdog and we had 90 percent of the country shouting for us. But Cork had the last laugh and we just didn't get a sniff on the third day.

I think we had nothing left in the tank, and they beat us by five points, 3-11 to 1-12. The Cork lads were so used to winning that they didn't even bother to stay out on the field while Brian Corcoran lifted the Cup. We would have partied for the year had we won it.

And yet, defeat didn't feel all that bad. We trooped off the field, out but not down. The crack had been unbelievable over those three weeks and we all enjoyed the buzz. To this day, I have some wonderful memories of those games, which were played in brilliant spring sunshine and with the whole country looking on.

After the saga eventually ended, the plan was to meet in Mary Willies pub, just outside Thurles, for a clear-the-air discussion. I was sure there would be plenty of strong words from the management; after all, we had thrown two good chances away and the fans were crushed. But instead what we got was a party. Like I say, no-one knew how to celebrate defeat like Wexford.

Don't get me wrong, we are a great sporting county and have had plenty of heroes. This past while alone, we have seen Gordon Darcy dazzle the world with the Irish rugby team, Matty Forde set the Gaelic football fields alight and Niall Griffin, Liam's son, make the Irish Olympic equestrian team. Before them, Nick Popplewell from Gorey was the main inspiration. I loved rugby union ever since Nick put Wexford on the map and took great pride in seeing a Wexford man on the world stage. Billy Walsh competed in the 1988 Seoul Olympics and another countyman, Jim O'Sullivan, won the Irish senior boxing title 10 times.

I just wished the county hurling team could start to make a bit of headway but that was unlikely while we hailed moral victories.

Mary Willies was waiting for me as I arrived, one of the last to make it in, still wondering what might have been. The first thing I noticed was a huge commotion inside, and as I opened the door, I was greeted by a sea of purple and gold, the fans congregated around Christy Keogh.

Now I expected Christy to be in a foul mood, pissed off that we failed him yet again, and I half-anticipated we might get a bollocking. But as the great man stood up and sang *The Hucklebuck*, it seemed unlikely we would.

There would hardly have been more excitement if we'd won the final, and I knew in my heart that even though they had the League trophy, the Cork camp weren't having half as much craic.

And that was the crux of our problem. We wouldn't know what to do with a trophy.

I hadn't heard Christy performing this song before, but by God, he was now the centre of attention and knew every line of it; it was great stuff. The crowd loved it too and cheered like hell as he showed off shakes and moves that Elvis would have been proud of. In fairness, despite the disappointment of losing, it was one of the most memorable moments of my time with Wexford.

Christy gave his heart and soul to Wexford hurling and even though he had fallen short after coming so close to guiding the county to a major title, he was still able to look on the bright side.

He had been in charge in 1981, 1984 and 1988 and each time ensured the set-up was much more professional. He brought Jimmy Furlong and Jimmy Prendergast in as selectors, which proved to be a success as we reached the final. And so it hurt that we couldn't do the job for him.

Dave Bernie had really developed the Supporters' Club and Jim Bolger, the racehorse trainer, was delighted to be involved. I remember coming out of training a few times and Jim would call you over for a chat, which usually ended up with Jim digging deep into the boot of his car and putting a few pairs of Puma King football boots into your gear bag. He enjoyed the League saga immensely and looked after the players out of his own pocket. Lads were always delighted to get the nod from Jim – they knew it usually meant coming away with a bit of gear.

The players also knew it was time to repay the faith so many had invested in us, and in the lead-up to the 1993 Championship we put in an enormous effort. It was mostly hurling with Cyril Farrell, but there was a huge emphasis on running this time, and Christy, who ran with us, put his own plan of action on the table.

Training may not have been as intense as it is now but we put in savage preparation, doing bleep tests in the Showgrounds in Enniscorthy, where the county senior footballers also trained, and undertaking those long stamina runs.

I always thought the Wexford footballers must have felt aggrieved because they trained a lot harder than us but missed out on all the glory. They had one star player, John O'Gorman, who would have made any team in the land, but the hurlers had the much bigger profile so the fans went for us. This has changed a bit in recent years; at least in 2004 they made something of a breakthrough.

It seems crazy to say but after the buzz and high jinks of the League, we went back to the 'humdrum' of the Championship and yet another meeting with Dublin – we beat them 1-14 to 0-10 – and Laois, who by now must have been sick to the back teeth of us.

There was a bit of expectation there this time and the media had really warmed to us so it was no surprise that a massive Wexford crowd drove to Nowlan Park to see the Laois game.

Adrian Fenlon, who had played no part in our League saga,

waltzed straight into the team as a fresh-faced 20-year-old. And I was delighted that Tomás retained his place on the team at wing back.

We hurled well enough on the day and were never going to lose if our heads were right.

Kilkenny were waiting for us in the Leinster final and I reckoned we'd win. Christy had done a marvellous job preparing us and we were primed and ready for action against our biggest rivals.

We gave it everything and had them on the rack for the entire first half. John O'Connor skinned Eamon Morrissey and Tomás skinned DJ Carey, but in a different sort of way. DJ seemed to spend a lot of time on the ground that day. Tomás claimed he had no part in that at all, but in fairness, he gave DJ a few leathers (something the Kilkenny superstar has had to get used to) just to unsettle him. But there were battles like that right the way up the field and we dominated most sectors against a damn good team.

Close to half time, we led by seven points and it looked like a breakthrough finally beckoned until Eamon Morrissey pinched a goal back just before the interval. That score changed the game as we only led by three at the break after hurling them off the pitch.

I think we were a lot like the current Limerick footballers, who came so close lately to slicing the old firm of Cork and Kerry apart but ultimately failed.

We stayed in touch in the second half and, with the game drawing to a close, DJ fell to the ground one more time and I looked across to see Tomás standing over him. My marker, John Power, went ape shit but I hit him with the end of the hurley under the ribs and told him to stay where he was.

He drew a box at me and hit me straight in the jaw.

I wasn't expecting the left hook and he drove me back nearly to the previous week. It was the last time I hit Power with the tip of the hurley – I decided to get on with the game after that.

John and I waged some real heavy battles and some of the spiciest encounters were under the dropping ball. I often cut the hand off him but when the next ball came down, he would pull twice as hard. Sometimes a lad would learn not to put his hand up against me more than once but not John Power.

With a few minutes left I went over to take a free we had done well to win and pumped my fist at the Wexford crowd. I was high on adrenalin and the crowd absolutely erupted onto their feet; they were now with us all the way and I sensed we could finally do the job.

But although I drove the free down the field it came back twice as quick and Kilkenny engineered one of the best points you will ever see to draw level. I was in a circle chasing after them as Liam Simpson, Adrian Ronan and Eamon Morrissey all combined. Morrissey finished off the move to make it Wexford 1-17, Kilkenny 2-14.

That was it: another chance blown. We headed back to Gorey that night and the kick had gone out of us. Totally depressed, Tomás and I hit the town and rumour spread the next day that we were seen punching each other's lights out in the early hours of the morning. If the truth be known, we were holding each other up. We knew our chance was gone.

Deep down Christy knew it too, and we got skinned the next day, 2-12 to 0-8. John Power destroyed me; I had done okay on him in the drawn game but he was a proud man and this was his answer.

The one Wexfordman I felt never got the recognition he deserved over those two games was Tomás, who had held DJ scoreless in the drawn game and limited him to just a goal in the replay.

It was the end of a busy year for the county. We had come so close but in the end we blew it. Kilkenny had ambushed us in the provincial final. To add to our misery in Oulart, the club was knocked out of the Wexford Championship by Buffers Alley.

I was only 25 but I still felt the years were slipping by and while other counties were busy writing romantic and elegant pieces of history, Wexford's contribution to hurling seemed to be one depressing chapter after another.

The 1994 Championship pitted us in another potential bloodbath against Dublin. It was always going to be stormy following the wars of 1990 and 1991, and again controversy was the order of the day. A good few lads were booked early in the game but it got worse. We went on to have George O'Connor and Tom Dempsey sent off while they lost Shay Boland and Tommy McKeown. The game ended in a draw: Wexford 3-13, Dublin 2-16.

Those Dubs were dirty bastards but they showed they could play a bit of hurling – two goals and 16 points is a nice haul. But they were out to get Tom Dempsey, no doubt about it, and I don't think they cared how badly they hurt him as long as he was out of the game. I suppose the fact Tom was sent off was mission accomplished for them. And it upset us because Georgie also lost his temper and walked.

Christy Keogh had given up being upset by their tackles; he was genuinely afraid one of our lads would lose an eye or get the fingers smashed, and when he saw Georgie getting a red card he sat down in the dugout and buried his head between his arms. The subs thought he was going to crack up.

'Poor Georgie, poor Georgie,' was all he muttered.

When he lifted his head, he found an even nicer surprise waiting: Tom Dempsey was there beside him.

'What the fuck are you doing here?' roared Christy.

'Never mind your poor Georgie – I got the line too,' snarled Dempsey.

If an intercounty Championship match hadn't been in the balance just then, it would have been hilarious but there was deadly serious business going ahead on the pitch.

We didn't want to be the team that lost to Dublin again but we were struggling, because even though they played nice hurling in patches, they also dragged us down to their level and we couldn't put them away.

Two days later, a number of players from both teams, including of course your truly, were summoned to a Leinster Council meeting and as we walked in the Dublin players came over to us. For 70 minutes the previous Sunday, they had tried their best to kill us, but we are all only human and we knew that each player who was in the dock wanted desperately to get off.

We reckoned we were lucky that we had Tom Dempsey on our side because he would sweet-talk a raging bull and we saw him as our trump card in the meeting.

But in the end, the Wexford lads didn't have to say much because Ciarán Barr, the former Antrim and then Dublin hurler, spoke for everyone and rambled on for half an hour.

When he finally stopped waffling, the bemused members of the Leinster Council went in to consider their verdicts. They handed Tommy McKeown a year's suspension and gave Georgie and Tom Dempsey a month each. The rest of us got off with severe warnings but the funniest part of the night came when they announced the county boards were fined £7,500 each.

With that news our county chairman, Paddy Wickham, nearly choked on the cigarette he had just lit. Spluttering with shock, he started ranting on about the cost to the county board. Wexford didn't have that sort of money and Paddy was doing his best just trying to keep the ship afloat so he wanted to know where in the name of God would he find the extra seven and a half grand?

But maybe the county board need not have worried. Some will argue that the money eventually went back to the two counties anyway. The Leinster Council slammed on the fines but once the fuss was over there was a fair chance that the money found its way back in the form of coaching grants to both county boards. The Council got their bans, the press got their headlines and the Wexford and Dublin committees probably got their money back in some shape or form.

You could never be up to the GAA!

These days the Council make sure a lot more goes in the direction of the players and I must say in passing that I got to know one of the current Leinster Council officials, Michael Delaney, very well over the past number of years, and he's a real players' man, which is nice to know.

But the bans Michael's predecessors handed out failed to do the job and things were no better in the replay, where Dublin had three men sent off.

This time we held our heads, came out of it with a bit of dignity and progressed easily by 3-22 to 1-11 to meet Laois in the next round. Again we demolished Laois, this time by 18 points, 4-24 to 4-6. I felt for Laois; it was an absolute disaster for them, one of their worst days ever.

In the Leinster final, though, we were on the receiving end. Offaly pulverised us by 1-18 to 0-14 and that match was the end of Christy Keogh's reign – he resigned after it.

Christy felt his time was up and so too did a few other guys who never played for Wexford again, including Garrett Kavanagh.

My heart went out to Christy and many others sympathised with him too. He had been so close at times to landing us either a League or Championship title. Over the years I had often wondered what he thought about when he went home after losing another final or big match by just a point or two.

I still feel he was the unluckiest manager in the game and while this was his third term, we were still being beaten by a point or two each time; there was no respite. Luck is a precious commodity – not everyone gets a taste of it. But he could eventually take heart from the fact he had built a team that would soon go forward and represent Wexford in style and some of the lads he had brought in would perform for the team for the next 10 or 12 years, something he can be justifiably proud of.

Christy was never far from my mind. At the end of the day, he was the one who gave me my first break. Incidentally, Christy had won county senior medals with both Shamrocks and Raparees and I often wondered what club he would support if push came to shove. Several times I asked him what medal would take pride of place on his mantelpiece and he always just smiled. Knowing him, I suspect they would have been side by side.

I also wondered if things would ever start to happen for me. By now, I had lost three Leinster finals, three League finals, two county finals and, damn it, I had even lost two Walsh Cups and two Oireachtas titles.

There was some respite from all the doom and gloom when Martin Storey, Tom Dempsey, Larry O'Gorman and I were picked for the Leinster Railway Cup team and we actually won a trophy. I'm not joking. We beat Connacht in the semi-final and then Ulster in the final. I was absolutely delighted because it was my first proper medal at adult level and the bonus arrived when, at the end of the year, I found myself in the running for an All Star again.

The hype had begun around the county but I ignored it because although everyone was telling me I was a certainty, I had heard the exact same in 1991 and had been devastated to lose out.

Anyway, the morning before the 1993 team was announced, Larry O rang my mother and told her I had made it. I refused to believe it and went to bed early but made sure to be up early to listen to the radio and actually hear my name being called out. In 1990, the hurling awards had been announced 'live' but it was the footballers' turn this year and so this time the hurlers knew their fate the day before.

Martin Storey made it on the team as well and up we went to the All Star function and had a great night.

Individually I suppose it had been a good year for the likes of Storey and me but what good is that? We needed success for Wexford. While I was delighted to win a Railway Cup, the second All Star meant more because I was still sore with Wexford for being dropped a few years earlier. As I said, winning personal awards just wasn't good enough anymore – I wanted to do it with the boys I grew up with.

There seemed to be little I could do about Wexford's slump but off the field, I decided to freshen things up a little by switching jobs. By now I had been 10 years with Andy Roche, who encouraged me to use my profile more.

The soft-drinks industry was an area that interested me; I had seen Billy Byrne working as a sales rep for one company and had been attracted by the company car and mobile phone that came with the job so I began to look into it.

Breda Flood had arranged a meeting for me with Liam Griffin, a Rosslare man who had a reputation as a big fish in the hotel business. I didn't ask any questions – people just said he was the man to talk to – and when we met, he told me I would have to bide my time because such jobs were hard to come by.

It was no surprise then, that I ended the 1994 intercounty season frustrated and wondering when our luck would change. At this stage all I had was a bit of respect, something I would lose a few years later.

I suppose when the county team gets knocked out, I did what every player does when reassurance and confidence is needed. I turned to my club.

What the Jaysus do you want going down to those louts for?
It's boxing gloves you'll need for them, not hurls.

Wexford follower to Tom Neville
when he agreed to manage Oulart-The-Ballagh

– C H A P T E R   N I N E –
Oulart-The-Ballagh

It took over 100 years for Oulart-The-Ballagh to win a senior Championship but what chance of success had the club when we were cursed? Legend has it that an angry priest put the hex on our club in the 1930s when the boys on the team refused to go to a funeral Mass and went training instead. The story goes that the priest told them they would never win a senior Championship, though we were only a junior club at the time.

Now the 'curse' was a load of rubbish but some people began to believe it after we lost final after final and certainly the Buffers Alley men delighted in sewing it into us and laughing at this so-called enchantment.

I think a few of our players started to believe in it as well because before we reached the 1994 decider, we had already lost five county finals and, believe me, that puts a few doubts in your mind.

Oulart could always produce plenty of intercounty players. Tom Byrne captained the Wexford minor team to an All-Ireland title in 1968 and Martin Storey led the seniors to the promised land 28 years later. In between, we had countless other great players but other clubs used to laugh at us because we never pulled together at club level. They saw Oulart players travelling to county training individually and laughed at the sight.

How could you win anything when lads you were playing

alongside wouldn't even talk to you sometimes? That's the way it was with us; you were never guaranteed to have everyone pulling in the one direction.

Still, the advert on the telly reminds us it's 'One life, one club' and that's the way I have always felt about Oulart-The-Ballagh. It's my home. I grew up here playing with my brothers and best friends and while there was a certain amount of bravado in our battles over the years, this is where it all started. And this is where it will all end in 2006 when I plan on completely retiring from the game.

We were never short of heroes growing up. Mick Jacob was the main man, but as I said, even he couldn't lead us to the breakthrough. We were starved of success, regularly losing county finals down the years. I was there to experience the feeling when we lost 3-16 to 2-13 in 1989 and again in 1992, when Buffers Alley beat us 1-11 to 1-5. And so when 1994 came around a few of us felt it was time to get rid of the old wives' tale for once and for all.

In fact we were desperate to win a county title. We felt like second-class citizens of Wexford, especially when we would meet teams like Buffers Alley, who were well used to winning. Maybe it was that desire that prompted us in the end to go ahead and bring in an outsider, something many would consider treason, a slur on those loyal club stalwarts who had spent years trying to get things off the ground.

Back then especially, the idea of going for an outside coach was treated with disdain. It was a case of is there no-one good enough in the club and if there's not, well we still won't appoint an outsider.

But that's not always the best view to take and in 1994 we needed a blow-in to lead us to our Holy Grail. Like it or not, we would not have won our first county title without Tom Neville.

In 1993 Brendan O'Connor, a guy who was heavily involved with the club and would have given his lung for the cause, called to the house and explained to me that he had a plan in mind for the Oulart-The-Ballagh senior team. But he didn't provide a huge amount of detail, and so when in January of 1994 Martin Storey and I travelled to Carlow with Brendan, on the basis that he had a pleasant surprise in store, we were not sure what to expect.

As we arrived closer to the town, Brendan told us we were meeting Tom Neville, who had won All-Ireland medals with Wexford and had trained them in 1976 and 1977.

Brendan had a fairly detailed brief on what was needed to manage our team and it was just as well because Tom bled him dry for information on the set-up. It was clear straightaway that if he was coming down, it wouldn't be for the fun of it.

It took a few meetings to persuade him that we had something worthwhile to offer but eventually Brendan broke through and was able to make the proposal at board level.

Inevitably, there were a few dissenters in Oulart, including Mick and Robbie Jacob and Pat Dempsey – guys who, in fairness, would have had the club's best interests at heart. But Tom's name somehow got through and we had a new manager.

From day one, Tom took no shit. On his first meeting with us, he revealed that people around the county thought he was mad coming to train us.

One wag had said to him: 'What the Jaysus do you want going down to those louts for? It's boxing gloves you'll need for them, not hurls.'

That was the perception people had of us. The Dunnes may have been no angels but the rest of the lads on the team were well able to look after themselves too. We had a name for being well up for a boxing match. Sadly, when it came to hurling, we didn't always end up winners.

Tom decided he had to change that mentality. He demanded a lot from Martin Storey and me, the two resident county players, and gave us no special treatment just because we were wearing the purple and gold. We had to go training with the club like the rest, and even when we were with the county two weeks before the 1994 Leinster final Tom expected us to train with the club – there was no layoff.

That hadn't happened before, Martin and I being on a par with the rest. But it was Tom's way or the highway and he got the respect he deserved.

The man just wanted to win every match he played and he changed how we trained to help achieve that ambition. If he wasn't running the shit out of us, we were doing ball work for a couple of hours at a time, and while it was heavy going, the results were clear for all to see.

Tom's training methods were unusual but effective. The first thing he did was penalise indiscipline; a guy could lose his place for persistent fouling and he would certainly have to do extra training if Tom wasn't happy with him. The result was we went the whole year without getting a man sent off.

He also hated the idea of five or six players looking for a pass from a team-mate at the one time so he introduced the idea of 'silent training', which meant you couldn't call a lad when he was about to offload. It was frustrating; lads who broke the silence had to hit the ground and give 20 press-ups and the boys on the team didn't like that. It led to fits of coughing being introduced into the Oulart-The-Ballagh training sessions. You would cough if you wanted a pass and cough even harder again if you wanted it more desperately than someone else.

Passers-by thought a flu epidemic had broken out in the village; here were the 30 fittest men in the parish coughing and wheezing at each other. It's a wonder someone didn't put Wexford hospital on alert. But how could you question Tom's methods when we came through the early stages of the Championship unbeaten and ended up in a county semi-final against Crossabeg-Ballymurn.

With a little bit of arrogance in us now, we cruised past them by 3-12 to 2-9 and qualified to meet St Martin's, backboned by the Wexford legends George and John O'Connor, in the final.

In previous years the village went ape-shit whenever we reached a county final but this time the build up was much different. Tom insisted on keeping it low-key, and you would have thought the club had been knocked out months earlier. There were no new togs or gearbags for the game. We didn't even get a pair of socks. Tom wanted no fuss, and he got his wish.

Off the field we were tighter than we'd ever been. There was always a good social element to the club but Tom had put a special bond between the lads.

We knew there were fellas who had lost finals going back 20 years and still didn't talk to each other, and we didn't like the notion of that.

As I write this in late 2004, we have one of the best club teams in Wexford, but we still have the odd guy who won't row in or pass the ball and that attitude won't win a county title for you.

You see, while the club is the be-all and end-all for many people, it's also the easiest place to fall out with your neighbours, family or friends. The amount of politics that goes on in clubs all over the country is crazy.

Tom and his selectors, Willie Sutherland, Jimmy Prendergast and Mick Jacob changed all that. They recognised the pitfalls right away and saw to it that we all sang from the one hymn sheet.

I enjoyed 1994. Tomás was captain and corner back and my other brother Seán was corner forward. In between them, I was centre back, and my old friend Martin Storey was wing forward.

As the days led up to the decider, I couldn't help comparing it to the 92 decider, when there were about 500 red and black Oulart flags hung on telegraph poles the whole way into Wexford town. This time, there was just one flag up; people wanted so badly for us to win that they were afraid to put anything up in case it would increase the pressure.

When the final came around, we were well drilled for the Martins, but the game itself was touch and go the whole way, a battle between two teams that had forgotten how to win and wanted it desperately – St Martin's had been out in the cold for almost as long as us.

I marked James Quirke, a good hurler who scored 10 points from frees and one from play. Then Rory McCarthy came in on me and he was another tough test. We were going down to the wire.

But Martin Redmond, Martin Dempsey, John Stamp and John Cleary were flying for us and we went into the half-time break a point up. With time almost up, and Oulart a point down, I was about to take a free from 80 yards out. Just as I made to lift the sliotar, Tomás came racing up like a lunatic looking for a short pass: 'Play the quick one! The quick one!'

I looked at him as if he had two heads, wondering where the silent hurling had gone, and replied: 'Will you ever fuck off – haven't I enough to be worrying about.'

Fortunately, the free was on target, though the sliotar barely cleared the keeper's hands and laboured over the bar. We were level again. Storey then shot a great point to put one between the teams. But the referee, Brian White, gave St Martin's two close-in frees, no more than 45 and 50 yards, the type of handy frees that can rip the guts out of you, but thank God they missed both. Fuming, I went over and told White what I thought of him and shortly after that he blew for time.

All mayhem broke out. We had won our first county title, by 1-14 to 0-16. I can honestly say it was the best feeling of my sporting life and when I rewind the memories, it still is. It's a moment I'll never forget, to see the looks of joy on the faces of friends and neighbours – it meant so much to them. Tomás got the man-of-the-match award and, as captain, lifted the cup too; it couldn't get much better for him.

I went over to George O'Connor and embraced him. I put my head on his chest and I don't mind saying a few tears fell out of my eyes. George had never won a county title either and his emotion was obvious.

Lifting my head up, he said: 'It had to be one of us, Liam. It had to be one of us.'

Four years later St Martin's went on to win the title but George wasn't playing, though I was delighted that John still was.

Meanwhile, we hit the town that night and partied for a year after. Even some guys who had carried grudges from previous losing teams put aside the bitterness and joined in the celebrations.

At one stage I looked around and I saw family, friends and neighbours; we got back to Oulart and thought that the village had never looked so well. There was a cup home now to make everything seem complete.

While we partied hard, Tom had a tough job reminding us that there was a Leinster title to be played for. In fairness, we put the pint glasses down for a few days and managed to beat Castletown in the semi-final, which meant we would meet Birr in the final.

As luck would have it, Birr were on the cusp of becoming one of the greatest club teams in history, with Brian Whelahan, the Pilkingtons and Joe Errity on board. It was no shame on us that they needed a replay to win.

Needless to say, Tom was by now the main man around the village. He had made it possible for us to at least look a Buffers Alley man in the face and say: 'Hey, we have a county title too.' That feeling was priceless. The curse was lifted. We knew it was a load of crap but the Alley lads had milked it all along. For good measure we shut them up again in the county League final later that year to put another trophy beside the Bob Bowe Cup, which now looked to be almost half the size it was when we first got our hands on it.

I went through so many emotions that year after playing with lads so long and then actually winning something together.

Winning that cup prolonged some lives in the parish by three or four years such happiness did the locals get out of it. A few of them went to their reward in the past year or two but I'm convinced they would have gone much earlier if not for that win.

I'm talking about lads like Lar 'The Boiler' Dempsey, a man who passed away recently but saw it all with the club over the years. Lar was club president for a long time and had watched us go from the junior ranks to senior county champions. After so many bad years, he finally got a taste of the big time.

We went on to retain our title in 95 when we beat Glynn-Barntown, who were playing their first county final, 2-15 to 2-9. We beat them again two years later to win our third title.

They were magic times. I was delighted that the club finally came good. For years, there were five major families in the village: the Cooneys, Clearys, Roches, Penders and Dunnes. And people like Brendan and Butch O'Connor, PJ Harris, Tom Byrne, The Boiler Dempsey, Paddy Keogh and the Jacob brothers all helped steer the ship in the right direction. But it took an outsider to get us to the top.

Tom Neville will always have the freedom of the village and maybe in a way he helped us adapt to outsiders coming into our parish. That's the way it's gone now. A generation ago everyone knew each other, but so many people have moved in lately it's no longer so.

The great thing is that 95 percent of them are lovely and have got fully involved in the community. My hope is that many of them will contribute to the club for the next generation.

Just lately we played a match and Tomás brought my young lad, Billy, into the dressing-room afterwards. It hit me then that, when I retire in a year or two, for the first time in over 30 years there will be no member of the Dunne family playing for Oulart, and I suppose that's the way it is. Playing for the village was always something special to me; for a long time it was much better than turning out for my county.

And then in late 94 we heard that Liam Griffin, a guy who had been involved in the underage set-up was taking over the Wexford team. Jesus, he was a committed man at underage level and had played for Clare, but what would he know about managing a Wexford senior hurling team?

Stick to frying rashers you long nosed hoor.
Disgruntled Wexford fan after the county's
loss to Meath in the 1995 League

– CHAPTER TEN –
A prophet in his own land

I spent the first meeting Liam Griffin had with the Wexford hurling
team staring at the size of his nose – I was fascinated by it. He was a
skinny bloke but, by Jesus, was he well equipped in the nasal
department. And did he love to talk, a chattering cyclone. As he stood
there in front of us, it was clear as day to any outsider that he was the
only winner in the room. Although we could all spot his big hooter, we
took in little or nothing of what he said. We were losers, you see. We
had thrown away every final we had reached and didn't really want to
listen. We were just too used to losing.

Griffin was born in Rosslare in 1946 and is one of a family of 10.
His father, Mick, came from Clare and Liam went there to study at the
Shannon College of Hotel Management and joined a nearby club,
Newmarket-on-Fergus. He had played all grades of hurling and football
for Wexford apart from senior but soon found himself on the Clare
senior hurling team that reached the National League semi-final of the
1967/1968 season.

He made his Championship debut that same season and scored 1-
2 against Waterford but his career at the top ended when he had to
travel to Switzerland to continue his hotel training.

His hurling ambition had, therefore, never been fully realised but
we were hardly going to help him either. This Wexford team had lost
every final it had reached and maybe we didn't even want to listen. But
not least because he had helped me in the past, I felt I owed him

something. Thank God I opened an ear and kept it opened through the bad times because we went on to share a piece of history together.

He didn't know me when he helped secure my first job; he didn't really know much more when he made me captain of Wexford, but it's fair to say he had learned a little when he quickly took it back again. It was never going to be a straight road.

I didn't know Liam from Adam when I first met him in his family hotel at Rosslare in the summer of 1989 and even now it's hard to think that one person could have such an effect on the rest of your life. Around the county, Griffin was seen as the man in the know, the guy to talk to if you wanted something, and if he trusted you or thought you were worth the effort, then you were on the way.

I badly wanted a job as a soft-drinks rep, mainly because Billy Byrne had a similar position and I liked the look of the lifestyle. Breda Flood arranged the meeting with the blessing of my employer at the time, Andy Roche, who encouraged me to move on in life and use my profile. I had decided the joinery business was not for me and had no intention of setting up a business on my own so it looked like I hadn't too many choices. I was only a kid, nervous as hell, but out Griffin came from the hotel offices to talk to me and I almost wet myself thinking how much he looked like Pinocchio. But I managed with a mighty effort to look him in the eye as we made a bit of small chat, and then it was straight down to business.

'What age are you, Liam?' he asked.

'I'm 20.'

'Well, it could take you five years to get this job, you know,' he continued, before scribbling down my details.

He didn't have to help. Liam Griffin owed Liam Dunne nothing. But that day he treated me like one of his own family. And a short while later he wrote off to Cantrell & Cochrane, Letts, Coca-Cola and all the big drinks companies on my behalf.

Of course I recognised that as a successful businessman he had enough to do without writing letters on my behalf, and I resolved that if

I ever got the job I would pay him back by working hard.

Little did I realise that five years later, when I eventually got the job and we got to know each other better, Griffin would maintain his incredible habit of making dreams come true on and off the field.

I suppose my first impression of him was that he was an ordinary Joe, apart from the nose, but he took a great interest in my career. Through the years, we'd meet every so often and he would stay in touch just to let me know he had not forgotten.

The news I'd been waiting for finally came in February 1994, when a position came up with G.H. Lett Ltd, the only independent drinks wholesaler in Ireland.

I hadn't a clue what the job entailed because I had given up all hope of getting it but they still gave me the nod. That was down to Griffin. Dougie Lett brought me around with him on a run for the day and as I had to fill in the order sheets I couldn't keep track of where we were going or what direction certain pubs were in, so when he left me on my own for the first time, I didn't finish the run until 9 pm. It was pitch dark but I felt like I was someone at last.

That was down to Griffin too. By that time, he had served as manager of the Wexford football team and had long been involved in the underage set-up and with his own club. He was known as a passionate GAA man but didn't have any real reputation as a miracle worker, so when word filtered through that he was the new county senior hurling manager, the team was surprised and didn't really know what to expect.

Word reached us that Griffin had absolutely bamboozled the county board, scarcely allowing them a word in edgeways to ask him any questions. After talking up a storm about tactics, players, discipline and training techniques, he himself ended the interview by saying: 'If I were in your shoes, I wouldn't appoint me. I'm a loose cannon. But I will help you find somebody else.'

It was too late – he had the job.

We had known Christy Keogh so well but here we had someone different and it must be said that not all the lads danced with joy at his appointment. He could well have been a great player but for injury and his studies but the lads wanted a bigger name as boss. I wanted to give him a chance but part of that goodwill disappeared three weeks into October of 1994 when he rang to tell me that I wouldn't be centre-back for Wexford in the following year's Championship.

'You're a better wing back than you are a centre back,' he insisted.

It was a strange enough phone call to get before the season even started. He softened the blow by telling me I was his captain but reiterated I would not be played in the heart of the defence. And then he hung up.

I felt both decisions were wrong. Centre back was my best position and Tomás should have been made captain instead of me. I didn't really want it and felt most of those in the club wanted Tomás for the job anyway, but from day one Liam thought he wouldn't get the necessary commitment from Tomás and that was the end of it; my brother was not in his plans.

Liam sent me a letter confirming I was captain and what was expected of me. He pointed out what a great honour it was for me and my family and added that he expected full consultation between both of us for the year ahead. I felt no added joy or elation at getting the job; we had to start winning things – that was more important.

Convincing the public we could be winners was going to be the hard part. Many in the county felt Griffin should have been let nowhere near the job; he had a lot of critics and still has, but then again, if you voice your opinion often enough people get envious or resentful and that's what happened with him as the years went on.

Liam does things right 99 percent of the time but we Wexford people have an awful habit of shooting ourselves in the foot and it seemed we resented anyone who would get off the fence and stand his ground for the county. We didn't know Liam had been offered the job previously and had turned it down, although he will tell you now that he regrets spurning the chance of taking us over a few years earlier.

He devised an individual training programme for each of us. There was no collective preparation until after Christmas. Griffin simply trusted us to work away on our own before regrouping after the holidays. I don't believe for a minute that anyone did the programme, and when we came back after the break it was clear we had taken a step back in terms of physical conditioning.

My brother Seán, Martin Storey and I did the training every so often but we would wash it down with a great haul of pints in one of the local pubs just as soon as it was over. To say the preparation was poor in 1995 is like saying modern Ireland is a rip-off, an understatement.

Liam also tried to take a psychological approach with us but it went in one ear and quickly flowed out the other. We were a macho lot at the time and had no business listening to this philosophy crap and reading the handouts he gave us. Most of the lads thought Griffin was a lunatic and it would take a full year for them to cop on there was method in his madness. He brought in Rory Kinsella and Séamus Barron as selectors. Those two were well respected but after beating Cork in the 1994 Oireachtas final by 2-7 to 1-8 and losing to Dublin 2-6 to 0-11 in the Walsh Cup final, we went through the whole 1995 season playing like children.

The week before our League clash with Meath at Belfield our club went away for a weekend in Killarney as a prize for winning our first county title. To get the ball rolling, Tomás and I started the session in the Danny Mann pub on Thursday at 1 pm and we went at it all day Friday and Saturday before eventually calling it a day in the early hours of Sunday morning.

Just a few hours later I lined out for Wexford against Meath. Seán and my friend Bartle Sinnott lay unconscious in the car as I drove to the match and they never had as much craic at a game in all their lives as they watched us go down by three points, 1-16 to 0-16.

As captain, I led the side out and went up for the toss, but that was the closest I got to leadership or action in that game. I don't remember hitting a sliotar in the first half, although my marker had scored a goal and a point. You'd think I would have grabbed a point or two because I had the choice of three balls – at least that's how many I was seeing most of the time.

Once, trying to run out for a ball, I tripped and fell, only to hear an old man in the crowd tell his pal: 'Dunne had never been the same since he broke his ankle.' If he knew how much Dunne had drunk in the previous 72 hours, he might have had more respect, or not.

The Meath lads were overjoyed at the result and as he walked off the field, Griffin was spat upon by a Wexford supporter. That was how bad things were; it was clear we had done nothing before Christmas and it was twice as obvious we were still only pissing around.

But we still didn't hurt enough. A few of us even chuckled at the result. It would have hurt more if we had cared enough, but then we would have had to do something about it.

As the Championship loomed we hoped for a change but failed to look within, where change was most needed. Griffin continued preaching but we would not be converted. While he wanted us reading articles on sports science and sports psychology, most of the lads wouldn't even bother reading a menu. We wanted to hurl alright, but weren't prepared to put the work in before games.

Griffin would give us handouts on diet and nutrition, but most lads threw them out the windows of their cars on the way home, though Storey and the two O'Connors used to take note of them. We were the fools though. Our new manager was trying to make changes but we had been around for a few years and thought we knew it all. We were set in our ways but they were not winning ways.

Surprisingly, Griffin never lost the rag with us and so we edgily progressed to the 1995 Championship. My debut as captain went well and we walloped Westmeath 6-23 to 1-7 to qualify for the Leinster semi-final with Offaly. That game proved to be more controversial in its build-up than anything else.

Oulart-The-Ballagh had a League game with Crossabeg-Ballymurn fixed for the Tuesday night before the Offaly match and, as we were under pressure to play from the club, I told the Wexford secretary, Mick Kinsella, that if the game was on we would play. He disagreed and told us to concentrate on the Leinster Championship as county board regulations suggested. I dug my heels in and made the point it had been seven weeks since the Oulart club had played a competitive game and our club officers wanted the complete panel together to get ready for the Championship match with St Martin's. I told him I felt the board could have put our Championship game back by two weeks like they had done for two clubs the year before. But this was Oulart, we were unfashionable and the board refused to switch.

But the club didn't budge either; we wanted to defend our League title so we took a stand. Tomás, Paul Finn and I all played against Crossabeg-Ballymurn – Martin Storey was injured and didn't play – and we won by 20 points.

But the sewage really hit the fan in county training the following night. It was clear when Griffin arrived that World War Three was about to break out.

Looking desperately hurt and deadly angry at the same time, he came up and really tore into me.

'I haven't slept a wink all night over this,' he said through gritted teeth. 'Playing a League game days before a Leinster semi-final. What in the name of Jesus are you at? I have to do something to you but I don't know what. I have to take some action.'

I had to say something but what could I say?

'Liam, whatever you decide to do, I'll back you 100 percent,' was all I could think of.

He walked away but some 45 minutes later, still with a face like thunder, he came over to me.

'I have to make a stand,' he sighed. 'I'm taking the captaincy off you.'

In fact he took the captaincy off the club completely and Martin

Storey was very angry with that because he hadn't played in the League game with Oulart. But Georgie O'Connor became the new leader of Wexford.

What followed was not pretty and there were meetings about meetings for days afterwards. I pointed out that we had a game ahead and we should try to focus on that but it split a lot of people in the camp. The club was very bitter and there was fury all around the village. It had been Oulart's first time winning the county title and our first shot at having a county captain and many of our members and supporters were disgusted at Griffin for taking it away from us. In fact many would still hold it against him. They would have settled for any of us, Tomás, Martin Storey or myself, leading the team out.

South East Radio read a statement from our club on the matter but the county board and the management team were furious they didn't get a chance to respond and the matter flared up all over again.

I didn't mind losing it, I really didn't, but I felt Liam made an awful blunder giving the captaincy to Georgie because he was too close to both him and John O – they were cousins and good friends as well.

I also felt he had put Georgie in an awkward position. And even though I didn't particularly want the captaincy, I was a bit annoyed. I remembered Griffin's phone call the previous October, when he told me I would not be centre back for the season ahead and began to put two and two together and get seven. Now I was getting paranoid.

I saw Georgie at centre back and captain of the side and knew it should have been one of our club members. Worse still, others on the team clearly felt the same and were grumbling behind Griffin's back. Most of the lads agreed the manager had to do something about the controversy but not all believed Georgie should have been captain. There were huge differences of opinion.

And so it was in that alarming frame of mind that we approached the Offaly match. We didn't have a chance. I knew it and Griffin knew it.

'Dunne sacked as captain' was the headline in the *Irish Independent* in the lead-up to the Croke Park clash. I was hounded by journalists looking for stories but I remembered all the effort Griffin had put in getting me a job and so I kept my mouth shut.

John Conran rang me and said it would be better to turn my phone off and go to Morriscastle beach for a walk. He was right; the fact I kept my views to myself would later stand in my favour. But one thing was for sure: as match preparation went, you could not find any worse. It was typical Wexford.

There was enough bitching between the players and the county board as it was without this. They would hardly even let us swap jerseys with opponents back then and there was a bad vibe towards the fixtures committee, who had refused to switch that club game.

When Sunday's televised game with Offaly arrived, the Wexford team was a total shambles. The game began but we might as well have been still in the dressing-room, and by the time we got back there at half-time, we were a beaten team.

Georgie tried to rally us by going around and roaring encouragement but I went into the toilets and didn't even listen. I was wrong but Seánie Flood and a few more of the lads followed me; it illustrated the split in the camp.

Despite everything, and even though I had been in the public eye all week, I had remained pretty focused and was actually happy with my game. And yet it wasn't worth a tinker's curse that I picked up a man-of-the-match award because they beat us again, 2-14 to 1-10.

Controversy would dog me for the rest of my career but this was my first experience of it. I was a key player in the further decline of Wexford hurling. We had become a pathetic, sad bunch, incapable of taking our chances.

In the early 90s, we had come so close to getting somewhere but here we were on our arses, having lost three Leinster finals in 1992, 93 and 94, and now this latest slump.

The 1995 season could have been the start of a new era for

Wexford hurling, what with live TV coverage and all that, but it had caved in on us and we could not get out of that dressing-room quickly enough – I doubt some lads even waited to have a shower.

As for the row surrounding the club, I felt I had let Liam Griffin down, but at least he had been given a two-year term and I hoped there would be a chance to repay him the next season.

I had been adamant I would stand by my club, even though I mightn't always have received their full backing when I was a minor. To this day I maintain it would have caused little bother for the Wexford fixtures committee to make a switch but they didn't bother their arses and we all were in the doldrums again. Good old Wexford – open a window and we'll jump out.

All sorts of jokes at our expense flew around the place but it wasn't funny at the time. By now the fans had had enough and wanted Griffin out. Oddly enough, the players had seen him take a stand on the Oulart incident and respected him for it, and they knew there were more to blame than just Griffin.

But the public failed to see it like that and on Monday September 4 about 20 members of the Wexford Supporters Club convened at Murphy Floods hotel to voice concern at the way the team was being handled.

Sensing a good story at a dead time of the year, the *Wexford People* newspaper rubbed their hands in anticipation and sent a reporter along.

'Griffin must go' was their headline the following week over a report on the supporters' meeting, where it was claimed, among other 'heated' exchanges, that Wexford would be a third-world county if things didn't change.

But the county board ignored the rebellion and Griffin, Rory Kinsella and Séamus Barron were ratified the following week for a second year in charge.

A proposal to get rid of the three was rejected when board chairman Paddy Wickham asked they be given a year's grace and there were only four dissenting voices.

Once he was safe in the knowledge he had a job for another year, Griffin travelled west to attend the 1995 All-Ireland final Clare homecoming. He had played for them for over two years – his father hailed from there – and understandably felt some affinity. It was a different Liam Griffin that came back from Clare the following day.

Meanwhile, the club-versus-county controversy had ensured that once again Oulart-The-Ballagh were Public Enemy Number One and we were under pressure to retain our title and shut our critics up. But after such a terrible year with the county, Tomás, Martin and myself were only too glad to get back to grassroots.

Tom Neville was waiting to get his hands on us again, of course. He insisted we had to compensate for the disasters on the intercounty front and off we went with another match against St Martin's, beating them by two points in the first round of the Wexford Championship. I got a lovely piece of crystal from South East Radio for winning man of the match and it was good to get back to playing decent hurling again.

Storey was captain this time and did a super job for the entire season. Although reigning champions are there to be shot down, it was no shock to me that we were in the county semi-final again just a year after winning the title for the first time. We were a damn good team. Our old friends Buffers Alley waited for us there and while they badly wanted our blood, there was no way we were going to bow to them, and so for the second year in a row we took them. Earlier that year, we had also beaten them in the League final but this Championship win was like all our Christmases and birthdays coming together.

The Alley had 12 county Championships but they would have given them all back just to deprive us of one – that was the extent of the mutual hatred at the time. It's not as bad these days because all the young lads play soccer together but back then it was fairly saucy to say the least. We beat them by seven points and didn't hold back in celebrating as they trudged off the field. In your face!

There was no talk of a curse now as we faced into our second county final in a row against Glynn-Barntown, a new team who had just reached their first ever decider at this level. They were peppered with good players, including Shane Carley, Eugene Furlong and Gary Laffan, but the occasion got to them and you could see it clearly even during the parade, as they waved and smiled into the crowd like pure novices. I knew there and then Oulart were more focused and we beat them 2-15 – 2-9. For the second year in a row, the Bob Bowe Cup came to the village and Martin Storey lifted it with a huge smile on his face.

This time, I wasn't completely satisfied just to win a club title. I still felt we were throwing everything away with the county, shooting ourselves in the foot.

Anyway, like Liam Griffin, I watched half in delight and half in envy as Clare went on to win the All-Ireland and change the face of hurling forever. Storey and I were so intrigued by their achievement that we agreed to go down and play them in the annual GOAL charity match on the Wednesday after their win over Offaly in the All-Ireland final. Oulart had a challenge game pencilled in for the Thursday, so the two of us had every intention of getting back for it, but we didn't factor in the danger of getting wrapped up in the celebrations in Ennis.

Over 16,000 turned up to watch the game, and Liam Doyle, who by now could hardly move, came over to mark me and chatted away, whenever the sliotar was down the far end of the field, about the countless early-morning training sessions they had put in. By the end of the match, I was under no illusions about Ger Loughnane's success – their All-Ireland was far from a fluke.

Daithí Regan and Kevin Kinahan were two of the few Offaly players to turn up and they deserved great credit for that and I remember thinking how down they must have felt but the Clare boys went out of their way to thank them and the rest of us for making it down. They were heroes for life but could still spare time for the ordinary Joes like ourselves.

I met Ger Loughnane and he asked me about Wexford, and seemed genuinely stunned when I told him my club team was better-prepared and fitter than the county squad.

It had done the Wexford team good to see Clare burying the so-called curse of Biddy Early and enjoying all the fruits of their success because it renewed our own hunger and showed us what winning an All-Ireland could do for you. At the same time, we weren't fully convinced we could get to that level because, quite simply, we were way off the pace. So our admiration of Clare was heavily mixed up with a fair bit of the green-eyed monster.

Griffin, however, thought the exact opposite. He began to draw up a plan and called an emergency meeting of the Wexford panel just a couple of weeks after the Clare win.

A few days before that gathering, I bumped into my sister-in-law Paula Sinnott, who worked for Liam at the Ferrycarrig Hotel, and spoke to her about the great year it had been for the club. I also remarked what a shambles of a season it had been for the county. Paula's response was immediate, emphatic and totally unexpected.

'I guarantee you,' she smiled, 'Liam Griffin will not leave this job until he achieves what he wants to do with that team. He will leave no stone unturned.'

To be honest, I seriously doubted he could achieve the miracle. Of course I didn't know then he had already plotted much of the way to the summit. It was an odyssey only Griffin could foresee, the road to emulating the Clare team of 1995 and laying hands on the MacCarthy Cup.

So come on ye full-time, small-town heroes, cast away your inbred fears /
Of standing out from all the rest, the cynics and the pessimists /
The self-indulgent, almost rich, the blatant hurlers on the ditch /
Time is passing so come on, face the ball, the game is on /
To win just once, oh to win just once, that would be enough.
The Saw Doctors, To Win Just Once

– CHAPTER ELEVEN –
The final countdown

The first sign that things were about to change in Wexford hurling came the Tuesday after the 1995 All-Ireland final when every squad member got a short phone call from the management.

There were no little chats or small talk; instead they issued us with a blunt message: Training resumes next week in the gym. This was new. Never had we gone back so early. But we all agreed something different was needed to dig Wexford out of the hole, and though we usually approached training with all the eagerness of someone going to a dentist to get a tooth yanked, this time there was a sense of willingness. In a sense it was imposed; you got the impression that now they weren't asking you to come in but were demanding it.

The Oulart lads were left alone, however, until our involvement in the Leinster club campaign ended. Our season finally ended after we were knocked out of the club Championship by Glenmore and beat Rathnure in the county League, and so just before Christmas Griffin asked us to the final two training sessions with the Wexford team.

The lads had been going strong for weeks, pumping iron in Dominic Kiernan's gym in Wexford town, but we had notions about ourselves – sure hadn't Oulart men long been the fittest in the county? We decided there wasn't much point to it and gave it a miss.

It was a big mistake because when we eventually did go back to

Dominic's we got the fright of our life. The lads had muscles on their muscles and were working like machines. There was no messing or joking as they threw themselves into their circuits and pumped iron to dance music. Seán Collier, a former international boxer and Ireland team trainer, was timing them at each station before moving them onto the next machine.

I looked at John O'Connor, who was paired with Damien Fitzhenry, and was astonished. John O had always been fit but he was absolutely flying now and Fitzy was all guns blazing too.

The pairs had been decided at the first training session and there was no slotting in with a lad just because you arrived together, no way. There was no-one getting between Fitzy and John O, or Tommy Kehoe and Adrian Fenlon, who was fast becoming the star performer in the gym by a country mile.

Storey and I went in together but we found working out to the music strange and didn't know the routine anyway, so like bold children, we did only half the repetitions and wouldn't be anywhere near finished when the boys were already on their next drill.

It was as clear as day Griffin had raised the bar and the Oulart contingent had failed to hurdle it. We were left embarrassed because it would take two days to get the soreness out of our shoulders and the back of our arms, but by then we were back in the gym again.

Weights are a part of life for the modern-day GAA player but for most of the Wexford panel this was their first hardcore experience of the gym. As it turned out they loved it. They seemed to rise to the bait Griffin, Collier and Kinsella had laid down, responding to the urgency of the drills, where everything was done at high speed.

Each player was asked to fill out a sheet on what he thought of Wexford hurling. In return, we were drowned with more handouts – sports literature, diet sheets and so on. Each player was told to drink four pints of water each day and stay away from alcohol.

Griffin told us that while other teams were running up hills we would be running down them as well to enhance our speed, but he said the gym work would continue for months until he was happy with our upper-body strength.

Wexford Wanderers gave us the use of tackle bags and suddenly I was going home with data on each muscle in my body tucked into my kit-bag. It was the first time I even knew I had muscles, to be honest.

There was no guesswork with the training; everything was done scientifically – well more or less everything. I remember Dave Guiney really getting into it in a bid to nail down his place on the team. He asked George O'Connor how much training he should be doing on his own and was duly told he should be doing at least 1,000 press-ups per day. It was a wind-up, of course, but a few days later Georgie got a phone call from Dave.

'Do your arms not get sore after a few days, George?'

The rest of us might have fallen around laughing but it just showed that Dave was ready to do what it took to make the team.

The issue of the captaincy arose around then. I ruled myself out because it didn't particularly interest me after what had happened the year before. Storey had replaced Tomás as club captain and had succeeded in getting everyone to row in behind him. He had to be the man to lead Wexford and I said as much to Griffin, reminding him of the great job Martin was doing with Oulart.

The announcement was made that Martin was the man, and though he and Liam may not have been bosom buddies, that had little or nothing to do with hurling and so they simply got on with it.

Early in 1996, when we played Offaly in the Walsh Cup, you could see everyone was starting to pull together. And of course the reason was that it was either Griffin's way or the highway.

It had all started with the pre-Christmas sessions in the gym, but the new attitude wasn't confined just to the gym. Just after the holidays, for example, he brought us up to the old golf links in Bunclody for a run. The course was unkind; it was hilly and bumpy and there was lots of it, the kind of place you'd bring an Army Ranger, or someone you didn't like, for training.

The Friday night before one of our first sessions there, Oulart had its club dinner dance, where we got our medals. Many large bottles of Bulmers were consumed as we gloated on the great year we'd had but the only drink we were involved with the following day was what came up through our throats and out our mouths.

As we arrived at Bunclody, we estimated it would take us 15 minutes to go around the course and we were not far wrong, but we didn't bank on having to run around it four times at nearly full stride.

It was a deadly course; there were little banks hidden everywhere and as I staggered onto my second lap I could see lads were well into their third. I swore then that never again would I drink before a session and do this to myself.

Yeah, it was a nice little learning curve, and as Tommy Kehoe, Larry O'Gorman and Adrian Fenlon were stuck at the front, the aim for me was to get up there within a few weeks. I was helped when I saw Ger Cushe, not normally known for his stamina, also improving with every outing.

You find out lots about your team-mates in these situations and it was clearer now who would make the cut and who was interested in going to a higher level. Cushe was not the fastest but he was pushing the boat out and staying at the front for as long as he could before drifting back a bit; the winner in him was coming out.

Under this regime, the games were a welcome respite from the training, even at this early stage of the season. We wanted to win every game we played and were thrilled to win the Walsh Cup against Offaly. It may not have seemed any big deal to outsiders at the time but for us it was massive. For good measure, we hammered them again in the League quarter-final, by 16 points, unheard of for a Wexford team.

People wondered what had changed and of course it was the players' attitudes. In a League game against Meath, Larry O'Gorman was whipped off the field in the first half because he didn't conform to

Griffin's game plan, and to ram the point home, he was dropped for the next game as well. He had been handed a specific job to do at half back but had tried to run the field and play his own game, and the manager was having none of it.

Griffin tried Ger Cushe at centre back and gave Damien Fitzhenry a run out the field, leaving Séamus Kavanagh in goal. He made sure all his theories and formations were tried out early in the year and assured us that by the time the Championship arrived everything would slot into place.

After games he would chat to us, rattling us with statistics compiled by John O'Leary, who'd been brought into the back-room team. The stats don't lie. I remember coming off the field many times chuffed with myself only to be told I'd been doing my own thing and not conforming to the team plan, which demanded more hooking and blocking and clearing the lines and less of the fouling and flaking.

Once we had absorbed the lessons, it was back to the heavy training during the week: two or three sessions in the gym and plenty of stamina running.

It had taken me six weeks to get the hang of the weights but then I became addicted to them and loved the buzz. For the first four or five weeks, I had found it hard to get out of bed with the pain and could hardly turn sideways, but I soon noticed my body changing, and my days of playing catch-up in the sweaty studio were over when I joined the lads who were doing the most reps on the bars.

Seán Collier used to bring us into the ring at Dominic's and invite us spar with him and while a few chanced their arm, the rest of the lads were at the weights and machines. With Griffin and Rory Kinsella treating the exercises like hurling drills, it was move, move, move. The backroom took a huge part in the sessions and gave us a one-minute breather between every set but they took no shit whatsoever.

One night, Tom Dempsey was doing his usual job of entertaining the troops while we suffered in training. As one of the funniest men I ever knew, Tom was invaluable to us on and off the field, but this particular night Griffin felt he was too much of a distraction and gave the signal to Collier, who beckoned poor old Tom into the ring for a bit of sparring.

We were all pumping away when Griffin ushered us ringside to admire Tom doing his best Sly Stallone impression. Suddenly, Collier let fly with a left hook and drove him into next week with a box. Tom hit the floor, blood dribbling down his mouth. It wasn't a bit funny – he had taken a fair old smack – but he didn't say a word to anyone.

In fairness to Tom, I don't think anyone else on the panel would have taken a box like that and stayed involved in the set-up. Eventually, everyone saw the funny side but the only thing Tom was raging about was that when he hit the floor, the first thing he could see was my red and black jersey of Oulart-The-Ballagh. Buffers Alley men always hated to see that shirt looking down on top of them.

From there, no-one was under any more illusions about what the management would and would not take and so we moved forward together, keeping the little transformation in the team quiet and well away from the Wexford people, who were expecting another disaster that summer.

Early in February, we travelled to Limerick for the League and they beat us 1-13 to 0-8 in the rain. The shocking thing was that they not only beat us on the scoreboard but also absolutely devoured us physically. Tommy Kehoe, a classy forward, was beat around the place that day.

I rarely saw Griffin angrier after a game, and he promised the team would never again be intimidated.

Despite the defeat, the Wexford fans must have had their hopes up once more.

We had gone through the early stages of the League in impressive fashion and, as I said, walloped Offaly before falling to Galway in the League semi-final.

We were not too downhearted about losing that game because we knew progress had been made; the team was still evolving and the dynamics of it were changing from week to week.

But the night I realised we really meant business was an evening late in April when we beat Cork 2-17 to 0-10 in a tournament game in Waterford.

There, the skeletons of the team of old were swept away into the night and replacing them was a psychological backbone that would carry us on for the remainder of the year.

Damien Fitzhenry was back in goal after his spell outfield, lighter and with an enhanced touch thanks to his stint there. Ger Cushe was on the edge of the square again but this time with the knowledge that he had played most of the year at centre back and had done fine there. If he survived that far outfield, he'd have little bother so close to goal.

I was at centre back, a position I loved because I felt I could have a big impact on games from there, and beside me was Larry O, who had played in so many positions by now that no-one could actually read the game better than him.

At midfield, the experience, skill and determination of Georgie was merged with the energy and ground hurling of Adrian Fenlon. Up front, Martin Storey and Tom Dempsey were fitter and stronger than ever and it was no coincidence that we absolutely blew Cork off the field that night. You could tell they had no idea what had happened to them but we knew and we wanted more.

For the first time in my era, the Wexford hurlers were pulling together. At least, most of us were. The Guiney brothers, Rod and Dave, hung together and there was always a little gap between them and us, but once we went on the field, I would give 100 percent for both of them and vice-versa.

Drink really did go out the door this time. For a few years, we had introduced phoney alcohol bans but this time, you carried the guilt of a serial killer on your shoulders if you guzzled even one pint.

Smoking, although it didn't affect me, went on the back burner as well, which meant purgatory for Seánie Flood and Martin Storey. Seánie used to love cans of coke as well and he could drink five or six of them every day in his tractor, but they went out the tractor door, replaced by water.

Our diet was completely changed at this stage. No more butter, no bread or anything sweeter. I lived on chicken, fruit, pasta, water and spinach after training; I ate so much of the bloody stuff it was little wonder I started to feel like Popeye.

Once training was over, we would head to the Talbot Hotel in Wexford town, where Griffin would usually have a five-minute meeting that lasted about two hours. While we waited, he would go into the chef and instruct him to take all fattening oils or creams off the menu. But being from Wexford, we couldn't do everything right and despite the fact that there was a huge BSE scare in the country back then, we shovelled juicy steaks into our mouths after each training session, just in case we wouldn't get infected.

The steaks were sponsored, would you believe, so to support the local farmers Larry O and Georgie were asked to pose for a picture and reassure the nation that beef was your only man. All around the county, you could see huge posters of the two boys loading steak into their big gobs. Priceless.

It wasn't just diet and physical preparation that we needed, though. Perhaps Liam Griffin's cleverest stroke was the introduction of a sports psychologist, Niamh Fitzpatrick, into the camp. Around six weeks before our Championship started, against Kilkenny, Niamh was presented to us in the Ferrycarrig Hotel and proceeded to tell us what Griffin had told us exactly a year earlier – only this time we were taking it in.

She went through every detail of our lives and each player was allotted a 20-minute slot to discuss things with her; you got half an hour if your head really was in bits. Once more, a circuit-like approach was adopted at those meetings; you had to be on time and ready to go in and talk to Niamh when your team-mate came out.

Niamh started to become more than just a sports psychologist for me. Gradually she got my life story. I wouldn't talk much about my father to anyone, about why he left home and so on, but she got it all and a lot more.

I spoke of bad things like the pressures of work and good things such as my upcoming wedding with Eithne. I told her stuff I wouldn't have told my mother but each time I felt a weight being lifted off my chest.

As well as the chats serving as great preparation for games, Niamh gave me real peace of mind as well and I found myself still chatting away when the time would arrive for the next player to come in. She would press pause and simply carry on the next time as though the conversation had never been interrupted in the first place.

We were given tapes, to be listened to especially before games, for mental preparation and relaxation. We would listen to them going to and from Croke Park as the year unfolded.

On top of that Liam Griffin gave us tapes of positive or motivational songs like *Search for a Hero* from M People, *We are the Champions* by Queen and two popular Wexford tunes, our 1996 anthem, *Dancing at the Crossroads*, and the ballad *Boolavogue*.

We had been way too manly to ever consider such airy-fairy methods before 96, but now I would close my eyes before training or a game and relax for five or 10 minutes at home, but at the same time suspecting that if my brothers or sisters could see me they would commit me to the men in the white coats.

One day I put the motivational tape on in the car for my brother Seán, and he was fairly wound up himself by the end of the journey.

So, as we headed into the Championship, there wasn't a stone left unturned and though a few months earlier we had believed Griffin to be insane, we could now see it all coming right in front of us.

Seeing these hard men going in front of a woman they hardly knew and blurting out their life stories to her, well, it just showed the change of attitude in the squad.

On the field our selectors, Rory Kinsella and Séamus Barron, who both knew everything there was to know about the game of hurling, hounded us in training, and our challenge games were reaching a ferocious tempo. After each match, with the help of John O'Leary, they pinned the stats up on the back of the door – just how many frees we won and conceded, how many line balls we got, scores, blocks and so on. There was just nowhere to hide.

With the Kilkenny game looming and Croke Park recently rebuilt and radically transformed, Niamh decided we should send a delegation to the stadium to report back on the alterations so we wouldn't be distracted by them on match day. Unfamiliarity, she said, can be seriously unsettling.

After her visit there with our PRO, Pat Murphy, she provided us with a comprehensive virtual tour of the place, describing the big yellow doors into the dressing-rooms, the inside of those changing rooms and the feel of the pitch.

Pat would lay out the jerseys from one to 15 in our virtual dressing-rooms so each of us knew where he would sit. Already it felt like we knew the stadium, though we had never seen it since the redesign. That was the sort of preparation we needed for Kilkenny because I and many of the lads had never beaten them in the Championship.

If we were doing our bit, Griffin was almost going overboard. That man was up some nights until 5 am dissecting videos, and though we would have played Kilkenny several times, he always had a new angle on them after watching those tapes.

We knew also that there were a few internal issues with their team, so when the game finally arrived, it really was shit or get off the pot, because we had never been so well prepared.

That game was in the melting pot for so long. We went five points up but back they came to within a point and we had to bring Billy Byrne on to rescue us with a goal – it wouldn't be his last time saving us that year.

When Billy came on, our game tactics went from: 'Get the ball in to the forwards quick and low' to 'Get the ball in any old way to Billy', because the man just seemed to gobble up any sort of supply that came his way and we were glad to see the Kilkenny net rattle soon after his arrival.

Griffin had told him to win the first ball and stop Pat O'Neill from lording it. When Billy got the sliotar, he was to jink one way and shoot the other.

He followed the orders to a T.

His goal came from a quick Adrian Fenlon pass and changed the game. A minute later, Feno took a quick line ball to Larry O which resulted in a point, and we hung on to win 1-14 to 0-14, a sensational result.

Only afterwards did it occur to me that we had never once even contemplated defeat. There was just no fear of losing; it was something that was never spoken about and that was incredible because we had discussed just about everything else.

But Griffin reminded us that the win was one step on the ladder and despite the fact county board officials had shed tears of joy in the dressing-room, we soon returned to normality on the following Wednesday night.

As with every game, we would sit down and pinpoint where we went wrong and then in training afterwards try to rectify the errors. There was always a huge emphasis on tactics in those sessions; Griffin insisted on six defenders marking eight forwards, which meant one defender would have to leave his man and someone else would have to look after his patch. It ensured cover play was always a strong part of our defence. Damien Fitzhenry's puck-outs were also analysed, and whichever way he stepped, every guy out the field knew where the ball was landing.

Niamh brought us back in to work on our minds so we were well prepared when we met Dublin and, after a desperate second half, just held on long enough to beat them 2-12 to 1-9, a poor winning margin considering we had played them off the field in the first half.

Just before the break, they got a penalty. Eamon Morrissey mishit the sliotar, but it somehow managed to get past Ger Cushe. After a few kind words were said to Ger, we went into the dressing-room and stayed there for the restart, because Dublin destroyed us in the first 15 minutes of the second half before we made a few changes, regained our shape and got through.

Our collapse in the second half was a sharp lesson because we had endured a scare. But rather than panic like we would have done in the past, we reacted well, made a few changes and played a get-out-of-jail card to ensure we would meet Offaly in the Leinster final.

I had watched Offaly destroy Laois in the other semi-final at Croke Park and when John Troy scored his second goal, I and Bartle Sinnott got up to leave – I had seen enough. The former Offaly hurler Pádraig Horan saw me leave and, pointing to Troy, heckled: 'That's your man, Liam.'

I kept my mouth shut but Bartle heard me mutter: 'He'll be my man alright.'

Troy scored 3-5 against Laois but with every score he and Offaly got, I wished them another one, which may be cruel on Laois but I wanted to build up the men in green, white and gold to the last and let them think they were invincible for the six weeks that remained to our big game.

We needed them to feel infallible because we had our own problems to iron out. It was clear as the spring water we were slugging by the gallon that our display against Dublin would not cut the mustard.

Sensing this, Griffin brought Niamh in to meet us shortly before the game. She asked us all to write down the reasons we felt Wexford were going to win the Leinster final. I had been talking to her a few days previously about the same subject, and when she didn't hear me speak up at the meeting she asked me why.

At this stage, we had heard the views of the whole squad: we're fitter; we're better prepared; our team is stronger. They were the theories but Niamh still wasn't satisfied.

'Liam,' she said, 'will you tell the lads the story you told me last week?'

I went red but proceeded to recall that a few days previously when I went home for dinner after one of our best ever training sessions, Mam asked: 'How did ye get on?' and my reply was: 'Mam, today we decided we're going to beat Offaly.'

As soon as I uttered those words, Niamh scribbled them on the board; it was the mantra she was looking for. It might sound cocky now, but I knew there was no way we could be beaten – we were just too well prepared.

With that, we were sent onto the training pitch in Wexford Park and as soon as we had done our warm-up drills, Griffin came up to me, caught me by the neck and growled: 'You don't forget what happened to you two years ago when the first ball came down between you and John Troy.'

I was taken aback. He had never spoken to me like that before. But he didn't have to remind me; my memory is long and I hadn't forgotten that Troy 'did' me with the first pull of the ball – he pulled early and caught my hand – when they hammered us in 94.

A while after the reminder about Troy, Griffin came back to me again, this time less pumped up.

'What do you think about Tom Dempsey?' he enquired.

Tom's brother-in-law had died just before the Offaly game, and Tom felt he wouldn't make the team and was anxious all week beforehand, so I felt maybe he might not be mentally right.

'I wouldn't play him,' I said. 'He's not right.'

Of course, Dempsey went on to have the game of his life and scored 1-5. It was his perfect game but the same applies to the rest of us as well. The memories and stories of that day will never be forgotten.

Going up to Croke Park on match day, Griffin stopped the bus on the Wexford-Wicklow border just past Inch and before the Arklow by-pass and asked us all to get off and move over to the ditch, where cows were mooing and passing cars were beeping their horns.

I'm sure the hundreds of Wexford supporters who passed us that day must have thought we were gone in the head but none of them dared stop to ask what the hell we were doing.

Griffin stood almost in the ditch and gave a speech – Christ, it still sends shivers down my spine! He gave a rendition of who we were and where we came from. He brought us back down the centuries to Vinegar Hill. The passionate way he spoke about Wexford brought tears to our eyes. It got worse when he spoke about our families and neighbours and ancestors and all the battles they'd had to fight over the years. And the fact they had risen, almost alone, in 1798 to give their blood in the cause of freedom.

By now there wasn't a dry eye on the ditch and to tell you the truth, the speech was so inspirational even the cows came over to have a look and listen. He asked for a complete focus and eventually, standing by the bus, brought his oration to an end.

'Lads,' he roared, 'we are walking out of our own county today but we are coming back as Leinster champions this evening! And we are walking out!' he reiterated, slapping the side of the bus and instructing the driver to move up the road and over the border.

Seánie Flood strolled alongside me and the two of us were in such shock at Griffin's speech that we scarcely heard the cars blowing their horns. When eventually we reached the bus and hopped on, there was complete silence – the lads were still trying to take in what had happened.

Larry Murphy looked over at me and while neither of us breathed a word, we were both thinking the same thing: Griffin was awesome. And so off we drove, heading to the Stillorgan Park Hotel, our pre-match base, to go through the usual ritual: pasta, Niamh Fitzpatrick, potatoes, Rory Kinsella, chicken and beans, Liam Griffin. You could eat what you wanted and speak to who you chose. In former times, we had been eating Mars bars on match days but now it was all hot food, full of energy.

On the way to Croke Park on the bus, Griffin showed us a video of his old favourite blockbuster *Braveheart*, which we watched every time without fail on the way to a big match. I was so entertained when I first saw the film before the League quarter-final against Galway that I didn't want to get off the bus.

The tape was switched on when the whole team was on board, but again, he never let us watch the end of it – just as the film entered its final stages, we had to hop off, tog out and warm up.

The lads used to love seeing bodies fly through the air, but Griffin was clever enough not to let us see the finale because the hero, William Wallace, dies in the end and we were so wrapped up in the film, it could have affected our minds. Seriously, that was the way we were thinking.

Of course *Braveheart* was a classic and all that, but by the time I got it for a Christmas present I was fairly sick of it.

Another part of the pre-match ritual was reading the newspapers. Nowadays, managers are paranoid about their players speaking to the press and if a team loses, the papers get the blame, while winning teams get accused of losing the run of themselves while talking to the press.

We didn't give a tráithnín what was said about us and would talk away to any journalist. Griffin knew the media had a big role to play and he knew how to handle the reporters, so he instructed everyone to talk away, and even before matches he would bring us back to newspapers by showing us the difference between photos of winning and losing players.

Adrian Fenlon was really the only guy who didn't like chatting to the press and, while I understand that, I can't fathom this bullshit of managers appointing two players to talk to the press before every game. It's manufactured and it's only putting more pressure on those lads who are chosen.

I read all the papers before the Offaly match and the pundits were split on the outcome but we were confident. Griffin called us into a huddle and did his usual prophecy act by predicting we would score a goal but within two minutes they would get one back. He warned us not to panic when that happened.

It had been 19 years since we won a provincial title so panicking should have been about the first port of call if we fell behind in a game.

Amazingly, though, Griffin's prediction came to pass. Early in the game, Gary Laffan, our big full-forward, flicked a lovely ball over to Tom Dempsey, who rifled a sweet goal, but almost straightaway, Michael Duignan cancelled it out by hitting one for Offaly. How could you panic when your manager had predicted exactly what would happen? Was it any wonder we had such faith in the man?

Soon after the goal, the first ball that landed between John Troy and I broke harmlessly between us but I pulled hard on the second ball alright and caught him in the mouth with the end of my hurl. It looked legitimate to the referee but I knew I had got him.

Blood spurted out of his mouth, but remembering what he had done to me two years before that, I didn't feel one bit of guilt. He was good at pulling off the ball himself; he had it down to a fine art.

Anyway, he was soon moved off me and into full-forward, where the big, welcoming arms of Ger Cushe opened for him.

'What happened you, John?' Cushe enquired politely.

'You know damn fucking well what happened,' Troy snarled.

Ger used to joke that lads would come in to mark him after a spell on me with bits of hurls stuck in them but this time we had a game to win and, with my revenge exacted, it was back to focusing on the ball.

Hassle! Next ball! Those were the key words in 96. They were drilled into us.

We started to pull away in the second half thanks to some heroic defending and even though Billy Dooley got a second goal for them, John O'Connor leapt around the full-back and half-back lines like a leopard, clearing ball after ball.

With time running out and Wexford leading by four points, Troy, who was back out marking me, decided to test me and leaning over, said: 'Congratulations! You deserve it.'

I didn't answer straightaway, aware he was probably playing mind games, but then we went six points up and I replied: 'Thanks, John.'

Just at the end, Brian Whelahan came out with the ball trying to make a huge clearance as he so often did to inspire his team, but for the umpteenth time that day Larry Murphy appeared out of nowhere and drove him back, as we had been instructed to do by Griffin before the game.

If we could plough their best player back and stop him from clearing ball, it would dishearten them, and seeing Brian being hounded, with time just up, drove our lads on to the final whistle.

For the first time in my career, I got a real sense of satisfaction as the seconds ticked away, a feeling of accomplishment. When the whistle blew, I just sprinted straight to the stand. I had been waiting so long for this moment and I just wanted to look on at the mayhem back on the field.

Storey was the first player I met and we wrapped our arms around each other. He walked up the steps to lift the Bob O'Keeffe Cup and Seánie Flood and I quickly followed him.

Maybe we got a little carried away. The two of us started swinging out of the little podium up there, and a steward told me to sit down.

'I will in my fuck,' I replied. 'I'm waiting 19 years to get up here.'

Looking back at the video of those celebrations in 96, well, it often raised the hairs on the back of my neck. Jim Berry, a Wexford man, was chairman of the Leinster Council at the time and he started us off talking about the 19-year gap and telling the nation we had done the county proud.

Below us, the crowd went nuts, and it took me ages to get back down to pitch level. I stood talking to reporters and when I did make it to the dressing-room, the mayhem had died down. But it was great to see the Bob O'Keeffe Cup inside.

The only thing that dampened the thrill that day was that I soon got one of my blinding headaches. In the 90s I suffered badly from post-match migraines and used to have to sit in the dressing-room and take painkillers after games. I would often feel sick with the pain and because of that I would avoid travelling back on the team bus. I just wanted peace and quiet so I used to go back to the car, which would be parked in Clonliffe College, munch on a few sandwiches, drink a pint of milk and slip home quietly on the back roads.

Those blazing headaches were deadly. Seánie Flood suffered from them as well and the two of us used to sit with our heads down after games. People must have wondered why we sometimes looked so upset after winning matches, but there was a reason.

It's a good thing there were no drug tests back then because I had so many painkillers inside me, I would surely have been done. But there was so much nervous energy entailed in playing in Croke Park that I used to get overwhelmed with pain once the final whistle blew.

And so while the rest of the team went mad in Wexford town the night of the Offaly game, I did my own thing. I was at home in bed early that night and didn't meet up with them until the night after, when we gathered for a reception in the town again.

We were back training on Wednesday and went for a run at Curracloe. It was great to see everyone on a high, and for good measure, Liam told us if we wanted a few pints that night there would be no problem, though in the same breath he warned us that training would resume in earnest the following night.

Of course, we needed no second invitation and retired to Hanrahan's of Curracloe, where the video of the game was still being replayed. Free pints were handed over the bar and we didn't hold back, but we suffered for our indulgence the next day.

Griffin ran the shite out of us, nearly killed us with those deadly 200-metre and 400-metre efforts. Ned Buggy was there watching and said he felt green at the gills just looking at us. We were back to reality, as if nothing had been won. Griffin told us to hit the showers and said he would be in with us in a few minutes to ask the squad one simple question.

With steam rising everywhere in the changing-room, he was hard to see but his voice was unmistakable.

'How many All-Ireland semi-finals are you guaranteed to play for the rest of your lives?' he asked.

No answer.

'The answer,' he replied, 'is this – you might never play in another one'.

Silence again. Just the sound of water splashing and guys trying to come to terms with what he had just said. And with that, we began to look forward to Galway, next up in four weeks' time with a confident manager, Mattie Murphy, who was talking up his men as the best in the business.

In the interim, the county really started to get behind us and at an A-versus-B training match, we spent hours just signing autographs for kids. It gave the lads a feeling of what life could be like for them, which was important as well. Banners and flags united the county and club rivalries went out the window. Our players were recognised everywhere they went. Of course my job entailed meeting publicans and shopkeepers, who were only too glad to collar me for a chat and go through the Leinster final blow by blow all over again.

Mam was sick in the run-up to the semi-final against Galway and I hadn't been in to see her. Maybe I was putting off going to the hospital – it's a trip I dislike at the best of times.

Anyway, I eventually got in to see her. None of the brothers or sisters had arrived, so though it soon came time to go training, I didn't want to leave her on her own and hung back. When the family eventually poured in I left and headed for training, arriving late. Griffin told me to do a few laps and then ate the face off me. I told him Mam was sick but he wasn't taking excuses and told me the next time I was to leave earlier. It was his way now.

The morning of the Galway match, Mam was still in hospital and Martin Storey and I went to see her.

'Martin,' she said. 'I won't make this game but make sure and give me a chance to see the final.'

Martin told her he'd do his best and we set off to Croke Park.

The game was only minutes old when John O'Connor was knocked unconscious after a tackle with Joe Rabbitte. The referee awarded a throw-in and Joe made the serious mistake of going in beside Georgie for it – he ended up with a broken bone in his ankle.

Another thing I recall about that game was the trouble I had with Cathal Moore. He scored 1-3 off me, and though there was nothing I could do for the goal, he really caught me for the points.

They were awarded a penalty in the second half and you can imagine my shock when I saw Ger Cushe alongside Damien Fitzhenry and Larry O'Gorman for the penalty. Cushe's record for saving penalties was not the best, and when I told him to get out of there he seemed fairly happy to do so.

I turned to the boys: 'Lads, if we stop this, we're in an All-Ireland final.'

Joe Cooney took the penalty and Fitzy dived, but I stopped it with my hurl and cleared it down the field.

For the rest of the game, we looked the better team and Tom Dempsey, Rory McCarthy, who got a brilliant goal, and Martin Storey gave us a bit of a cushion as the final minutes ticked away.

Galway looked rattled and drove loads of wides and while I still feel they wouldn't have beaten us, they did spurn a huge number of chances. But we got there.

Back home, everything went crazy and that night Bartle Sinnott and I came out of Phil Redmond's pub. I pointed across the road to a group singing and dancing at the crossroads, just like the song suggested.

'We might never see it again,' I said to Bartle.

Within three months, we had become the heroes of the county. We had a back-up team to look after our every need and ensure no-one was taking advantage of us. Not that it was likely to happen. Any step we took, there was someone waiting for us to put a blanket on the ground before us. It was incredible. You would get a punnet of strawberries sent over to you after training; people were coming over to us in restaurants and asking what way we wanted our steaks cooked; there were free boots for everyone. It was unreal and I had never seen anything like it. We even got free suits and shoes – some of the lads are still wearing them.

The management stopped us from taking the Bob O'Keeffe Cup around the county, however, and Griffin made sure we knew the journey wasn't over yet. He called us back into training after the Galway game, brought us into the room and told us we didn't have to train if we didn't want to. Most of us gave it a skip and tried on our new boots but that was the last night the showbiz stuff was allowed into the camp.

There and then, he spoke to us about every aspect of All-Ireland final day. I still reckon this was the night everything fell into place. He went as far as explaining how to greet President Mary Robinson before the game, instructing us to stand with our hands behind our backs and look straight at her. After that, we were to focus on the Liam MacCarthy Cup above on the podium, and that was to be our point of visual contact until we were called to walk behind the band with our socks up and look into the crowd to remember who we were and why we were there.

That night, there and then, two and a half weeks before the game against Limerick, the All-Ireland final was won. He had a list longer than Santa Claus himself, the most comprehensive guide to playing in a big match you will ever see. We knew our every movement from the talk that night to the moment the ball was thrown in against Limerick.

In the lead-up to the big match, I was best man at the wedding of my cousin Robert Dunne, and as old habits die hard, I got home from the Tuscar House hotel at a quarter to five the next morning.

It was a great wedding. Robert and I were close; he had lost his Dad, my godfather, in a car accident in 1972 and we had played a lot of hurling together. I found the occasion a great release from hurling, Griffin had relented and given me a dispensation from training, but I still felt all eyes were on me in the residents' bar to see if I was having a drink.

I took a few Budweisers and thought I had behaved fairly well, but Griffin didn't appreciate my honesty one little bit when I told him about it and I got another earful.

And so the training went ahead for the biggest game of our lives. We just worked hard and listened. Griffin reminded us how Tommy Kehoe had been pulverised by Limerick's Seán O'Neill in a League match earlier that year and how the home crowd in Kilmallock jeered Tommy.

Rows broke out everywhere that day but we didn't come out on top in too many and when Griffin brought us back into Dominic's Gym the day after that game, he demanded it would never happen again.

'No intimidation!' he roared.

'As long as I live, what happened you in Kilmallock will never happen one of my players again,' he screamed at Tommy Kehoe.

'What's the word, lads?' he shouted.

'No intimidation!' we roared back, and with the music pumping in the background we must have looked the unlikeliest bunch of thugs. From then on, if Griffin ever felt training was slipping, he would haul us into a big circle and get us to roar that mantra at the top of our voices.

But we were disciplined and maybe the idea of bringing us to an Army tent at Ballytrent beach had the desired effect. We had been there earlier in the year but a couple of weeks before the final we were back, sleeping in a huge tent erected by the backroom team.

It was straight out of boot camp with little camper beds just six inches off the ground. We slept there on Friday nights, travelled to Rosslare to train the next day and played a match between ourselves. Afterwards, we would go for a walk together and then it was back to camp, where one of the manager's friends, Tony Kehoe, was cooking a big barbecue with lashings of sponsored food. Martin Storey and John O'Connor were his commis chefs and helped him prepare the mountain of steaks. Some more of the lads set a big bonfire, and while we waited for the main course, we drank Ballygowan water, tea and orange juice by the litre or dug into large baskets of fruit. It was the best of grub and the best of times.

At night we would huddle up around the bonfire and Tom Dempsey would lead the way in a singsong. Of course Larry O was the headline act, belting out the numbers, aided and abetted by Seánie Flood on guitar. It was a great bonding, serious stuff.

Blankets were thrown on the bed and the lights went out. Then the real fun started. Boots and other heavy objects flew through the darkness and there were desperate roars and gasps as men were suffocated by pillows. What do you expect from 30 redblooded chaps deprived of a social life for so long?

At 5.15 the wake-up call for Sunday sounded. Griffin said he was calling a team meeting to discuss the Limerick players, but first we had to train. We went for a run, and then started pulling hurleys on rows of old tyres to develop our weak sides.

When he was called in to give us a hand, Griffin actually brought us back there again in 2001, the week before the All-Ireland semi-final with Tipperary. It was the same set-up only this time we didn't stay overnight.

Billy Byrne, the two O'Connors, Tom Dempsey and Martin Storey, who had retired by then but was drafted back into the squad, all came and we tore into the mountain of steaks and sandwiches.

Griffin got up at one stage and arrived back with crates of Budweiser and Heineken.

'Have a drink, lads,' he said. 'Next weekend, we will beat Tipperary and reach the All-Ireland final.'

He would be proved wrong of course, but it was close – the man is never far off the mark.

But the two camps we went on in 96 were the brainwave of a genius. You could see everyone growing closer together. The chats, the sing-songs, the grub, the fun – I will never forget it.

But when we got the wake-up call at 5.15 am before the final with Limerick, I wasn't too delighted with the whole thing.

'For Christ's sake, could he not have called us at half nine or something?' I moaned. No, he wanted to do it then.

We dragged ourselves out, battled our way through the training and settled down for the theory bit. Griffin proceeded to go through the Limerick team, dissecting them one by one.

'Joe Quaid, a great shot-stopper so try and place your shots but his puck-outs are predictable and won't go too far away from Gary Kirby. Ciarán Carey, will run all day but try to drag him out of position and he won't like it.'

Martin Storey was to play his usual game and we were to be confident that would work. He came to Gary Kirby but didn't get a chance to voice his opinion on him because George O'Connor interrupted: 'Liam will take care of Gary Kirby – we don't have to worry about him.'

Griffin looked up and moved on. I was a bit taken aback at the faith George and the boys had invested in me. But there was no fuss and the rest of the Limerick team quickly got the once over before the manager switched on a video.

He showed more highlights of the Clare team coming home after winning the 95 All-Ireland final. We could see the crowd going nuts and the joy that greeted them, but again, just as we got carried away with the footage, he turned it off and told us it was ours if we wanted it badly enough.

We did, of course, so there was no better time to spring a weights session on us while the squad was still starry-eyed from the Clare footage. Seán Collier had a mini-gym built around the tent and we used boots, tyres and sandbags to reinforce our muscles.

As we beavered away at all hours in the morning, Griffin and the selectors went around to each one of us individually.

'While we are down here getting ready for Limerick, they are asleep in Dublin. They are up there in a cosy hotel trying to get used to the pre-match routine but look at us and what we are doing. We are ready for them.'

And he was right. We were fine-tuned now. We went back to bed for a while and then turned up for breakfast before being 'released' back to our families. Amazingly, no stories or tales of our camp were leaked to the press; it showed the loyalty that existed in the set-up. By now lads totally believed in Griffin; they would have done ballet dancing for him, Rory, Séamus, Seán and Niamh. It was a time of confidence and belief.

But we still had to win the All-Ireland final and it wasn't all claps on the back; there were a few disappointments on the road to the big day. Our build-up had been marred by an injury to Seánie Flood, who had to retire injured against Galway. Seánie was one of the team's best and most tigerish players and we needed him as much as he desperately wanted to play himself. With a fortnight to go, he tried to give himself every chance by running but he wasn't able to and it was heartbreaking to see. His biggest problem was trying to find out what the injury was. A number of specialists offered opinions, but by the time he realised he had a hairline fracture it was too late – Seánie was going to miss the biggest day in the county's history.

Another upset for me was the fact that Tomás was not on the squad. I felt he should have been because there were others there not half as good as him. Of course he was no saint. I don't know if he would have stuck to the same torrid training regime as the rest of us, but Liam Griffin certainly cannot have been sure he wouldn't knuckle down. I had asked the manager about Tomás early in the season; he didn't get back to me, and Tomás's hopes of making the cut just seemed to fizzle out.

I didn't allow it to affect me and didn't sulk but I was disappointed he wasn't there. We had grown a lot closer travelling to matches in and around 93 and 94 and it would have been great to go in and out of training with him. But I got on with it and Griffin never raised the matter again.

So that was it, the All-Ireland final checklist was drawn up. Liam even had a local artist draw cartoons of us beating Limerick. But he had the serious stuff sorted out as well, and that included the scenario where one of our men, or one of theirs, was sent off.

Anytime we sat down to eat, Griffin had a man come over and take the butter off the table. Instead of apple tart and cream, we got spinach. We had lovely new shoes and suits – some of the lads even looked respectable. I had enough boots, togs and socks to kit out a whole team. I knew the personal statistics of every man on the team and would spend training matches trying to clear more and more balls so I would have a higher average than anyone else.

We all knew the Limerick team inside out. Gary Kirby was my man. The in-form forward in the country, he had scored 1-33 on the way to the final.

But when I woke up on September 1, the morning of the 1996 All-Ireland final, I was ready for him. I switched off the alarm and the first thought that came to me was the film *Braveheart*. I wondered if we would finally get to see the end of it, and if it would after all have an heroic ending.

I suspected it would.

MAKING HAY AT HOME IN OULART: Kieran, Tomás, Seán and I in the back garden in 1972

THE FIRST OF MANY: I won my first ever hurling medal in the Nicky Rackard League

The red and black of Oulart-The Ballagh: I am pictured here playing against St. Martins in the county final. The club means everything to me.

Grin and bear it: Myself and Seánie Flood at the 1996 All-Ireland Final banquet. Seán was so unlucky to miss the final through injury but was an exceptional hurler.

FROM WEXFORD PARK TO ST PETER'S SQUARE: Six Kilkenny men surround me at the Vatican. John Hoyne, James McGarry, Derek Lyng, me, Michael Kavanagh, Noel Hickey and Henry Shefflin during our Railway Cup trip in 2003.

HENRY THE GREAT: I am pictured here at the 2003 All Stars with my friend Henry Shefflin, one of the game's greatest hurlers In the foreground is the late Cormac McAnallen whom I had the pleasure of sitting beside that night.

HOME IS WHERE THE HEART IS: With Mam and Dad after winning my first All Star award in 1990

WOULD YOU BUY A USED CAR FROM THESE MEN?: Martin Storey, Larry O'Gorman and I at the 1993 GAA All Stars

WORLD AT OUR FEET: I'm pictured here with clubmate Martin Storey and Dublin football legend Charlie Redmond picking up my second All Star award in 1993.

MINE'S A PINT!: Tipperary legend John Leahy and I have the craic at the 1990 GAA All Stars banquet. I found him to be great company.

ACROSS THE BORDER: Wexford men at the 2004 Wexford/Carlow dinner dance
Back row: Mick Doyle, Darragh Ryan, Tom O'Keeffe, Liam Dunne, Jim English
Front: Jim Doyle, Ned Wheeler, Tom Neville

REACH FOR THE STARS: Life really changed for me after I won my first All Star award. Two years previously I wasn't even good enough for the Wexford team.

Rise and follow Charlie! Here I am receiving my first All Star from GAA President John Dowling, Frank O'Rourke from Bank of Ireland and Taoiseach Charlie Haughey

Two tribes come together: A Buffers Alley man in Oulart. Only Tom Dempsey would get away with it!

THE WEXFORD WAGON: This car followed us everywhere in 1996. How, I don't know!

THE START OF THE CONTROVERSY: Gary Kirby and I get ready to pull on the first ball that came our way in the 1996 All-Ireland final. We all know what happened next!

What more could you ask for: A glowing bride, Eithne, and the Liam McCarthy Cup. It doesn't get better than this.

Safe hands: Damien Fitzhenry with Billy

WELL ARMED: With my Man-of-the-Match trophy and the Liam McCarthy
Cup and below with my brother Kieran

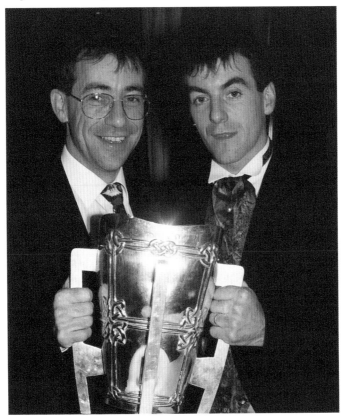

CRAMPER VAN!: David Beckham may have a Mercedes but in 1996 all Martin Storey and I had to bring the cup around the county was Paul Finn's Renault 5 van!

HATS OFF TO THE BROTHERS!: Seán and Tomás play the whistle at one of the homecoming celebrations in Oulart in 1996

Eye on the ball: Making my international debut for Ireland in the 1988 U-21 Shinty Championship against Scotland

On the Run: Dashing out of defence against Offaly in the 1991 League Final. Michael Duignan and Daithí Regan are behind me while George O'Connor waits in support.

CHASING DJ: This was not the first or last time I was left trailing in DJ's wake – one of the best hurlers of all time

CHASING MICKEY: Rory McCarthy and I in pursuit of Cork midfielder Mickey O'Connell in the 2003 All-Ireland semi-final

FAME AT LAST!: Signing autographs for fans in the run up to the 1996 All-Ireland

BEYOND THE TUNNEL: I run out into a sea of purple and gold at Croke Park for the 1996 All-Ireland semi-final with Galway.

THE END OF AN ERA: Shaking hands with Cork's Joe Deane after they had defeated us in the 2003 All-Ireland semi-final replay. My last game for Wexford.

SEEING RED AGAIN: Picking up my second red card from Pat Horan after a clash with Tipperary's Brian O'Meara in the 2001 All-Ireland semi-final replay. Brian missed out on a final appearance after this dismissal.

FROM RED TO TOE: Ger Harrington issues me with my third consecutive red card in the 2002 Leinster hurling final against Kilkenny. This signalled the start of my decline.

DOGS OF WAR!: Kilkenny's John Power and I had many saucy battles over the years. I came out on top on this occasion in the 1997 Leinster Hurling Final.

LOOKING AFTER MY OWN PATCH: While my teammates follow the ball, Tipperary's Liam Cahill and I get to know each other during the 2001 Championship.

BROTHERS IN ARMS: Celebrating qualifying for the 1996 All-Ireland final after a thrilling win over Galway.

THE MAESTRO: Liam Griffin

IT'S MY FIELD BULL!: L–R: Bartle 'Jacks' Redmond, Bartle 'Foxten' Sinnott, Martin 'Sport' Dempsey, Ned Evans, Tom Sinnott, Pat 'The Boiler' Dempsey, Liam Dunne and Johnny Hayden at the new Oulart-The-Ballagh GAA pitch

OULART'S GREATEST SUPPORTER: Stephen Hayden is surrounded by a likely lot! Seán Dunne, Liam Dunne, Tom Byrne, Jimmy Prendergast, Martin Storey, Paul Fnn, Mick Jacob and Tomás Dunne.

IF YOU WANT IT, PHIL HAS IT!: Phil Redmond and I at his pub and shop in Raheen Duff. He sells everything from pig meal to curry powder.

HISTORY ON THE DOUBLE: The Oulart men who won All-Ireland titles for Wexford in front of the 1798 Rebellion monument. Front row L-R: Darren Stamp, Liam Dunne, Christy Jacob, Seán Dunne, Jimmy Prendergast; Back row L-R: Rory Jacob, Paul Finn, Keith Rossiter, Martin Storey, Mick Jacob, Tom Byrne, Tomás Dunne, Michael Jacob

FAMILY TIES: Eithne, Aoife and Billy

TIME OUT: Taking a stroll on Morriscastle beach

In every bar down on the Main Street, they were hanging from the rafters,
And they sang the Boys of Wexford, like it was going out of style,
All the bingo halls were empty and the Masses finished early,
Sure no-one ever saw the like of it since the time of JFK.
The Wild Swans, Dancing at the Crossroads

– CHAPTER TWELVE –
Heaven can wait

After thinking of Gary Kirby and *Braveheart*, my next memory of All-Ireland final day was being called to the telephone to speak to Christy Jacob, who had won an All-Ireland medal with Wexford in 1968, the last time we had won the Liam MacCarthy Cup.

It was strange for me to get a call from Christy because we hadn't always seen eye to eye but it was a nice touch and it sort of put me in good humour for the day.

When I looked out the window after that conversation, the day got even better and I couldn't help laughing. At the start of the season, around 20 people from the village would gather in the middle of Oulart to see us off to Croke Park, but this time there were close to 200, all of them looking for autographs.

It wasn't hard to enjoy their enthusiasm; again it left me feeling positive and bright. I smiled as I looked at the tractors that had been painted purple and gold, the beloved Wexford colours in all their glory. These were your neighbours, the people you grew up with, the ones that were looking out for you, and if they didn't inspire you nothing would.

I joined up with Storey and we hopped on the team bus. Once we were all present and correct, Griffin slapped on our favourite flick for what felt like the 100th time, and yet the lads were still glued to it. We didn't need to look at William Wallace to have legs flying around the place; we had John O'Connor, who did the job just fine on his own.

The lads were tense and as we pulled into the Stillorgan Park Hotel in Dublin, the amount of support for us was frightening. Each of us individually attended to his various little rituals before we came together for one last team meeting.

And strangely, Griffin took no part in it. After steering us through the year and showing leadership Martin Luther King would be proud of, he left us to our own devices. He just said the work had been done and it was now up to us, quickly went through the game plan and was gone. Jesus, we'd have to do it on our own after all!

Niamh Fitzpatrick said her few words, and it was over to us. The meeting had a nervous edge to it, but soon players chipped in with their tuppenceworth. Then Seánie Flood stood up.

We had seen Seánie break down in Wexford Park as he tried to push himself into All-Ireland final contention and we broke down with him; it hurt us as much as it hurt him. Each time he had tried to string two runs together, he had just made the problem worse. He knew himself he had no chance but would find out exactly how serious the injury was only after the All-Ireland final.

As he stood up, the room went totally silent. What followed was something I will never forget. For years after, people would talk about the rousing and passionate speech Seánie Flood had made and how he'd inspired us to victory, but if the truth be told, he said hardly anything at all because he soon broke down, and I'm not ashamed to say I quietly let the tears well and almost broke down with him.

'Lads,' he whispered. 'You will never realise what you have until it's taken away from you.'

And with that, he wept. I put my head down so no-one could see me at it, but there were plenty others in the same boat.

Seánie couldn't continue; amid total silence he went over to the window and gazed out at the legions of Wexford fans on their way to Croke Park.

After what seemed like an eternity, that eerie stillness, more at place in a library than a team meeting, was finally broken by a loud thump on the table. It was Georgie O'Connor, of course.

'Come on to fuck, lads! We're going to win this! We have to!'

He stood up, and with that the mood in the room changed completely.

Defiance.

Lads went over to Seánie to console him. It was tough, but the tears were not finished yet. Before we took off from the hotel, Griffin held us in the team bus and read out a telegram he had received. He read the whole thing from start to finish: about what the team had done for the county and people of Wexford, about the pride and delight we had inspired. And he finished with a few words that basically wished us every blessing in the world for the big match.

'And that telegram,' Griffin concluded, as he placed his hand on my shoulder, 'is from Eileen Dunne, Liam's mother.'

Bang! My mother. Jesus, if he was looking for a weak spot, he had found it. She was the one person who always had full faith in me. There all the time, when my father had left, she was the one who picked up the pieces. Each time I got into trouble, my mother stood up for me – it was someone else's fault, you see.

A strong woman, she had guided eight of us through life with the help of little but a wooden spoon or poker, both of which she used to good effect. She and my aunt Ann used to travel to games; they were enthralled by the whole Wexford thing. They would gather on the Friday before the game, my aunt Ann having travelled from Cork, and I would spend Saturday trying to avoid them because all they wanted to talk about was the match and that was the last thing I wanted to chat about. Each morning of a game, I would pop up to see them but the first thing they would ask for was inside gossip and the latest match tactics.

Now Griffin had caught me again, just hours before the match. I thought back to how Mam had been sick for the semi-final; it was heart-wrenching stuff. I half expected Griffin to put on *Sleepless in Seattle* instead of *Braveheart*. But what more motivation could you ask for? Somehow, I stayed focused. This was the chance of a lifetime. None of us had ever reached an All-Ireland final before and there was no guarantee we would get back. As it happens, I never did play in another one after that.

The bus started and with the rev of an engine began the final part of our odyssey. I looked out the window and took it all in. Larry O and the rest of the lads were also taking everything in. Every good-looking woman that passed was subjected to an admiring whistle from him, with support from the rest of the crew. In fairness to Larry O, he could spot a well-formed woman a mile away, and on big match days the scenery always seemed to be exceptional. Nerves always play a part but the Wexford players were too busy spotting talent to suffer unbearable tension.

As we drew nearer the stadium, I tried to memorise everything I saw. Sometimes, when I close my eyes at night, the thoughts are still there, only a dream away. Thousands of fans waving at you with their eyes wide open and full of hope, the colour of it all, the mix of purple and gold and green and white jerseys, as they made their way to the ground.

The start of the minor match; we hankered for it to end but had to let on to have some sort of an interest in it just to keep our minds off the big game for a while longer.

It seemed like an eternity to throw-in. The wait was a lengthy definition of what my life was all about up to that point. Over the years, I had asked many questions of myself and now it was time for answers.

In the dressing-room, it was as tense as I had ever seen it. I made 10 visits to the toilet and kept meeting the same lads the whole time, Seánie Flood, Ger Cushe, Larry O.

'Jaysus,' I thought to myself, 'are they still pissing?' But I could have sourced a river myself that day.

Our PRO, Pat Murphy, handed the jerseys out, and I went into the jacks again, found a cubicle, sat down on the seat and pulled on the jersey. Before all big games, I used to lock myself in the toilet cubicle. The rest of the lads probably thought I had the scutters, but I would just sit down, pull the Wexford shirt down on me and spend a few moments thinking about my Dad. For some reason, it always helped me do the job on the field.

It goes without saying that I thought of my mother but I also thought of my father, whom I hadn't seen for so long. Why hadn't he called? Jesus, he started me off hurling. It would have killed him to miss a game like this. I couldn't understand why he didn't get in touch. But of course Dad had a different life now; working in St Helena, off the coast of South Africa, he didn't want to come home. And although we found it hard to take, we had to move on.

Dad had missed everything but we had missed him too. The gap between us grew wider each year from 1992 onwards as we began to see less and less of him. At first, it was a six-week gap but that soon became three or four months and then we were lucky to have him home once a year. When he started to skip Christmas time, we knew it was all over and just rallied around Mam.

It seemed to be a blow each time Dad missed a big game, like when we won the club's first ever county final in 1994, when Tomás led the team home. Tomás and I used to travel to training together and spoke about Dad a fair bit, but what could you say really? Here he was, missing us reaping the harvest after he had helped to sow the seeds.

I had my own thoughts on the whole situation but it must have been hard for the old man as well. When he would make the rare journey home, people in the parish were blowing him up, telling him what a great tan he had and saying that he looked twice as fit and healthy as his sons. But that soon changed too, and when he came back the year after we won the 94 county final, the locals reminded him of what he had missed. The fact he was now missing the All-Ireland final, well it hurt a little bit.

There were no letters or cards, and yet we just carried on. And while I would spend time thinking about him before matches, my mother was the last person I would think of before going out of the dressing-room. The cubicle is a quiet place. It's small and may not smell the best but you can lock yourself away before you go out and place yourself in front of the whole country. I did a lot of thinking there before games, personal thoughts. The team stuff was confined to the dressing-room. People never came looking for me – maybe they knew I had my own routine to act out.

The Wexford jersey always lifted me; it was an honour to put it on and when I locked that door, it was all about the county, my family and myself. Let's just say I wasn't short of motivational tools when I went out to hurl.

Snapping out of the zone, I left my hiding place and stepped back into the dressing-room, where the atmosphere was even more tingling than it had been in that little cubicle.

'Jesus, Brother,' Griffin was telling Larry O'Gorman, 'get us going! Come on, Brother!'

Then Larry brought us into the warm-up room and started to inject a bit of humour into proceedings. We huddled together fiercely, like best friends out to say their goodbyes for the last time. While the Limerick team were jostling lads out of the way going into their dressing-room and beating their hurls like lunatics inside, we were saying prayers. They were way too hyped up; we were controlled. The look in our eyes said it all: it was shit or bust, and after offering up a prayer, we nearly took the hinges off the doors when the call from the stewards came to vacate the room.

The run out onto the field will stay with me for life. While I was hyped, I couldn't but sneak a little smile into the TV cameras that greeted us at the entrance to the tunnel.

Boom! Jesus, the roar was deafening. I'd never heard anything like it. I gave one big sprint out of the tunnel. My helmet barely stayed on. I ran nowhere and ran everywhere at the same time, tried to get water in and then remembered I couldn't go to the toilet anymore so I stopped. I was in the middle of the pitch. My legs were strong. That was good. Yet I wanted to hide and there was no hiding place. I was never as dumbstruck in all my life. The fright I got when I ran out onto the field that day will live forever with me.

The noise, the people, lack of space, it shocked me and I turned around and saw Seánie Flood, which didn't help me much either. Seánie went to walk to the bench but I dragged him back, like he had defiantly pulled us out of the fire all year.

'No way, Seánie!' I told him. 'You're in this with us.'

He was a real character, a witty, funny lad who made his money as a self-employed contractor and tried to make it to Slane in his spare time with his rock band Running on Empty. They were no Beatles, but all the same they were a fairly lively bunch and would go on to get a fair few gigs after this match.

Seánie had been unflappable in defence for so long and there was no chance we were letting him go now. So I caught him by the neck, marched him over for the team photograph and threw him in the middle of the bench. But of course, Larry O had decided to go missing, and to this day people still think it was a Griffin ploy to leave out a team member from the photo just to confuse the opposition.

That theory is crap, because Larry O was off somewhere getting his own few photos taken, I think. Anyway, it was important to have Seánie in the picture; he was a big part of our camp and had quietened Johnny Dooley and Kevin Broderick in previous games to help us get this far.

Would you believe that the nerves then started to disappear a little, and as I warmed up, I thought what an awesome feeling this was to be here pucking around just before an All-Ireland final. I envied the Kilkenny lads who got to sample this occasion most of the time.

This may seem a trivial matter, but when the call then came to stand for President Robinson we felt we were seasoned professionals at this lark. After all, Griffin had coached us for this moment a fortnight earlier. As per orders, I stood with my hands behind my back and looked for the Liam MacCarthy Cup, but it was not on the podium.

'Never mind,' I thought. 'I'll see it soon enough.'

It's only a little thing but it matters on All-Ireland final day, and if you contrasted the Wexford and Limerick teams on their presentation to the President, you may have picked the winners out before the ball was even thrown in. We stood in a straight line, chests forward, backs straight, and even paid her compliments.

Amid all the tension, it was one of the funniest moments of my career when Larry O even praised Mary Robinson on her choice of dress, while nearby the Limerick lads hopped nervously in and out of line, bending and stretching and looking seriously on edge.

I looked up and down the line at our lads and my heart just thumped; I marvelled at the way they appeared so calm and focused. How great it had been to travel the road alongside these lads over the past year! Fitzy, then only 22, was beside me. From day one, we knew he was possibly the best goalkeeper in Ireland. What I didn't know while standing there meeting the President was that later in the day he would create one of the defining moments by laying his body on the line and stopping a certain goal.

Then there was Cushe, sound and solid, a lionheart. He could not have been blamed if he'd thrown his hat at it when Griffin dropped him in 95 for John O'Connor. We had to win for the likes of him, who had always watched out for others.

After Larry O had finished giving the President fashion tips, I sneaked a look down his direction. Free entertainment, they were the words that popped into my head when I saw his big grin. But the hoor was also the best hurler I ever played alongside.

John O'Connor was in contrast to Larry O because he was a serious fellow and didn't take any messing. Like Georgie, he was superfit. Looking along the line at the two of them, I was glad they were on my side.

Adrian Fenlon, another iron man, was also a key reason why we had to win this match. He hadn't even been on the team for the League but here he was, vital to the cause, inspiring other youngsters for the future. He would lead us from centrefield. I was sure of that.

Colm Kehoe was cut from the same mould. He was someone I didn't really know until 96. Now, when I looked over at him, he was quiet as usual but you could see the desire.

And then I looked over at Rod and Dave Guiney, or the Gooneys, as I used to call them. They didn't mix that much with us, but Griffin had a great hold on them, and just as with the rest of the team, I was willing to burst a gut for either brother.

Just because you don't always get on with someone doesn't mean you can't hurl with him. At this stage, I was trained to keep away from them in the warm-ups before matches. They were like rocket-launchers, firing the ball from one to the other, trying to kill each other; I almost laughed aloud as I remembered the constant competition between them.

Dave didn't start that day, and alongside him on the bench was Billy Byrne. Jesus, if you couldn't try to win for that man, you had no hope. Here he was, 36 years old, eight years older than me, but he had done all the training with no bother and there was no complaining out of him. Win, lose or draw, he had left his mark on the Championship.

We got the call to fall in behind the Artane Boys Band, a part of the proceedings we had rehearsed from way back. As we marched, I spotted some local photographers by the Canal End and gave them a nod – they'd been with us all year as well and it meant as much to them as it did to the rest of the county.

The big TV screen glared down ominously at us like Big Brother. Niamh warned it would be a daunting experience but had prepared us well, and so we were calm and assured marching around the field, which is more than can be said for Limerick, who had broken away and run into their field positions before we were even halfway down the Cusack Stand side.

We didn't bat an eyelid. Wexford were staying behind the band all the way around and that was it. Around by Hill 16 we rallied on our own, right over to where the Wexford fans dominated the terrace. You can imagine the lift we got passing in front of them on our own. At the same time, Limerick must have felt like spare pricks at a wedding, because I looked down and saw Mike Nash, Declan Nash and Stephen MacDonagh jogging on the spot, running over and back to each other. They didn't even do a half lap of the field. Too impatient.

One thing we neglected to do was to listen to Martin Storey's final few words after we broke. Martin called us back but Fitzy was off like a rocket and down to his goal. Four of us stayed back, but then we said to hell with it, the time for talking was done.

I ran to my position and shook hands with Gary Kirby. I had my homework done on him. I had studied videos of Joe Quaid's puck-outs, so each time he went to deliver a ball on the left, I knew it was coming my way. Two weeks before the final, I had phoned Griffin to ask him how I should deal with Kirby and he warned me that discipline was the key. He rammed home the fact that from frees Kirby had scored almost everything he'd hit so far that season. By the end of the conversation, I was in no doubt that this guy could well beat us on his own.

'If we keep Kirby to four points from frees, we'll win the game,' Griffin said and added that he had every confidence in me. Before he hung up, he finished: 'Liamy, the great Liamy Dunne, you will be man of the match on All-Ireland final day.'

I wasn't exactly sure about that but now there was no time to think. Seconds after the ball was thrown in, Seán O'Neill, who had flattened Tommy Kehoe in the League earlier that year, hit Georgie a right shot. The referee, Pat Horan, awarded a throw-in between the two and Seán ended up on the ground and I don't think he hit a ball after that or since; he had met someone who was mentally and physically strong and Georgie absolutely flaked him.

Soon, the second puck-out of the day landed between Gary Kirby and I. We both pulled on it at the same time, and as I pulled he came in sideways with that unusual style of his. We made contact and the ball broke to Martin Storey, who gave a 70-metre free away.

I didn't feel there was anything out of the ordinary during our exchange; Gary didn't go down and there wasn't even a break or stoppage in the play. He went over to the Cusack Stand side instead and pointed the free.

A few minutes later, Rod Guiney gave a free away and he stuck that over as well. Later, a young lad came in with a towel to wipe blood from his finger, but Gary was fine and played on. He had two points from frees by the break.

But a lot more dangerous at the time was Ciarán Carey, who really seemed to be getting into his game. Joe Quaid started off brilliantly but his tactics didn't work for him. Joe started hitting the ball as far as he could, raining puck-outs down on top of Georgie and I, who just retreated as far back as we had to and mopped up.

I didn't hit the ball five times during the second half but I didn't have to; in my opinion, my opponent's body language suggested that he was going to do no damage. And yet, they left him centre-forward for the entire game.

But still, the picture wasn't much rosier for us and we trailed by four points, 0-5 to 0-1, early in the game. Mike Houlihan broke his hurley across Larry O'Gorman, John O'Connor was having trouble with Owen O'Neill and Ger Cushe gave Damien Quigley a slap to test his reaction.

It was a stormy opening and, not surprisingly, both John O and Owen were soon booked. As Horan wrote their names in, I drew his attention to Houlihan's tackle on Larry O and, in fairness, he booked the second Limerickman as well.

At the other end of the pitch, Joe Quaid made a great save from Gary Laffan. I thought it was going to be one of those days but then a row started involving 15 lads. We were supposed to be minding our discipline but here we were again, fighting all over the place.

This time, Adrian Fenlon, Martin Storey and Ciarán Carey were booked. Then, after a throw-in, our corner-forward Eamon Scallan followed them into Horan's notepad.

Play continued and Scallan and Stephen MacDonagh pulled across each other but Scallan pulled again and, after 23 minutes of the first half, the referee decided this was going no further. He called our man aside and flashed a red card.

Now, three weeks before, we had spoken of this possibility, but you could have got some odds on Eamon getting the line. We were good friends over the years. He was very witty and good company, but he was far from being the giddiest guy on the team and was the last fellow I would have expected to walk the line.

We needed something to save our All-Ireland and we needed it quickly. Griffin calmly created a two-man full-forward line and instructed them to keep switching onto Limerick defenders so they couldn't settle. He kept the rest of the team intact.

Limerick decided Davy Clarke was their loose man but we threw one of the lads over on him and they seemed to play him all wrong, leaving him in defence, instead of switching Ciarán Carey into that role and moving him up the field, where he could have drawn one of the defenders out and created space for someone else. They left Clarke where he was and allowed Joe Quaid to boom huge puck-outs down on top of our defence. We lapped it up.

And the Man Above, this time, gave us a sign that it could yet be our day when he helped John O'Connor float a 91-yard free over the bar soon after Eamon was sent off. It gave us an awful lift. John O had missed a similar score that would have won the 93 League final, but here he was, doing it when it counted most.

Like a rolling stone, the momentum continued to gather. Almost immediately Tom Dempsey got a goal that was like an organ transplant for the team because it handed us back our belief. Larry O added another quick point. We were thriving in the face of adversity and went to the dressing-rooms a point to the good.

The halfway house was calm and controlled, but it was hard to keep cool because we were like bulls, raging and frantic to get back into the ring. The one thing that kept things in perspective was the sight of Eamon Scallan, and we took turns to offer words of comfort to him. The buzz word was discipline for the second half. Kirby was still capable of winning the game from frees, but not if we didn't concede any. And with the game half over, we could concede two more frees and still meet the challenge Griffin had set us. Up stepped the manager.

'You have put your lives on the line for this!' he roared. 'This is it. I believe you are 35 minutes away from destiny. We have that feeling lads – it's been building up all year and you know it. Believe in one another. We had guys up at five in the morning training with us and they didn't even get a jersey today but look at them, part of us.'

He referred to guys like Thomas Codd, MJ Reck and Joe Kearns, who had trained their arses off all year and didn't even have a jersey on match day.

Griffin was right, we owed it to them as much as each other.

'You've put in 187 sessions from day one to today, the All-Ireland final,' he reminded us. 'That's a lot of time. But today is payback for your families.'

And out we went, the light blinding us as we ran head first into destiny, not knowing how we were going to get there but determined and confident we would arrive.

Gary Laffan ran the show in the opening minutes, hitting two bad wides but eventually nailing a point that settled us. Quaid made another great save from him, though, and all over the field, Limerickmen were clashing swords with us. Rory MacCarthy was struggling with Mark Foley but working his ass off. Barry Foley, who had scored a point off Larry O, was called ashore and we breathed a sigh of relief that Limerick had no Mike Galligan to bring on.

As the game became more frantic, our full-back Ger Cushe went down injured. There was nothing wrong with him but from his vantage point he could see we needed a breather. As Cushe hit the ground, John O went over to Hill 16 and got the massive Wexford crowd going, and we breathed in what little inspiration our lungs would allow us to.

Playing with 14 men was starting to take its toll. Yet we didn't give away one free in defence for the 35 minutes of the second half. I always maintain that if we had fouled, Kirby would have pointed six or seven frees, but we showed some bottle to rein in our violent urges and cut out that aspect of the game, which I'm sure contributed to Gary having a stinker of a final.

Going into this game, I had developed a reputation for not being a tight marker but that game I shed the label, and a few yards behind, Ger Cushe, who was said to be too big and too slow for the top level, was having a stormer. There was no better day to shut people up.

As the game entered the magic moments where life will change either way, we clung onto a two-point lead, more precious to us than any gem or jewel in the world. With time almost up, I got the ball, soloed out of defence and waited for a Limerickman to come and clatter me. It was the only time in my career where I wanted to be upended, and I kept hobbling away, waiting for the free to come.

But no-one fouled, and suddenly Seán O'Neill arrived and whipped the ball away as I lost control and slipped. Trying to catch him, I found my legs would not move – they had gone to jelly – and I just sighed in colossal relief as Storey came to my rescue and won the ball back.

'The hill-running in Bunclody stood to him anyway,' I thought, before realising I was on the ground, dreaming, in an All-Ireland final.

I prayed to God and shouted at Pat Horan in the one gasp: 'Jesus, Pat, time must be up.'

I think he heard me because though they won a free, he blew the next whistle. Unsure that we had really won the game, I looked up at the scoreboard to double-check. WEXFORD 1-13 - LIMERICK 0-

14. Yep! The first thing I did was shake hands with Gary. I genuinely felt sorry for him. It was their second time losing a final in three years. What a pill to swallow!

Still, we had waited 28 years ourselves and that was no picnic either. In a daze, I walked to the stand, all the strength sapped out of me. I met Bartle Redmond on the field, my old pal, put my hand on his shoulder and started crying.

We walked side by side over to the Hogan Stand, until fans got me and threw me on their shoulders. I got down again and kept walking. It was strange: supporters were running past me, ignoring me, and in the end I had to turn around to a few of them to try and get in with the rest of the team.

'Jaysus, I'm after hurling here. Will some of ye try and throw me in,' I begged.

Eventually, I reached the inner circle and saw Storey lift the Liam MacCarthy Cup. What a funny feeling to see your own clubman lift the cup! I tried to take it all in but I could barely see Martin, there were so many ribbons on the piece of silver.

For a moment, the team went back under the Hogan Stand because the gardaí wanted the crowd to break up, and in those few moments we bonded with each other – the pictures in Monday's papers would show Oulart and Buffers Alley men crying in each other's arms – and the team just reflected quietly on what we had achieved before going back out onto the field.

Thousands were milling around out there, but in the middle of the purple and gold blur, among the legions of whooping and back-slapping supporters, I saw my mother, crying with delight. I looked her in the face and saw pride. I felt the very same. Hugging her, I bowed my head. 'Mam,' I said, 'I have no more tears left for you.'

I was told before the game that they were going to do me.

**Gary Kirby of Limerick on the 1996 final,
which left him with broken fingers**

– CHAPTER THIRTEEN –
Victory and Kirby

Life just changed. The win was for ourselves and for the supporters,
who just put us up on a pedestal. From then on, nothing was the same.
Wexford: 1996 All-Ireland champions. The win was made all the
sweeter by the fact that I was named RTÉ Man of the Match. I don't
know how because I cleared only four or five balls all during the game.
The TV cameras hovered ominously around me all night so I realised
Jim Bolger must have known something in advance when he told me I
was getting the nod.

Commentator Ger Canning called my name and everyone stood
up and clapped as I received my award, crystal worth £750, so they told
me, but I still couldn't figure out why I had got it. Sure I had stopped
Gary Kirby but I hadn't hit five balls all day and felt my hurling had
been sacrificed for the purpose of that specific job. Even going in to that
winners' banquet in Malahide, the extent of what we had done didn't
sink in, but as we met great hurlers from a past era and saw their eyes
twinkle with delight, we knew we had achieved something rare and
wonderful.

The Wexford fans had taken so much hurt over the years, and it
was great to be able to sit back and watch them enjoy this with us. I
thought in particular of our number one fan, Marcella Meehan from
Charleton Hill, who was in the audience wearing her beloved
Wexford geansaí.

I had met Marcella for the first time when I was presenting medals to the winners of a pool tournament in New Ross. She was confined to a wheelchair, but we got to know her well because she would never miss a game. Her bedroom was a shrine to Wexford hurling and she would send birthday cards to all the lads – how she used to get the dates I don't know.

She got on particularly well with Damien Fitzhenry, who always reckoned he could hear her behind his goal, no matter where we were playing. He gave her his jersey, Ger Cushe presented her with his hurley, Rod Guiney gave her a purple tiger teddy and George O'Connor was only too happy to make a presentation of a bronze statue of a hurling boot. Tom Dempsey and she shared tears of joy after the All-Ireland final win and the Wexford Supporters Club named her their official Number One Fan. From time to time, she would ring Eithne and chat away and even though she went through several operations for her illness she wouldn't miss a game.

Larry Murphy wrote her a lovely note once saying: 'We will keep your courage in our hearts forever.' And he was right.

Her wish was that, when she died, the Wexford team of 96 would carry her coffin. Sadly, that moment would come to pass in January 2003, when Marcella passed away.

The funeral was terribly sad. In fairness to Rod Guiney, he did a marvellous job and went up to the altar to speak on behalf of the players. His words were poignant and real. The team took turns to carry the coffin, and walking down to the graveyard I was beside Rory McCarthy and in front of me were George and John O'Connor, Billy Byrne, Martin Storey, Tom Dempsey, Seán Flood and Larry O'Gorman. They were all devastated. If I ever needed a reminder that we had all shared in something special, this was it.

'I can't understand why we didn't win more, Rory,' I said. 'Just look at those lads around you.'

Marcella would have approved. She was buried in New Ross and as we left the church, the strains of *The Purple and Gold*, her favourite song, carried across the churchyard. It was one of the saddest experiences of my life.

Thank God she saw the good times! The night of the 96 final would have been the happiest of her life. The team got a glow when we saw people like Marcella beaming from ear to ear.

The rest of that night was a blur to me. I do remember, however, the Wild Swans getting up on stage to sing *Dancing at the Crossroads* and we enjoyed the formalities and informalities of it all. The years 93 to 95 had been rollercoasters but to win an All-Ireland after 28 years was incredible, especially when you considered how many Leinster titles we had lost along the way.

The fun stopped momentarily when we were informed there would be a team meeting, at 11 am the next day in the hotel, and true to form, no-one was late. With the breakfast eaten and the papers read, we gathered in a room to listen to Griffin one more time. By this stage, if he'd told us we should become transvestites, we would have gone shopping for bras and nylons, so the whole squad attended, all eyes and ears, to hear his thoughts on what had just happened. Not for the first time, his words were loaded with meaning.

'This,' he whispered, 'is probably the last time we will ever be together as a group.'

Again, he had caught our attention, and again he would turn out to be right. At least one guy didn't even make it to the official medal presentation later that year, and one or two didn't make it on the team holiday the next year either. I can understand holidays, but missing the medal presentation was a crime. One of our subs, Liam Turley, a Galway native, was the man who missed out.

Liam was a nice lad and a decent hurler who had transferred to St Martin's and had managed to attract the selectors' attention, and to his credit, he trained and hurled away with us all year. But I felt his absence showed just what that All-Ireland meant to him. It seemed a little bit of a snub when he didn't turn up to the medal ceremony.

But Griffin had predicted someone would miss out and there we were, startled to hear such a stark prediction hours after we had won an All-Ireland, the fruits of slaving together for nine months on the trot. And he wasn't finished there. He went on to warn us of the dangers of booze. He hadn't been wrong once all year so we listened intently as he advised us not to go near the winners' podiums all over the county if we had drink taken.

'You are All-Ireland champions now. Conduct yourselves like All-Ireland champions,' he concluded.

After that, we had to go to the Burlington Hotel for the traditional post-All-Ireland banquet for both teams, which I always felt was terribly unfair on the losers. I shook hands with Mike Nash from Limerick and Davy Clarke but we didn't speak much.

Then Gary Kirby came into view and just as I was about to go over, because obviously he was disappointed, I saw he had a big bandage on his finger and his arm was in a sling. That just turned me off, and I didn't bother approaching him.

Of course, that's when all the innuendo started: the rumours that we had agreed in training that I would break his hand so he wouldn't be able to take frees, the theory that I had deliberately pulled on his fingers as the second ball came our way. And that's all I've heard ever since.

'Ah yeah, you're the man who broke Kirby's fingers in the 96 final. Stopped him from hitting frees.'

Word got back to me that Gary had been telling people he knew it was going to happen, but as far as I'm concerned, Limerick beat themselves that day. I haven't a clue if he broke his fingers or not. If he did, I certainly didn't set out to break them. The two of us pulled on the ball at the same time and, as far as I'm concerned, if he had struck correctly he would have got no contact from me. There was nothing said about the 70-metre free he pointed from under the Cusack Stand a moment or two after we had pulled. And there was even less said about the fact that the Wexford backs gave away no free in the second half of the final, which I reckon is a record.

Nothing was premeditated. No Wexford player went out to take any Limerickman out of it. The whole incident was blown out of proportion. To anyone who still doubts me, I would say take the video out, slow it down when it comes to that notorious exchange between us and you will see there was no malice on my part.

A few years later, I was in the Anner Hotel in Thurles when Philip Ryan, a C&C sales rep, said there was an old friend of mine nearby that I had to meet. He ushered me into a room and left me there with none other than G Kirby. We spoke for about 10 minutes, chatted about hurling in general and shook hands before leaving. There was no awkwardness.

But then, in 2003, I was told of an episode of the TV series *Laochra Gael*, where he had plenty to say about me and the incident. It was in that broadcast he told the world Wexford had a pre-match plan to go out and do him.

He said: 'As I pulled, my hand met a hurl and broke a bone in my finger. If I was pulling on the ball, it meant that the ball was a hurley length from my hand. So whoever hit me was pulling low below the ball.

'You lose games, but we all have to go to work the following morning and you don't do things like that.'

It's clear he was very sore over what happened; I can't do much about that. What annoyed me more was the insistence by the Limerick players that they had thrown the 1996 final away. Thrown it away? Who were they trying to cod?

We were on the wrong end of an 0-5 to 0-1 scoreline and reduced to 14 men for about 35 minutes of the game, yet we cut the free count down to almost zero and they say they threw it away. What about the 1994 final when they had it in the bag but let Offaly take it from them? Maybe Limerick threw that one away – they certainly didn't in 1996.

I have to say the whole affair didn't occupy much space on my mind at the time but I was damned angry when it all flared up again from 2000 onward when I got my first red card. That's when it really got to me.

I hope this finally sets the record straight. I didn't go out to 'do' Gary Kirby. There was no preconceived plan to take him out. In case you think I protest too much, maybe consider Liam Griffin's purist philosophy when it comes to hurling. He would rather you miss a point from 70 metres than cheat by moving it forward five metres and score. To suggest he would encourage me to do something that went so strongly against his principles is defying all logic.

Another defender would never have heard of the incident again but my reputation landed me with this. That's my take on the affair. It also seems to me that whenever you win something, there will always be people who want to take from it.

It was no wonder that we enjoyed the homecoming so much. On our way to Gorey, Billy Byrne told me he had often imagined coming home as a winner and wondering if the streets would be packed. He didn't have long to wait for his answer because from there to Enniscorthy and on to Wexford town, the county was thronged.

Heading into Enniscorthy, we negotiated the corner around Cinema Lane and there I saw the Kilkenny hurling legend Christy Heffernan, clapping and cheering the team bus on. To see a Kilkenny man obviously delighted for us was something to behold; he was really enjoying the craic.

The entire panel went up on to a platform and were introduced one by one to the crowd. By this stage, we were almost fed up of the ritual, which had to be performed in every town the team bus stopped in, and so it was a relief when we reached the Ferrycarrig Hotel, where the team stayed and enjoyed a buffet dinner.

I don't know what got into me but the next morning I woke up and drove into Wexford town in search of a flower shop. The woman who worked there hadn't a clue I had played in the final but she must have thought I was soft in the head when I asked her to create a bouquet of purple and gold flowers and requested they be sent to Liam Griffin and his wife, Mary, at the hotel.

The GOAL match was the next item on the agenda, and of course a drinking session broke out in the Talbot Hotel before we even got to play the Rest of Ireland outfit. About 12,000 turned up and, to their credit, a lot of the Limerick guys showed their faces as well, although I only managed a half hour against them because I was green to the gills from drink. But it didn't stop me from heading back to the Talbot after, where we rocked the night away until about 5 am.

Sometime during the celebrations I had to nip out to find a hole in the wall and extract a few quid, and passing the County Hotel, I was invited in by the manager. The place was jointed and before I knew it I was hoisted shoulder high and planted on stage by a crowd of cheering supporters, who demanded I sing a song with Joe Monaghan's band.

Joe started singing some tune – I still don't know what it was – but all of a sudden I was centre stage with a microphone, not knowing the words and looking like a right clown. I had to do something.

'Up Wexford!' I roared, and the place went bananas.

I said I'd push it a bit more.

'Yyuuupp Wexfooorrrd!' I shouted even louder, shaking my fist in the air. It wasn't the most original stage performance of all time, but the crowd nearly went through the roof before shouldering me off the stage in triumphal procession.

Eventually, I managed to sneak away and rejoin the lads. It would be like that for the rest of the year.

Going back to your roots is always special, and so I wanted to be clear in the head when Martin Storey, Paul Finn and I visited the schools in Oulart, starting with Church of Ireland, Kilnamanagh, and then set off to meet the villagers.

Now style was not a big thing with any of the three of us and while the likes of Manchester United are used to limos and Mercs, we piled into the back of Paul Finn's old van with the Liam MacCarthy Cup to meet the club chairman, Fintan Cooney, and all the various families and aunts and uncles.

Joe Quaid was gracious enough to come down to us that night and stayed over with Tom Dempsey. The TV cameras were also around and no-one ever saw a livelier buzz around the place. That evening, we went over to Storey's end of the village, the Ballagh, and it was the same all over again.

For six solid months after we won the Cup, the celebrations continued and only then did I get a chance to bring Liam MacCarthy back to Raheen Duff, where he was warmly received.

For any lad who likes the taste of a few pints it was a dangerous time, though. I was working with GH Lett Soft Drinks of Enniscorthy before moving to C&C, and with both jobs I was expected to be at certain pubs at night if the Cup was also there.

I never disliked the taste of drink anyway but this didn't help and I was too conscientious to refuse anyone an appearance. I feared word would go around that I was too big for my boots.

But the reality was that I was being asked out to pubs every night. I should have drawn a line but publicans I dealt with in the line of business took it as a personal slight if I was not there to bring the MacCarthy Cup to them.

And so I had more 5 am sessions than an Olympic athlete and although I had never been looked after better in my life, not having to pay for drink or food, I was falling into a trap, an easy one to slip into. Still, it was better that we had a piece of silverware than to be stuck in the doldrums, I thought, and I got on with it.

There were one or two tricky and uncomfortable moments, including a day when I visited a pub in Ferns, and asked the owner to open an account with my new employers, C&C. He refused, saying I had given him a kick in the teeth by not making it to his pub the night the Cup arrived and now it was his turn to give me a kick back. What could I do except apologise?

But that was an isolated incident and generally we were worshipped and treated like heroes, and we made no bones about using our new-found status to boost the Wexford hurlers' holiday fund.

The squad raised so much money for that American holiday in January 1997 that the married guys received £2,500 spending money each, the single players with a girlfriend got £2,000 and the totally single chaps received a nice £1,500 in their back pockets.

Of the 13 of the side nominated for an All Star award, seven of us got the nod, though Ger Cushe should have been the eighth – I remember Brian Lohan saying he had taken Cushe's All Star.

But it didn't stop there. Martin Storey got the Players' Player of the Year award; Larry O'Gorman got the Sports Writers' Hurler of the Year; and I got the *Star* newspaper/Waterford Crystal equivalent. And just about every Wexford hurler got some recognition for his efforts.

We were gods and the freebies just kept on flowing in. The night before the 96 senior football All-Ireland final between Meath and Mayo, Martin Storey and I were invited by Guinness up to their corporate box to watch the game. We were put up and handed £100 spending money and watched the two teams box the shit out of each other and play a little bit of football as well.

There was also a three-week holiday to the US coming up and the trip with the All Stars after that. Suddenly, everything had clicked into place and although I was still a little upset not to have heard anything from my Dad, who hadn't contacted me after the final, I was getting married in a few weeks' time to Eithne and hoped he would make it.

Suddenly there seemed to be no need to worry anymore. The vouchers, holidays, gifts and stuff were only small tokens but life could not get much better. We were All-Ireland champions for the first time since 1968. These were the days that every player dreamt about. Only now, there was no need to dream.

A real friend is one who walks in when the rest of the world walks out.
Friendship is one mind in two bodies.
Mencius, Confucian philosopher

– CHAPTER FOURTEEN –
From feast to famine

On October 18 1996 my mother finally had a challenger for the role of leading lady in my life.

I first met Eithne Sinnott in the Hydro nightclub in Wexford in 1989 although I had known her brother, Eamon, who hurled for Wexford, a long time before. Eamon was a fine bloke but the Sinnotts came from Buffers Alley territory so there was no way I could have been seen around any of them. Nevertheless, I found Eithne, who worked at the time as a hairdresser in Kilmuckridge, to be easy on the eye and wonderfully easygoing and so it took off from there.

There's probably never a convenient time to be introduced to your future in-laws, and so my initial visit to the Sinnott household was clouded in fear and discomfort. After a few pints to pluck up the courage, I eventually made my way in and Eithne's Mam and Dad, May and Paddy, were having tea.

Paddy was in dire form because Eamon had shipped a right smack in a county training match in which I was involved with the other team. Paddy was big into hurling and not too happy about it.

'Get me out of here quick,' I thought.

The Sinnotts loved their hurling. Stellah, Eithne's sister, had played in an All-Ireland final with my sister Siobhán, so that was a link straightaway. Eithne herself had played a bit and represented Wexford at under-14. Her sisters Paula and Kate also played and Eamon was a class act; he captained Wexford at one stage and did really well on minor and under-21 teams before then. But though the family were hurling-mad and naturally friendly, they probably would have preferred anyone but an Oulart man to be arriving in courting the lovely Eithne.

Of course love conquers all, or so they say, and gradually I got totally comfortable with the Sinnott family and always got a warm welcome anytime I called.

I proposed to Eithne at the end of 1995. It was a real romantic moment as I popped the question in my car. Eithne was surprised; she hadn't seen it coming at all, but to my colossal relief she said yes.

We bought the ring in Waterford, arrived back at her house and said nothing. Her Mam got a right shock when she saw the gleam on her finger.

The wedding was fixed for October 18 1996 at the Ferrycarrig Hotel and to be fair to my fiancée, she excelled herself with the preparations and did most of the work. I was a disaster, totally consumed by hurling. All I really contributed to the effort was to ring Liam Griffin and book the hotel.

Liam was great to us. For good measure, Paula Sinnott worked in the Ferrycarrig, so from my point of view it was ideal – it was only a matter of me turning up with the ring on the day.

But as I say, I'm a laid-back person and not much fazes me, not even the fact we had nowhere to live three weeks before we got married. I found it amusing but few others did. All I could do was tell them not to panic, and add that it was actually too late for that anyway.

Eventually, I asked a friend, Kevin Cooney, about the living quarters over Phil Redmond's pub in Raheen Duff and he said there was no problem; we could stay there till we got sorted out. Little did I expect we would spend three years there, boosting Phil's bank account by a huge amount along the way.

Our wedding was like a hurling match; there were 10 of the 1996 All-Ireland team invited and many of my Oulart team-mates were there as

well, as were the cousins and the usual circle of friends. My brother
Seán was best man. Carol, another of Eithne's sisters, was bridesmaid.

We had sent the invitation to my father, unsure if he would travel.
But even though he was working in St Helena he made the long
journey home. He had been home around the time of the 1996
Wexford-Galway All-Ireland semi-final but we had lost touch
completely apart from that. It was great to have him there for the big
day. Mam had been sick around then so it was nice to have her up and
well and enjoying the wedding also.

I really enjoyed the ceremony and it flew by, to be honest,
although the day after was just as pleasing, when most of the party
headed into the Centenary Stores, a popular hostelry in Wexford town.

Mind you, Eithne was seriously displeased to see me disappear
into a corner of the Stores for several hours for an interview with Tom
Williams, a local writer who was compiling a book, *With Hand on
Heart*, the inside story of our All-Ireland win, at the time.

But the woman was a saint and still is. I have to confess she has
put up with a lot from me over the years. I overstepped the mark several
times, but she has never given up on me.

Before I went to chat to Tom, Dad phoned me from Dublin
Airport to tell me he was on his away again and we chatted for a few
minutes. I didn't realise it would be five years before we would speak
again.

Dad wished me luck and went off to his other life but there was
no time to get down about it. I went ahead to do the interview and join
in the sing-song that was after breaking out.

We had a great day and as the Wexford team and their partners
would soon be heading to the US for three weeks, there was no point in
honeymooning straightaway, so instead we retreated to the West of
Ireland and visited Galway and Ennis with our friends Bartle and Josie
Sinnott.

We enjoyed that little trip. It was the start of our new life together
and when we came back to our new home over Phil Redmond's pub,

we tried to make it homely and lived in. Well Eithne did. My main contribution to homemaking was to set about 200 traps around the place to keep the mice at bay.

There was some craic in that house when we first moved in. We loved it there, though my frequent trips downstairs to the pub nearly killed me and my bank balance. It was way too handy.

It was also too accessible for the thieves who broke in and robbed us blind while Eithne and I were asleep some time in March 97. I had a number of work-related cheques in the house but they were traceable and of no use, so the burglars just lined them up on the sink and left them there. But they took just about everything else.

When I came downstairs the following morning and saw we had been fleeced, my first thought was of my All-Ireland medal. I dashed to the press and went searching for it but dropped my head in despair when I saw it had been removed.

Shocked, I turned to sit down, and was astonished to see an array of medals lined up along the edge of the table with my All-Ireland medal taking pride of place in the middle.

The thieves had opened the box so that the medal sat gleaming out at me. They had more or less put it on show. I was just relieved they hadn't swiped it.

They got away with cash, other belongings and a lovely Wexford tracksuit I had just received from the county board. I reported it to the Gardai but the culprits were never found.

Amid the fuss over the All-Ireland final triumph, which still hadn't died down, the wedding and the hullabaloo over the robbery, it was obvious something had to give, and this time Oulart-The-Ballagh suffered. We could all see what was happening; there was still too much rejoicing about the place. Tom Neville tried to get it going again for the 97 club championship but what could he do?

We ploughed away and got to the quarter-final against Glynn-

Barntown, whom we'd beaten in the final just a year before. It was a miserable evening, I remember, but we managed to get past them before losing to Rathnure in the semi-final.

The team had suffered because of the All-Ireland win. Paul Finn and I were dragged all over the place with the Liam MacCarthy Cup, but I really felt sorry for Storey, who was asked to go everywhere and even had to take a few weeks off work to cope.

From here, things started to get worse for me and Wexford. In January of 97, the team went on holidays to the US. Near the end of the stay, Griffin called us together for a meal and meeting, to which wives and partners were also invited.

He made a one-hour speech but it was not as morale-boosting as the rest of the talks he had given us over the past year, for the simple reason he told us he was leaving. He went through all of 95 and 96, analysing the ups and downs, the highs and lows. And at the end of it all, he said he was stepping down.

Disappointment seeped through all of us, but strangely, we kind of knew that this was coming because Mary had been sick. So we accepted his decision.

What could we do? He had made his move.

Straight away, I wound my mind back to a chat I had with my sister-in-law Paula Sinnott and remembered how at the end of 95 she had told me Liam wouldn't walk away until he felt the job had been done. Well, here we were now, undoubtedly with the job done, and although Martin Storey stood up and made a passionate plea for him to stay on, it was never going to happen.

Liam had to devote everything to Mary, who had given him so much encouragement when he took the job, and his decision was quite understandable after all the time he had given to us the year before. We knew there and then things would never be the same again. Fair enough, the set-up was good and there was a decent base there for us to build on, but there would never be another Liam Griffin.

Plenty of counties would, though, have killed to have a man of the calibre of Rory Kinsella as their manager, and we were damn lucky to have him. Rory had been there as a selector with Séamus Barron, who also stepped down, and was widely respected as a real hurling coach among all of us. He introduced Eddie McDonald and Paudge Courtney to the set-up.

It was a comical sight to see us going back to the grindstone a few weeks after the holiday and it was no wonder we had a terrible League. I felt sorry for Rory because the expectation levels were huge and yet we were absolutely way out of shape when we returned.

We played our first League match against Galway and what a shock the crowd must have got. The last time many of them had seen us togged out, we were like whippets: lean muscular machines who had reached the top of the summit. We stood out and so did the muscles and veins in our necks and calves. You could tell at a glance we were fit and bursting to go.

Well, when we trotted out onto Wexford Park for that first League game, you could almost hear the disbelief that greeted us, because most of the team were like Oompa Loompas.

Ger Cushe had gone absolutely huge after a winter of enjoying life as an All-Ireland champion. But he wasn't the only one doing impressions of Mr Blobby. Gary Laffan and Tom Dempsey certainly bore no resemblance to Kate Moss and I was a good stone overweight myself.

I looked around the dressing-room that day and could see Griffin's words in the Burlington Hotel had already rung true. We, the men that won the All-Ireland final for the county, would never be in the same group or room ever again and it was a numbing old thought.

There was no Georgie O'Connor. It was strange not to have him beside me in a dressing-room before a game, staring at some point on the wall and inspiring us just by being there in all his bloody-minded glory.

John O was not in the best of form either and had been demoted to the bench.

And we had a few new faces in the set-up. Guys like Eugene Furlong came in and went straight onto the team, which was a sign to all of us that no place was safe.

I immediately liked Eugene. He had initially arrived on the scene a few years previously but hadn't reappeared since. I asked what brought him back and could only laugh at his blunt reply.

'I'm hurling the shite out of Gary Laffan every night at club training and there he is with an All-Ireland medal so I thought I'd be well able for it.'

Anyway, by the end of the League, a blind man could see that Rory Kinsella had been a brave guy to have taken this job on. We were in bits and certainly not helping Rory fill the shoes of Griffin, which seemed to be getting bigger all the time. We needed to snap out of it if we were to get anywhere that year.

But you don't become a bad team overnight and I remember doing an interview with the journalist Martin Breheny just before the start of the Championship and telling him that at last the corner had been turned and this team meant business again.

First up were Offaly and though Griffin was gone, at least some of his structures had stayed in place. Niamh Fitzpatrick was still involved, and for the three weeks leading up to our first Championship game of the season we trained like demons.

The 96 party was still going on around us, would you believe, but for once we avoided the celebrations and knuckled down to support Rory for once and for all.

I suffered a bit of a blow on the eve of the match when Fintan Cooney, the man who had been so good to my family when I was a child, got a heart attack in Oulart and passed away. The funeral was arranged for the Sunday evening, a few hours after the Leinster semifinal, and it was hard enough to focus on hurling.

Surprisingly, we went 10 points up against Offaly, but they came right back at us and it took a flukey goal from me, which went in off the stick of their goalkeeper, David Hughes, and a Damien Fitzhenry save to get us through in the end by three points, 3-12 to 2-12.

Before we knew it, we were in a big build-up to the Leinster final, and if we thought the hype was big in 96, it seemed to be much more widespread this time around. Everywhere I went with work, it was hurling, and when you are trying to drum up new business accounts, you can't exactly be rude by trying to ignore it all and stay away from it.

But I have to say that I was a little bit drained from talking hurling at this stage and was shocked that I couldn't even get away from it at the funeral, where the club members formed a guard of honour in Fintan's memory.

People kept coming over to me, shaking hands and talking about the Offaly match. It just showed how deeply they felt for Wexford hurling but at the same time I thought it was a bit much.

I spoke to Fintan's wife, also my godmother, Clare. She said she just knew I got my goal earlier that afternoon for Fintan. When she mentioned the goal, I just remembered what a loss her husband was, not just to us but to the whole community. I was a bit upset and let the funeral go to the graveyard, a place I would not often frequent – that's just my way.

You never really get over losing someone close but time passes and lets you deal with it. So winning the Leinster final in Fintan's memory was the next priority and when we learned we would be up against Kilkenny, well, it made the challenge all the more spicy because our current crop of players had never beaten them in a provincial final.

Preparation had been going well; I think Rory had us fine-tuned.

And one week ahead of the game, an old friend came to visit us and have a chat.

Into a team meeting at Murphy Floods Hotel arrived Griffin with a big huge box. It was great to see him again and we wondered what he had in store for us this time. Maybe some new gear?

While we were wondering, out he stepped again, only to come back in with another big box. We thought we were in for a right haul here.

We listened to Liam as he spoke about defending our titles. Delving into one box, he lifted out the Bob O'Keeffe Cup and told us we had a choice – we could either hold onto it or give it back to Kilkenny. Then he lifted out the Liam MacCarthy Cup.

'You gave up your lives to win this,' he said. 'Are you going to let it slip away just like that, without a fight? The choice is yours.'

And looking around the room, I could sense we didn't want to give either of those cups back just yet.

The Kilkenny game was never going to be pretty and with Aodhán MacSuibhne refereeing, it was going to take a strong display from him to keep us apart. I say that because within a few minutes of the start, Andy Comerford took a go at Tom Dempsey and hit him a right belt. Not being shy on the field, I bided my time and drew a dart at him as he returned from a big solo up the field.

As Andy went down, my old friend John Power came over and sent me flying. I got up and had my name taken.

'You little bastard!' Comerford roared at me, with his two hands where you don't want to get hit.

'Andy,' I replied. 'If you want to act the bollox, you'll get plenty of it back.'

Anyway, the laugh seemed to be on the other side of my face when Kilkenny went into the break five points up thanks mostly to a PJ Delaney goal. Ger Cushe had been taken off with an eye injury and our backs were totally against the wall. Things looked bleaker than a

December Sunday in Tramore.

Rory sent on Dave Guiney. Jesus, I now had a Guiney brother on either side of me. I couldn't believe it. But they did well in what was a strange finale to the game.

Kilkenny didn't hold their places at all and we just decided to follow our men, meaning I actually ended up at full back for the last few minutes. It was strange to see Seánie Flood, who had recovered from injury, out at centre back. But that's the way we played them and it worked, because we hauled the lead back and won by six points: 2-14 to 1-11.

It was Billy Byrne's day. All throughout 96, he had come on as a substitute and done the business, but this really took the biscuit because he almost single-handedly won the match for us by scoring 1-2 in the space of a few minutes. Thank God he didn't retire!

Early in the second half, I was fouled and stood over the ball to take the free but Billy was coming on and told me not to take it until he got into position at the other end of the field.

'Wait till I get to the square!' he shouted, giving our game plan away in literally two seconds. Not that it was a surprise or anything. I lobbed it in to him and bang!, he rattled the net. Then we started to target him like Newcastle with Alan Shearer, and he scored another two points, which just gave us a massive lift.

We hung on to win and it was as good a feeling as I have enjoyed after a game. I went running off the pitch with my hands in the air. My brother Seán and a friend, Pat Dempsey, came toward me but I just smiled and sped past them like a hare on amphetamines. I wanted to get to the platform; there was a cup there waiting to be brought home again.

As I got up towards the stand, I stuck a Wexford flag in one of the flower pots and waited for Rod Guiney, our new captain, to lift the cup again. I just thought of what we had done: beaten Offaly in the semi-final and Kilkenny in the final. We deserved this and no-one could argue with that.

Tom Dempsey and Seánie Flood sang *The Purple and Gold* from the steps of the Hogan Stand, which didn't go down too well with some of the Kilkenny lads, but they are used to winning every year; this was still fairly new to us.

Something else that didn't go down too well was Rod forgetting to offer three cheers for Kilkenny, but I grabbed the mike and did the honours.

And still, I wanted a bit more. There was no point in getting too carried away. We were flying it and there was more to be won. I had a taste for it now and knew the team might never see days like these again.

After that game, people were queueing up to come over and hug me, shake my hand and chat about the final. But I took it all with a pinch of salt. I knew supporters were fickle and reminded them there would be plenty of days when they wouldn't want to hug me.

As I made my way back to the car in Clonliffe College for a quiet mug of tea and a sandwich, little did I realise how soon I would be proven right.

Although thousands turned up in Gorey to greet the team, the boys were by now seriously hankering after another crack at the All-Ireland and were determined to treat the drink with caution. So while they enjoyed the fun that night, the session didn't really linger.

It was back to training, and with the new back-door format now in operation, we had to wait a while before learning Tipperary were next up. They had lost to Clare in the Munster final and then beaten Down to get through to the All-Ireland semi-final.

And then something seemed to change. In the run-up to meeting Len Gaynor's team, you could sense things were slipping in our camp. The final proof was that while both Rod Guiney and Gary Laffan had injuries, they still ended up starting that game, which I saw as a big mistake on their part.

I admired Rod for wanting to play for his county but he was captain and should have stepped down. He had a fitness test on what turned out to be a cruciate-ligament injury. The test only involved running in a straight line and so of course he was going to be fine. One twist or turn on that area of the knee and you would have known it was all over, so from that point of view the fitness test was a waste of time.

And just to ram the point home, not long into the game the two boys were taken off injured, and that had a fierce unsettling effect on us. I'm not saying that we would otherwise have beaten Tipp, but we were wrong, everyone was wrong, the lads shouldn't have played and they shouldn't have been let play. The management and the medical team slipped up badly.

As if that wasn't bad enough, we had to endure losing Rory McCarthy at midfield, who was a great player for us. He got turned over in the air by Conor Gleeson. In my view it was an accident and Gleeson never went to do him, though an awful lot was made of it afterwards. At the same time, I felt Conal Bonnar should not have got away with kicking Rory over the sideline after the initial incident, and I know if I had drawn a kick like that, not only would I be barred from the game, I would probably be still hiding in my house as well.

Anyway, Tipp beat us, knocked us off our perch and qualified for the All-Ireland final. They beat us by seven points, 2-16 to 0-15, but it should have been more. I was marking Declan Ryan and needed all my concentration to keep tabs on him, but what really killed us off was when Brian O'Meara got a goal in the second half.

One thing that hadn't helped us was the pre-match build-up. The *Examiner* printed an interview with Ger Loughnane, who slated us for using 'roughhouse' tactics. Those comments went down like a lead balloon in Wexford. Even now there are people who will tell you he was way out of line. I'm sure Ger thought Clare could end up meeting us in the final, but it just wasn't the sort of psychological ploy Liam Griffin would have used.

Anyway, Tipp drew strength from those comments and on the day they physically blew us away, and the back-to-back dream was over.

The Loughnane thing was a huge controversy at the time and

while he claimed he was misinterpreted, we would have loved to ram those words back down Clare throats in the final.

That's one of the biggest regrets I have, that we didn't get to play them in the Championship after we learned so much from them and got inspiration from their breakthrough. The only time I had played against them was in GOAL matches. It would have been nice to meet in the thick of the Championship if only to see which really was the better team.

So here we were, out of the All-Ireland series, and yet I considered it to be a successful year though I don't for one second feel we got the recognition we deserved for retaining the Bob O'Keeffe Cup. That was evident in the All Star selection, where only one Wexfordman, Fitzy, got the nod and despite the fact we had come from six points down to beat them by six in the provincial final, Kilkenny got three awards.

I suppose we had another Leinster medal and that was the important thing, although I looked on, envious as hell, as Clare beat Tipp in the final a few weeks later.

Life had changed for me the year before, but it really went head over heels on August 23 1997. Little Billy Dunne arrived into the world and in the space of a few seconds changed the lives of Eithne and me forever.

We had been married just under a year and he came on the scene much sharper than we'd expected. I brought Eithne into the hospital on that Saturday morning at 4.30. Neither of us had much notion of what to do but we both knew the time had arrived.

I spent the day in the hospital until the hunger got the better of me and I headed for a Chinese takeaway in the Lotus House. In hindsight, I shouldn't have gone back to the ward so soon, because Eithne wasn't feeling well and the smell of me and my Chinese hardly helped her. But maybe it brought the birth forward a little. Either way, Billy was born at around 5.30 pm.

It's hard to know what to say when your first child comes into the world. I just kind of looked on, dumb-struck. I rang the two grannies, Mam and Eithne's mother, May, and told them their grandson had arrived.

Naturally enough, Martin Storey and the boys soon heard the news and the good wishes poured in, but I had to travel to Galway to play Sarsfields in a practice match the following day and for once my mind wasn't totally consumed with hurling, one of the few times I could ever say that.

Eithne and I hadn't discussed names, but the lads kept asking me what we were going to call the child, so just to give them an answer and keep them happy I replied: 'Billy.' And that became the standard response for those around the village wanting to know his name.

After I had missed most of the day because of the hurling match, Eithne's sister, Paula, was out for my blood so I hurried to the hospital to discuss names.

'We better call him Billy,' I told Eithne. 'The whole village thinks that's his name anyway.'

Of course, there was another reason. My uncle and godfather was killed in 1972 and I'd been thinking we hadn't seen a Billy Dunne in the parish for a long time. That all changed with the arrival of our son and, would you believe, a year or two later my cousin Robert had a baby boy and they called him Billy as well. Now there were two of them around the place. Uncle Billy would have loved that.

Buoyed by the arrival of the little lad, Eithne and I learned to adapt, but I must admit his mother learned a lot quicker than his father. I loved the idea of having him around and could not wait for him to see me hurling. That would take a few years, however, so as we got used to this third member of the Dunne family, and with Wexford out of the reckoning, it was back to the drawing board with Oulart for the rest of the year.

We drew Faythe Harriers in the semi-final and beat them in a replay to qualify to meet Glynn-Barntown in the final. They must have been sick of the sight of us. We beat them again, by three points, and I became the third Dunne brother to win a man-of-the-match award in a county final, following in the footsteps of Seán and Tomás, something else for Mam to boast about.

It was all still happening but things soon turned sour. There was plenty of hassle over having to play three Sundays in a row, but when we drew Castletown of Laois in the Leinster semi-final that scenario was on the cards. We played them at Rathdowney the same day the Wexford team were flying out on holidays to Spain. We sent our bags to Dublin Airport in the hope of meeting up after the game but – wouldn't you know it? – the game was a draw.

We wanted to go on holidays but Tom Neville and Mick Jacob didn't want that at all; they were afraid we'd go on the tear in Spain and not be right for the replay the following week. In fairness to Castletown, they agreed to put the match back for a fortnight but our own mentors would have none of it, and despite a spate of meetings, Storey and I were deprived of our holiday in the sun, a break we both badly needed.

We'd had too much hurling by now, and after 20 minutes of the replay, in Belfield, I went over on my leg and knew straightaway it was broken. The ball had cut loose; my clubmate Pearse Redmond went to pick it up and missed; he kicked it on and David Cuddy went in to get it; I shouldered David and as I jostled him my leg snapped and I went down in a heap.

I did not hear the snap but there was a shot of pain all the way down my leg and I suspected something was seriously wrong. That suspicion was confirmed a moment later when I looked down and saw a huge bend in the leg.

In agony, I put my hands under my calf and looked up at Brendan O'Connor and Martin Dempsey, who were roaring to the sideline for medical attention. It was a pain you wouldn't wish on your worst enemy. It was so bad I wanted to die.

My brother Seán came running to me. He knew it was serious because none of us ever stayed down unless we had to. Pat Delaney, the Castletown manager and former Offaly player, also came over but was less sympathetic.

'You fucking deserve that, Dunne. You fucking deserve that,' he sneered. It was raw and it was bitter. Pat obviously had issues with me. I wasn't able to answer but Seán was and told him where to go. I pleaded for a bit of silence; all I wanted was peace and quiet.

One of the women involved with the club, Mary Doyle, came running in with a tracksuit to cover me but the aroma of her perfume was too strong for me and I had to tell the poor woman to go away. I felt really sick and was in awful pain.

A few moments later, I was even less comfortable when they produced an advertising board and used it as a stretcher to bring me into the dressing-room.

'Jesus Christ,' I thought. 'Can it get any worse?' It could.

Dr Derek Forde came in and was about to give me a relieving injection. I almost grabbed the needle out of his hands so desperate was I to stick it into the leg myself but just as he was about to do so, he got another emergency call from the field, where the Castletown full forward had managed to get a bit of a hurley stuck in his jaw. Talk about a bloodbath.

'The boys are following the game plan to a T,' I smirked, half unconscious, half crying.

Anyway, Dr Forde sorted him out, came back and gave me an injection in the shoulder, which brought me more relief than I ever thought possible. It was blissful. The pain just went, and it demonstrated to me how important the presence of a doctor is at all GAA games. A stretcher wouldn't be a bad idea either; those advertising boards are not the best.

An ambulance brought me to Ardkeen Hospital, Waterford, where I was told I would need an operation the following morning. They put a cast on my leg but only for Derek Forde I probably would have been left waiting there and God knows what sort of an infection I would have got.

I looked at the date on the calendar, Saturday November 8, and decided I wouldn't forget it in a hurry. The pain had been extreme. But Pat Delaney's words, well, I would remember them too.

When my brother Kieran arrived at the hospital, I was still in my hurling gear and he was so concerned for my welfare that the first thing he asked for was my jersey. Brothers!

We started chatting and after a while I didn't feel too sorry for myself because I remembered the terrible story of a young guy from the village back home. It just came into my head.

In 1992, Stephen Hayden, a promising hurler, was rushing for training for the club under-21 team. I was a selector with the team and knew him well; Stephen was a lovely chap. As usual before training, he was finishing off his chores on the farm, inflating a tyre with one of those pressure machines when it suddenly blew up and hit him in the face. It was a freak accident and it drove him almost 25 feet in the air and left him with brain damage.

The accident had a terrible effect on the village. Stephen is such a top lad that we hated seeing something so terrible happening to him of all people. Stephen's Dad, Johnny, brings him to all the matches, and when we won our first county final two years later I gave my jersey to him, and Tomás dedicated the win to him. In fact, the entire team went up to Stephen afterwards. We knew that if things had turned out differently, he could have been there on the field with us as well.

And rightly so, thinking of Stephen stopped me from feeling sorry for myself. His bravery and his family's love for him should be an example for all of us because they look after him so well.

Me? Well, I got away lightly in comparison. The surgeon operated, put a plate and a few screws into my leg, and that was it. The whole of the village seemed to descend on Ardkeen and those wonderful women the nurses were driven mad because the phone rang so often.

I stayed there for a few weeks and all my old pals came down for a look, the lads from the county team, Griffin, Seánie Flood, Rory Kinsella, Paul Codd, John O, and it was great to see them. It relieved the boredom and took away the anxiety I felt over the injury and how it would affect my work.

Only four months previously, I had joined Cantrell & Cochrane, a job I had wanted for so long, and now here I was with a broken leg, not worth a shit to them. I had a new wife and little Billy, who was only three months at this stage.

With C&C, I had taken a cut in wages, but I had been pushing hard for the job as sales developer and knew it would take time. I was willing to bide my time there until my job prospects and wages improved.

Soon after breaking my leg, in an interview with Vincent Hogan, I articulated my feelings. I was 29, had no permanent job, had a four-month-old child and was newly married. The GAA insurance scheme was crap, absolute shite, and for the six months or so that I was out of work, I got £29.33 per week for all my efforts over the years. Cantrell & Cochrane were decent to me; they paid me a month's salary, which they didn't have to do. Furthermore, while I moaned about the GAA insurance scheme, I have to say that only for the people who make up the association at grassroots level, I don't know how I would have survived.

Pat Dempsey had been chairman of the Oulart club since Fintan's death and he organised a benefit night for me in Cooney's pub. I was humbled and grateful but embarrassed as well, so I kept well away from the bar the night of the fundraiser. And so you can imagine my shock a few days later when Pat arrived up to the house with a cheque for £4,500.

'Every penny of it is yours, Liam,' he said. I was stunned. But that wasn't the only kindness bestowed on me. One fellow I had never even met, Ned Kavanagh from Carlow, sent me £100 in the post. Pat 'Stack' Murphy, a businessman, sent me £350 in the post. Brendan O'Connor was also very good to me. None of these guys ever looked for thanks and I would have been too embarrassed to give it to them, but at the same time I never forgot.

The county board was excellent too and paid for my medical bills. So although it was a tough time, I was well looked after.

Once I left hospital I went back to our home over Phil Redmond's pub and, to be straight, I was a hard man to live with. There was the usual feeling sorry for myself; I just wanted to get out of the house and usually the first resort was the bar downstairs.

I probably didn't see what was happening at first but it didn't take long for the danger signs to start flashing. The winter nights are dark, weary and boring at the best of times, but when you can't walk it's even more depressing.

The first night I was home, Ger Cushe and his wife, Mag, came to see me and the two of us went into the bar downstairs. I wasn't in the form for drinking but ended up having a few anyway.

And that's the way it turned out for the next three months. Friends would call up to see how I was keeping and, inevitably, the bar was the first stop. It was just too handy for me: a 20-second trip to the stool.

All the boys visited, from Storey to Brendan O'Connor, and I started to get sucked into a rut. During the day, I was bored out of my wits and could do very little for Eithne and young Billy. I longed for the evening, the chance to chat to someone about hurling and have a few drinks.

Before long, Storey could see I was drinking too much and urged me to cut down because it would prevent my leg from healing properly. But of course I paid no notice; I was getting too fond of my evening sessions in Phil's bar.

Out of the £4,500 raised by the club, I would say Phil got a fair old chunk, which was fierce selfish of me, considering I was newly married and had a child only a few months old. But the same lads who were urging me to cut down were often there in the evenings helping me lower the hard stuff.

Phil's pub, there was something about it I just couldn't resist. For a stranger walking in off the street, there would be no great appeal to Phil's bar but stay there for a while and the man himself would have your family tree traced right back to its roots. You wouldn't be long feeling at home.

It's not much to look at: I suppose if push came to shove, 20 people might fit into it. But it has the spirit of a busy down-town New York bar. In such a place, not much bigger than a kitchen, you can be yourself, and it represents a part of Ireland that is untouched and honest to goodness. On the side of the bar is a little shop, where some lads prefer to sip their pint, and outside the actual counter is the fridge where the drink is stored. On the wall is a rings board, just in case you fancy a game, there were many nights when I was so drunk I didn't even connect with the board, but sure that was all part of the craic.

It just became too easy for me to drink the nights away there. Neighbours loved to gather there and the warm, cosy atmosphere made it a hard place to leave.

I was fast becoming 'the one' Griffin had warned us about. I slept during the day and wanted to get out of the house at night. It was mostly pints of beer and cider; at least I managed to keep away from shorts, but it didn't feel like that the following morning.

Other wives would have shown me the door or walked out but Eithne just kept the show on the road.

No wonder the injury took 16 months to heal properly and little wonder again that my hurling suffered for almost two years afterwards. I was digging a hole for myself and, as not a night went by without a visit downstairs, the hole would get deeper. Some lads would call over almost every evening. We would have a cup of tea, head downstairs for a few hours and then maybe come back up and watch a hurling video or something and eat the sandwiches Eithne had left out for us. Often, if the craic was good, we would even fill a box with a few takeaway bottles and bring them upstairs. It was the best fun I ever had while injured but for my life and career, it was a ridiculous scenario, and yet I could still persuade myself I hadn't gone too far,

Maybe that was the most worrying aspect. I was 29 and should have had more sense but I was in a ball of self-pity, and this was a way of dealing with the frustration: the night-time, the pints, the lads and a chance to get out of the house.

Amazingly, Eithne never said much to me; she had her hands full with little Billy. All I was concerned about was how tough it was to be out of hurling with a broken leg. Me, myself and I.

Worse again, the plaudits still kept flowing, though not for me, and awards like Wexford Sports Star of the Month and another All Star nomination reminded me what I was missing out on.

But I was to miss out on more than just awards. In fact the entire 1998 season went by without my involvement and that was down to inappropriate recovery methods; the leg was completely out of shape.

Eventually, I started to cop on and realised that unless I took care of myself the leg might never come right so I used the swimming pool at the Ferrycarrig Hotel. That in itself was a hassle. I couldn't drive so someone had to be at my beck and call to ferry me there, which I found hugely frustrating. Still, I stuck at it, and after 15 months I was at least able to walk properly again.

I had stayed on the crutches as long as possible to give myself some chance of playing hurling in 98 but, realistically, it was never going to happen. Because though I got the all-clear in August, I still couldn't even jog. that's what I got for skulling pints every night and feeling sorry for myself.

It was a conscious decision not to go to training in Wexford Park much that year. I kept my distance from the team during the week but still travelled with them to games, for my own sanity more than anything else. It didn't help my despair as I looked at them getting caught on the hop by Offaly.

Before the game, the team assembled for a photograph and left a gap of about two feet at the end of the bench. I used to sit there at that end, always had done for some reason. No-one ever sat there bar me, and Rory MacCarthy would have his space at the other end. Maybe it's just habit but when you're playing big games, it's nice to be able to look around and take it in.

This time, I waited for my spot to be filled but they left it vacant. My space was still there. If you look back at that team picture from 98, you will see what I'm talking about. Maybe the lads weren't aware they were doing it, and that little gap would have meant nothing to anyone else in the ground, but to me it came across as a great gesture,

Rod Guiney and Gary Laffan were also injured and yet I still felt we were good enough to keep the run going and pull off a win. I was almost right.

I talked to the lads before the game and recalled Pat Delaney's words of sympathy to me while I lay writhing in agony after breaking my leg. My intention was to strike a motivational chord with one or two of the team, and I could see Seánie Flood responding; he was just back from injury and knew the loneliness a player feels when his career is almost taken away from him. But it was all to no avail. Wexford had the game in their hands right until the final minutes but were caught by a Johnny Dooley sucker punch at the end of normal time and that was it, they were gone: 1-15 to 0-17.

Dooley's goal was brilliant but I felt Aodhán Mac Suibhne made some terrible decisions that day.

And so the season ended in disaster and I got little comfort even from Oulart-The-Ballagh, who were knocked out in the first round of the Wexford Championship. My sporting world had well and truly caved in, and I was learning all over again just how cruel and fickle sport could be.

Life is just one damned thing after another.
Elbert Hubbard, Author

– CHAPTER FIFTEEN –
Return to the fold

I got a chance to wipe the slate clean. Not everyone gets that opportunity. After a four-month slump of sleeping late, moping around the house and drinking even later, I managed to snap out of my self-pity and worked on my leg.

I gave it a right go to get fit again. I went swimming, used the gym, tried jogging in a straight line when I felt I could manage it and soon rejoined the Wexford squad.

When, in February 1999, I played my first game for Wexford since the injury, I decided, for the first time in my life, to put a shin guard on; I had already begun to worry about taking a belt on the site of the injury.

We played a game of Probables versus Possibles, but even though I had more experience than most of the new lads put together, I was way off the pace. I knew then it would be extremely hard to get back to the level of skill and fitness I had managed just a couple of years earlier.

I got through the League way below par but Rory Kinsella never criticised me, and I was in the half-back line when we played Dublin in Nowlan Park in the first round of the Championship.

Although we beat them by a point, 1-13 to 1-12, I was just awful. Their manager, Michael O'Grady, who had spent time with Wexford, was most gracious and said how delighted he was to see me back in the game. But Michael was too kind; the game had just passed me by completely. I was simply miles off the pace.

By the time our game with Offaly came around, I have to say the improvement had not been staggering. I was marking Michael Duignan, and in fairness to him, he came over to see how my leg was by letting a lovely pull of the hurl land just where I had broken it.

'I'd say it's fully healed, Mike,' I laughed.

I didn't mind taking a belt from Duignan because I respected him, and anyway there was no point in getting thick that day because they totally overpowered us and gave us a nice 3-17 to 0-15 beating.

It was clear as day that this team was starting to slip now and Rory was also coming to the end of his reign. The team was stale and, apart from Declan Ruth, no-one was coming through. Declan had broken onto the team in 1998 at wing back but was dropped in 99, so even he didn't look like setting the world alight back then, and the underage structures had produced no-one else.

In fairness, very few of the team had got completely carried away with the hysteria of 96 and 97 and I sensed most of the team still wanted more. Larry O would be the first to tell you he started to believe in the hype for a while and got a little excited by it all. But no man wanted more and he was as hungry as any of us. The trouble was that the team had learned to accept defeat all over again.

Everyone was working hard, so complacency could not be used as an excuse for defeat. Staleness could, however. Jesus, the truth is harsh, but the team just wasn't good enough anymore.

I started to look back and remind myself how lucky I had been, a bad move for any hurler. Apart from the trophies, I had the All Stars as well, which the likes of Ger Cushe somehow missed out on, so even though I felt the end was near, I had nothing to complain about.

Cushe should definitely have got an All Star in 96 or 97 or both but he was ignored. Griffin had called him into the bar of the Burlington the night of the 96 ceremony to warn him he hadn't made the shortlist. I remember praying that for once Griffin was wrong, but of course he wasn't. I never felt that Ger got the credit he deserved and here he was now, bowing out, and I felt that personally I was losing not just a great team-mate but also a loyal friend.

Rory Kinsella was another guy I felt for. He had shown huge trust in me while I was injured and even though I was struggling for form he kept me in the team and stuck by me. This was the end of him as Wexford manager and to me it felt like the end of an era. Once more, I remembered Griffin's prediction, the morning after our All-Ireland win, that we would never be together as a group again; it seemed unbelievable at the time but he was never more accurate.

It had gone from a famine to a feast back to a famine and, as I said, we held out no great hope of winning anything in 2000, when we heard Joachim Kelly was the new manager. He was a sound guy but he wasn't the man for us at all and it soon became apparent. It was a waste of a year and, as I look back now, I would give anything to have a season like that back, so you could try and make more use of it.

By the end of the year, we were lower even than we'd been in 95. Our League was terrible and the one Championship game we played was against Offaly, Joachim's own county, and they murdered us for the second year in a row, 3-15 to 1-8.

They had great motivation playing us because Joachim was our manager, but in truth, we could have had Seán Boylan, Brian Cody and Liam Griffin pulling the strings for us that day and Offaly would still have come out on top. We were the worst-prepared Wexford team ever. My mother would have breezed through some of the drills laid out for us in training.

It wasn't all Joachim's fault. My being sent off didn't help the team much either. So it's little wonder I have a sour taste in my mouth when I remember 2000. It was a long way from what we had achieved just a few years earlier. There was no queue of Wexford supporters lining up to shake my hand or hug me when I left Croke Park the evening of the Offaly game.

The following day Vincent Hogan wrote in the *Irish Independent* of my wild pull on John Troy, but to the grave I'll argue that I simply flicked the ball off him with one hand on the hurl. Then again, the way

Troy went down you would swear he had been shot.

I avoided Griffin for weeks afterwards for fear of the tongue-lashing I would get off him and sat back and waited to see who would leave the set-up.

There was a brief respite from all the gloom when Oulart won the 2000 League final against St Martin's but we had a lot of hassle in that camp as well by the time the Championship came around. Tony Cottrell from Kilkenny was our trainer and had raised plenty of hackles during the League final when he sneered at the fact that Anthony O'Leary and my brother Tomás were getting rubs from the physio at the interval.

'You wouldn't see that in Kilkenny,' Tony smiled.

Tomás must have been in serious pain because it would take a bullet in the back of his leg to see him wincing, and so Tony's remark pissed a lot of us off.

Nonetheless, we reached the Championship final, where we played Darragh Ryan's club, St Anne's, who had developed from the junior ranks since 96 and won the county senior football title earlier in 2000. We thought we were on the way after we'd gone six points up but they came back at us and brought it level. Again we went four points up and looked to have the game won, but they staged a late rally to win their first senior hurling title by two points.

They were a team of giants: most of them stood over six-foot-one, and the word went around that we had been horsed out of the title. People around the village couldn't accept that and we were slated, but I think Anne's brought more than just brute force to the game and deserved their win. Their club was on a roll from the football campaign and we were not good enough on the day to stop their momentum.

I believe 13 of them were on the football as well as the hurling team, and that's some achievement. But the people of Oulart felt we should have been able to push home our advantage on the scoreboard and so that season ended in a welter of disappointment as well.

The next time I saw the boys from St Anne's was when we were brought together for a Wexford hurlers' meeting with our new manager, Tony Dempsey. I found it strange to look at Tony and see Ger Cushe, now a selector, there beside him with the third member of the management, Davy Morris. I had battled for so long with Cushe and now here he was on the other side of the set-up. We had been great mates but Ger rightly kept his distance from me for a while.

It suddenly dawned on me that with Larry O, I was now the elder statesman on the team, and the point was made when Tony asked me to say a few words, something I would seldom have chosen to do in all my years with the squad. I was tentative enough at the start but I found what I wanted to say and it went something like this.

'We're fighting with the county board one minute and ourselves the next. We need enthusiasm for this now. The buzz has gone out of us and the set-up is stale, but it's down to us to get Wexford back on top.

'Tony will be a players' man. We will want for nothing and it's our responsibility from here onwards.'

I kept it short and sweet but Tony was a lot like Liam Griffin with words – you could stay listening to him all evening. He told us pride was the buzzword. He needed to bring pride back to Wexford and, true to his word, Dempsey would go a long way towards that end.

It was clear as day even then that Tony would wind up in Dáil Éireann because the man was always on the go. He was just starting his political career and it was amazing how he could combine both careers: sport and politics. But somehow he did. Probably the three mobile phones he was constantly talking into helped. One night, after training in Farmleigh, he was chatting with Adrian Fenlon and myself when he took out one of the phones; it had recorded 19 missed calls during the previous 90 minutes. Now that was pressure, and yet he never let the hurling suffer. At the time, Fenlon, Darragh Ryan, who had been the best player for St Anne's that season, and I were elected onto a players' committee, and because Damien Fitzhenry used to put so many great ideas from the floor, we decided to draft him in as well. The Three Musketeers found their d'Artagnan.

Fitzy became the head spokesman and anything we wanted we got. There was a county board chequebook there for us, and every so often he would produce a few gear-bags or other pieces of equipment to keep the camp happy. Some managers might have come back and said they couldn't do this or that but Tony would take out the chequebook and if a player was in trouble he would look after him. He was out for our best interests. For example, if a guy was having problems getting off work to make training, Tony would pay for a replacement at the workplace so the player could be freed up.

With such an approach, it's no surprise he was not only a successful businessman but also principal of Enniscorthy Vocational School. Anywhere he went, success followed. He had been chairman of the Wexford GAA board at 29, was on a number of high-powered committees in Croke Park and had also managed county under-21 teams, leading the 1979 team to a Leinster title.

It also encouraged us that we won the Walsh Cup within a few months of him taking over. It was my first time meeting Laois and marking David Cuddy since I broke my leg and we shook hands. I had never put an ounce of blame on him. But when the first ball arrived in, I drove it 10 yards out of his hand and when the second one came in, David was left shaking his paw again. Just to let all concerned know that my nerve hadn't gone.

With the game well won, I was taken off with five minutes to go and got a nice round of applause from the Wexford supporters, which was good to hear considering I had been jeered by the Offaly supporters the last time I had left a field early.

For us, it was just another Walsh Cup medal but you could see the disappointment on the Laois players' faces; the Cup would have meant the world to them.

We went into the League with a bit of confidence, and though we got nowhere we knew we would have the measure of Laois again in the Championship. And so it was no shock to anyone when we beat them by 17 points to 10. But it was all for nothing when Kilkenny destroyed us again in the Leinster final. They beat us by 2-19 to 0-12 this time; we seemed to be falling further and further behind them. Young Billy was baffled after the presentation and asked me why Denis Byrne from Kilkenny was lifting the cup when I had told him before the game that Wexford would be bringing it home.

I was almost afraid to explain; it looked like it would be a long time before the Bob O'Keeffe Cup would be home again. But Billy didn't need that harsh dose of reality at his age; I just told him Denis was borrowing the cup for a while.

With the back door looming, we tried to pick ourselves up the week after with a challenge match against Galway but might as well have sprayed graffiti all over the dressing-room because the writing was well and truly on the wall.

We went into that game aiming to restore confidence, and Galway beat us out the gate by 20 points. We were in big trouble and Tony Dempsey knew that the squad was more than a little short of the required standard. He decided it was time to bring Liam Griffin back on the scene. Boy, were we delighted when we saw the familiar skinny frame, preceded of course by that magnificent nose, walking back into Wexford Park! Griffin has some sort of an aura about him. There is no-one I know quite like the man. He is blessed with some sort of a reassuring presence that is enough for me any day of the week.

He returned to take a few sessions just before we were drawn to play Limerick in the All-Ireland quarter-final. Before he came in, we the players had a couple of heart-to-hearts, during which I pointed out to the rest of the boys that one man couldn't do it all for us. But of course he almost did. Before we knew it, after just a couple of coaching sessions, Griffin had us motoring well.

A few nights before we played Limerick, he brought us into a circle and started going through match tactics.

'Liam Dunne, where are you?' he roared.

'Oh, Jaysus,' I thought as I hesitantly stepped forward. 'What's going to happen here?'

Griffin grabbed me and put me in front of the squad.

'This is what's going to happen you on Sunday. A high ball will come down between you and the lad you are marking. You will pull on the ball and he will go to ground, holding his head. Their manager, Eamon Cregan, will run in from the line shouting "Dunne, you dirty bastard, you're at it again!"

'The referee will call you over and issue a yellow card. He might even give you a red card. But that is their game plan and no matter what happens, we will be ready for it. We are one step ahead.'

I stood there, not knowing whether to laugh or cry. This was Griffin's way of impressing on the lads that whatever the match threw up, Wexford would be ready for it.

That game turned out to be one of the most exciting and dramatic of my career, although the Wexford fans, suspecting we were in for a trouncing, stayed away. Without a shadow of a doubt, we were outnumbered five to one by the Limerick crowd, who were still hungry for glory.

The game started at 100 miles per hour and ended over an hour later at 120 mph. I never saw or played in such a sharp opening to a match. But Griffin had known this would happen and for weeks beforehand had us training on a tighter pitch and with two or three sliotars on the go at all times from the sideline or end-line.

After 10 minutes Ollie Moran, a sound guy, went to catch a ball and I pulled. I don't think I hit him, there wasn't much contact made anyway and the ball just broke in behind us. But as it did I saw Ollie was holding his left ear.

The referee, Michael Wadding, thought I hit him. His whistle blew and suddenly in came Cregan, roaring and shouting at me. Larry O made a run to stop him, and Declan Ruth lent a hand, while Wadding called me over.

'Michael,' I almost laughed, feeling like this was a snippet from *Back to the Future*, 'Liam Griffin told me last Wednesday night this would happen. Eamon Cregan is probably going nuts around here somewhere, but honest to God, I didn't hit the ball or the man.'

Wadding didn't listen. Out came the yellow card. I still could hardly believe Griffin's prediction had come through. Stunned, I went over to Ollie and asked him if he was okay.

'I'm grand, Liam, not a bother on me,' he smiled, and I smiled back. In fairness that sort of stuff happens in hurling matches everyday of the year.

That was it. After that I knew they couldn't have much else in their armoury. If that was their plan A, I knew we were one step ahead. So now we had a bit more belief, but all the same it took a Paul Codd goal just before the break to keep the scoreboard healthy.

The small band of Wexford fans present stood to clap us into the dressing-room, where Tony Dempsey was waiting to stoke the adrenalin. He had an easy job to get me going.

'We're doing this to show that there's a future for Wexford hurling,' he bellowed. 'We're doing this for the young lads all over the county who need new heroes today, lads the likes of young Billy Dunne.'

Always a great man for asking the players their opinion during games, Tony looked at me and said: 'Well, Dunner, what have you to say?'

I let rip. I had never lost it in a dressing-room before then but there was a first time for everything. People say that frenzied speeches will only get you so far and I agree, but on that day words were exactly what we needed, and so with Billy's disappointment over the Bob O'Keeffe Cup fresh in my mind, I stepped forward.

'I'd die for young Billy,' I bellowed. 'And I'd die for the Wexford fans who bothered to come up here today. But there are 14 men alongside me that I'd die for as well.'

I grabbed my jersey and reminded the lads of what we were fighting for.

'It's for the fucking county, lads! It's for this jersey that we all put so much in. To get the smiles back on people's faces at home. For our families and friends.

'This is our day, lads! Limerick are going to drive us all the way. Let us be the ones standing when it's all over!'

The message got through. I could see the astonishment on the faces of young lads like Rory Mallon and Nicky Lambert. This was a rude awakening for them but I had to show them there was something good and worthwhile about being a Wexford hurler because some had forgotten what it felt like and the new guys didn't really know what it should feel like at all.

As for myself, after a depressing four years, finally there was a sense that we could get out of the hole and I wasn't missing the lift. This was the day to put the spring back into my hurling.

The door nearly went off the hinges as we burst back out onto the field but this time we could hear our own fans. There was no game-plan but to win. If Limerick wanted to test this vulnerable Wexford team one more time, we were going to fight them all the way.

The second half never once slowed down. In all there were six goals and 25 points scored. Near the end, I started to feel my words had been in vain as we trailed by two points.

Our tongues hung out of our mouths and we looked dead and buried. But then Clem Smith took down Rory McCarthy around 21 yards from the Limerick goal and we were awarded a free. I looked around to call for Fitzy but leaders do not need to be beckoned and our goalkeeper was already sprinting up the field, ready to take the responsibility of firing us into an All-Ireland semi-final. We needed a goal and Fitzy had the most powerful shot of the lot of us.

There may have been nerves but it didn't show as he absolutely buried the ball to the back of the net. Seconds later the Limerickmen collapsed to their knees as the final whistle blew. I just wanted to run, anywhere. I needed to celebrate; it hadn't felt this good in years. Christ! I had nearly forgotten why I loved the game.

Several of the lads were on the same high. Some of them mentioned my half-time rant to reporters, who asked me what exactly I had said. But by now the dreaded migraine had kicked in and, there in the dressing-room with what felt like a spear going through my head, I couldn't concentrate enough to recall my words. I suspect some journalists thought I was being thick when I replied that I couldn't actually remember what I'd said. The game had taken a lot out of me and my main concern was to take a painkiller to get rid of the pressure building up between my ears.

It didn't take the people of Wexford long to realise the significance of what had happened: we were in an All-Ireland semi-final against Tipperary. I just gave myself a day or two to celebrate and unwind and it was back to the grindstone.

A few days later I was going about my business with C&C when I got a phone call from Griffin asking me to meet him for a chat. We duly met and discussed the challenge ahead. The purpose of the meeting soon emerged: he was touting the idea of bringing Martin Storey back into the panel.

Storey had retired a year earlier but Griffin felt his introduction as a sub could unhinge the Tipp defence and also unsettle Nicky English, who was relatively new to management.

One of our selectors, Davy Morris, disagreed, but Griffin prevailed and I was delighted to see my old buddy returning; we had great craic travelling to training together just like in the old days.

And so the big man came back. And to this day, Griffin will tell you he made a mistake. That was, he didn't bring Tom Dempsey back as well. But that is another story.

We felt we had prepared well and had a fair chance of beating Tipp. But they came out of the blocks at 90 miles an hour and we were eight or nine points down at the break. I felt we could still salvage the game but inside in the dressing-room it was general doom and gloom.

Doc O'Connor, a guy not long on the scene, came over and hit me a dig.

'Jesus, say something, will you? Get it going!' he said through gritted teeth.

Now, I had never really spoken before the Limerick outburst, but I gathered my thoughts, took a drink of water and started talking. There was no point in coming out with more bravado stuff because it won't work every time. Instead I asked the lads to raise their game and, quite calmly, told them I wasn't waiting for any Tipperary man to come out in front of us. Nicky's boys could take the hind tit. I opened the door, and as we filed out I just reminded them we had 35 minutes to save our season.

Enter Larry O'Gorman. How he managed to score those two incredible goals from midfield is still beyond me but he rattled the net twice and, almost singlehandedly, had Tipp on the ropes.

As the game went on, we brought Martin Storey on and he completely unsettled the Tipp full-back line, causing so much chaos and confusion they fumbled ball after ball.

That's where a guy like Tom Dempsey, who was still playing brilliant stuff at club level, could really have made them pay. As it was, and despite Storey's heroics, we were wasteful and our shooting was erratic, and we still trailed until Rory McCarthy grabbed a late goal.

The ding dong battle continued until, near the end, we were awarded a free 45 metres out when Paul Codd was fouled. The ball sailed wide and I had a sickening feeling that with it had gone our 2001 All-Ireland hopes.

With 45 seconds left on the clock, the scores level, and Tipp on the rack, Pat O'Connor, the best referee I have encountered, blew the game up. I was angry because there was still time on the clock, and maybe deep in my heart I knew we had lost our chance.

Again, the county came alive and there was huge spirit and enthusiasm around the place as we looked forward to the replay, which was played the following Saturday evening in a drizzle and a downpour. I started at centre back on John Carroll, who got in behind me, soloed through and kicked a goal to the back of the net. Then I was dispatched onto Brian O'Meara and we all know what happened from there. The two of us were sent off.

Mitch Jordan joined me a moment or two afterwards and in a farcical game, Tipp ran out easy winners by 3-12 to 0-10.

As I have said, the fact Brian got a straight red card and missed the All-Ireland final is something I regret but there wasn't a whole lot going on between us and although I spoke on his behalf at the GAC meeting, from time to time I have had to remind people it wasn't all one-way traffic. I was sent off as well.

For the second time in a year, I sat in the dressing-room as my team got destroyed out on the field. I had let the lads down but really felt sick at what had been one of the worst refereeing decisions of all time.
Even now, taking Brian and I out of the equation, it's universally agreed that Pat Horan's job on that All-Ireland semi-final was nothing short of a vaudeville act. He was a joke and I have been living ever since with the consequences of his disastrous decision-making.

Sure, I might have deserved it but Brian O'Meara missed an All-Ireland final because the referee was so poor. Of course we had started it and ultimately had ourselves to blame, but in games all over Ireland, from under-eight to junior B to intercounty senior, that sort of handbags stuff goes on. Pat decided to be a hero and went with the ill-advised counsel of his linesman Pat Aherne, who has also proved a disaster on occasions over the years. Technically, they applied the letter of the law, but if you applied that in every game you wouldn't have six men left on the field at the end of the 70 minutes.

I had tapped Brian and he had hit me back. It was so on and so forth, but to have officials like those two making decisions in an All-

Ireland semi-final, well it just shows what the GAA know sometimes.

The Star newspaper ran a 'Let Brian play' campaign and underneath the logo was a 'Men not wimps' catch-line. They were right but Croke Park's top brass didn't get it and despite all the hype that surrounded the case afterwards, Horan had his report submitted within a few hours of the final whistle.

Nothing anyone could say or do was going to change minds, if any, in Croke Park. I was reported for striking and was back hurling a month later, while Brian missed out on playing in an All-Ireland final. But if people think I got off lightly, they need not worry. That red card and that incident meant I had walked two years on the trot in the Guinness Hurling Championship and by now referees were making extra special efforts to keep an eye on me. I was a marked man. You could have sworn I had killed someone; there was kind of a 'leper factor' about me as far as some people outside Wexford were concerned.

I got many phone calls. Some offered consolation and support; others were less complimentary to say the least. Sometimes it was a case of just putting down the phone to cut off the stream of abuse. Some letters arrived and sometimes I regret I didn't keep them – they might have made colourful material for this book – but really, the bin was the only place for them.

I stood up and took it on the chin and I have to say that those around the village, my neighbours and those close to me, never made an issue of the sending-off. When my mother got over the disappointment, she never blamed me at all but everyone else got a blast alright.

I met Brian at a League match in Nenagh the following year and I walked back 15 yards to shake hands with him but he looked away as he shook and maybe I couldn't blame him. But we met in Wexford Park after that again and he walked by me so I knew that was it. Again, I don't know if I could blame him.

It was the end of an eventful year but I had consolation in the fact that we had at least put the pride back into Wexford hurling. We were rewarded with a holiday to Lanzarote and did a fair bit of fundraising to generate spending money, which was no bother because the goodwill factor was high in the county again.

We raised £20,000 with a race night alone. We put pressure on the county board to get a donation from Croke Park to help the students on the team enjoy their holiday a little better. We were aware the GAA had raked in £535,000 from the replay with Tipperary alone, and while we didn't win the All-Ireland we contributed enormously to the excitement and shape of the season in our games with Laois, Kilkenny, Limerick and Tipperary. And so we wanted just £10,000 to divide among the lads still at college and asked the GAA president, Seán McCague, and his top table, but they refused and we never got a penny from them.

Whether he was directly involved or not, I felt the president should have made a name for himself on this issue, and though I've often been told McCague was a players' man, I don't believe for a moment he was.

On a trip to Amsterdam with C&C, I met a work colleague, Gene Sherry, who was from Scotstown, McCague's stamping ground. Gene sang his praises but I had my own theory.

Darragh Ó Sé could get out of a suspension incurred in a club game and be back to play with Kerry in the All-Ireland series but John Boland, a minor hurler from Tipperary, had to take the GAA to court to play the biggest game of his life.

Although John took the case, the GAA tried to stop him from playing in an All-Ireland final after he had been sent off in the North Tipp minor championship with his club, Toomevara. They wanted to deprive a young chap of playing in an All-Ireland final, a massive opportunity for him, yet the president and his colleagues allowed Ó Sé to return to the fold when, according to the rules, he was suspended and should have missed the final.

It disgusted me.

I met Seán on an All Stars trip early in 2004 and briefly spoke to him. My own feeling is he was not the players' man he was cracked up to be, and I know plenty of the Wexford lads would share my view after our plan to raise a few quid for the students was scuppered. My own opinion is that the current office holder, Seán Kelly, is twice the president, and thank God, we have moved a little in terms of player welfare.

Players don't ask for much. I mean the holiday to Lanzarote was a great break, but apart from that, some mileage expenses for travelling to training and a bit of gear, we pretty much get on with it.

Anyway we had our little break, which was very much male-dominated – about 95 percent of the players decided they wanted to travel without wives or partners.

When we got back some of the lads were wondering if I would call it a day but I had no such intentions. I was hurling well and greatly enjoying the game again after my slump in 1999 and 2000, so I earmarked 2002 as a season of further progress.

Our first Championship game that year was against Dublin, and in a welter of scores we beat them 3-15 to 2-12 in Thurles to qualify for another date with our old pals Kilkenny in the Leinster final at Croke Park. Unfortunately, the script here was pretty much the same as the previous two years. Though they beat us by only two points this time, I became the first ever intercounty senior hurler to be sent off in three Championships in a row.

We were pipped 0-19 to 0-17 but I wasn't on the pitch to witness the end, and to be brutally honest, the referee, Ger Harrington, had to send me off.

It was a wild pull on Martin Comerford. Harrington did very well in that game and leaving me on the field would have been a black mark on his copybook.

This wasn't the way I wanted to make history and while Wexford got ready for the qualifier match against Clare, I resigned myself to the fact that my season was over and there was no escape. I duly received a two-month ban from the game.

And so, unsure of how to cope, I hit the drink and carried the piss-up over for five months. I had been in the media spotlight in the past but this was the worst ever. I believe I got a small taste of how Vinny Jones or Alan Smith or one of those Premiership bad boys must feel when he turns on the TV or picks up the tabloids. There were snide remarks on television, the odd stab in the newspapers and a nasty focus on my mother and family.

Apart from letting my own people down, I had let myself down. It had taken me so long to make my name as a hurler but I had gone from people telling me I was the county's best player in 25 years to just being a dirty little bastard who didn't have the sense to quit when he was losing it. Thing was, deep down I knew I wasn't losing my hurling and had faith that there was a little bit more in the tank.

But after almost six months of drinking, it took an innocent but piercing look from my own two children at around seven o'clock on a November morning to make me see sense. Their Dad coming into the house, rotten drunk, in the half-light of dawn. Was this something they were going to have to put up with for the rest of their childhood?

On many occasions over the year, and I know this might sound melodramatic, I felt my situation resembled that of Roy Keane, who had just walked out on the World Cup. The Saipan incident is history now and the Cork genius is back playing with Ireland, but for 18 months or so he had to live with the tag of letting people down.

Of course Roy's situation split a nation. Mine was far less newsworthy, but it was no less important to me and my family and I was always wondering how the constant controversy was damaging them. The fact I always admired Keane so much, I suppose, created a few parallels in my mind between the two of us. We both had our problems with the drink; neither of us was a stranger to the early shower; and though we played different sports, we would both have built up reputations as loose cannons prone to the red mist followed smartly by the dreaded red card. On top of that, the two of us had suffered bad leg injuries.

I suppose a failed drugs test was about the only thing I didn't get landed with during my career. Roy had also sampled many of the downsides to his sport, though the stakes, at least the financial ones, are obviously higher as captain of Manchester United.

Maybe drawing a little strength from what he went through to get back playing with club and country, I finally decided there was still a little willpower left in my alcohol-soaked brain, and so I arranged the meeting with Griffin.

We spoke for hours. He agreed that maybe there was a last chance at bowing out on a high, one last hope of salvation.

At Vinegar Hill, o'er the pleasant Slaney
Our heroes vainly stood back to back;
And the Yeos at Tullow took Father Murphy
And burned his body upon the rack
Boolavogue

– CHAPTER SIXTEEN –
Vinegar Hill, the farewell

Vinegar Hill holds lots of history for Wexford but I never really saw its beauty for a long time. When Ray Keogh and I were sprinting up and down it, I certainly didn't appreciate its view or historical significance.

Running on Morriscastle beach was not enough for me; I had to push myself to the extreme limit if I was going to make it back with Wexford for one last time and get a chance to redeem myself by hurling my way out of the game. That's what Griffin had told me anyway.

This time it was about Liam Dunne. That may seem selfish to anyone else in the county but it had to be that way. It was time to do my own thing. I took the social element out of my game and almost turned into a hermit.

Jim Bolger the racehorse trainer, who loves Wexford hurling, sent me a cheque for €250 and with it a little note asking me not to retire.

'Don't worry, Jim, I have other things on my mind,' I thought.

To be in the best physical shape of my life, to get back to the level I had achieved in 1996, I had to be in the best mental state of my career as well.

That's where the real battle started because I felt under heavy pressure. Before Christmas, I made up my mind to go at it hell for leather, persuading myself each time I went for a run on Vinegar Hill or the beach. It was a time for keeping your mouth shut and getting on with the job. The beach each morning and evening – such was the plan anyway.

Ray was also keen to lose a bit of weight so he said he would join me on a few runs to The Hill as well. As the two of us were by now associated closely with the bar stool, no-one really believed we were doing the runs together, but we were and it was serious stuff.

It suited me. I had a bit of company now, someone who wouldn't be streets ahead of me and put me off the job before I had even started. The first day I went with Ray, I confessed to him that I had never been to The Hill before and deadly in earnest, he turned around and told me that as a Wexford man I should be ashamed of myself with all that had happened there so many years before.

I was a little embarrassed by Ray's rebuke, but there was no time to wallow anymore and I set about conquering the killer peaks and slopes. The punishment was unreal. For my runs on the beach, I would throw on layers of clothing to sweat out all the toxins and alcohol. But after a few sprints, I would throw off a few layers at the foot of the hill to give me some chance of making it to the top.

Although a friend, Declan O'Connor, and I had put in some groundwork by running four miles every so often, I was coming under brutal pressure on The Hill, which was dominated by a deadly incline so steep I wouldn't even send John Troy up it.

I seized up several times and threw up many more, wondering what the hell I was doing. But I persevered. Some people thought I had lost the plot but I knew what I was doing.

One day, Declan Ruth came out with me and, without intending, he demonstrated the fitness I needed to reach to hurl my way back onto the Wexford team. He was way ahead of me. But later I went back on my own and managed to negotiate the huge sandbags five times in one session.

That was it for me. Every limb and muscle had tightened near the end of my third run and I felt like giving in but stamina was my biggest problem and if I was going to play against the likes of Kilkenny again, I needed to be able to keep up and compete.

One night, with the wind howling and the rain pouring down, I was about 10 seconds away from jacking my session in. I had 'conquered' The Hill three times and felt I hadn't the strength to raise the flag a fourth time. But just as I was about to throw in the towel, Pat Delaney came into my head and I remembered the way he'd roared at me when I lay on the ground in Belfield with my leg smashed.

Pat doesn't know this but he got me up Vinegar Hill a fourth time and gave me all the motivation I needed to make it up a fifth. With tears of pain welling, I ground out the fourth ascent, jogged slowly back down, thought of Delaney with every step and, though almost reduced to walking pace, got back up a fifth time.

I sat down at the top. The wind was howling and it was lonely. I thought of what I had put those closest to me through and what a selfish prick I had been. There, on top of that historic hill, I recalled the way I had neglected my wife and children and what an absolute waste of space I had been for the 16 months I had spent moping in the absence of hurling.

I also wondered what encouragement Griffin might offer if he could see me here now, on top of The Hill, exhausted but with no badness or drink in my system. And fuck it, for a few minutes I was proud of myself again. I got up and stumbled back down, the legs like jelly, going from under me.

The following night I was there again and undertook the same regime. In a perverse sort of a way, I grew to love that hill; it reminded me of who I was and who I needed to be. But while The Hill was a test, the beaches were just as challenging. I wouldn't let a day go by without doing two runs at either Morriscastle or Kilmuckridge and, would you believe, by now I was enjoying it.

Morriscastle at 7 am frightened the shit out of me just as it did at 7 pm – you couldn't see your hand in front of you. But I was ready for it. Togs and socks, wet-suit and plastic bag, jersey and tracksuit bottoms, a cap: they were all I needed. The rest I would do myself.

After two weeks, I decided to cut out the little breaks I'd been giving myself during the training runs and instead chalked out a little circuit, where I would stop and do stomach exercises instead of waiting to get the breath back. My circuit was a 20-minute run, sit-ups and press-ups until my stomach looked like a six-pack, another run against the wind and then three shuttle runs and 10 hill runs. I spent an hour there in the morning and an hour each evening for well over two months.

The windy nights were miserable and I was often afraid of my life that, like my uncle Seán Woulfe, I would be swept out to the raging sea by the howling gales. I sometimes imagined there was someone behind me, someone not too friendly. I was a bit like the man in the poem we learnt at school, *The Ancient Mariner*, 'Like one that on a lonesome road doth walk in fear and dread, and having once turned round walks on and turns no more his head, because he knows a frightful fiend doth close behind him tread.'

I adopted a friendly street light in the distance as comfort, a light I never let out of my sight for long. It was the one bit of assurance I had.

I trained from the first week in November until Christmas and managed to stay out of the pub. Eithne thought the holiday season had come early. The only time I stirred out it would be to have a game of cards with the lads. I had gone from one extreme to the other: from drinking heavily every night to not touching the stuff. People couldn't really believe it but I kept my head down, already thinking ahead to the following summer.

I took a little break from training on Christmas Day and New Year's Day but nearly felt guilty about it when chatting to Doc O'Connor soon after. Doc informed me he had even trained on Christmas Day so I knew the bar had been raised higher again. Even though I was bursting my hole, someone was doing more than me; it only motivated me even more.

As weird and masochistic as it sounds, I grew to love the training regime. It allowed me time on my own and gave me the discipline I needed if I was to go back hurling with the county team again. But the runs, climbs and sprints – I knew in my heart and soul this would be the final such extreme effort. I would never be able to go through such a purgatory again. Never.

My mother in law, May Sinnott would see me running, the rain pissing down and the wind almost driving me back into the sand. She never said anything but I swear she thought I had lost the plot.

When we went away on holidays to Lanzarote with the Wexford team in the new year. I decided to let my limbs and muscles settle in the sea, relax and take the week off training. I had a few drinks every day as well but there was no danger of slipping back into the hole; this was my therapy and I spent a happy week with Ray Keogh, Chris 'Hopper' McGrath and Mitch Jordan.

I didn't feel one bit bad about having a few pints, not even after what I had put people through. This time I felt in control of my life and felt I could stop if I wanted to. This suggested to me I was not after all 'the one' Griffin had referred to.

Sure I had gone overboard on the drink and people might say, with some justification, I had a problem. But as for being an alcoholic? Well, the fact I took a few drinks for a week and then gave it up again reassured me my problem was not full-blown.

So I tried to enjoy the holiday and although it was great craic, there were plenty of times when I was the subject of the team's wit and wisecracks. The lads used to conduct little quizzes in the bar. One day as I walked in some smartass called out: 'And who was the first intercounty hurler to be sent off in three Championships in a row?'

'LIAM DUNNE,' they all roared in unison and fell around laughing. All very well. I can take a slagging from the best of them. But this was not the way I wanted to be remembered after giving 16 years with the team. Instead I stored it. Any motivation was welcome. I just kept repeating the goals I had set for myself. Metaphorically, even though we were away, I had pinned the words 'Honour' and 'Respect' on the walls of my hotel room.

I revealed very little to any of the lads about what I was doing but I knew that when it came to pre-season training and those long runs I used to dread, I would be ready and better than any of the lads at them. And if I could manage those bloody runs so early in the year, there was every chance my hurling would speak for itself later in the season.

The new Wexford manager, John Conran, had been onto me about going back and had assured me I was a big part of his plans but even though I was training my arse off and awaiting the chance to meet Offaly and their selector Pat Delaney, I didn't let onto John that my mind was fully made up. I told him I needed time to think about it.

He was stern: 'People tell me I'm stone mad to be even thinking about you,' he warned. 'But as I said, you're a big part of my plans, Liam, and although some people don't want you involved, I do.'

He called a fitness test for the Tuesday night after we returned from our team holiday. The night before the test, I rang him and told him I was coming back 100 percent.

'That's all I wanted to hear,' he said before hanging up. It was a short conversation and in fairness, there was nothing much to be said. When the fitness test was held, most of the lads had faces on them like they had to hand over a winning lottery ticket but this time I was up at the front, for the first time in ages.

As Sod's Law would have it, they decided to abolish those lung-wrenching and mind-numbing long runs I used to dread. I was looking forward to a chance to show what I could do, but the training had changed completely. We had shuttle runs and heart monitors, sprints and strides. All around me, lads were stretched out on the ground, suffering with their lungs and thighs. But I got through it okay and the lads started to twig I had been doing extra training.

I had let it be known I meant business, and though I was only a sub for the first League game against Derry, I was on the Club Lemon the night before. Most players are off the beer at that stage of the season anyway but this was a big deal for me.

Before that game, Dickie Murphy, a top senior referee and a former Wexford selector, took me by surprise by asking me would I now feel under pressure with referees after all the sendings-off.

'No, I wouldn't think so, Dickie,' I replied without thinking. But he had hit the nail on the head, and later that evening I mentioned our conversation to John Conran and Martin Quigley.

'Well, do you feel under pressure?' came the question.

'Yeah, I'll be bricking it every day I go out, to be honest,' I replied.

And it was true. One wild pull from Liam Dunne and I was off again and the reputation was totally gone this time. So I made a few decisions before the start of the season. My main task was to get to the ball first; I had never been the fastest thing on two legs so, now more than ever, I would have to fall back on experience and an ability to read the game. Secondly, I would no longer pull on the ball. That might sound crazy for an intercounty hurler but I couldn't afford to get sent off again and I knew I was a marked man in every match I played. No, instead I would bat or block.

And I would do it my own way. I even decided to go over to Parkhead and watch Celtic play Hearts just before the start of the League. Nowadays a manager would laugh at you if you asked for time off to go and get married, never mind tear away with the lads for a few days. But I knew what I was doing and had a feeling the break back to reality would do me no harm at all. I had trained my guts out for several months, a little respite would do me the world of good.

John Conran agreed and so a few of us went over to watch the Celts, and in particular my hero Henrik Larsson. It was a great crew that included my brother Seán and some old friends. It was a brilliant experience, capped by the fact the Bhoys won 3-0. I spent much of the game observing Martin O'Neill on the sideline; it would have been nice to meet him.

When I returned to the county team, my focus was on writing more history and not wallowing in the past. And do you know what?

Playing Derry in my first game back was a grand way to begin a season of redemption. There was no glare or spotlight, no expectations and few supporters.

As the game went on, however, the team almost collapsed and I came on. I had just arrived when a Derry player stared at me like I'd just been released from jail.

'Are you the lad who was sent off last year?' he nervously enquired.

'Yep,' I replied, 'and the year before and before that again.'

He was supposed to be my marker but after that he kept his distance, maybe half afraid I'd hit him a tip.

Anyway, we were five points down when I came in at centrefield, got a point and set Mitch Jordan up for another one. First game over. We won by two.

The Wexford papers, who had been good to me during my troublesome three years, wrote that I changed the game, but that was rubbish; I had hit only about four balls. And so I was again named as a sub for the game against Tipperary at Nenagh.

Once again, we were being destroyed. My clubmate Keith Rossiter was taken off, which I felt was a disgrace because Mark O'Leary had scored only a point off him. I came on and O'Leary said to me: 'What are they doing taking him off?'

I agreed with the Tipp man and let the selectors know what I felt at the half-time break. But we were well beaten again and had to beat Offaly at Wexford Park by at least 12 points, just to make the second stage of the League.

This was the first time I'd been in the same stadium with my pal Pat Delaney since the broken-leg episode in 1997 and I really revelled in beating them by 14, though we had been six points down at one stage.

It was nice to get a chance to hurl on young Brian Carroll that day, though. I had remembered Brian's late father, Pat, very well and recalled Pat Fleury's great speech when Offaly won the 1985 All-Ireland final. I would later play Railway Cup with Brian in Rome; he could be as good as his Dad.

I was selected at centre back for the Offaly game and scored a point from 100 yards to a huge roar from the stands. That put us eight up and a Paul Codd goal left us on our way to the big win we needed. I ran towards the tunnel, raised my fist to the crowd and suddenly saw Delaney in front of me.

He turned away.

'That's the first part of the job,' I thought to myself. 'The next will be at Nowlan Park in the Championship.'

Galway ended our League hopes after that and we prepared to face Offaly on the June Bank Holiday Monday. I remember saying to Eithne before that game that it was the first time in my career I thought I wouldn't make the first 15 for a Championship game. I don't know what it was but I had a premonition I wouldn't make it.

And the next thing we heard, Rory Mallon, who was flying it at corner-back, just left us and headed off to America. They moved Keith Rossiter back to cover for him and, to my huge relief, I was named at wing-back.

It would have been a dire feeling to have started from the bench for the first time in my Championship career and I later mentioned my pre-match jitters to Conran. He said he couldn't understand where I was getting this from because I was the first name on his team-sheet.

I was still concerned about my status, however. In the past, I had always used a heavy hurl, but in latter years, wary I would get roasted by some guy 10 years younger, I decided to lighten my hurls. Albert Randall, my hurley-maker and old friend, knew what I was about and though the sticks were now lighter, he still managed to make ones that fitted me like a glove.

We knew the game was speeding up. Albert left out three or four sticks and asked me to pick my favourite. He then pointed out those he considered best for me, and 10 times out of 10 over the years he would be right and I would bow to his superior wisdom.

Of course, in the Offaly game Rory Hanniffy and I clashed on the first pull of a ball and my hurley broke. But I had my spares well broken in and ready to play a high-speed Championship match.

I have never understood how lads play with just the one stick every year and then when it comes to the Championship they break their number-one hurl and have to use a replacement they have no connection with.

And this Offaly game was a typical Championship match. I needed my stick to be light so I could swing it fast and under pressure. I had to use my head and experience to compensate for my lack of pace. Still, all the experience in the world cannot legislate for playing with Wexford. And this was a typical display; we went from eight points down to winning by one, 0-16 to 1-12.

Near the end, Brian Carroll missed a free for them from 40 yards out and I screamed at Pat O'Connor that he owed us 45 seconds from the Tipperary game two years earlier. I'm not sure he understood what I was on about but in the end we hung on for dear life to get through to meet Kilkenny yet again, our fourth Leinster final meeting in six years.

After the Offaly game, I was introduced to official GAA drug-testing for the first time. It was like a scene straight from *Fr Ted*. The former Kilkenny hurler Richie Power was a steward that day and part of his job was to haul four players, two from each team, into the dressing-room for the tests.

Of course, my name was called, and as I ran into the tunnel, waving and pumping my fists at the crowd, Richie nabbed me and almost cringed with the embarrassment of having to tell me what lay ahead.

In a newspaper interview with the journalist Christy O'Connor earlier that day, I had joked that I'd been caught for everything else so it would be no surprise if I was done for failing a drugs test. But to tell the truth, I wasn't laughing as I was led into a tiny room just away from the dressing-rooms.

My team-mate MJ Furlong was dragged in with me and we were

handed little tubs by an official of the Irish Sports Council and told to piddle 75 milligrams of our best.

It was one hell of a farce. MJ was grand. He had been on the pitch for only the last two minutes and could fill the River Slaney at the driest of times anyway. He was done and dusted after a minute or two.

But I was in trouble. Forgive the graphic description, but I was so dehydrated I couldn't even force out a dribble.

'I'll turn on the taps for you, that might help,' the guy from the Sports Council ventured.

'What in the name of Jaysus difference will that make?' I asked in disbelief, as MJ roared laughing on his way out of the room.

Looking around, I saw the two Offaly lads, Damien Murray and one of the subs, had done the sensible thing and brought their gear into the room with them. They were showered and changed by the time they had their business complete.

Anyway, with all the water I consumed, things finally started to happen and as I went about my business I was horrified to notice the guy from the Sports Council staring at my family jewels while I filled his tub.

'What in the name of Christ are you looking at?' I roared.

'Oh sorry, we have to keep an eye on things in case anyone tries to slip a foreign substance into the tub.'

'Oh sweet Jesus!'

I nearly cried but managed to produce 70 milligrams and, embarrassed as hell, handed it to him.

'You're still five mills short,' he pointed out.

I burst out laughing, tilted the tub to one side so the precious liquid reached the 75-milligram line and said: 'Don't spill any of it and you'll be alright.' Then I left the room.

Two weeks later, I received a letter saying I had passed the test with flying colours, so obviously your man had done a good job keeping it all in the tub.

And so it was all set up for another tilt with Kilkenny in the Leinster final. You would get so sick of playing these lads after all the beatings they dished out since 1997. That's why the 2004 team enjoyed so much beating them, because it was totally unexpected and out of the blue.

Before the game, Griffin rang to tell me I would be marking John Hoyne. All he kept saying was: 'He's a hardy bastard, a tough hoor.'

I didn't need Liam to tell me that. It was like marking John Power all over again. But Brian Cody knew who he wanted on me.

Before the throw-in, we started the parade and I broke momentarily because I saw Cody out of the corner of my eye. He had always backed me up, especially in the three years I'd been sent off. Even after the clash with Martin Comerford, he spoke in my favour. The man has a ferocious appetite to win and I think he is the driving force behind that Kilkenny team because even when their hunger dips, Cody keeps the ship on course.

I don't really know why but I went over to Brian and shook hands with him as we headed up along the Hogan Stand. People asked me afterwards why I did it and I just replied that it was something I wanted to do.

I still wanted to take his crown. We had run Kilkenny close in 2002 but, to be frank, they could have ended this game at half-time and Eddie Brennan and DJ Carey could have had six goals between them.

We absolutely caved in after the break, though I was reasonably happy with the firefighting job I had done on my own patch and was mildly surprised when one newspaper, the *Irish Mirror*, gave me a rating of five the following morning and predicted I had graced Croke Park for the last time.

Players do read papers but I smiled when I read this, knowing I had marked four Kilkenny lads, including Hoyne, Martin Comerford and Henry Shefflin, and held them all scoreless.

Like I said, I had changed my whole game so I didn't stand out anymore. I don't remember one incident in that match where I pulled on the ball. I just blocked, and when my opponent went to shoot, I tried to shoo him away from the posts, keeping him at bay. And while I succeeded, Kilkenny were awesome and the result went against us.

In the end, and believe me, the end couldn't come quick enough, they beat us 2-23 to 2-12. It was my sixth time losing a Leinster final. I had been beaten in 92, 93, 94, 2001, 2002 and now in 2003, which I have to say was one of the worst thrashings of the lot.

To be truthful, I had expected a few smart comments or jibes from the Kilkenny lads during that game about my three red cards in a row but to be fair, there wasn't a word out of any of them, and no other player from any team I faced in the 2003 Championship offered an opinion on the matter, which just shows the character of the players.

The Wexford team needed to show some character now. We had an unmerciful row at our first training session back after the final. John Conran had a go at us because some lads on the team didn't have their socks pulled up for the parade. Management also tore strips off us for throwing water bottles around the field, expecting them to come in like lackeys and gather them up. The county board had been fined €750 or something because only Darren Stamp had his socks pulled up for the parade, but I thought this focus on the pre-match hullabaloo was the greatest load of horse manure and I walked off the field in disgust.

Dave Guiney came over to me and put his arm around me.

'Take your hands off me, Dave,' I snapped.

He had a go back and then Adrian Fenlon had a go at him. Most of the boys got involved in one way or another but I kept going into the dressing-room, where John Conran followed me.

'This is a load of shite, John. We're after getting hammered in a Leinster final and all we're worried about is who had their socks pulled up and who didn't and who was throwing water bottles around the pitch. It's a load of bollocks.'

But John was only a scapegoat for my anger. We had been rolled over by Kilkenny and I was furious because there is no county I hate losing to more than them. John had his own problems and I shouldn't have had a go at him. He found it difficult to get instructions to our players that day; anytime he stepped onto the pitch, he knew the county board would be hammered with another fine, the victims of another idiotic GAA rule.

It also didn't help matters that Niamh Fitzpatrick, someone all the players knew and trusted, had left the camp. She and John didn't see eye to eye on a number of issues and we were without her services for the Leinster final. I felt she was always worth having around but it was the manager's call.

For me, Niamh had been an absolute star; it was no surprise to me that she was snapped up by the Irish Olympic team straightaway. Many times I had poured my heart out to her and she had greatly assisted my mental preparation before games.

It was my own fault that I felt I needed her more than most in the 2003 season but I couldn't blame John Conran for deciding she was surplus to requirements. I had put my hands into the fire in 2000, 2001 and 2002 and had come out burned but the manager had the whole team to look after, not just me.

But as the year went on we missed her. And the year did go on, despite the fact we were annihilated by Kilkenny and drew Waterford in the qualifiers.

Waterford are the biggest enigma in the GAA; they had just been beaten by Cork in the Munster final, and on their day, well, they were likely to blow us away.

We travelled down to Nowlan Park to play them on a Saturday evening in July and as we walked out onto the pitch, we could see it was like a billiard table, it was so smooth. The Wexford fans had made the journey in force as did the Waterford supporters and the atmosphere was unreal.

Of course, true to the great tradition of the Irish weather, by the time we changed and emerged from the dressing-room, there was a gale and a monsoon to greet us. In fact the rain was so strong you could hardly see in front of you.

Well, we couldn't, but the Waterford lads certainly had no problem and within 10 minutes they went ahead by eight points to three and it looked like we were about to get creamed, something that looked even more likely when we lost Adrian Fenlon through injury.

But sometimes fate intervenes, and though Adrian is one of our best ever players, his substitution allowed Larry Murphy in from the bench. Larry had been injured earlier in the year and frustrated because he couldn't get his place but, by Jesus, he turned the game around that day.

He started to create havoc in the Waterford defence and each time the ball went his way, he either scored or broke it to the likes of Rory Jacob, meaning that although we were played off the field for most of the first half, they led by only a point and you could already tell the pressure of being overwhelming favourites was getting to them. I would go as far as saying they got a mental block in the second half. We tore out of the traps and hit two or three quick points and it seemed as if Larry was involved in all of them. We dictated the game from there on and Waterford started their usual trick of switching forwards all over the place.

Dan Shanahan was moved away from me and out came Paul Flynn.

'Jaysus,' he groaned. 'I didn't think I'd have to face you today.'

And while I chuckled back at him, he had the ball over the bar, which wiped the smile off my face.

Near the end, big Dan came by me again and I tugged his jersey and asked him if I could have it afterwards.

'It would be an honour to have yours as well, Liam boy,' he said, with a sort of a smile that made it look like he had half his front teeth missing.

Dan had the year of his life in 2004 but I had felt for years that he must have been the victim of local politics because Dave Bennett and he, both Lismore men, were the first to be taken off whenever the team went bad. Both of them can hurl and, from what I hear, are dedicated trainers, so it must have been local stuff that kept them down – the politics isn't just confined to Wexford after all.

We clung on in one of the most tension-filled endings to a game and came out on top 1-20 to 18 points, and they were just devastated. As the final whistle blew, I ran to the sideline, where young Billy was thrust in front of a steward, who lifted him out to me. The young lad knew it had been a great day at the office and just smiled and looked around the field, taking everything in.

I think Billy will be a great little hurler. It's only better he's getting and he can strike cleanly with both sides already even though he's only seven. Griffin asked me about him one day and I said all he needed to be a fine player was the heart, to which our former manager responded: 'Ah, would you leave him alone, his little heart is only growing.'

Suddenly, people recognised the Wexford hurlers again. They didn't shy away as you walked by them in the street or pretend not to see as you slumped out of Croke Park, destroyed by another sending-off. No, we were heroes again. It's so fickle. The county went berserk but in fairness to the fans there has always been a core support around.

Just after we had beaten Offaly and qualified for the provincial final, we held a barbecue and race night and raised an amazing €45,000 for the Supporters' Club. It showed what was out there for us if we could get back to winning ways. It felt like we were on our way back when the All-Ireland quarter-final draw pitted us against Antrim. The excitement only increased. No offence to the lads up north – they're fighting an uphill battle all the time – but we were expected to win this one easily and the supporters could smell an All-Ireland semi-final.

At the back of our heads, we couldn't help but look forward to an All-Ireland semi-final. We never really knuckled down to the prospect of playing Antrim; the challenge just didn't really faze us. But it should have.

Dinny Cahill had them fine-tuned when we met them in Croke Park, ahead of the semi-final between Tipperary and Offaly. They got two goals in the first half and another that was disallowed for no reason at all. That score would surely have put them out of sight.

The year before, they had tested Tipp, but in all fairness, they couldn't beat us, could they? Well, they had us on the ropes until late in the second half, when Paul Codd stepped up and buried a 21-yard free. We got another straightaway and that left them on the ropes.

But they weren't finished yet and brought on Aidan Delargy at corner forward, who scored some lovely points. If he'd been brought on earlier, we were finished. We got them by three points in the end, 2-15 to 2-12, but we can thank Rory McCarthy for that win because he really saved us. Like several others I had fallen into the complacency trap and had a stinker, but at least we survived.

At the end of the game, the referee, my old friend Pat Horan, ran 50-odd yards in my direction. Pat had sent me off in 2001, and as he approached me the Wexford lads must have wondered what reception he would get. He stuck out his hand.

'I wish you the very best of luck in the All-Ireland semi-final,' he said.

'Thanks, Pat.'

He wasn't finished: 'I sincerely mean that.'

'I know you do.'

He didn't have to do that but our relationship didn't just go back to the Brian O'Meara incident. I had known him from a shinty trip in 1988 and while it's hard, sometimes it's better to just leave stuff on the field. Besides, we had a semi-final with Cork to look forward to. I played the best hurling of my career against them in those epic 1993 League final games.

This time one or two of that Wexford team were still intact, while they had an entire line-up of new faces.

It was a huge task for us to stand up to them. Around 10 years previously, I peaked against them and received an All Star for my efforts, but it would be asking a lot to reproduce that form in a different era, especially at the ripe old age of 35 and marking possibly the fastest hurler in the land, Ben O'Connor.

We had two weeks to prepare, though, so I was going to give it everything. Wexford went Boom! Kids on the streets wore our jersey; the feel-good factor was back and everyone wanted to hurl the game as you went about your work.

Our build-up was intense and on the ball. Mick Kinsella started to do a lot of coaching work with us and Griffin was around again to help out. We knew one area of great concern to us was the half-forward line. Cork had dominated that sector all year long and had snuffed out teams by winning the battles on that line. So we devised a game-plan to disrupt their lethal half-forwards. The entire defence, midfield and goalkeepers met for video analysis one evening and we drew up a blueprint that would stop the likes of O'Connor and the McCarthys, Timmy and Niall, from running amok.

My bit was simple. Their goalkeeper, Donal Óg Cusack, hit 95 percent of his puck-outs down on top of their big corner forward Alan Browne, which didn't make sense to me when you had the speedster Ben O'Connor on the far side of the field.

Before the game, I rang Griffin to ask him his opinion on stopping Ben the Bullet. 'Get to the ball first,' was his curt reply.

And so our instructions were that each time the Cork half-forward line retreated inside their own half for our puck-outs we should go back with them and either win the break or prevent them from flying down into our half. We had to take risks, take a chance, try and get to the sliotar first and then hope like hell it would break in your favour.

It was potentially my last game for the county, something I dreaded. And in the past, under such pressure, I would have retreated home and got all wrapped up in the tension. But this year, I was taking a different path. I was happy that my fitness would ensure that discipline would not be a problem and while I lived most of the year like a hermit, if I wanted to go and relax, I would do so.

Armed with the security that I was in great shape and had plenty of tactical knowledge of both the Wexford and Cork teams, I decided to kick the heels up one Friday night, just 12 days before the big match. Eithne and I had arranged to take a trip to Wexford town to see the film *Veronica Guerin*. Martin Storey and Rosaleen decided they would come along and so we agreed to meet up outside the cinema a few minutes before the film started.

Storey went to pay but was told all the seats had been sold. I could see he was disappointed as we had been looking forward to a night's company so I suggested we go to Charlie Kavanagh's pub for a quick pint.

'Jesus, you're not supposed to be drinking,' he said.

'One won't kill me,' I replied.

And up we went. I was immediately aware people were looking at me so I sent Storey to the bar and we sipped away for a while. Again, eyes turned in my direction but I was my own man and didn't need some fellow in a bar to tell me what I should and shouldn't be doing.

So we ordered a few more and it turned out to be a great night between the four of us, and while I hoped and prayed Adrian Fenlon and the lads wouldn't hear about it, I knew it was just the relaxation I needed in the lead-up to that Cork game.

Of course when I woke up the next morning I didn't exactly feel like a primed athlete. But I dragged myself out of the bed and went to work. I had to lacquer a stairs for someone and the smell of that didn't help me either.

I arrived back home at 5 pm and even though Liam Griffin was taking a training session at 6.30 in Wexford Park, I knew I wouldn't be able to make it. So dialling John Conran's number, I came clean – well mostly clean.

'John, I have a sick stomach. I won't be able to make training and I'm actually in bed right now.'

Not a word of a lie and John was fine about the whole thing. Of course, I didn't tell him fully why I had a sick stomach.

If you ask me, that little bit of craic with Martin Storey and the two wives was the best fun I had in ages. Like the visit to Parkhead, it crowned me. My preparation had been intense but you can't maintain that all day, every day, and in order to be fresh for the All-Ireland semi-final, I knew those few pints were as good as any sprint or stamina run. And when match day came along, I felt like a million dollars: refreshed, confident and ready to restore my reputation. I knew how important it was for Wexford to win that game but it was equally important that if I was going to retire, people would remember me as a hurler.

And in the dressing-room, I reminded myself once more that it could be my last game for Wexford, and as I went through my normal pre-match routine, I did it more solemnly than ever before. Thinking of Mam one last time, I burst out of the dressing-room like Carl Lewis and out into the light.

After the game, Larry O'Gorman asked me what was that sprint out of the blocks all about.

'You made me look bad,' he said, deadly serious. 'I had to make a break after you and it nearly killed me!'

Jesus, Croke Park never looked as well. I looked around and made sure to take in everything. There were over 50,000 people cheering or jeering. It was a daunting arena to be in. I knew I might never get back there again so I made a mental recording of everything I saw.

The glare. It seems everyone is staring at you with a big bright lens.

The colour. Sprinting out in front of the purple and gold rainbow in front of Hill 16, all of us hoping to find the gold at the end of it.

The concentration. From Fitzy to the referee, everyone is focused, and even in the pre-match puck-around, no-one wants to drop a ball.

The goons or match-day stewards. The gents on the sideline who walk around Croke Park with the puffed-up air of a US President about to hit the red button but serve little purpose.

The opponents. Sometimes, though not always, I can tell if a guy really wants to be out here. It's written on his face.

There were a lot more Cork fans than Wexford fans in the stadium, which was strange because they don't usually bother turning up in droves for semi-finals down there. Maybe they were expecting something special. Or else they just wanted this win as much as we did. Like ourselves, Cork hadn't exactly set the world alight with All-Ireland titles in recent years.

The whole day went by me like a rocket but something I do remember was the stupid warm-up we undertook in front of Hill 16. These bloody drills are all the rave now, but in my book they are a load of baloney and are used on match days mainly to justify the trainer's existence.

Anyway, within a few minutes, I heard the unmistakable voice of Marty Morrissey calling out the names of the Cork team.

'Would you please welcome the Rock of Cloyne, the one and only Diarmuid O'Sullivan' and 'One of Ireland's top forwards, Joe Deane.'

The Cork crowd lapped it up and cheered in delight as their heroes were announced in glowing terms, but it really got up my nose.

'Would you listen to those arrogant bastards?' I roared at our lads. 'Who the fuck do they think they are?'

I kept drilling the message into the team, trying to hammer home the message that this Cork team were way ahead of themselves. Next thing, just as my words were sinking in, I heard, 'And now, the marvellous Damien Fitzhenry.'

'Waaahhheeeyyy!'

The roar from our lot was almost as deafening as Cork's. It was a circus, and the lads started laughing. To tell the truth, by the time Marty called out, 'The ageless wonder, Liam Dunne,' I was half looking forward to the cheer I would get.

With my main motivational tool out the window, I shrugged my shoulders and smirked as the rest of the names were called out and the

Wexford supporters went berserk. Now for my battle with Ben the Bullet.

We actually played the game-plan to a T, but to be frank, I was very lucky all during that game, because when Ben and I retreated for a break from the Wexford puck-out, the ball just seemed to hop in my path. If I took two steps to the left, it came with me, and if I hopped to the right, well, it was there as well. I motored along pretty impressively on the wing before John Conran opted to move me into the centre-back spot in a switch with Declan Ruth. Our men followed and Ben O'Connor zipped in after me towards the centre-forward spot.

'Jaysus, Ben,' I thought. 'Would you ever feck off and give an old man a bit of peace.'

We could have been a little bit sharper in the full-back line, however. Setanta Ó hAilpín was on Doc O'Connor, leaving Dave Guiney to look after Alan Browne, who was winning most of their puck-outs. I would have swapped our corner-backs and let Dave plague Setanta for the 70 minutes. But with me being back in the centre, the whole thing had gone full circle and it was a fine feeling to be there again in an All-Ireland semi-final, 10 years after playing the best stuff of my life there. Against Cork as well.

I really enjoyed the game, especially when we went five points up and looked like we were on our way to an All-Ireland final.

'Oh Christ,' I whispered, 'we're nearly there.'

Maybe after all the shit that had gone on for the past three years, I wasn't too far away from the summit once more. As the sun shone down, I appreciated why I had been in tears climbing Vinegar Hill and running in Kilmuckridge and Morriscastle on all those early mornings. This was the feeling I lived for every day of my life.

But Wexford hurlers are famous for snatching defeat from the jaws of victory, and while I knew we wouldn't cruise into the final, I didn't think we would cave in like we did either.

In the space of 11 lousy and agonising minutes, our five-point lead turned into a six-point deficit. Cork nabbed two goals. I'm not sure if either of them was legal but the ref, Aodhán Mac Suibhne, decreed they were. Alan Browne shot over a great point with time just up. It left them three ahead.

My lungs stopped pumping air and, desperately looking into the vast blue sky above Croke Park, I pleaded with God to lend us a hand. I'm not a religious man and the last time I had chatted with the Man Upstairs was during the last few minutes of the 1996 All-Ireland final, when I begged Him not to let Mike Houlihan's late free hit the back of the net.

God must have felt sorry for me because He listened to my prayers back then and He did it again in 2003. For whatever reason, He came up trumps once more and I will never as long as I live forget the sequence that followed.

Fitzy took a long puck-out and the ball broke to Tom Kenny, who was brilliantly hooked by Mick Jacob, who robbed him and sent a pass towards Mitch Jordan, who didn't hang around long and instead sent a pass to Rory McCarthy, who was on the run and heading away from the Cork goal. Still, it didn't seem to matter to Rory where he was heading because he almost ripped open Donal Óg Cusack's net with a rasping shot.

'Oh God, thank you!' I cried, with my face to the heavens.

Ben O'Connor was also staring at the sky but for a different reason, I would guess.

The final whistle blew straightaway and I tapped Ben on the chest and as we swopped jerseys I started to babble about, of all things, the Celtic soccer team. Earlier in the week, I had read that Donal Óg was a huge Celtic fan and was organising a trip to Parkhead and so I started waffling to Ben, who probably hadn't a clue what I was on about.

But this was a great feeling, one I had forgotten existed. Excited and drained at the same time, I went to the sideline to look for Billy and approached a member of the Garda to ask for his help.

'Where's the child?' the garda enquired.

'Somewhere in the Cusack Stand,' I panted.

'You may find him yourself,' the garda laughed and walked off, leaving me to pace the sideline up and down like a weary donkey, looking for the young lad.

As the crowd cheered I spotted my great pal Martin Dempsey in the crowd and went over and gave him Ben's jersey. The crowd cheered louder as, barechested, I shook a defiant fist in their direction before tearing back into the dressing-room. I cringed later that night when I saw TV footage of it because I looked like William Wallace from *Braveheart* rallying his troops but I suppose it was one of those days.

The replay proved to be my last game in Croke Park. We gave it everything in the drawn game and even though we hit two early goals in the rematch, I knew deep down we were never going to play as well again. I was moved to centre-back. And despite the fact we started brightly, and a big crowd turned up to support us, we mostly huffed and puffed around the place while Cork did all the hurling.

I hurled my own patch pretty well even though The Bullet did nab two points off me. Again there were one or two doubts over some of Cork's goals but they were by far the better team and deserved to make it through. They came at us in droves and we had no answer in the second half.

It was funny. Looking around with the game over and still 10 minutes to play, I had an eerie feeling and turned around to talk to Ben in between a break of play.

'Win, lose or draw, at least you have some chance of being here many more days,' I told him.

'Not at all,' he replied. 'There's plenty of hurling left in you.'

But I knew that time was up, and when the final whistle blew, we shook hands and I dropped my head in disappointment. Walking off the field, I looked around at the four corners of the great field of dreams and knew I would never be back as a player again.

Before I had time to think, Diarmuid O'Sullivan, the Cork full-back, came over to shake my hand. Billy was with me this time and

Diarmuid took off his jersey and gave it to him. The young lad was delighted because while Sully had a tough time in the first game, he was absolutely awesome in the replay and Billy was fascinated as he burst out of the square and drove the sliotar down the field.

I was last into the dressing-room, where Mick Kinsella grabbed me and sort of pinned me against the wall.

'This is not a time to make any rash decisions,' he said. 'You're after having the year of your life – you've hurled as well as ever.'

At the start, Mick and I hadn't been the best of buddies. As an officer of the county board, he went mad one year and demanded our shirts back after we swapped jerseys with Laois. I lost the plot with him and threw a jersey in his face. But we had mellowed since then and got on a lot better in recent years. And I think both of us had the same interest at heart and that was Wexford hurling.

And here I was at the end of my particular role for Wexford hurling, finished. Dejected, I sat there in the dressing-room, saying nothing and taking everything in. This was my last time in a Wexford dressing-room. I looked over at Fitzy, one of the best of them. Sometimes it was his way or the highway, but he was a friend, an old reliable.

Darren Stamp was in one of his trances; he often goes into them after losing games. He dropped off the Wexford panel in 2004 but maybe he can come back a better man and carry on Oulart's tradition of supplying defenders for Wexford.

Beside Darren was Darragh Ryan. The man is just awesome, an inspiration on and off the field. I wished we had more years on the field together.

Skippy Ruth was there as well, one of the lads. His standards went so high there at one stage that they would inevitably slip for a little time. And now they are back up there again.

I looked over at Rory Mac. He was baby-faced when all this started for him in 1996 but the innocence of it all is gone now. He grew up a lot after that All-Ireland final win.

Adrian Fenlon, the iron-man of the team, was close by.

Larry O was drying himself, absolutely gutted. He was the best hurler I ever shared a field with and that includes Brian Whelahan, Willie O'Connor, any of them you care to mention. He would have been Hurler of the Year two or three times if he was with Kilkenny.

There was Paul Codd beside me. There's only one Paul Codd. You couldn't possibly make another.

I didn't want to take my jersey off just then. It didn't feel right. Instead, I put my head down and thought of older team-mates with whom I used to sit all those years ago. The ghosts of Wexford past.

Ger Cushe: I would trust him with my life. Martin Storey: one of my closest friends – the craic we had. The O'Connors: they would go through a wall for you. Billy Byrne: respect.

All the old names and faces came back to me and, more than ever before, I took in the atmosphere and just sat back to look at the lads. John Conran came over and shook hands with me.

'Good luck, Liam. I'll be talking to you. Don't make any decisions yet.'

But there was no need to even respond to John. I nodded at him and thought about something I had dreaded for several years. For what I took to be the last time, I pulled my purple and gold jersey over my head. It felt like a piece of me went with it.

Did you ever really doubt when you set out at the start?
Did you hope that you'd achieve the goals on which you set your heart?
At times it must have been so hard to keep your focus true;
At last you're past the post and congratulations due
Card from Anne Woulfe to Liam Dunne

– CHAPTER SEVENTEEN –
Respect in the heel of the hunt

Rome, November 8, 2003. Hurling had left me in a mess a year ago but it got me to within an inch of the Pope as well. Since I retired, I have learned never to underestimate the power of hurling. A lot of my work contacts are made through the game. The little perks and bonuses that come with the sport have set me up nicely and even though you are gone, you are not forgotten.

Just a year ago, I was getting out of my bed in Kilmuckridge and drinking cans of beer at two o clock in the morning. Now I'm in the foyer of a hotel in Rome, getting ready to meet Il Papa with seven or eight lads from the Kilkenny hurling team, each one of them a superstar. And although I put the work into getting here, it's because of hurling that I have got my life back in order in such a short space of time.

Henry Shefflin, John Hoyne, Brian Whelahan, Brian Carroll, young Tommy Walsh, and the Hanniffys were all in the hotel lobby, waiting to play against Connacht in the Railway Cup final and then visit the Vatican. They treated me as though I was their team-mate and, for that weekend only, I was. I loved every minute of it.

The Railway Cup may have become the laughing stock of the GAA world but it had been 10 years since I won my last medal in that competition and it was time for another. We were in Rome to do the job. Not long after Cork knocked us out of the Championship, Mick Jacob rang my house, told me he was a selector and wondered if I was interested in playing in the competition.

'Jaysus, Mick, I've forgotten about the Railway Cup a long time ago. It's the other direction I'm heading in. Forget about me.'

But Mick wasn't done: 'We have Ulster in the semi-final and the final is in Rome.'

'Count me in, Mick,' I interrupted. 'Jaysus, do your best for me now.'

I nodded like a headbanger at a rock concert as he told me the plan. The prospect of playing in this competition had suddenly become strangely attractive.

Rome. What a great and unique way to say goodbye to top-flight hurling! If I could just get on the panel, there would be a seat on the plane with my name on it. When we travelled to Casement Park to play Ulster, the pre-match training session turned into a booze-up for some of the Wexford lads on the team, myself included. Darragh Ryan was off to Boston and Skippy Ruth were heading to Lanzarote so both of them were going to miss the final anyway, and they weren't too bothered about playing Ulster.

But Noel Skehan, the manager, was and he had words with Skippy after we eventually made the team hotel at 2 am. I said nothing and headed off to bed.

When I awoke, I was amazed to hear I had been picked to play at left-wing back. To be honest, I felt I was just making up the numbers and that Skehan had never been a fan of mine, but fair dues to him, he picked me and we beat Ulster.

Some friends and I had a trip to Parkhead organised for the same weekend as the Railway Cup final in Rome so that had to be cancelled. And so I headed off to Italy to play the men from the west in the final.

I took it seriously, trained hard on my own for it. And when we arrived over there I was glad I did, because it turned out to be one of the best weekends of my life.

Not only did I maintain my fitness and form at maximum but once the game was out of the way we absolutely tore the arse out of the trip. I got to know the likes of John Hoyne, with whom I'd had many battles, and Brendan Murphy, all those lads I had played against but didn't really know.

In the final itself, Connacht were well up at half-time, but even in a much-maligned competition like the Railway Cup, which people said was on its knees, I noticed how much the Kilkenny men wanted to win.

First up for the half-time pep talk was Henry Shefflin, who said we were a disgrace, and he wasn't far wrong. Then Michael Kavanagh had a few words about what winning another Railway Cup medal would mean to everyone, especially the likes of me, who had won one a decade earlier.

Brian Whelahan wanted it too and said so, and we were a different team in the second half. Hoyne started the ball rolling with a goal. Gary Hanniffy made a huge difference when he came on as a sub. At the end of the match, which we won by two points, 3-9 to 2-10, Tommy Walsh ran over to me and we started hugging; it meant a lot to the Leinster team and that just made the weekend.

Afterwards, Tom O'Riordan of the *Irish Independent* wrote a report headed 'Dunne's Railway Cup of honour', in which he referred to me holding my medal 'like a boy clutching a toy'.

It did feel that way but the fact I got to know so many lads I had hurled against was another really enjoyable aspect of the tour. Shefflin and I became great old friends over there and he kept asking if I was going to call it a day. I told him the Railway Cup had been my last game.

At the banquet that night, the Leinster Council organised a free bar for us, but by the time we reached the hotel most of us were well hydrated anyway. Manchester United were playing Liverpool on the box so a crowd of us gathered around to watch that before heading back for the dinner. Derek Lyng, Don Hyland from Wicklow and about six other lads came back late for the official meal so we were put sitting in a room of our own.

Seán Kelly didn't forget us, though, and came in for a chat.

'I hear this is your last year, Liam. You'd be mad to go now and you going so well,' he said.

Liam Mulvihill, the Director-General, arrived over.

'Well done, you had a great year,' he told me, 'I hear you're retiring but why don't you keep going?'

Nice words and great to hear them. It just added to the trip, as did the next morning, when I went down to the hotel lobby to meet Hoyne, as we had arranged to visit the Vatican. We missed the Pope by a few minutes; he had been out on the balcony but left just as we arrived in St. Peter's Square. It would have been great to see him but we contented ourselves with a tour of the area and bought some souvenirs for the folks at home.

When I got back home, all the talk was that I was set for a fourth All Star. Noel Skehan had told us the All Star selectors would have noticed who played well in the Railway Cup, and while I didn't believe him for a minute because he just used it as motivation for the team, I still felt I was in the shake-up.

My hopes were raised even higher when I was voted Wexford Hurler of the Year for the first time. Hughie Byrne from the Supporters Club contacted me with the news.

'We must have got 600 votes and your name was on all of them,' he said.

The brilliant Matty Forde got the Footballer of the Year award. It can be only a matter of time before Matty gets his first All Star – the man is phenomenal.

And so expectations rose. But experience taught me not to get too carried away and despite the local papers and fans launching a campaign on my behalf, I decided to keep my feet on the ground.

Mick Kinsella told me he felt I was a certainty but again I reminded him of my 1991 experience, when I really deserved an award but didn't get it. That contrasted with the season before, when, incredibly, I got my first award and didn't deserve it at all. But Mick told me after the season I'd had and the level I'd reached, they'd get it hard to ignore me.

Still, one piercing phone call from Damien Fitzhenry, the day before the All Stars were announced, dashed all hopes.

'We're only going up for the spin,' Fitzy said, referring to the Wexford players' hopes of walking up those famous steps. 'They didn't even give us one.'

Well, he didn't put it as politely as that. Around Wexford, people went nuts. Martin felt very aggrieved but at this stage I was well comfortable handling the rollercoaster ride that is hurling.

Sure it would have been nice to end my career with an award but others were more disappointed than me. John Conran called for a Wexford boycott of the ceremony, which I'm glad we didn't operate, because as I said earlier, I had the pleasure of sitting with Cormac McAnallen that evening.

The week after the All Stars, my itinerary for their trip to Arizona arrived. Brian Cody had ensured I was picked as a replacement. With such a fuss over the fact no Wexfordman had made the team, I knew there was a chance a few of us could make the trip and sure enough, I got the nod. It was a real bonus; we had another great trip and here I met lads like Eoin and Paul Kelly for the first time.

I had really enjoyed the past season. It's not often that trips to Rome and Arizona come out of the blue. During the Arizona trip, four or five reporters were trying to establish if I had made any decision about hanging up the camán but though I spoke away, I wasn't going to officially announce anything over there.

Only one man knew my plan and that was Liam Griffin. My Mam and Eithne had encouraged me to go back for another year but I knew I would be doing it for all the wrong reasons. There was no point going back to Wexford hurling just to keep your contacts in place, help your job prospects or get some free gear. Too many players had done that and it didn't work.

People started pointing out that I would make a grand little corner forward but as far as I was concerned, if I couldn't get my place on the half-back line, then it was all over.

On my return, I got a text message from Offaly's Brendan Murphy, who was with me on both trips: 'Well, Dunner, will I get Santa Claus to get me an Ashguard glove for my hand or what are you doing?'

I had to laugh out loud when I read it. But Brendan didn't have to go and buy that protective glove after all; I was definitely gone. I delayed the decision until we came back from our Wexford team holiday in San Francisco. By now I could have got a job with RTÉ's *No Frontiers* because there were more stamps on my passport in a month than many people have in a lifetime.

For the third year in a row, the Wexford hurlers voted to go on holidays without wives, partners or girlfriends, and while that may seem selfish, the fact is only three of the team were married. The decision was almost unanimous: 27 out of 28 opted for the solo run.

Dave Guiney from Rathnure wanted to bring his wife, Brenda, and in fairness, he was perfectly entitled to. But on our arrival at Dublin Airport, the members of the Players' Committee, Darragh Ryan, Adrian Fenlon, Damien Fitzhenry and I, received a letter from Dave. He took us to task for voting against taking partners along and pointed out that Brenda and he had given huge commitment to Wexford hurling over the years. Dave wasn't coming on the holiday.

The first thing I said to the lads was does this fellow think the rest of us have done shag all for Wexford over the years. We were disappointed with his attitude, and even more so when we heard Dave had gone public with his views.

It was that time of the year when the GAA columns are short of material and this story was as juicy as you would hope to get. It spread like wildfire all over the national media, and the local papers and radio stations went to town on it.

Beyond in Frisco, in a fit of exasperation, I told a few of the Rathnure boys it would take one of their own to stir things up. But they retorted that Dave originally came from Rosslare, which shows what they were thinking as well.

Jesus, at the back of it I could see where he was coming from. All of us gave huge commitment over the years and Dave had been around a long time. We knew our partners made all the sacrifices as well. No holidays, no social life. Christ, no-one knew better than Eithne, who watched me almost fall apart because of Wexford hurling.

Dave didn't have to go public on the issue. It was a squad decision. The year before, Ger Cushe declined to go to Lanzarote. Ger wouldn't go because his wife, Mag, wasn't invited, but you didn't see him in the newspapers. He just rowed in with the decision.

Anyway, on behalf of the team, I was asked when I returned to respond to Dave's comments and did so. We could have done without the whole controversy, though he probably still feels he was right to speak up.

Soon after, I phoned John Conran and told him I was finished. There were no dramatic statements or behind-the-scenes manoeuvres. John just said he would do the same thing if he were in my shoes.

After that I rang county secretary Mick Kinsella and he alerted the local media, who had always been fair to me over the years. When the local press got hold of the story, word wasn't long in spreading to the national media but nothing prepared me for the response the announcement received. It was absolutely overwhelming. The kind wishes and words of hundreds of people really helped me cope. It was a tough decision, a really complex one, when you have known little else for 16 years.

I still feel the GAA world must have been itching for news on the week in March 2004 when I retired, because it dominated newspapers for almost seven days. The lads in TV3 would hardly be renowned for their hurling coverage but even they sent cameras down, and RTÉ TV and radio did interviews as well. The whole affair blew up once more at the weekend when the Sunday papers came out and I got an even bigger farewell.

Overall, the coverage of my departure blew me away as did the response from the people of Wexford, who I like to think appreciated the effort I had put into wearing the jersey.

I got a lovely parcel from the Clare hurler Seánie McMahon, with one of his famous number-six shirts enclosed. Seánie had been the only intercounty player from outside Wexford to send me a card when I broke my leg in 1997. The man is a real class act.

But now there were so many goodwill cards I didn't know what to do with them, from the likes of the former Wexford and Dublin manager Michael O'Grady to the Laois hurler Niall Rigney. People and clubs presented me with gift tokens, crystal and vouchers.

Some of the more memorable functions included the one hosted by the Wexford Association in Carlow, where Tom Neville, Jim English and Ned Wheeler greeted me and led a standing ovation. The same thing happened at the Bunclody Dinner Dance and on each occasion, though naturally delighted, I wanted the ground to open and swallow me. On my first League game with Oulart after my intercounty retirement, the captain of Oylegate-Glenbrien made a presentation to me in front of the stands before the match. He gave me a lovely piece of crystal but afterwards, their chairman, Séamus Walsh, came into our dressing-room and apologised to me because he was after having a smashing time! Séamus had let the precious crystal fall. Fair dues to them, within a fortnight they had a replacement piece up to me, another lovely touch.

Perhaps the biggest compliment ever paid was a throwaway comment by a former Wexford goalkeeper, Pat Nolan. Pat was just chatting to Tomás and I one evening when he asserted that of all the Wexford players of the modern era, only one would have made the famous team of the 50s and 60s, and I was the man.

That meant an awful lot coming from him, because retirement

had left a big gap in my life, and such positive feedback helped me ease into life after Wexford hurling. Albert Randall, who used to make hurleys for us in 1996, presented me with a lamp carved out of ash, with two little hurls on its sides. It was and is a beautiful piece. Underneath, it has 'Liam Dunne, Oulart-The-Ballagh, 1994, 1995 & 1997' in honour of the three county titles we won. Below that it has the years I won the three All Stars inscribed, a lovely job. In return I handed Albert the last intercounty hurley I wielded and one of my last Wexford jerseys.

Albert has sticks from all sorts of past players, including legends like Billy Rackard and Mick Mackey, but he was reluctant to take mine because he said there was more hurling left in it. It wasn't as if I felt my legs were going to go. As I've admitted many a time, pace was never my big asset anyway. The harsh reality was that I couldn't face doing the training programme I had set out for myself a year earlier. To keep up with the Tommy Walshes of this world, that was what a guy my age would have had to do. And probably even more. Even the great DJ Carey went into training at Nowlan Park an hour earlier than everyone else to retain his sharpness.

In my own mind, I was full sure I could have retained my place on the Wexford team, but that wasn't sufficient reason to go back. Again, you must really want to go back, and not just because you will get your game and your free gear and your holidays.

My old friend Larry O also went soon after and even though I was up in the stands in the summer of 2004 to see Wexford, without my input, pull off the biggest hurling shock in a decade by running the Cody gang out of town (unfortunately, they snuck back in a while later), I knew I had made the right decision.

I stuck to my guns in the close season but kept ticking over in training, just in case something clicked and changed my mind. I suppose if Adrian Fenlon, Darragh Ryan or Damien Fitzhenry had arrived at my door, I just might have done a U-turn. Now the boys are always welcome at my door but this was one time when I was glad they didn't ring the bell.

My family had enjoyed all the fuss of 2003 and probably wanted more but I had set out to prove a point and achieved the three aims I set: Honour; Respect; Wexford Hurler of the Year. The only way was down. One bad belt or one roasting and I was back to square one all over again.

In the heel of the hunt, I felt that in some way I had restored my reputation and my name. And maybe now when people spoke of Liam Dunne, 'Dirty little fucker' might not be the first words out of their mouths. The critics might even remember I played fairly well in my last year, almost as good as I had ever done. Maybe they would say: 'Hardy little bastard but he was a good hurler.' That would be more like it.

I also got to move back home in 2003. No wonder I look back on the year with affection and real peace of mind. There is no doubt the switch had a settling effect on me. In five years we had lived in five different houses but I always knew I wanted to go back home to Kyle Cross, and when my mother moved out and into a house beside Tomás, I moved back in. We had just built a house in Kilnamanagh but when the opportunity to move home came up, I couldn't ignore it. To be frank, I always felt that if the old homestead were sold to someone else I would never be able to pass by and would regret it for the rest of my life.

Things had come together nicely. Closure at last.

Win together, lose together, play together, stay together.
Debra Mancuso

– CHAPTER EIGHTEEN –
The hurler on the ditch

Expectations were hardly ever lower in Wexford than in 2004 but typically we delivered a Leinster title out of the blue. During the League, the writing was on the wall. Players left the panel quicker than the sun deserted our summer and we got some woeful drubbings in the League. We had to face Kilkenny in the Leinster Championship on June 13 and that would be the beginning and end of the team, many felt.

When Darren Stamp decided he didn't want any more, Robbie Codd, Anthony O'Leary and Barry Goff all jumped ship as well. And with Larry O and myself out of the equation, it didn't look great for the team.

We seemed to fall lower and lower during the early part of the season. Cork destroyed us under lights at Páirc Uí Rinn at the end of February. Tipperary gave us another hiding, 4-18 to 1-13. Kilkenny hammered us as well.

John Conran came under huge pressure and all sorts of rumours and stories hit the national press, having been leaked from Wexford. Many of them were untrue but there was some substance at the back of it. The harsh reality is that some of the players were unhappy with the manager and wanted a change.

Behind the scenes, people worked frantically to keep him in the job because they were afraid of who might take over and I bet they are glad now they didn't decide to act on that impulse because 'Wexford:

Leinster Champions 2004' has a nice ring to it.

At the end of the League, the popular theory was that the team had overtrained, but I think we were just looking for excuses, and after about six weeks of being slated, the lads finally decided enough was enough. After a lock-in meeting one night, they all rowed in together.

Jim Kilty, the athletics coach and former Tipperary trainer who specialises in what is now known as SAQ – speed, agility and quickness – started to spread his gospel, and John Conran let his defence go to work on tactics for the Kilkenny match.

Paul Carley decided he had suffered a pain in his ass long enough being sub keeper to Fitzy and so made the wing-forward slot his own. The Jacob brothers picked up their form. Eoin Quigley, who had joined the panel out of nowhere after leaving a soccer career at Bohemians in Dublin, looked the part.

No-one gave us a hope in hell of beating Kilkenny in the Leinster semi-final and they were right. Why should they? In the eyes of most people, Wexford were on the way out. But they hadn't bargained for the new leaders who emerged in the team when Larry O and I left.

The Friday before the Kilkenny match, I rang five players: Adrian Fenlon, Darragh Ryan, Declan Ruth, Damien Fitzhenry and Rory McCarthy. Each one told me we would win and I felt I had no choice but to believe them. They told me the preparation had been good. There were no overblown expectations but they had a game-plan and were sticking to it.

In the past few years, Kilkenny have dominated the half-back department and players like Peter Barry, JJ Delaney and now Tommy Walsh have routinely chewed up and spit out opposing forwards for fun. This time, Wexford decided to avoid these key players as much as possible.

Fitzy played short puck-outs to a good stick man like Rory Mac and what balls arrived in the half-forward line were low into a guy who had made a crossfield run, hungrily looking for it.

On my way into Croke Park, I was swallowed up by Wexford

supporters wanting to ask about my retirement. But there was no danger of getting lost in the crowd, because only 27,000 turned up for the game. Not even our own supporters believed and that itself was rare. And yet by half-time, the Cats were only a point ahead, 0-11 to 0-10, and the onlookers in purple and gold knew we were in with a shout.

I didn't find it too hard to look on at first but it was torture as the game reached a dramatic conclusion. With time up, we were two points down and when Adrian Fenlon cut a brilliant sideline into Peter Barry's hands, I groaned with despair, thinking we had blown our chance.

Suddenly, Mick Jacob hooked him, turned around and goaled in the same breath and you just can't defend against play like that. We won the game in the last second, 2-15 to 1-16.

In the stand, I went nuts. Billy looked at me as though I had two heads but it was one of the greatest feelings I ever experienced. Charging onto the field, I jumped on any of the lads I could find and shared a few hugs with some old team-mates.

A despondent looking Brian Cody walked into the tunnel and I went over to him and said: 'Brian, you can't begrudge us this.' He looked back at me and simply replied: 'Well done, well done.'

Eddie Brennan came over and shook hands, but in the Wexford dressing-room I was pleasantly shocked to hear Declan Ruth and Darragh Ryan talking about how this win would be no use unless the team won the Leinster final. I really admired that attitude. My lot would have gone haywire, but this is a different Wexford team than in the past. We failed to build on our 1996 success but maybe this time it will be different; there are five pioneers on this present side and everyone else eats, drinks and sleeps hurling. Now is the time to bring the younger lads on, when we have inspirational players like Ruth, Fenlon, McCarthy, Ryan and Fitzhenry still involved.

We played Offaly in the Leinster final on July 4 but I dreaded that as well because I felt they were waiting in the long grass for us. We had done the hard work knocking Kilkenny out and it was nicely teed up for them to throw us out now and leave us with egg on our face.

Maybe it was the fact I had soldiered with the team for the three years before that and each time we had lost Leinster finals that I was kind of glad to be in the stands again for that match. Of course I have to admit there was a pang of sadness when the lads came out onto the field for the warm-up but that didn't last too long because Offaly hopped out onto Croke Park like toned sprinters and played like demons for the first 15 minutes.

Folding my arms and looking on as they dogged us in the opening quarter, I just sat back and prayed.

'That pitch is not made for old lads anymore,' I thought.

And as Eithne, Billy, Aoife and I looked on as a family, I knew this was the way it had to be from now on.

At half-time, I was asked by RTÉ to go down to the sideline and do an interview with Jim Carney. I offered an honest view of Wexford's display, pointing out that only for four great saves from Damien Fitzhenry we were history.

The second half was just as edgy, and it wasn't until the last few moments that we pulled away. A great goal from Paul Carley and two late points from Rory Jacob made it 2-12 to 1-11. We were through to the All-Ireland semi-final.

It was bedlam after that. I grabbed Billy. To go into the dressing-room, shake the lads' hands and share the joy after that game meant a lot to me. I got a thump on the back and a hug from the happiest man in Croke Park, John Conran.

'It's an awful pity you weren't with us,' he smiled.

'Jesus, John, I was with ye,' I said.

Only a liar would say he wouldn't have loved to be out there. Of course I would, but that wasn't the case when we got hammered in the League by the likes of Cork, Tipperary and Kilkenny. You can't have it both ways.

I mean, I wasn't sad I had retired when in the semi-final we got walloped by Cork, 1-27 to 0-12. Jesus, Cork were good but who could have seen that one coming?

Doing an interview with RTÉ at the break, I could see the lads' heads were down as they trooped off the field 11 points in arrears. Again, only for Fitzy it would have been several times worse.

I would think after that drubbing a couple of the lads are wondering if they can go on any longer and it goes back to what I said; the Leinster title win was great to get but it only papered over the cracks. We needed guys steaming through the ranks to replace the fellows who left and give the squad strength in depth, but Cork had a much stronger bench than we had and they were on fire. It was disappointing for us to lose like that. I privately thought we had a great chance of winning and felt we could take Kilkenny in the final. How wrong was I?

If some of the lads do quit, then their wishes should be respected. I had my time, made my mistakes and moved on. I did my best for the cause of Wexford but no-one is irreplaceable. Generations evolve and now we have Metal Mickey and Razor Rory Jacob and the boys leading the charge, waiting to take over from Adrian Fenlon and company as the new leaders.

That's the way it should be. Michael is getting his chance now. He hurled with a bit of mettle this year and apart from the Cork game, his brother was razor sharp in the corner.

I'm still waiting for my clubmate Keith Rossiter to really get over his injuries and become the player I know he can be. Maybe Darren Stamp will also come back next year and show us what a man he is as well.

Just as Martin Storey and Tom Dempsey once made their names in Croke Park, we had a young lad, Eoin Quigley, coming in and hitting 0-3 in a Leinster final out of the blue. Eoin didn't get going against Cork either but it was his first season and Ronan Curran was All Star material.

John O'Connor had a bad day at the office against the Rebels too. Few outside the county even knew who he was before the provincial final, but the Rathnure man is now captain of the side and will gain in confidence.

We're still waiting to get the best out of Paul Codd. He can do it if he wants to do it, when he wants to do it. But that's not good enough; we need him all the time. It's as simple as that. He is crucial to Wexford.

And if this time we learn our lessons from the success and failure of the 2004 season, which we didn't from the 1996 success, and get the production line at underage level going, we can do even better.

The harsh reality, though, is that juvenile structures in Wexford are a shambles. There are too many people with too many private agendas and not all of them about trying to get Wexford hurling back to where it should be. And if this situation persists we're in big trouble regardless of the relative successes of 2004.

Take the 2004 minors for example. We were beaten in the provincial semi-final by Dublin and it's common knowledge around the county that some of the backroom team weren't even on speaking terms. That would be funny if it weren't so tragic, and to make it worse you still have clubs trying to get the sons and nephews of cronies on the team. It has happened with all county teams over the years and until we can get shot of it and play the best players we will struggle.

I witnessed these backroom shenanigans so many times from my progression from underage to senior. Only I had the opposite experience – lads in my club were pushing for me not to be played. But it's a silly situation. Our 2004 minors had to bring in Tom Dempsey and George O'Connor to help them, and while both did a job, Dublin beat us and Kilkenny hammered them, which is worrying to say the least.

It's time for the Kilkenny dominance to be stopped. I respect them for what they've achieved, but it's time for the rest of us to stand up now. Two years ago, they lost one Leinster minor final in 10 years and had a crisis meeting. We could have one of them every week in Wexford and it still wouldn't make a difference.

Liam Griffin is finally getting somewhere, though. It was heartening to see so many people from different clubs at the recent launch of the development squads. These squads will be an enormous help because they will keep the groups together the whole time. Players should have thundered through since we won the All-Ireland title but they didn't.

I'm not saying we have a divine right to win the All-Ireland every year, and I don't set a whole lot of store by tradition. But the brutal reality is that we haven't moved forward since 96 and I would go as far as saying we have actually gone backward; the structures have weakened and some of those running our underage teams should be ashamed of themselves.

It's sad and sickening to see the direction we have gone and in case you think I'm talking sentimental shite just for the sake of it, here are the facts. Just say we don't win another All-Ireland title by the time 2008 comes around, and that is quite likely. That will mean Wexford have won the Liam MacCarthy Cup just once in 40 years. You would see a better strike rate with Emile Heskey in front of goal. If that statistic comes to pass, it's a bloody serious problem in anyone's language.

We are in deep trouble. I mean, it took us 19 years to end the Leinster final hoodoo and 28 years to end the All-Ireland drought and even though we brought success to the county, nothing has been done since to ensure the next generation get a chance to emulate us.

The last time we won a Leinster minor title was in 1985 and although we won under-21 provincial titles in 86 and 87, it was 10 years before we did the trick again in 96 and 97. That's inconsistency. And while I was lucky enough to be there on that team that ended the famine, it gives me no great pleasure to sit back and watch another start all over again.

Tradition is gone out the window in Wexford hurling. If we keep harping back to the men of the 50s and 60s, we are only fooling ourselves. We have not moved on and I'm going to put my money where my mouth is and sink my teeth into this deficiency that is killing hurling in the county.

I want to put a stop to all the talk and get the right personnel in place to bring future hurlers along. Just look at Mick Kinsella, one of the best hurling coaches in the county, who is stuck behind a desk doing administration work when he is most needed out on the field. The likes of Jim English and Ned Wheeler put Wexford hurling at a certain level and really it hasn't moved on a whole lot.

To progress, we have to change the framework of the county senior hurling Championship, which at the time of writing is farcical. A team could be out in the first round of the Championship at the end of May and might not play again for seven weeks. There are no midweek games of any value and so players, finding they are not getting enough action, have turned to rugby or soccer. Can you blame them? At least they get a chance to raise a bit of sweat.

I have noticed how bad the situation is only since I retired from the county scene. Unless a guy is actually on the first 15 for Wexford, he has no hope of getting a game. The club Championship is put on hold until the county team are well into their campaign, and even if you are a sub on that county side you cannot get a game for your club. The county board won't allow you to play. So the lads at club level are stuck with 12 or 13 senior players at training while others go off and train with the county minor, under-21, intermediate or senior teams.

I know damn well we all have to get along and I'm only too well aware how important the county scene is to everyone, but we are only shooting ourselves in the foot at grassroots level. Lads only have Mickey Mouse games to contend with during the summer, when they should be playing serious Championship affairs.

But there are more problems. Some are now starting to use the emergence of the county footballers as an excuse for the lack of progress we are making on the hurling fields. And it's just stupid to blame them. The reality is that players have always tried to get along by playing both codes. If you go back through the early years of the GAA, you will find that Wexford were always very strong at football, people forget we were the first county to do the football four-in-a-row, from 1915 to 1918. There are still certain people in the county that would have little interest in hurling and fair play to them, they are looking after their own patch.

But the finger is pointed in their direction and that's just a load of baloney. And when you have a lad like Matty Forde setting the world alight and pushing for an All Star, well I think everyone should row in behind him and support the footballers as well.

There is plenty of room for two successful intercounty codes in Wexford. We are surely not so flush with success in hurling that we have to begrudge the footballers their days in the sun.

Why not consider midweek games for both county League and Championship? And if a county under-21 player does not have a game with Wexford for two weeks let him play for his club.

I would also recommend we cut the number of senior hurling teams in the county from 16 average sides to 12 decent outfits. Give the Wexford League a makeover. The board are running this competition for the sake of it and if I was the sponsor I would be upset – they put little or no effort into it.

And now to something more uplifting. For the record, here are the best 15 Wexford players I have hurled with:

Damien Fitzhenry in goal; he was one of the greatest of them all.

The full-back line has to be Niall McDonald, Ger Cushe and John O'Connor. McDonald was one of the most underrated hurlers in the county.

My half-back line is Seán Flood, Darragh Ryan, whose father, Tossie, always argued he was better there than at full-back, and Larry O'Gorman on the other wing.

I include my brother Tomás at number eight and for once in Wexford that's not a case of jobs for the family. And partnering him is John Conran.

My half-forward line is Martin Storey, Georgie O'Connor and Adrian Fenlon. Martin I would pick at number 10. Georgie would be my centre-forward and Adrian would line out at number 12.

Tom Dempsey has to be in the corner. Billy Byrne is a shoo-in at full forward. And for his sheer goalscoring opportunism, I put Rory

McCarthy in the other corner.

The likes of David 'Doc' O'Connor, Colm Kehoe and Larry Murphy will be justifiably disappointed, but these are the guys I would like beside me if I were in the trenches tomorrow.

As for the future, I feel now is the time that Griffin must call most of his 1996 troops together to decide what is the best way forward for Wexford. That is what happened in Kilkenny; they called anyone who won an All-Ireland with the county back to help out at underage level. And if you can't beat them, join them. We are a proud county but in this instance there is no shame in learning from Kilkenny.

Georgie and Tom were involved with the county minors in 2004. Storey is heavily involved with Oulart-The-Ballagh. But you also need the likes of Billy Byrne and Ger Cushe coming back into the scene some time soon.

This is the best way forward. Learn from Kilkenny. We were all great men when we won the All-Ireland but you have your time as a player and if you can put something back into it as a coach it's all the better. As a group we must try to come up with different ideas on how to progress, but hurling is a simple game and the fault is that we are inclined to make it complicated.

Maybe we are also suffering from the changes in Irish society, like the drinking culture and the counterattractions of other social activities that leave people with less time for sport and fitness.

Initially, I was opposed to the 'back door' but how wrong I was. We really need it now for the game to survive. You have to change with the times and Croke Park officials have to do the same. And if we are to save the game, it's time for an open draw.

If you came from rural Ireland in the past, you played either hurling or Gaelic football. Now there's soccer, rugby, basketball, squash, golf, cars, music, television, women, men, whatever turns you on, and the reality is that what happened 15 years ago will not do.

Jesus, the GAA won't even entertain a debate on Rule 42 or the potential opening of Croke Park to either soccer or rugby. They are almost €100 million in debt and still won't even discuss the matter. It's no wonder tickets cost €35 for a replay like the Clare and Kilkenny game in Thurles in the summer of 2004.

I think a debate will happen sooner or later but the fact they didn't even table a discussion of the affair was the biggest PR disaster in the history of the Association. And believe me, I'm an expert in PR disasters.

There was no great wringing of hands when we played the Railway Cup final on a rugby pitch in Rome, and yet they won't entertain the prospect of gaining a few million euro from the rent of the ground to the Government, FAI or IRFU.

As for the game in general, well I look at the likes of Laois and just don't know what can be done to save them. I don't know what's going to happen to them. During all our battles, we rarely used to beat them by more than three or four points and now they're hurling at a tempo slower than you would see in many a third-tier county. Their manager, Paudie Butler, knows his hurling and is doing all he can, but I just think they need to focus on the age groups from eight to 16, try and get a few good minors coming through at the one time and take it from there.

Just look at what happened their footballers when they won a couple of minor All-Irelands in the late 90s. It took them a while to come through but they are getting there.

It was the same with the Westmeath football team. All of a sudden the team wins a Leinster title in 2004 after threatening for the past four years.

The Laois and Wexford hurlers need to start winning minor titles, bring them to under-21 straightaway and then see how they do at the top. But they are not getting much support because the ruling classes in the GAA are ignoring hurling. You can even see it with small things like TV coverage; you have football games on TV most of the time. Yet there was huge scope with this year's hurling qualifier draw to televise more games and they failed to do so.

The Sunday Game is dominated by football and even if there is more unpredictability in that code, they are not giving hurling a sufficient profile at all; I would say the show is 70 percent football.

I suppose the GAA can do a lot more with the footballers, who at least go off to Australia and play in a high-profile international series, while the hurlers are stuck with a domestic Championship that only three or four teams can really win at present.

County boards who choose not to promote the game and focus on Gaelic football instead, and there are many, should also be called to heel. Maybe the GAA could decrease grant allocation and other funding until boards begin serious development programmes.

And county boards who forbid hurlers to play both codes should be penalised, because that is a personal decision and no player should be deprived of the chance to wear a county jersey.

Seeing Laois play hurling like Longford is not good for anyone. We need them motoring through trying to carve out a breakthrough in the Leinster Championship, but they simply won't get there playing at walking speed.

The same applies to Wexford. Just because we won a provincial title this year doesn't mean we can take the foot off the pedal. We have only realised in the past few years how bad we were when Kilkenny hammered us by playing at 100 miles an hour. After those defeats we at least went into the qualifiers knowing we had to up the pace to get anywhere.

With the safety net taken away from us and a do-or-die qualifier ahead, the mantra was always speed, speed and more speed. Speed is why Kilkenny are that bit ahead all the time. They consistently use it – just look at how they demolished Galway in the 2004 Championship.

But other counties have failed to get to that level and I suppose I shouldn't single out Laois because others are more culpable and, for example, I just don't know for the life of me what goes on in Galway either. Take a look at the hurlers they've had over the years and ask how in the name of God they've won so little. Even the team of 1987 and 1988 should have won more than the two All-Irelands they managed. They won the 2004 National League and instead of growing in confidence went on to get murdered by Kilkenny in the Qualifiers with players like Eugene Cloonan, Damien Hayes, Alan Kerins and Kevin Broderick.

Of course, they should have taken their move into the Leinster Championship. It would have brightened up our competition and at the same time given them a much better chance in the All-Ireland series.

There is so much to do and so little time but I intend to do more than just bellyache about it. Now that I've stopped playing, I want to earn my spurs as a coach and put something back in.

It's not just hurling that's in crisis. The Association has many problems waiting to explode. When you see the Circuit Court and High Court cropping up in the GAA pages of our newspapers, you know there's something seriously wrong.

Take the Gerry Quinn and Henry Shefflin incident in July 2004. I was no angel over the years, but I felt that Gerry had to go for that offence and yet he wasn't even booked. Pat Horan, the referee, didn't see the incident so nothing happened.

The same Pat is an amazing character. He didn't see the incident between Brian O'Meara and me in 2001 and yet he sent the two of us off.

When I see the 'fouls' I got red cards for and compare them with incidents that have gone unpunished since, my transgressions look petty. Look again at the video of the 2004 game between Tipp and Cork. There was a brawl on the sideline and hurls driven into ribs and Pat Horan was there again, and again nothing happened. The inconsistency is crazy and that is leading us to court cases.

When Brian O'Meara and I were banned a few years back we could have produced a watertight defence by showing videotapes of our little bout of handbags and the following day's mayhem between

Kilkenny and Galway and comparing the two, but of course that didn't happen.

This is going to be a serious obstacle for the GAA. If players are going to miss big games, they will see an opportunity to go to court. And in Quinn's case, if he is 'done' by video evidence, then he is entitled to go to court to fight the action. After all, he wasn't even booked in the match.

The whole area is a minefield. If a guy who isn't booked or sent off gets caught on video evidence and misses a big game, the Four Goldmines is going to be his next port of call.

I picked my all-time great Wexford hurling team and would like to do the same for those I played against over my 16 years. I think picking a Team of the Millennium or a Team of the Century is a waste of time. How can you possibly make worthwhile judgements over that length of time? Instead, I'm going for men I played against.

Offaly's Jim Troy was the best keeper I ever faced.

Willie O'Connor broke my heart several times at corner-back; Brian Lohan was the best full-back in that era; and Martin Hanamy was just as good in the other corner.

Brian Whelahan is a shoo-in on the half-back line; Seánie McMahon was the greatest centre-back in my time; and Niall Rigney from Laois takes the other half-back role.

My midfield pairing is Teddy McCarthy and Ciarán Carey. Johnny Dooley, John Power and Joe Cooney form my star-studded half-forward line.

I opt for Henry Shefflin at corner-forward; Declan Ryan is an automatic choice at full-forward; and DJ has to go in at number 15.

That's a team I would love to manage and would love to pit them against anyone. There is not a position I would change.

I wish hurling had as many genuine superstars on the way through the ranks but I suspect that's not the case. And there are many other problems facing the GAA apart from the decline of hurling.

Apart from on-the-field problems, they also have a problem with the field of dreams. They need to rip up that Croke Park pitch as quickly as possible. After sinking €2.5 million into it, they produce the worst playing surface you will ever see. It's an abomination. You can't stand up on it. It's terrible watching lads slipping and sliding chasing after the ball and when you have guys trying to twist and turn on such a surface there are going to be huge problems with knees and ankles. What genius thought artificial grass was going to work?

They tried for 30 years to promote an artificial hurley and had to go back to ash. The sooner the Croke Park brass go back to grass, or get put out to grass, the better. Thurles is the best pitch in Ireland by far and they should try to replicate that. Players deserve the best and a good pitch is the least they could ask for. Their welfare should be the number-one item on the agenda.

As for pay for play, I don't expect players will go professional, but there are already a number who are doing well out of their image and reputation and getting by without having to do full-time day jobs. Fair play to them. I think company endorsements and private deals are the way forward. For the €1,500 involved, the Paddy Power deal with Paul Codd unsettled the Wexford team in 2003, but if the business is conducted properly, then that's fine.

If I was starting out again, I would go straight to DJ Carey and chat with him on this issue. He is the one player who has used his image to the maximum. When a guy has nine All Stars in the bag he would be foolish not to.

I can see DJ going into that end of looking after players when he retires. He would be an ideal agent for players, someone they could trust, a man who has done it all.

Tom Dempsey would be my choice in Wexford. He has the intelligence, diplomacy, personality and contacts to broker deals to look after players. It's already happening. Hurlers and footballers pull up with their names on cars, and while not all of them want to turn professional, they want to get money out of it. The perks are few and far between for players; even the hurlers were stopped going to the US to play a year or two back.

The rugby player Gordon Darcy got a few quid for endorsing Wexford Creamery this year. Some of us have worn their jersey for 14 years but if we individually endorsed their products there would be a big fuss over it and we probably would be discouraged for fear of upsetting the applecart.

In this context, the GPA is a disaster. Certain players have done well out of it. The top five, the likes of DJ, Henry Shefflin, Jason Sherlock, Peter Canavan and Kieran McGeeney.

Wexford played their third All-Ireland semi-final in four years this season and the GPA has not even organised a boot deal for any of our players. When we joined the association we were supposed to get a fleece top and a mobile phone from the Carphone Warehouse. Rod and Dave Guiney went up to collect them and the warehouse was closed.

I am a member of the GPA but think it is fading big time. It didn't help that the GAA had their own players' union, headed by Jarlath Burns, two years ago. You need one voice, an official one, but the GAA won't merge with the GPA. They wouldn't like the players dictating on any policy matters.

The most annoying thing for players is that it's common knowledge that big-name managers and even managers at local level are getting well paid under the counter for their efforts.

Lots of people can manage a club team and get a good few quid for it. In fact, the only way you won't get a few bob is if you train your local team, because insiders generally get nothing.

But some of the amounts big-name managers receive are just crazy. If there are thousands of euro going to club managers, you can imagine what the high-profile county managers are pulling in. That's something the GAA has shied away from.

Another is of course the above-mentioned Rule 42. I would totally open up Croke Park. Maybe it would be hard to listen to *God*

Save the Queen there, but surely you could come to some arrangement. Why would you deprive the likes of Brian O'Driscoll and Gordon Darcy the chance to play in the finest stadium in the land?

As with everything in the GAA, we will be a long time waiting for an answer.

Yes, there were times, I'm sure you knew
When I bit off more than I could chew;
But through it all, when there was doubt,
I ate it up and spit it out.
I faced it all and I stood tall;
And did it my way.
Frank Sinatra

– CHAPTER NINETEEN –
Passing the camán

It still feels strange to take my wife and children to Croke Park and watch Wexford play. Part of me is still on that team bus listening to Tom Dempsey and Larry O having the craic, or putting the headphones on and letting the music take my mind away.

Those tapes Griffin gave us, *Search for a Hero* and *Simply the Best*, did the job. The lyrics may have been simple and straightforward but they were honest and helped us focus.

These days I listen to *Sunday Sport* on Radio One on the way to Dublin and keep an eye in the mirror to check that the youngsters are okay in the back seat. And now I have Billy blowing those bloody hooters in my ear. Mind you, I took it off him and blew it myself when we won the Leinster final this year. He's the one now. Only a child, but he can hit the ball just as good off his left as he can off the right and for a child seven years of age, well let's just say the signs are good.

I started bringing him into the Wexford dressing-room in 2001 when I felt he was old enough to realise what was going on around him, and somehow we always managed to get to him after games. He would hop out over the wire and walk into the dressing-room to share some minerals and biscuits with the lads.

At the beginning, he would shy behind me and you couldn't get a word out of him. When I was suspended for the Clare game, I brought him into the dressing-room before the game and that was a major mistake; he was afraid of his life at the noise, and I said I would never do it again. But he persisted and progressed to sitting on Declan Ruth's knee while I was drug-tested after the Offaly game in 2003. Now, you can't stop him.

I was sitting in the players' lounge hours after we won the Leinster final and, realising I hadn't seen him in a while, went searching. I found Rory McCarthy and himself sitting back on a couch, chatting away like old buddies.

'He's telling me some stories about you,' Rory Mac laughed.

It was grand for Billy to see me playing at Croke Park for the couple of years although he probably saw the worst times. He loves watching hurling videos too. When we moved into our new house we never brought them down from the attic because Eithne was sick to the teeth of watching them. She was right – there were a few I wouldn't want to see as well. But Billy loves them all.

He's hurling with the six-to-10-year-olds at the moment and is handy enough but if I let him go up through the ranks too quick, he could get a bad belt and be finished with the game.

As for his club loyalties, there was a bit of confusion in the early days, through no fault of his own. If Eithne and I had been away for a few days, he could come home from the Sinnott house with a Buffers Alley jersey, a terrible-looking geansaí altogether. That was soon nipped in the bud, I can promise you.

There are times he just leaves me in stitches. Like last Christmas, when the Sinnotts brought him the present he wanted, a set of goalposts, and we started taking shots on one another. He was pretending to be Rory Jacob, Roy Keane and Setanta Ó hAilpín because he got a sliotar, a football and an Aussie Rules ball as well.

I took a fairly hard shot and he never even saw the ball go by him, but, quick as a flash, he turned around and roared: 'Jesus Christ, Daddy!

I'm only a kid!' He went to fetch the ball but I was gone into the house in howls of laughter.

Aoife has the same effect on us. She's five now and it's gas watching her grow up. She adapted a lot quicker to being an Oulart girl than Billy did to being an Oulart boy and is starting to get stuck in on the camogie end of things now, just like her mother.

I will never forget the day Aoife hugged me after I was sent off in the 2001 All-Ireland semi-final. She is a sweet child and I don't think she can yet believe her Dad is coming in from work and not flying straight back out the door with a gear-bag every night of the week.

She will soon have me around the house most of the time. In the next year or two, I will hang up my boots for Oulart. For some reason, I feel the 2006 season will be the final chapter in Liam Dunne's hurling career.

I look at Martin Storey, who at 40 is still as fit as a fiddle and loves the game. I see him training like a demon for Oulart and still making the senior team. I don't think I'll still be playing for the club when I'm that age and I'm near enough to it now. Maybe it will be hard for me to retire when the day comes; maybe I will want to hang on a bit more. But the feeling right now is just one more year.

As I write this, I'm still adjusting to intercounty retirement. I've had a few offers to go coaching here and there but I'm quite content to help look after the Oulart juniors and seniors. In the future, I would love to help out with the underage structure in Wexford and maybe take charge of the minor team.

Will I ever manage the Wexford senior team? To be honest, I don't know. It's the road I want to go down but you have to take these things step by step.

It's the end of 2004 now. Another year has flown by and instead of getting ready for another gruelling pre-season training campaign, I'm quite happy to look out the window at Billy and Aoife playing together.

Breda Jacob was my first teacher and she was Billy's as well. It's funny how things go. Now Billy wants to get Rory Jacob's name and number on the back of my old jersey. He's already looking for new heroes.

The days when I went to matches in Dublin with my Mam and Dad don't seem that long ago but my time has come and gone. While Oulart and Wexford will always be a huge part of my life, I have a new home and a family to look after.

It's just a pity the old man never got to see the house. It's a fine job: a dormer bungalow that Eithne and I put our own stamp on.

Shortly after Christmas 2003, we found out he was dying of leukaemia and for a while my mind was far away from hurling. My father was in hospital in Southampton all during the summer of 2004 and received bone-marrow treatment. But we knew it would make no difference so the brothers and sisters went over to see him.

It took a while for me to go over and when I did, it wasn't exactly a moment I was looking forward to. Dad asked about retirement and then asked about the house at Kyle Cross, enquiring what it was like and looking for a description. I couldn't really describe it to him; I just said it was a nice dormer bungalow and it was different. I felt like joking: 'Yeah, and I finished it, not like the way you left it.' A few years back, I had told him of my intention to buy and renovate it and had made the same crack about actually finishing the job, so this time I just left it alone.

He asked me about the 2004 Wexford team but though the boys had reached the Leinster final at this stage, my father was dying and I knew that once I walked out the door I would never see him again, so hurling was way down my agenda.

My mind was all over the place, angry with him for going away and yet at the end of the day knowing he was my father. I know Dad had done his own thing and that was his decision and so I tried just to chat away. We spoke of different things but inevitably it returned to hurling again and I told him I intended going into the hurley-making business. He recalled how he used to make and splice them for me when I was a small child.

When I got up to go, I shook hands with him.

'I was always a proud man at Croke Park,' I told him,

And he just looked at me and replied: 'Yeah, the spliced hurls got to Croke Park.'

'They'll be there again,' I said and left the hospital.

And that was it. I came back home glad I had seen him.

He passed away in England on July 23 2004 at 71 years of age but, thank God, his body came back to Oulart, after such a long time away. When news of his death came, we didn't know if he was staying in England or coming home to be buried. The good thing was that my eldest brother, Kieran, had a foot in both camps – he had stayed in contact with Dad through the years – and he made sure things were right from Mam's point of view before looking after the details.

The crowds that turned out on Friday and Saturday were overwhelming. And our parish priest, Fr Jordan, handled the funeral, and the whole weekend, with great sensitivity, knowing it was a complex situation.

When Dad left home we found it hard to deal with and at the same time we all got on with our own lives. But Mam was left there to cope and I think she coped brilliantly. And it had been difficult all through the years when people were afraid to mention my father in case they would overstep the mark.

Years ago, Dad had remarked the number of Buffers Alley people that turned up to my grandmother's funeral and it was funny that they also came in their droves to Dad's funeral. We and the Buffers Alley crowd had half-killed each other over the years and it usually took a wedding or a funeral to get us together. But when all is said and done they are decent people. Tony Doran probably got the biggest reception from us; I think I shook his hand three or four times.

With his coming home, Dad was at peace and so were we. The

locals had found it difficult over the years but the fact of bringing him back and having so many turn up at his funeral, it was a bit of honour and respect restored to him in the end.

There was a huge crowd; he had 28 grandchildren alone; and I could even smile at the sight of a Buffers Alley hurl, something that under different circumstances would get my dander up big-time, being brought up to the altar as one of the symbols of his life.

All the older guys who had started the Oulart club wore jerseys over their shoulders as a mark of respect, and for the removal, the current players formed a guard of honour. My brothers played their tin whistles at the altar; Dad loved traditional Irish music and the boys played their hearts out.

We got great comfort, my mother and sisters especially, that he came home. It was a chapter that was finally closed. Dad would have been shocked and humbled at the numbers who turned up in his memory. And under the circumstances, it was a weekend that went very well.

A couple of days after the funeral, I looked out the back garden and saw Billy getting ready for the All-Ireland semi-final with Cork. He was buzzing around with his mop of blond hair shouting 'Razor Rory hits the ball to the back of the net!' and dreaming a million different dreams, all of them played out at Croke Park.

Maybe Billy will wear the Purple and Gold some day. If he doesn't, other young lads will. They can draw confidence and inspiration from the memory of the days the county beat Kilkenny and Offaly to win the 2004 Leinster final, just as new heroes emerged when our 1996 team did the job.

Life passes by all too easily. It's sometimes hard to believe I'm finished my intercounty career after 16 frustrating and unpredictable but downright brilliant years.

But the wheel keeps turning for Wexford hurling. I hope I gave it a right good spin.

I like to think I did.

LIAM DUNNE'S ROLL OF HONOUR

Played 126 competitive games for Wexford.

1 All-Ireland SHC 1996

2 Leinster SHC 1996 and 1997

3 All Stars, 1990, 1993 and 1996

2 Railway Cups, 1993 and 2003

6 Walsh Cups

2 Leinster Under 21 HC medals 1986 and 1987

Wexford Sportstar of the Year 1997

Wexford Hurler of the Year 2003

The *Star* newspaper/Waterford Crystal Hurler of the Year 1997

Shinty Under 21 International 1986 and 1987 and senior 1993

4 Wexford SHC medals

(captained Oulart-the-Ballagh 2004 team to success).

TANGLED UP IN YOU

ROGUE SERIES - BOOK ONE

LARA WARD COSIO

ROGUE PUBLICATIONS

This is a work of fiction. Names, characters, businesses, places, events and incidents are either the products of the author's imagination or used in a fictitious manner.

Editor: Serena Clarke

Also by Lara Ward Cosio
Tangled Up In You (Rogue Series Book 1)
Playing At Love (Rogue Series Book 2)
Hitting That Sweet Spot (Rogue Series Book 3)
Finding Rhythm (Rogue Series Book 4)
Looking For Trouble (Rogue Series Book 5)
Felicity Found (Rogue Series Book 6)
Rogue Christmas Story (Rogue Series Book 7)
Problematic Love (Rogue Series Book 8)
Rock Star on the Verge (Rogue Series Book 9)

Full On Rogue: The Complete Books #1-4
Rogue Extra: The Complete Books #5-8

Hula Girl: A Standalone Romance

For my girls, Paloma and Emma.

FOREWORD

rogue

    pronunciation: / rōg /

    noun

    1. A dishonest or unprincipled man

    1.2 A person whose behavior one disapproves of but one who is nonetheless likable or attractive

    (often used as a playful term of reproof)

PART I

1

SOPHIE

2002

It was just a silly drinking game. She was only expected to make up an answer—to *lie*. So why did she immediately think of offering up her most cherished, intimate, *real*, memory?

The beer buzz probably had a lot to do with it.

Sitting with a group of friends in a dive bar not far from the University of Southern California campus, she surveyed the empty bottles of beer littering the small round table. The place was grungy and just lax enough that they weren't carded for drinks.

"What's it going to be then, Sophie?" Tobin asked and grabbed her arm, shaking her with mock eagerness.

She laughed as he obviously intended, but also noticed that when he released his grip, he let his fingers trail gently over the fine blonde hair of her forearm. He was in her *Foundations of Western Art* class and had been angling to get her alone rather than in a group outing like this since the semester started. She'd successfully put him off but his patience and persistence was beginning to wear her down. With sandy hair and pale blue eyes, he was cute, even if he did stare at her a little too intensely.

It was her turn in the game called "You Wouldn't Believe . . ." in which they each had to divulge either a hard-to-believe truth or make

3

something up and successfully defend the lie before declaring which it was.

"Okay, okay," she said and took a deep breath. "You wouldn't believe that . . . Gavin McManus asked me to marry him when I was sixteen years old."

The four of them—Tobin, Rachel, Zach, and Gracelynn—watched her in silence and then as if orchestrated, they all burst out laughing at precisely the same second.

"Yeah, right!" Rachel said, pulling her long straight hair over one shoulder.

"How on earth do you think you can pull that one off?" Zach asked.

"You *do* know that you're supposed to choose something at least halfway believable, right?" Gracelyn said, leaning over the table and patting her on the hand.

"It's true, though!" she said, smiling at the memory. She had to remind herself that, to them, her declaration couldn't be remotely true. Not when given the fact that Gavin McManus was the singer for the up and coming Irish rock band Rogue and she was an American college sophomore. *He* supposedly proposed to her? Two years ago, when she was sixteen? Nothing about that computed.

"Totally," Rachel said. "And then there was the time that Justin Timberlake asked me to be his backup singer."

They all laughed and the conversation escalated into how Justin supposedly serenaded Rachel with "Rock Your Body" and how he had rocked it so well that she was now expecting his baby.

Sophie watched the others distractedly as the vivid memory of the first time she ever saw Gavin came to the forefront of her mind. It was in the halls of her new school in Ireland. She had been full of dread over being the new girl.

Make that the *foreign* new girl.

Moving from Silicon Valley in northern California to Dublin hadn't exactly been a well-thought-out plan. She'd mentioned the idea of doing so out of a fit of frustration and desperation after a particularly bad day at school. For reasons she could never figure out, her former tight circle of friends had turned against her and become relentless mean girls. Though she hadn't confessed her motives for wanting to escape to another country, her parents, the workaholic founders of their own tech company, had warmed to the idea right away. They declared it a wonderful learning opportunity and quickly arranged for her to stay with a trusted employee who was helping to set up their company's manufacturing expansion in the business-friendly country. They shipped her off with plans to visit when it aligned with progress checks on their business venture.

The family hosting her at their home on the Southside of Dublin was warm and welcoming. But once the initial excitement of exploring the tourist areas of the city wore off, she began to panic at the idea of what she had done. At sixteen, she was suddenly in a new country all on her own.

On her first day at school, a student volunteer gave her a brief tour of the essentials and then she was left to fight the nerves that formed a knot in her stomach. What had she been thinking? Running away from home? All because of some bullies she didn't want to face? And now she was in a place where she knew *no one*. What she wouldn't give for one of those mean girls to call out to her in their sickening taunt. Because at least she wouldn't feel so completely alone.

Knowing she had no choice in the matter now, she started toward her first class. But the hallway was blocked by a large, boisterous, group of kids. There was a ring-leader of the bunch commanding all the attention. The crowd circled around him, hanging on every word as he gestured wildly.

Inching her way closer, she watched the boy. His hair was chestnut brown, untamed and past his collar. He wore his school uniform with obvious reluctance. His gray and blue striped tie was loose around his neck, the top button of his white shirt undone, and his gray trousers were slung low on his hips. His blue eyes were incredibly expressive and he had a square jaw set off by a sensual mouth with lips that had an alluring "just kissed" redness to them. She'd never known a boy to possess such raw magnetism. As if pulled by some invisible gravitational force, she took another step closer.

"How did you know the fella wasn't about to take his car out?" asked one of the onlookers.

"Well, I didn't, did I?"

"You're mental!"

"The added risk is what makes the joyride all that much better, anyway," the ring-leader said with a grin. The crowd laughed appreciatively. "So, we went out for about an hour or so, me and Seamus did. As we're turning the corner to get the car back, I could just make out this figure under the streetlamp looking up and down the street wondering where in bleedin' hell his car went. I take one look at Seamus and he gets me right away, pulling the most incredible move. He threw it straight into reverse and back we went right around the corner and out of sight."

"Didn't the sorry bastard see you then, Gavin?"

So, this charismatic boy had a name. *Gavin*. Being so far away from home just got a whole lot more interesting.

Gavin hesitated, building the anticipation. "He didn't. What's better, though, is he goes back inside long enough for us to park the thing back where we found it so, in the end, he was none the wiser. It was magic, I tell you. Seamus is a wizard at driving, don't you know?"

The group erupted into laughter and cheers and it soon became clear that the boy Gavin called Seamus had been among them but reluctant to take center stage. As Sophie was examining the way Seamus' cheeks turned crimson under the attention of congratulatory slaps on the back and handshakes, she sensed she was being watched in return.

Looking back at Gavin, she saw he had his eyes fixed on her and a rush of heat filled her body. She expected him to appraise her from head to toe as most boys did, but instead, he held eye contact with her. She couldn't have broken the connection if she tried. They stayed locked into each other's spell, even when a teacher poked his head out from a classroom and tried to rally everyone to begin the school day. It must have lasted mere seconds but it felt like a lifetime as sound muffled and the movements of others blurred and receded.

Finally, another boy, taller and with jet-black hair and deep blue eyes, threw his arm around Gavin's neck and pulled him from the others.

She saw Gavin mouth something with a nod of his head in her direction. But she was so overwhelmed by the intensity of their silent connection that she didn't sort out exactly what he had said until she was seated in class, trying and failing to focus on the teacher at the whiteboard.

Gorgeous. That was what Gavin had told his friend as he motioned to her.

And with that realization, she had been a goner.

2

GAVIN

"Oh, get out of there. Get out of there! We're gonna die!"

"Steady on, Marty. We've got them where we want them."

Gavin barely registered his bandmates' videogame-inspired banter—not just because he was distracted, but because the dynamic playing out between bassist Martin and drummer Shay was typical. Shay was the solid force within their rhythm section, the one to impose some discipline onto Martin. Whereas Martin was stocky, baby-faced, and aimless, Shay was all compact muscles, prominent Irish cheekbones, and laser-focused. Gavin had no doubt that Shay would be the one to lead the two of them to victory in their *Call of Duty* gaming battle.

The band was on their bus heading to Los Angeles after sold-out shows in San Francisco and San Jose. This was their first time in America and it had been a wild ride as first the college scene, then alternative radio, latched onto them. They were touring in support of their debut album, *It Could Be Now*, thrilled to have two singles charting in the top ten, and having sold just over three million albums worldwide.

At eighteen, Gavin was the rock star he had always known he'd become. It had just happened more quickly than even he believed it would. It seemed that both his innate charm and his propensity for oversharing a wounded, romantic core not only made him the exact right person to be the frontman of a rock band like Rogue but helped propel them to the kind of success he had always wanted.

So why was he feeling such a strong sense of desolation? He looked out the window, surveying the barren view off the freeway, all beige and lifeless in temperatures so hot and foreign to him that the heat of the sunbaked glass nearly singed his fingertips.

"What's rattling around in that head of yours?"

He reluctantly pulled his eyes away from the window to look at Conor, his best friend and the guitarist for the band. Conor was lounging on the sole sofa in the bus, his long legs stretched out and crossed at the ankles with his head resting in the crook of his folded arm as he read a book. If Gavin showed the slightest interest in the book with the cartoonish tiger on the cover that didn't jibe with the title—*Life of Pi*—Conor could recite an on-the-spot essay on its literary merits. Besides being the best-looking guy in the band, Conor was also the smartest.

"What's that?" Gavin asked, still feeling out of sorts.

Conor didn't look up from his book. "What's keeping you from finalizing that setlist?"

He couldn't help but smile. His friend knew him well. So well, it seemed that he didn't even have to study him very hard to know something was occupying his mind. It must have been the silence of his inaction. A sheet of paper was on the table before him, a pen clutched in his fist, but he hadn't made any progress.

"Just feeling a little fuzzy," he said and rubbed his face. The truth was that he had been lost in thoughts of Sophie Kavanaugh.

In fact, he'd been thinking of her nonstop since their most recent shows in northern California. Fantasies that Sophie might be in the audience of one of those shows had swirled in his head, tripping him up during a couple songs before he regained his concentration. Knowing Sophie had grown up in nearby Menlo Park in Silicon Valley and returned there after her year of studies in Dublin made him hope she would turn up for the band's shows.

But she hadn't.

And he'd partied especially hard after each show to numb the disappointment he felt.

Apparently, Conor had deciphered as much because he said, "I hear having a beer helps sort that out. You know, hair of the dog that bit you and all."

"Wanker," Gavin muttered.

Conor was notorious for never overindulging in alcohol. Not only could he hold his liquor, but he never got hungover. Hell, no matter how late they were out partying, Conor always got up early the next day to work out. He possessed a rare and, honestly, annoying, kind of discipline.

Dropping his book low enough to make eye contact, Conor said, "*You* could have reached out to *her*, you know?"

Gavin grimaced. Once again, Conor could read him. Though he was a confessional person by nature, Gavin hadn't spoken to Conor about Sophie in ages. Not since she had left Dublin and his love for her had withered before being replaced by an inexplicable bitterness.

She had been his everything for an entire school year, their connection far too intense for sixteen-year-olds. And especially far too intense given they were never meant to last, not with it clear from the start that she'd only be there for a limited time. But their attraction couldn't be denied. They were a rare match. She filled a void in his life, and he liked to believe that he did the same for her.

In the end, though, she walked away, despite his desperate entreaties for her to stay. And there'd been no stopping the hurt and sadness he felt. Before long, that pain morphed into an all-too-familiar sense of abandonment. Resentment soon followed. Resentment, mostly, for how her leaving made him feel he wasn't worthy of sticking around for all over again.

So, he'd gone on with his life, dismissing her from his heart.

But then the band actually gained some traction and made it to America. And not just any part of the States, but the same area where Sophie lived. He'd stupidly allowed himself to think she might show up, that he might open his heart to her again if she did.

All he got instead was disappointment and a reawakening of the sting and ache of how she'd walked away.

Still, as the bus rocked smoothly down the open road, he couldn't keep from thinking of her. Especially, of that moment when he saw her for the first time.

Having an American show up at school had been an anomaly. That this American was also so beautiful had sent a buzz through the building. Gavin hadn't yet been clued in, however, as he was too busy regaling a group of friends with the story of how he and Shay had nicked a car for a joyride. As a natural leader, other kids looked to him for both direction and, as in this case, entertainment. He both courted and thrived under that kind of attention.

When he first saw Sophie, she was watching Shay burn up in embarrassment over the accolades from the crowd for his driving ability. Tall, blonde, and strikingly pretty, she literally stood apart from everyone else. But what captivated him more than her beauty was the soulfulness in her hazel eyes. They held a compelling mixture of compassion and intelligence that he couldn't turn away from. Then she leveled those eyes on his and they shared a moment of silent connection so intense he was left dumbstruck.

It was only when Conor pulled him onward toward class that he regained his senses. He said the first thing that came to mind, declaring the new girl "gorgeous." But even as he said the word, he somehow knew it was insufficient for her. He instinctively knew there was much more to her than her gorgeous outward appearance.

"Let's do 'So Real.'"

He shook off his reverie and found Conor had abandoned his book and was sitting opposite him at the small table.

Thankfully, Conor had dropped his question about Gavin being the one to reach out to Sophie. Focusing on music instead was just what he needed, not reminiscing about a girl he'd never see again.

Having just one album of their own songs to play, they had to flesh out their sets with covers and had been working lately on a couple songs from Jeff Buckley's album *Grace*. Conor had long been itching to put "So Real" on the setlist since it would give him the chance to toy with feedback on the guitar.

"What about 'Lover, You Should've Come Over'?" Gavin suggested and sang the line about being too young to keep love from going wrong. It was one of those hurts-so-good lines that he wished he had written for himself. It was so fitting to his experience, after all.

"Nah, let's not indulge your moodiness with that one," Conor said.

Gavin laughed, not taking offense. Conor, like everyone else who knew him, accepted his sudden swings in temperament as being the prerogative of an artist.

"Here's what we'll do," Gavin said, and wrote the song title "Last Goodbye" because he knew it would make the girls in the audience scream when he sang one particular line that sounded like a flirty invitation.

Conor nodded.

"What did you decide?" Shay asked, not taking his eyes off the wall-mounted monitor. He and Martin were still deep into their game.

When Gavin told him the name of the song, Martin sang the line Gavin had had in mind when he chose it, belting out an ear-splitting falsetto: "Kiss me, please kiss me."

"You're rubbish, Marty. Never do that again," Gavin said with a laugh.

Martin and the others joined in the laughter. Soon he and Shay were back to their game and Conor had returned to his book.

Gavin looked down at the setlist but all he saw was a fleeting image of Sophie. It was her smiling at him before turning away, her long blonde hair swinging over her shoulder. He had played that memory in his mind over and over in the last few years. It was the promise of her smile before he lost sight of it that captivated him. There was warmth, sweetness, and a teasing flirt in that small gesture. It was everything Sophie. But he knew there was no point in holding on to that vision.

He had moved on in pursuit of this rock star dream.

And she obviously had moved on with her life, too.

3

SOPHIE

"It's okay," Tobin said as the others continued in their fanciful stories. "I believe you, Sophie."

She was slow to smile as she came out of her own thoughts, but she did recognize that Tobin's wink belied his vote of confidence.

He emptied his Heineken bottle into her glass, and she knew his "generosity" was motivated by a desire to increase her beer buzz. "Tell me more about this episode where you almost became a child bride."

Despite the sarcasm—or maybe because of it—she was beginning to like him more. "I lived in Dublin for a year," she said, forcing the words out at first. The urge to share this had probably been a bad one. Even if he did believe her, there was no way he could understand what her time with Gavin really meant. But she forged ahead, recounting to him in broad strokes what had amounted to the best time of her life. "My parents were expanding their business there and I wanted a change, so they agreed to let me go. It turned out to be an amazing experience. I hated to leave. Gavin asked me to marry him when we were in the car on the way to the airport. He didn't want me to go. It was sweet and it was sort of desperate." She looked down at the amber liquid in her glass. "But I think he meant it."

Tobin watched her for a moment before breaking out into a grin. "You are so good at this game," he said. "Really, your dedication is amazing."

Sophie nodded. "Got ya." There was no need to try to convince him of her truth.

Her truth. While it was true that Gavin McManus had asked her to marry him, their first meeting hadn't suggested anything like that was to come. It turned out that they shared a history class, so it wasn't long before their hallway stare-down had the chance to become more.

She'd been digging through her backpack to find a pen when she sensed someone watching her. Without even looking, she somehow knew it was Gavin. A rush of heat pinked her cheeks.

"What's the craic, darlin'?" he asked smoothly, as if they were picking up a conversation that had only recently been interrupted.

Thrown by both his familiar manner and the unfamiliar expression, she stayed mute.

"What I mean by that," he said, flattening his brogue into a comical American accent, "is, how are you? How are you enjoying our little island here?"

Ah, so he had learned she was American. She sighed and resigned herself to the fact that she had already been gossiped about. Though she knew it was to be expected, she'd rather it went on without her knowledge.

"It's been great. So far," she said, unable to keep the wariness from her voice.

"What brings you to these parts?"

He was watching her intently, his earlier casual nature suddenly replaced with open interest.

"Just wanted something new. New experiences."

That made him smile and she realized how it might have sounded. Coming off as the eager new girl, ready for anything. Not exactly what she meant, and she scrambled to explain, telling him in a rush about her parents' foray into the local burgeoning tech industry.

"Oh, so you're a rich girl slumming it with us Paddies, is that it?"

His teasing had an edge to it, and she wasn't sure how to respond.

"*Paddy*, darlin', is another word for Irishman," he continued. "It can be harmless or a put-down." He sat back in his chair. "If you've come here thinking you're better than us lot, go ahead and use Paddy as you like."

She was taken aback by this line of attack, and her first instinct was to retreat from him. Almost as quickly, she was surprised to find the inner reserve to push back. She had spent the last few months suffering at the hands of former friends who had inexplicably turned on her, making her an outcast at school. Hadn't she come all this way to free herself from that kind of senseless bullying?

"Actually," she said, "I'm not one to make assumptions or talk down to others—not even in retaliation for the same thing being done to me."

He opened his mouth, hesitated, and then pressed his lips together. Furrowing his brow, he watched her in silence. She returned his stare, only unlike in the hallway earlier, this was about him trying to figure her out and her trying to hold her ground.

"Oh, would you look at what you've done," a girl to Sophie's left said.

The girl's chocolate-brown hair was cut into a severe, but cute, bob. Heavy makeup covered her eyes and multiple earrings filled her lobes. But her genuine smile made her instantly trustworthy to Sophie.

"What *I've* done?" Sophie asked softly.

"You've done the impossible. You've shut up Gavin McManus. Fair play to you." She gave Sophie a round of applause and Gavin smiled sourly. "I'm Felicity, by the way. Look, class is about to start, but I want you to promise me we'll have lunch together. You can tell me all about America, yeah?"

Sophie smiled at this kind welcome. It was the opposite of what she had just experienced with Gavin and immediately set her at ease.

"Sure, that'd be great," she said.

THE SCHOOL'S lunchroom was just like the one back home with large rows of picnic-style tables and noisy with the chatter of dozens of conversations going on at once. Sophie had brought a simple sandwich but was too nervous to eat. Looking around the room for some place to sit out the lunch break was nerve-wracking. But then, she spotted Felicity at a table with Gavin and some others at the same moment that Felicity called out to her.

"Sophie! Come sit here, my dear."

The room seemed to go quiet as Sophie took the empty spot next to Felicity. The silent scrutiny she felt in that moment was uncomfortably intense, making her desperate for some distraction. Before she could come up with a way to divert the unwanted attention, Felicity came to the rescue.

"All right, everyone," Felicity said, standing up, "since none of yous could mind your own bloody business, even if you actually tried, this is my new best mate in all the world, Sophie. She's from the States."

Sophie was grateful for the way Felicity assumed the role of guide and protector. She was proving to be a friend already.

A few kids said hello and Sophie smiled shyly in return.

"So, how are you enjoying our sunshine and prosperity?" the boy next to her asked.

She laughed. "It's overwhelming."

"My name's Conor. Good to meet you," he said. "Where is it you're from?"

"California," Gavin interrupted from his position at the opposite, far end of the table.

"And how do you know that, Gav?" Conor asked.

"Just look at that Baywatch tan—doesn't that say it all?"

The crowd tittered and Sophie's stomach dropped at the derisive comment. He was the one they all looked to and now he was setting the tone for how she should be viewed. The hint of schoolyard meanness was déjà vu. But this time, she wouldn't let it go unchallenged.

"Oh, so you're going to pretend that I didn't tell you I was from California? Just so you can show off?" she asked, and the group quieted. The instinct to push back against Gavin's taunts surprised her once more. Maybe this move to another country had been a good decision after all. She felt renewed confidence.

"You smart-arse, Gav," Conor said. "Don't give the new kid hassle. You've probably frightened her to death of all Irishmen."

"I don't think she's frightened at all," Gavin said, locking eyes with her.

That same feeling of connection swept over her and she was drawn to him all over again, despite their combative episodes. Their gaze was broken when a girl leaned down, wrapped her arm around Gavin from behind, and kissed him on the cheek.

He turned and looked up at her with a smile. She had a broad, freckled face, and her long, unruly brown hair worked as a shield when Gavin pulled her down to him for a kiss on the mouth. The crowd of kids at the table howled.

Sophie turned distractedly to Conor, confused by the sting of jealousy she felt at Gavin so quickly giving his attention to another girl. She noticed for the first time the striking way Conor's blue eyes contrasted with this black hair and brows. His cheekbones were high and his jawline defined, but thick eyelashes and a quick smile softened those edges.

"You okay, Sophie?" he asked.

"Um, yeah. I think I'm still jet-lagged, though." With a glance, she saw that Gavin had pulled away from his girlfriend and was watching her interaction with Conor.

"So, have you had a chance yet to see Dublin at all?" Conor asked.

"I did get a bit of the tourist's view over the weekend."

"Ah, let's see, that would be Grafton Street, Trinity Library, and St. Patrick's Cathedral?" he asked and she laughed and nodded. "You'll have to see the city with more of an insider's feel. I could show you some unique spots."

"Unique?" The way he was looking at her conveyed more than a friendly invitation.

"You know, places off the beaten path—"

"Word to the wise, darlin'," Gavin said with a wink and a wicked grin, "Conor's my best mate, but I'd be careful. He's a heartbreaker!" Gavin said and laughed.

"Fuck off, Gav," Conor returned with a laugh.

"Oh, yeah? Put 'em up, pretty boy," he replied, getting up from the table and moving to the end of it so he could assume a boxing stance.

Conor rose to join him and the two held up fists but when they swiped at each other it was with an open hand, trying to land a slap rather than a punch.

"Boys—they're nothing but hormones, aye?" Felicity asked with a nod to the two of them.

"Seems that way. Is that girl Gavin's . . . ?

"Well that's about rightly put. Her name's Mary, by the way. Don't know if he considers it serious. He's a bit of a player, always running with someone new. Someone more like *you*, actually."

"What does that mean?"

Felicity glanced at Mary and then back at Sophie. "Him being with Mary is a bit of a departure. She's sweet, but a tad plain and plump. Odd that she was able to snatch him, really. He's usually with stunners like you."

Sophie laughed. "Stunner is not how I'd describe myself, but thanks."

"The more I think of it, the more I think you are exactly Gavin's type."

"Me?" Sophie hated the hopeful note in her voice. Why was she so attracted to the boy who had taken an instant dislike to her? She usually prided herself on rejecting the schoolyard notion that when a boy is mean it's because he likes you. Besides, a couple of heated gazes wasn't enough to explain this. Was it?

"Don't tell me you're interested?" Felicity asked. "With the way he's treated you today?"

Apparently, Felicity could see right through her. Still, she tried to play it off. "Oh, no. I was just curious."

Felicity watched her for a moment and then nodded sagely. "Well, let me give you the lay of the land, so to speak. You've met Gavin and Conor, yeah?"

Sophie nodded and watched the two continue to swipe at each other as their friends cheered them on. Mary stood to the side, her eyes fixed on Gavin.

"They've been best mates since God was a boy. They started a band together, too."

"A band?"

Felicity threw Sophie a knowing glance. "Sexy, yeah? Young rockers. Gavin's the singer—got a nice voice, really. Conor plays guitar. And see that fella over there?"

Sophie followed her nod and saw a lanky boy on the outskirts. He was sitting by himself with headphones on and head bowed. His strawberry-blond hair fell over his eyes but she recognized him from earlier.

"That's Shay—drummer. He's so wrapped up in music that a lot of us suspect he doesn't even know what a girl is," Felicity said with a laugh.

"It can't be that bad," Sophie said. "He seems sweet."

"He's hopeless. Just try talking to him—you'll see. He won't be able to string two words together. It's a bit of a joke."

"Aw, poor thing."

"Ah, he takes it all in stride. Anyway, last, but not least . . . see that one there?" She pointed to a stocky boy with an affable smile. "That's Martin—the bass player. He's the sort who's happy to do whatever he's told. Now, you tell me all about you, love."

Sophie launched into her own story, fielding Felicity's questions as she went. They had an easy, natural rapport and the break went by fast. As everyone stood and gathered their things in preparation for their next classes, Sophie couldn't keep from looking for Gavin.

And it seemed he had the same instinct, because she soon found herself locked in his gaze once again. He'd been walking away, his arm around Mary's neck, but then he'd hesitated and turned back to look for her. After telling Mary something, he made his way through the opposing stream of kids to join her.

"Hey," she said as nonchalantly as she could, aware both of her heartbeat quickening and of Felicity moving away, smirking at them.

"I, em," he started, pushing his hand through his hair and looking away. "I'm sorry if I came at you aggressive-like or something. I'm not really that way. I guess Felicity was right."

She forced herself to swallow. "Right about what?"

He met her eyes without wavering now and she could feel herself leaning toward him in anticipation.

"You've had some kind of effect on me, I'll say that much," he told her. "It's just, well, you're like some sort of exotic creature."

"Oh," she replied, unsure what else to say. The first part about her having an *effect* on him was flattering. But she didn't know what to make of being called an *exotic creature*.

"I really hope you enjoy your time here."

She nodded.

"And that offer of Conor's? To show you around? Forget about him. If you're after seeing some of Dublin, I'm your man."

The flirt was clear. He wanted her to disregard Conor and instead consider him.

And she did so. Without a second thought. Because she knew she wanted him since they first locked eyes in the hall earlier.

But then she glanced over his shoulder and was quickly reminded of reality. Mary stood at a distance, watching them.

"I thought you were Mary's man?" she challenged, finding that inner reserve once again. The last thing she wanted was to get in between a couple. He'd have to break up with Mary before anything else could happen.

He smiled ruefully before laughing and shaking his head, a response that she took to mean he understood her expectations. Taking a few steps backward, he held up his hands in a helpless gesture.

"Who knows what the future holds, yeah?" he asked, tossing her a wink before turning away.

Despite herself, she smiled.

4

SOPHIE

"Oh!" Rachel started, and everyone turned to her. Sophie was jolted back to the present at the bar near USC. "You do know that your *husband* is in town this weekend, right, Sophie?"

"What?"

"Rogue is playing two nights at the Palladium."

"I, uh, I didn't realize." Her heart thudded at the thought of Gavin being within reach.

"Maybe you can work your magic to get tickets!" Gracelyn said. "And backstage passes! Their guitarist is so hot!"

"Oh, but what about the shy one? The drummer? He's cute," Rachel said.

"That's Shay," Sophie said.

"What kind of name is Shay?"

"It's short for Seamus. Only, his parents were these weird, checked-out people. They didn't even bother to put the full name on his birth certificate. It was like they never understood what having kids meant and let him and his brother raise themselves. Gavin always called him Seamus, though. It was sweet."

"Um, okay . . . anyway, do you think we can get another round of drinks?" Zach asked.

Clearly, Zach didn't believe this bit of inside information. The group went off on another tangent and Sophie was happy to turn her thoughts to her first encounter with Shay.

It was the day after her back-and-forth with Gavin. They'd all gathered at lunch at the same table again, but Gavin had made a concerted effort to avoid talking to her, both in class and now on the break.

Feeling awkward by his purposeful indifference to her, she'd distracted herself by focusing on Shay. He had his head bowed as he got lost in whatever was playing on his headphones, isolating himself once again.

"I'm going to introduce myself," Sophie said.

"Don't do it," Felicity warned. "He'll take one look at you, see this pretty blonde, and faint before he can conjure up a word to you!"

"It can't be that bad!" Sophie said. "And besides, I'm up for a challenge."

"All right, then. Have at it!"

Sophie stood and headed toward Shay. Glancing back, she saw Felicity and Conor huddling together as they watched the scene unfold. She also saw Gavin interrupt his own storytelling to a different part of their group to see where she was going.

Stopping in front of Shay, she waited a moment for him to look up and acknowledge her. When he continued to stare at the ground, she heard some giggles behind her. Refusing to be dissuaded, she bent over at the waist, inadvertently providing a teasing view down the front of her shirt which Shay saw when he finally glanced up.

With flushed cheeks, he jumped to his feet and took a step away. The scene elicited a few hoots and more snickering, which only made Sophie more determined. Wasn't Shay their friend? This felt too much like the mean behavior she had endured.

"I'm sorry," she said, smiling. "I didn't mean to scare you."

Shay responded with silence and furrowed brows.

She tapped her own ears to suggest he remove his headphones so they could speak. He got her point and hastily pulled them from his head.

"Hi. Shay, right?" she asked.

He nodded, dumbfounded.

"I'm Sophie. I'm new here—from America. I just wanted to introduce myself."

There was a long silence as she waited for him to say something.

"I'm Shay," he finally said, and then blushed again. "Shite—you already know that."

The group broke out into riotous laughter and applause at Shay's faux pas. He looked down and started to put his headphones back on.

"Wait," Sophie whispered, stopping him. "Take my hand, say something sweet. Anything."

Shay hesitated, glancing at his friends, who continued to laugh and make jokes at his expense. Then he took her hand in his.

"Well, then, it's lovely to meet you," he said.

"Very nice to meet you, Shay. Thanks so much," she said before leaning forward and kissing his cheek.

"Yeah, Shay!" Felicity shouted and was joined by most of the others.

The incident created an unspoken bond between her and Shay, as she thereafter made sure he was actively engaged in their group.

It also got Gavin's attention because he tracked Sophie down as she was leaving school that day.

"Hey," he said, "I'll walk with you."

She glanced at him, trying not to reveal how thrilled she was by the prospect of spending time with him. She knew she shouldn't flirt with him. He had a girlfriend. But there was just something … *irresistible* about him.

"Oh, sure, " she said.

"You're not far past where I live, I think. On Alma, right?"

"Yep," she said with a shake of her head. "I guess everyone knows everything about me?"

"People do talk. But no, you're still a mystery to most."

She nodded.

"Though, what you did today with Shay tells me a lot about who you are."

She shot him a look and held it. There was no taunt in his blue eyes, though. Instead, there was admiration.

"You can't possibly know how much that meant to him, Sophie. He's incredibly shy, but he still wants to be included. You somehow saw that right away."

She shrugged. "I've always rooted for the underdog."

He laughed. "What's that mean? You're saying Shay's a dog?"

She blushed. "No, that's not what I meant."

"I know. I was only messing." He reached around and gave her bicep a reassuring squeeze and for a moment, she had to fight against leaning into him to make the gesture into something of an embrace.

When he removed his hand from her, she regained herself. "I guess I just thought he looked like he needed someone. And, I … like to be needed. To help, if I can."

He watched her for so long that she finally turned away and focused on the sidewalk. There was more concrete than greenery in this neighborhood, but the narrow, mostly attached houses were well-tended. The sky was cloudy, of course, with rain sure to come soon.

"Well, I think—" he started.

"Gav, where do you think you're going?"

Sophie followed the voice calling after Gavin and saw a man across the street gesturing at them. His brown hair was slicked back with some kind of product that left it greasy looking rather than styled. He'd missed a button so that his shirt was done up crookedly. Though he was only a few years older than Gavin, his sloppy appearance and hectoring tone made him seem practically middle-aged.

"I'll be back in a few minutes," Gavin said dismissively.

"In my hole, you will! You know you're meant to be coming straight home. I'll tell Da, so I will."

"Fuck's sake," Gavin muttered.

"It's okay if you have to go," she told him.

"It's fine. Let's just keep on."

He took her hand then and picked up the pace. It was a confident, protective move that made her smile.

"That's your problem! You always think the rules don't apply to you! Like you're better than everyone else!"

Gavin kept walking, kept holding her hand. And soon, they were on her street.

"Sorry about that," he said. He released her hand abruptly, almost as if he only then realized he'd been holding it. "My brother is an arsehole. There's no other word for it."

"It's fine."

"Well, hopefully you can ignore him like I do. Though, I'll admit I've had a lifetime of practice and so have quite the head start."

She laughed, but there was something in his expression that gave her pause. His brother wasn't just an annoyance, there was more to it.

The thing he'd said about Gavin thinking he was better than others came back to her. It was what Gavin had told her when they first met. She realized that he'd probably heard that quite a few times.

Though he left after another minute of small talk, that brief time together let her see another side to him. Before, he'd come off as alternately combative, charming, and confident. But it was in their shared moments of silence that she recognized the vulnerability he tried to hide beneath his otherwise boisterous personality. It drew her to him even more. It made her want to protect him.

Remembering how intensely they connected during that unplanned walk left her anxious now to see how he had changed after the last couple years. All she had to do was somehow not only get tickets to Rogue's show, but also get backstage passes.

5

GAVIN

Sound check had gone well, but Gavin couldn't shake his uneasiness. While his bandmates made their way backstage to cool down and grab a bite to eat, he lingered at the mic. They had played to a sold-out crowd at the four-thousand-person capacity Hollywood Palladium the previous night, but it was quiet now, with only occasional tinkering by the sound and light engineers.

Gripping the microphone with both hands and looking up, he focused on the large chandelier at the back of the wide, curved room. Something about its unexpected elegance in the same place where thousands of teenagers would once more sweat to their music tonight brought Sophie to mind. Similarly, she had seemed out of place with him and his friends in Ireland. She was this sophisticated and poised American who he had thought of as an *exotic creature*.

As she became a regular in their group, she joined Felicity in watching the band fumble in early sessions.

"So, what's the name of the band, anyway?" she had asked after one jam session.

"Good question. We can't seem to settle on one. Any ideas?"

She thought a moment. "Well, what inspires you?"

He looked at her in surprise. He had been kidding. It hadn't occurred to him that she'd be halfway interested in the minutiae of the band.

"How do you mean?" he asked.

"As far as music, I mean. Who has inspired you to do this, to be a singer?"

"There's quite a few on that list. John Lennon, Joe Strummer, Jeff Buckley, Liam Gallagher, Bono—of course. But David Bowie most of all."

"For a name, then, I'd say think about what exactly they inspire in you."

"Eh," he started, unsure what she was getting at.

"What do you love about the way their music makes you feel? Maybe something will sound right if you do that. For a name, I mean."

He smiled at her and was again struck by her thoughtfulness. She had a generous way about her. What he had seen her do with Shay was no fluke.

"It's just an idea. It probably sounds really stupid, right? I—"

"No, it's brilliant, Sophie." He hesitated before continuing. "Actually, do you know Bowie's song 'Heroes'?"

"Sure."

"I got stuck on a line in it. It goes . . . ." He sang the lines about being lovers and nothing keeping them together, followed by, "We could steal time, just for one day."

He was momentarily distracted by the effect his singing seemed to have on her. She was watching him with a far-off look, a trace of a smile on her lips. Those lips were perfectly, naturally, smooth and pink. They looked so soft. So kissable. *Biteable*, even. Jesus, he wanted her. And he got the feeling that she felt the same way in return.

But he had Mary.

She had proclaimed her status as his girlfriend a few days before the start of school, making sure everyone knew it. He hadn't minded at the time because he didn't take it seriously.

Now, it seemed terribly inconvenient and not at all what he wanted.

"What I get stuck on," he said, forcing himself to continue, "is the part about stealing time. It's such a powerful idea, you know, to be able to create a space in which there's another chance to get it right, to say the right things . . . ."

She nodded, encouraging him to continue.

"And then I think maybe it's not just about wanting to steal time, but to *still* time. There are some moments that you never want to end, some times that you wish to freeze and linger in—"

"And isn't it amazing that that's what you have the power to do with songwriting?" she asked excitedly.

"Do I?"

"You do! You can capture a moment, a feeling, so precisely in a song that it will live forever. It will always be what you felt at the time. And the most amazing thing is that everyone else gets a chance to claim it as their own depending on how they interpret it. That's what's so beautiful about music."

That was the moment when he was truly lost to her. It manifested as the sensation of falling, as if mistiming the step off of a curb. The resulting delicious dizziness made him smile.

Never one for confrontation, he'd gone from that encounter to Mary's with the gentle suggestion that they take a step back in seeing each other. He was, he suggested, just so busy with school and the band. He thought he got the point across without being hurtful and left feeling hopeful about being able to pursue Sophie instead.

Sophie was who he wanted. Who he *needed*. This insane connection he felt with her was too rare, too precious. Not only did she believe in him as a songwriter and musician, but she had a kind of … tenderness he craved.

Her faith in him as a musician had proven well placed, he thought, as his eyes focused again on the chandelier of the Palladium. He may not have kept the girl in the end, but he got the musical career he wanted, which wasn't all bad.

If only it didn't still hurt so much to have lost her.

6

SOPHIE

Though Sophie was supposed to use her "magic" to procure tickets to see Rogue, it was Gracelyn who managed to arrange things. Her uncle had connections at Rogue's label, and got them tickets and backstage passes for the second show at the Palladium.

In the brief time leading up to the show, Sophie went along with the gentle ribbing Gracelyn gave her over her claim that she had a relationship with the lead singer of Rogue. She was too nervous about the chance to actually see Gavin again to spend energy convincing Gracelyn her story was true.

Though she considered Gracelyn a friend, she wasn't a *close* friend. Since returning to the States, she'd had trouble forming close friendships that measured up to what she had with Gavin and Felicity. She attributed this at least in part to the fact that her parents had invested in a "getaway" beach house in Malibu, so she spent summers and other school breaks away, making it difficult to keep up with friends whose worlds were limited to Menlo Park.

Felicity's bold introduction of Sophie as her "best mate in all the world" had fast become reality, even though they outwardly appeared to have nothing in common. At a visit to the nail salon, Sophie got her usual French manicure. Felicity had her short nails painted crimson with black tips. Sophie loved the indulgence of getting a pedicure, complete with paraffin wax dip to keep her feet soft. Felicity mocked the idea of paying someone to touch her feet.

When out shopping, Sophie bought Chanel perfume and a silk body-hugging dress in an eye-catching fuchsia color, and Felicity spent all she had on a pair of eight-hole, steel-toe black patent leather Dr. Martens boots. Sophie's mother was intent on instilling self-reliance in her daughter. Felicity's mother relied heavily on her daughter to be her best friend and confidant as she dated a string of men destined to break her heart. In the end, those differences mattered little as they both understood what mattered more was that they shared the same sense of humor, which allowed them to quickly establish a free and honest intimacy with each other.

After returning home, Sophie's friendship with Felicity had turned into a sporadic email connection. And she hadn't seen Gavin since that trip to the airport two years ago. They had written and spoken on the phone a few times, but their once-unshakable connection dissipated all too quickly. It had hurt, of course, but Sophie knew that Gavin was obsessively focused on making something happen with the band in Ireland. She was in high school in America. They were truly worlds apart.

She had watched Rogue's debut album make an impact in the college scene. But no longer being part of their inner circle, it soon felt strange to simply be a fan. So she purposely distanced herself from following their progress, which meant she hadn't even known they were in town.

But she was soon about to find out what had become of her old high school boyfriend. And she couldn't stop trembling from the anticipation of it all.

————

SOPHIE COULD FEEL every beat of her heart as she watched Gavin from her stage-left vantage point at the Palladium.

She had always thought he exuded that rare kind of star power that makes others stop and pay attention, but this performance was on another level. In just the last couple years, he had grown into a true frontman who could *own* the stage. The audience was in his thrall, responding to his slightest command as he gripped the microphone and sang with that distinctive, slightly raspy, and intensely passionate voice. Sweat dripped down his face, and his eyes were wide as he implored the fans to sing with him.

Seeing the band perform here was a far cry from the first time she saw them really play live. It was just a few days after she and Gavin had talked about inspiration for a band name. She and Felicity had settled on a makeshift bench made from a piece of wood supported at either end by a stack of concrete blocks in Conor's back garden. They watched as the boys fiddled with their instruments in a show of preparation.

Sophie's eyes naturally wandered to Gavin. There was an easiness he had in his own skin that was so attractive. With a tug on Felicity's sleeve, she whispered, "Gavin looks so good today!"

Felicity responded by rolling her eyes. "Please. He looks like he hasn't bathed in a week. Conor, on the other hand—he looks delicious."

Taken aback, Sophie looked at her friend. Felicity had never said she was interested in Conor before, but now that Sophie thought about it, there did seem to be some kind of closeness between them that went beyond friendship. She knew that Conor had a habit of showing up to group outings with Felicity in tow. Sophie had seen them tease each other or join forces in arguments against others. They even had nicknames for each other that no one else used. It all added up to a natural fit for a romantic relationship, and Sophie was surprised she hadn't put it together sooner.

"Why didn't you tell me you like him?" Sophie asked excitedly.

"'Cause I don't. I just think he's sexy. So sometimes we do it, is all," Felicity replied nonchalantly.

At the same time that Sophie was forcibly closing her mouth, Conor caught her eye. He swung his guitar strap over his head and the instrument hung low against his hips. At almost six feet, he was a couple inches taller than Gavin. His build was athletic, probably because whenever he wasn't with Gavin, he was playing soccer. Today he wore crisp Levi's that were still dark blue and unblemished, while Gavin wore faded jeans with a hole in one knee. Whereas Conor's dark hair was cut short and neat and his face was cleanly shaven, Gavin wore his hair longish and unkempt and had a few days of wispy beard growth. Conor was all cool and control, while Gavin oozed confidence and charisma.

"But—you mean you just have sex with him?" Sophie blurted out.

"Shh! Sophie, you're the only other person who knows about it. But, yeah, every so often we just . . . get together."

"And that's all you want?" Sophie touched her friend's hand and eyed her with concern.

Felicity smiled and then laughed. "It's really okay. Maybe I'd want something more if things were different. But it's okay. When we're together, it's actually . . . sweet."

"What do you mean—if things were different?"

"I've told you my plan. I want away from here. Away from my Ma. And even if I wasn't planning on leaving, there's no way I could be serious with someone like Conor."

"I don't get it. If you like him and he likes you, what's stopping you?"

"Only because he's in a band, Sophie. And they're good. They're determined to go all the way. There is no way in the world I'd let my heart get involved with a guy who wants to be a rock star. He'll end up going on the road, cheating on me, and forgetting me altogether. Believe it or not, I have too much self-respect to do that to myself."

Sophie nodded with distraction, unable to even take in the music as the boys began to piece together a song. The idea of casual sex was incomprehensible. She had never been with anyone in that way and couldn't imagine doing so without love and commitment being involved. Despite her mother's pragmatic personality—or perhaps in subconscious rebellion against it—she had grown up with Disney princess ideals of finding that one true love.

Felicity nudged Sophie. "He wrote a fucking song about you, Sophie!"

"What?" Sophie asked with confusion.

"Haven't you been listening? It's called 'Exotic Creature'."

Exotic creature. That was how Gavin had described her in his attempt to explain away the aggressive way he had challenged her upon their first meeting. He'd said that a girl like her was an *exotic creature* in his world. She hadn't known what to make of that. But she'd taken it as an apology. Now, she suddenly realized he had meant something very special with those words, that it wasn't just a throwaway line.

"Look at Mary's face. He's made a bollocks out of it, and that's for sure," Felicity said with perverse pleasure. "Though, I heard that he told her they should take a break, so I'm not sure why she's in a strop over this."

But Sophie didn't look to see what Mary's reaction was because she couldn't keep from staring at Gavin's rose-hued lips as he sang, "You take my breath, darlin', and I like this dizzy feeling."

Being sung to—sung about—felt just as intimate as she imagined sex would. Especially when they locked eyes. Their connection was obvious and undeniable in this moment. It was only broken by Mary moving into their sight line.

But when she started in on him over his obviously divided attention, he took her a few feet away so they couldn't be heard. Sophie didn't know what was said after that, but when Mary stormed off, Gavin did not follow her.

Sophie watched as he instead waited a beat before turning and locking eyes with her. It felt like that moment in the hallway all over again where everyone and everything else faded away. This time, instead of just sharing a heated gaze, he made his way to her.

"So," he said with a sheepish grin.

"Um, yeah," she said lamely.

They both understood the awkwardness and inevitability of the situation, though, and shared a laugh.

"I hope you like the song," he said. "It's a bit rough still, but—"

"I love it," she said, touching her chest.

His eyes dropped to where her hand covered her heart. She swallowed hard when he gently took her hand in his. At first, he just held it warmly. His touch sent a jolt of electricity through her body but that changed to the most intense sensation of longing she'd ever experienced when he leaned down and pressed his lips to the inside of her wrist. The sensation of his soft lips combined with the stubble of his beard brushing against her tender skin made her come alive in a way she never had before.

"I want to know you better, Sophie," he said softly

It could have been taken as a pickup line. If she had been at all jaded about wanting the same thing from him, she might have scoffed at it.

But she didn't. Instead, she said, "You do?"

"I have since the moment I saw you at school. In the hall." He still held her hand in his but now he used his other hand to stroke her cheek. "Jesus, but you're beautiful. It's not just that, though. There's something about you. Something in your eyes. I just want to get lost in them."

There had been no turning back after that. They had become inseparable. He was her first love, and eventually, her first sexual experience. And just as she had suspected, he was broken inside. He shared with her what caused the fractures of his heart and she did everything she could to seal them, wanting desperately to help heal him. It was an uncommon connection that they clung to for as long as they could, but there had been no choice but to return to California after the school year was over. It was that separation that gave her a taste of the kind of emotional pain he had long battled.

Now, Sophie felt a different kind of pain as Gracelyn squeezed her arm and jumped in rhythm to the chest-thumping bass and drum combo of Rogue's Palladium show. Beyond that, though, the show felt like an out-of-body experience, flying by without her really registering anything other than the fact that her eyes never left Gavin.

7

SOPHIE

I t took a moment to adjust to the activity in the room as Sophie surveyed the crowded backstage area. It was already in full party mode, even though the final thunderous applause after the last encore had only happened ten minutes before. The air was heavy with perfume, weed, and sweat.

She felt acutely out of place as she took in the hangers-on filling the room, most of whom still wore their designer sunglasses and spoke loudly to compete against the music. They were young, hip, and a sure sign that Rogue was on its way to becoming the next big band.

"This is your big moment!" Gracelyn said. "You have to introduce me to the guitarist. What's his name again?"

She opened her mouth to respond but there was a sudden sharp burst of laughter, making her instinctively look for Gavin as the source of the reaction. He was the type of person others flocked to, and his stories usually resulted in such delighted outbursts. But before she could locate him, she fixated on two scantily clad girls dancing provocatively and kissing each other with elaborate tongue.

It wasn't the sexuality of the girls that interested her, as much as *who* they were performing for. Their current audience of one was Conor Quinn, the band's guitar player and Gavin's best friend. He was sitting by himself on a sofa, a bottle of Beck's in his hand as he stared at the show before him. He wore new but faded jeans and his well-defined chest was bare. His short black hair was carefully askew, a striking contrast to his deep blue eyes. He had always been the most conventionally handsome of the group, and now that he had grown into his looks, he wouldn't have been out of place on a catwalk modeling the latest fashions.

As Sophie took in the sight of him, a flood of memories rushed through her head and heart. Just as she was thinking he would be perfectly happy to ogle the pseudo-lesbian dancers forever, he glanced up and met her eyes.

The recognition was instantaneous. Conor smiled broadly and stood. He stepped past the girls without hesitation and their faces fell in disappointment. It took only a moment for them to rebound, however, as they were soon scanning the room for other band members.

"Sophie Kavanaugh, I don't believe it!" Conor said and surprised her with a quick kiss on the lips and a long, tight hug. "I adore that you're here," he murmured into her ear as he pulled away.

"I was so excited when I heard that you guys were in L.A.," she replied. "I had to come, to see . . . ."

"Good you did. God, you look amazing!" He eyed her up and down.

She smiled but also felt her cheeks burning at the hungry way he appraised her. The choice of what to wear had been agonizing. In the end, she decided to dress in what she was most comfortable in— form-fitting, low-rise jeans with sandals and a shrunken peasant top left untied at the neck to give a hint of cleavage. She had left her long blonde hair down and nervously toyed with it now.

"I can't believe you were telling the truth," Gracelyn said into her ear.

"Oh, um," Sophie said, "Conor, this is my friend Gracelyn."

"Good to meet you," he said quickly. Gracelyn was a tall, thin Chinese-American beauty but that didn't stop him from turning his attention back to Sophie. "So, you saw us play? What'd you think?"

"Oh my gosh. You guys *owned* that stage. It was amazing."

"Thanks. It's lovely to hear you say so."

They fell silent, taking each other in for a moment. She then reached out and touched his forearm, and he leaned forward expectantly.

"Conor, I really want to catch up with you, but I need to find Gavin. I have to just . . . see."

"Oh." He reached out and grabbed her hand. "Well, listen, before you run off, just what sort of reunion were you expecting?"

But she had already tuned him out, having spotted Gavin across the room. Conor held onto her fingers until the last second, even as she gravitated toward Gavin. There was no trepidation or doubt on her part, only impatience to meet with the man who had owned her heart since she first saw him three years earlier.

8

GAVIN

Gavin thought the gig had been one of their best—the acoustics were sharp, the crowd was in their thrall, and his vocals and stage presence had been on point. He'd still been riding the high of that performance when he saw Sophie slip into their backstage party room. As incongruous as it was for her to be at this show, rather than the ones in northern California, his first thought upon recognizing her to wonder if a part of him had somehow known all along that she was out there in the audience.

The last two years had seen her mature into a beautiful young woman. She had always been pretty—maybe even too pretty for her years. Now her long legs were less coltish and more shapely. The sophisticated, delicate beauty of her high cheekbones and thin, straight nose, which had made her appear older than her peers in school, were now a graceful, natural fit. The eyes were the same, though. Those extraordinary hazel eyes could turn green so deeply and suddenly that they took your breath away. He had gotten blissfully lost in those eyes so many times.

He was ready to forget the resentment he'd built up toward her and get lost in her all over again tonight. But then he watched her hug Conor and touch him, and he felt his heart fracture just like it had the last time he'd seen her.

Wasn't she here to see *him*? Why take the extended time to chat up his best friend?

The sting of rejection before they had even spoken was sharp and undeniable. And he sank into it, finding comfort in the familiarity of it.

He'd spent the last couple of years thinking of her as the one who'd rejected him, after all.

When her parents arranged for her flight home, he'd begged her to stay in Ireland with him instead of returning to the States. First he pitched it as breaking free from her parents' expectations of school and other conformities, inviting her to travel with the band to London, where they planned to scrape together gigs. When she rejected that idea, he accused her of lacking an artist's soul. He'd said she would never survive without the cushy lifestyle of her rich parents. Neither was true, but he'd been unable to keep from lashing out. She was the truest thing he had ever known or felt beyond music and letting her go was unfathomable.

Which was why he'd asked her in all seriousness to marry him. It was a last-ditch effort on the way to the airport, sure, but he had meant it. He would have married her as soon as it was legally allowed, when they were both eighteen in just over a year. But she'd scoffed, and that had broken his heart.

He knew he had the tendency to romanticize things and that it was selfish to have turned their separation into a case of tragic love where he was the victim. But it was how he'd been able to move on.

Now that she was here, he found himself at war over how he felt. On the one hand, he wanted to rush to her and pull her into his arms. On the other, he saw that her priority seemed to be Conor, and he felt renewed bitterness.

As she turned to make her way toward him, he focused on the way she held onto Conor's fingers until the last second. It was the same thing she had done with him at the airport. Bitterness won the war in that moment and he went into self-protection mode, transforming into a cocky rock star who couldn't be bothered with his ex-girlfriend.

9

As she made her way to Gavin, she noticed the way he had also filled out his frame. His longish, wavy brown hair was pushed back from his face and the sensual shape of his mouth was exactly as she remembered. He had the kind of naturally just-kissed-hued lips girls were drawn to watching as he spoke. And his rugged good looks and natural charm meant girls were also drawn to want to kiss those lips. *She* still wanted to kiss those lips.

But so did the platinum blonde who had wrapped her arm around his waist as they sat closely together on another sofa. Her halter top barely covered the nipples of her very large breasts. She either had implants or an impressive push-up bra because her breasts were practically an offering on display. They were certainly captivating Gavin's attention as he didn't even look up as she approached.

Oddly, seeing Gavin with another girl like this didn't make her jealous. Rather, she instinctively knew that this girl could never really own his heart. But then he used the back of his hand to stroke the upper swell of her breasts and it occurred to Sophie that he seemed less concerned with satisfying his heart than another part of his body. She had never wanted to think about him being intimate with other girls, but this scenario made it all too real. It made his rock star life— the life he had created without her—all too real.

Even so, she knew she had to find out what could be between

them now because she couldn't accept that the bond they had once shared was dead.

"Gavin?" She held her breath as she waited for him to look up at her.

After a prolonged moment, he did, and there was a hardness in his blue eyes. Oddly, he didn't seem surprised to see her. Had he already seen her and decided to ignore her? Incomprehension and disappointment coursed through her.

"Hi," she said brightly, forcing herself to go through with this reunion whether he was interested or not. "I saw the show. You guys were great."

"Thanks," he said shortly and wrapped his arm around the blonde, who in turn smiled triumphantly at Sophie.

Her stomach tightened and she struggled to get enough air. But she didn't want him to see the effect he had on her. "Are you in town long?"

"Few days, then we're off to the next city, next show, next girl," he said and squeezed the girl at his side. She rewarded him with a high-pitched giggle.

Sophie was frozen silent for a moment, her heart aching at his indifference. It didn't seem possible that this was the same guy who had spent a year loving her.

"Well, good for you," she finally said, ignoring the taunt of his response. "Do you have time to catch up? I'd love to talk."

"Em, I don't know. Our schedule is pretty crazy."

"Yes, I can see how *busy* you are." She eyed the girl at his side again.

"What exactly did you expect by coming here?"

The question hit her hard. It was so cold. *He* was so cold. It wasn't like him. Something was off, but she could see in his blank expression that he wasn't going to back down from this frosty reception of her. Still, she answered him honestly.

"What did I expect? I expected to see you. To—"

"And now you have. You saw Conor, too. Seemed to me that was a *special* moment. You can say hello to Shay and Marty if you like—maybe on your way out?"

He was dismissing her. But she couldn't understand why. Why was he acting as if she was some *acquaintance*? She should just walk away and cut her losses. She shouldn't give him the satisfaction of treating her like this. But before she went, she wanted him to know that he had just ruined everything good they had shared. He had placed his rock star ego above their connection and that was a mistake they would both regret for the rest of their lives.

"Do you even *know* what you're doing?" she asked.

When he simply shook his head with a smirk that seemed to say he couldn't care less, she felt the anger and hurt rise up in her chest.

"You've," she started, ready to tell him off. But then tears clouded her vision and strangled her throat and she looked down, struggling to regain her composure.

This finally got a genuine reaction out of him, as he sat up and pulled away from the blonde.

"What have I done, Sophie?" he asked softly, tilting his head to meet her eyes.

But she lost her nerve, suddenly feeling foolish for imposing on an old high school boyfriend who had clearly moved on. Felicity had understood what rock star ambitions meant all too well. She should have listened.

"Forget it. Never mind. This," she said and gestured first to herself and then to him, "was *my* mistake." She turned away before he could see the tears fall from her eyes.

"What a jerk."

Gracelyn made the remark loud enough for Gavin to hear, and while Sophie appreciated the support, she just wanted to get out of there. She glanced around and though her vision was unfocused, she saw that Shay was watching her from one corner of the room, a sympathetic look on his face. Martin was at the bar, but also watching her. It seemed her interaction with Gavin had garnered everyone's attention. At least that hadn't changed, she thought and laughed bitterly.

She and Gracelyn were halfway down the long hallway in the backstage maze of the venue when a man call her name. For the briefest second, she imagined it to be Gavin running after her with apologies.

Instead, it was Conor who was by her side in a moment, offering her a cloth bandana for the tears welling in her eyes. In addition to donning a long-sleeve T-shirt, he had also obviously witnessed her disastrous encounter with Gavin.

"What was that about? Why did he act like we never meant anything?" she asked as she took the cloth and dabbed at her eyes.

"Things are just different now, Soph. I tried to warn you," he said gently.

"It really was a mistake to come here." She blinked back more tears. "I have to go."

"You're sure? You don't have to leave. Hang out with me. I'd love to catch up with you."

"I, uh, I can't." She stood on her toes and kissed Conor on the cheek. "But, thanks for being so sweet to me."

"Sure," he replied with a sigh as she and Gracelyn moved away.

Sophie had sensed that Conor had more to say, but she really couldn't stay. She needed the space to try to process the confusion and heartbreak of her encounter with Gavin.

The fact of the matter was that they hadn't seen each other in two years and his first instinct had been to deliberately hurt her.

She had no idea why.

This blasé rock star persona wasn't like him. It couldn't have been the *real* him.

Maybe it was just bad timing with catching him all hyped up after a show. That was the likeliest explanation.

She just didn't know whether she'd ever find out if she was right about that.

10

GAVIN

2003

"So, which one of you came up with the name 'Rogue'?"

Gavin was the first to burst out into laughter, but Conor, Shay, and Martin quickly joined him. They were crammed into KROQ's studio doing a live appearance to promote their appearance as headliners of the radio station's upcoming summer music festival in Irvine, just outside of Los Angeles. They sat elbow to elbow in swivel barstools, headphones on in the low light of an amber wash.

"Ah, I suspect there's a story there," the DJ said. He stood opposite them, as he would have been blocked from their view by the various computer monitors and other equipment if he sat down. "Let's go ahead and use this momentous occasion of your first visit here with us to come clean."

"No can do," Gavin said. "We took a solemn vow never to reveal the origins of our band name."

The others laughed, but the DJ wasn't deterred.

"All right, here's what I'm going to do. The first caller who can tell me the story will win VIP tickets to see you—Rogue—at the Weenie Roast."

The first two calls were fans who didn't even try to take a guess and instead begged for tickets. But the next call changed everything.

"Hello, caller, you're on the air with the members of Rogue. Can you tell us what the origin of their name is?"

"I'm calling for my friend," a female voice said. "She's the one that knows the story but she won't get on the line."

"Okay, and what's your name?"

"Gracelyn."

"Let's hear it, then, Gracelyn."

"I'm not sure I have it exactly right because she started to tell me and then when I said I was going to call in she freaked out. She wants me to hang up right now."

"This is intriguing," Gavin said with a laugh. This mystery was a welcome departure from the usual promotional appearances they made on radio stations and he was game to switch things up.

"Anyway," the caller continued, "she said it has something to do with Marty—Martin?—getting confused between the word rogue and a scholarship? Rhodes scholarship?"

"Fuck me," Conor said.

"Sophie," Gavin said. There was no doubt in his mind that this caller's friend was his Sophie. She had been the only person besides the band members there when they came up with the name for their band, after all.

Adrenaline coursed through his body as flashes of that day came to mind.

They'd all been crowded into Conor's room, hanging out and listening to Beck's *Midnite Vultures*. Conor sat on the end of his bed, toying with an acoustic guitar version of their song, "Feel It." Gavin beat the floor in time, silently mouthing the lyrics.

Their idle conversations turned, as it increasingly did, to the inevitable need for the band to go to London to get recognized.

"What we need is a manager," Shay said. "If we could get someone to work for us, someone who actually knows what the fuck he's doing—"

"Unlike us!" Martin added with a laugh.

"Aye, we're not the greatest band in the world, but we will be," Gavin said, interrupting himself mid-lyric as Conor played on.

"True enough," Shay said. "But to get there, we have to find someone who has a bleeding clue about the music industry. I'm not sure going to London just for the sake of it will help us much."

"When would you go?" Sophie asked, eyeing Gavin.

"Dunno, darlin'."

"There's not much to stick around here for," Conor said.

"Well . . . ." Gavin looked at his girlfriend and gave her a reassuring smile.

"What, you're going to let a girl stop you, Gav?" Conor shot back. "You—the most ambitious of us all?"

"There's no rush at this very moment, Con. We haven't even played a single gig yet. Let's not get ahead of ourselves."

"Yeah, and Sophie's not going to be here forever, either," Martin reminded them.

"Just the school year," Sophie agreed, unable to keep the sadness from her voice.

"Look, Sophie, you can work it out," Martin suggested. "You're a smart girl—get yourself a rogue scholarship and come back for university."

Gavin met Sophie's eyes and after a moment they both laughed.

"What?" Martin asked, his face coloring.

"I'm sorry," Gavin said with a grin, "what kind of scholarship?"

"*Rogue*." Martin said it as if it were the simplest thing in the world and weren't they idiots for not knowing what he was saying.

But his response was met with laughter from all of them this time. Conor put down his guitar, went to his bookshelf and pulled out a thick, antiquated dictionary. He let it drop with a thud in Martin's lap.

"Do us a favor, then. Look up rogue and tell us what it means."

"Just tell me what I did wrong," Martin said mournfully.

"Now, now—you'll never learn 'til you look for yourself," Gavin chimed in, grinning.

"Thanks very much, *mother*," Martin replied as he opened the fat text.

They all waited in anticipation as he flipped through the pages.

"Ha ha. So I was a wee bit off. 'Rogue: somebody who is unscrupulous or dishonest, especially somebody who is nevertheless likable,'" he read with a flat voice. "'A fun-loving, mischievous person; an individual varying markedly from the standard.' There, happy?"

"Good word," Sophie said.

"Wrong one though, I get it," Martin said and smiled with a shake of his head.

"Let me see that," Gavin said, taking the book from him. He scanned the other definitions and found one marked "dated" and read it aloud to the others. "'A rogue is also a person who jokes and behaves in a way which you do not approve of but whom you do not want to criticize because you like them too much.'"

"All right! I get it—joke's not funny anymore," Martin said.

"No, Marty, I'm not joking you," Gavin said. "It is a good word. Seems to me . . . it's a good name for our band."

There was silence as they all contemplated the idea. Finally, Conor nodded, and without a word picked up his guitar and began to play again. Gavin looked at Martin and was met with a proud grin—he had discovered it after all. Shay appeared unsure as he squinted at the thought of it for a moment. At last, he nodded in approval.

"Then it's settled," Gavin said. "Rogue."

Now, Gavin pushed away both those memories and his stool as he stood in the radio station studio. "Sophie? Are you there?"

"Who is Sophie?" the DJ asked.

"Please, Gracelyn? It's Gracelyn, is it?" Gavin closed his eyes and bowed his head, pressing his headphones tighter to his ears with both hands.

"Uh, yeah."

"Can you put Sophie on the line? I need to speak with her."

"Gavin, not like this," Conor said urgently, but Gavin ignored him.

It had been nine months since the show at the Palladium where he had cruelly dismissed Sophie. In that time, he had thought of her every day. There was no doubt in his mind that he had been an immature ass but he hadn't been able to find the courage to reach out to her. Now it seemed she had made the first effort once again and he wasn't going to screw it up this time.

There was a muffled conversation on the line, the reluctance on Sophie's part clear enough.

But then he heard her voice as she said a soft hello.

He let out his breath in relief. Opening his eyes, he fixated on the chrome pole holding the microphone in front of him. "Sophie, I'm so glad you called."

"I didn't call, actually," she replied. "That was Gracelyn. I got the message last time. I'm not trying to force anything, okay?"

"No, don't say that." He squeezed his eyes shut, grimacing at what a mess he had made of things. There was nothing he could do but give her his honesty. He opened his eyes and said, "I know I was a dick then. But it wasn't the real me, I swear. It was *my* mistake and nothing to do with you. Let me apologize in person. I need to see you. I need it like oxygen, darlin'."

With a glance, he saw Conor shaking his head. Their manager, James Kelly, was squeezed into a corner just beyond them and his face was flushed red, matching the color of his hair. The DJ was watching him with barely contained glee at the juiciness of it all. Let them gawk, Gavin thought. His need to connect with Sophie far outweighed any of their concerns.

"Look, I know I've a slagging coming," he continued. "And I'll only welcome it. As long as you give it to me in person. As long as I can get lost in your eyes while you do it. Say yes, Sophie."

There was an uncomfortably long pause before she replied. "Um, I guess we won the VIP tickets to the Weenie Roast? I can see you there?"

"Is that the best you can do?" He hoped she would remember the expression. They had often used it to challenge each other, both playfully and during a row.

"It is."

He nodded to himself, despite the disappointment of her response. "That's grand, then. I can't wait to see you tomorrow."

The connection was broken as the DJ told Sophie to hold the line so that she could give her information to a production assistant.

For the rest of their segment, Conor diligently pushed the conversation back to the band and their upcoming performance while Gavin retreated to his own thoughts. They were thoughts that mingled with music and lyrics as he tried to conjure up the right way to make amends with the girl he was sure he still loved.

11

Gavin exited the hotel elevator, feeling happily buzzed. The band was staying at Chateau Marmont in West Hollywood for a few days and had already taken full advantage of the pool during the day and the hotel bar during the evenings, including this one.

If he hadn't forgotten his cell phone, he would still be at the bar with the others, indulging in drinks despite being underage. They'd all quickly learned that the late 1920s hotel had a reputation for cultivating a celebrity clientele, carefully marketing the prospect of stargazing opportunities for other guests who craved proximity to fame. And now Rogue was staying there as both minor celebrities and tourists themselves. It meant they got to enjoy the perks of the bar, especially after the management saw how much attention he and Conor could generate. They had an ever-growing crowd of new "friends" wanting their company who were all too happy to pay for the bands' overpriced drinks.

But as soon as he rounded the corner toward his room he knew his evening plans had completely changed.

"Sophie," he said, his smile wide and beyond his control.

It had taken him less than a second to recognize her.

She sat on the floor in front of his door, wearing a light summer dress with a cropped jean jacket and toying with her own cell phone. Startled, she looked up at him and scrambled to her feet at the same time. "I'm sorry to bother you like this," she said quickly. "I just didn't want to meet again in the middle of a crowded room."

"Come here," he said. He reached out to hug her but she shook her head.

"I just wanted you to know I'm not coming tomorrow. In case it mattered."

"In case it mattered? Of course, it matters. Darlin', I meant it when I said I was desperate to see you."

"You mean, just long enough to send me on my way? Like last year at the Palladium. I won't do that again."

"Jesus, Sophie." He'd known he would have to atone for the shitty way he'd treated her, but he hadn't realized how hurt she would still be. It sobered him up in the worst way, as he realized she was only here to tell him off. Dragging his hand through his unruly hair, he let out a sigh and decided his best hope was to remind her of their history. "So, that's it then?"

"I—"

"You want nothing to do with me? After what we had? I mean, we had something real. Something that I know I fucked up last time. But I'm trying now. You can't walk away like this."

"Gavin, don't—"

"You can't give up. You can't—"

"You broke my heart! You broke it."

The raw pain in her voice froze him. When her eyes teared up and darkened, his threatened to do the same. It nearly did him in to see her this hurt. To see that he had caused this.

"Darlin'," he said softly, "I didn't mean it. Just—"

A well-dressed couple in their thirties appeared at the end of the hall, hanging on to each other as they staggered and laughed drunkenly. They seemed to find it hilarious that they were having such a hard time getting their key to open the door to their room.

Gavin used the distraction to open his own door. "Come in. So we can talk for just a minute." He searched her eyes but couldn't read her. He guessed it was because she didn't know her own mind at that second. "Please."

Holding the door open wide, he gestured for her to enter with his other arm. She hesitated but stepped inside, and he knew he needed to be careful not to spook her.

12

SOPHIE

Sophie felt claustrophobic the second Gavin shut the door behind him. The room was small, with antique furnishings, but it wasn't the space that bothered her. Her heart was beating too fast, her head swimming. That outburst of a confession, that he had broken her heart, was true. She'd spent months after that encounter at the Palladium so depressed she barely got through her classes. The worst part was that she had hoped every day for Gavin to make some effort to reach out to her. She'd even had elaborate fantasies that he might track her down. But he never did.

Gradually, she put him out of her mind and moved on. But then, he and Rogue came to her city once again.

One minute she and Gracelyn were talking about going to a party to celebrate the end of finals, and the next minute the radio in the background caught their attention. Sophie had tried to pretend disinterest but her friend would have none of it. Before she knew it, Gracelyn had coaxed out of her a brief description of how the name Rogue came to be.

She'd never intended to reach out to Gavin again. Not after how he had treated her last time. Despite her belief that he had been putting on an insensitive rock star attitude for show and that he couldn't have really meant to be so cruel, she knew the bottom line was that whatever they had was over.

But hearing his pleading voice over the phone had felt so good, so reminiscent of the boy she had known. And she had come close to being seduced by it. But after the adrenaline rush faded, she realized she had no desire to set herself up to experience a repeat of the casual arrogance he had displayed at the Palladium. Especially not in another backstage scenario with groupies and other hangers-on watching the spectacle.

It wasn't hard to sort out that the band was staying at this well-known hotel. Gavin was a rock music aficionado and would have been curious about its history of wild escapades from the likes of Led Zeppelin and Jim Morrison of The Doors. She had called and asked for Gavin's room and was put through without delay. The band wasn't big enough to need false names.

And now she was here, in front of him. To what end? Why hadn't she just not shown up at the festival? The answer was obvious to them both as they locked eyes. He closed the short distance between them. Her heartbeat quickened all over again and her breathing went shallow. The heat of mutual desire was palpable.

"This heart," he said, his voice husky and seductive as he brushed his fingertips over the bare skin just above her breast. "If I broke it, I want to mend it now."

Sophie shivered with the tickle of his touch and caught him trying to hold back a smile. She took a step back.

"I may have been waiting for you at your hotel room, but I'm *not* your groupie. Don't insult me with a line like that."

His face fell but she saw that her words had reached his core. He took a step back and had the decency to look embarrassed.

"This is why I didn't want to see you in the mix of all the 'rock star' stuff. I know things have changed, but don't forget that I *know* you."

He looked away from her, to windows that were only partially covered by sheer curtains. The bright city lights shone through, and the Sunset Boulevard traffic was a constant hum.

"At least," she continued, "I know who you *were*. I don't know the person I saw last time. I guess part of why I came tonight is to find out why you were like that. With me. *Me*, Gavin."

He looked back at her and she could see him pulling up a wall around himself. His body lost its natural fluidity and his eyes lost focus.

"I'll admit I was a bastard. Okay? I was just caught up in the whole scene we're in now. It's a fucking head-trip, suddenly being catered to for any little whim. I guess I've gotten carried away with it. I'm sorry."

She eyed him but he didn't continue. "Is that the best you can do?"

"Fuck's sake. I'm sorry, Sophie. What more can I say?"

"I guess that's it." She nodded while at the same time blinking back tears. There was nothing else to say. That spark, the magic they had shared, hadn't just faded. It was dead.

"No, don't go," he said when she took a step toward the door. "Sophie," he said, desperation in his voice, "you broke my heart too. You broke it first."

13

There he went again. Exposing his wounded heart. Sophie had always held the key to unlocking his most tortured and unvarnished emotions. This was different from the reputation he had fast been earning for being confessional in his songs and interviews. Those efforts were more calibrated than what they appeared. He had a natural instinct for how to manipulate his songs and image. That didn't carry over into how to handle his emotions when it came to Sophie.

She turned back to him, incredulous. "What does that mean?"

"Darlin', don't you know it gutted me when you left?"

"It was hard for both of us, but what other choice was there?"

He watched her for a moment, trying to conjure up something other than his truth. Fuck it. Might as well go for broke and confess all.

"You know very well that the choice was for you to stay and for us to get married."

Sophie mirrored the reaction she had given him the first time he suggested this two years earlier. It was a quick dismissal of the idea.

"I was sixteen—"

"Nearly seventeen."

"Gavin, it was romantic and amazing for you to even consider such a thing. But we both knew it was impossible."

"I knew no such thing. I was willing to remake my life for you, Sophie."

"But—"

"And you walked away. *You walked away.*"

The silence stretched out between them as she watched him, and he did everything he could to not look away. He wanted to hide the hurt and fear he knew was naked in his eyes. And yet she was the only one he had ever been able to be this honest with. There was enormous relief in that. In letting go.

He thought she might tell him she had never meant to provoke that sense of desertion in him. Or that it wasn't fair to compare her going home to finish high school to the same thing as the abandonment he'd known as a child.

Instead, she moved to him, took his face in both her hands and kissed him with a tenderness and longing he gratefully surrendered to.

Wrapping his arm around her slim waist and holding her close, they quickly found the rhythm they had perfected in all those make-out sessions during school. Her lips were soft but her kiss was insistent. He thought fleetingly about the fact that she still knew exactly how to manage him. She still knew him well enough to sense that he hated to even vaguely admit that her leaving had brought up tortured memories from his childhood.

But at the same time, a part of him had known his confession would trigger her desire to drop her own needs to instead take care of his. He'd known she was wired this way since the day he walked her home from school and she'd admitted she was a person who liked to be *needed*. And Jesus, was he ever in need. They'd been fiercely connected in this way, to a level that was well beyond what a simple teenage relationship should have been.

And here she was again, providing the warmth and familiarity he had craved these past few years. The scent on her skin was the same light floral one she had always worn. He smiled at the comforting pleasure of it, breaking their kiss.

She met his eyes, silently questioning the interruption, and he shook his head to dismiss her concern. He took her face into his hands and brought his mouth to hers, oblivious to everything else.

His bandmates down at the bar didn't register in his thoughts, the world outside of their room didn't exist.

He had all he wanted and needed at the moment.

Sophie was everything.

14

SOPHIE

Though his mouth tasted like alcohol, his instant familiarity was what she found intoxicating. The pressure of his lips against hers, the searching movement of his tongue, and the rhythm of their kisses was so easy, so *right*, that she almost sighed from the pleasure of it.

Their chemistry was unlike anything she had ever experienced with anyone else. He was handsome and confident with undeniable sensuality that was magnetic. All of this was transported to the stage when he performed, as she saw at that Palladium gig. The screaming girls had almost drowned out the music.

If they only knew that their fantasies about him were her current reality.

As if reading her thoughts, he pulled away just enough to assess her back.

The way he leveled his eyes upon her now thrilled her to her core.

He looked at her as if he wanted to *consume* her.

And she was willing.

She was willing to be taken by him body and soul. He'd always had that power over her, ever since that first moment in the hallway at school. And even more so once she realized that he wasn't just the popular kid everyone looked to but was, in fact, damaged. In *need*. It made her want to be the one to fix him. To be the one who could soothe his rough, tortured, edges.

This, between them now, was a need of a more physical kind. And she didn't hesitate to pursue it, despite the fact that she knew in the back of her mind that he'd be leaving town with the band soon. She craved the connection that only the two of them could create, even if it would be fleeting.

Sliding her fingers into his hair, she playfully tugged his wavy locks and elicited a happy moan from him. The moan he made when she then grasped him over his jeans was of a more tortured nature.

"I'm so fucking happy to see you, darlin'," he told her in between the kisses he trailed along her neck.

She peeled off her jacket as he pulled the straps of her dress down, revealing her braless breasts. He trailed his kisses over her sensitive nipples, taking each one in turn into his mouth hungrily. Her breasts weren't large but they were nicely shaped and he had always made sure she knew how much he loved them. His sucking and teasing bites made her catch her breath, and he looked up at her.

"Don't stop," she told him, making him smile.

15

GAVIN

She was everything he remembered: exceedingly receptive to his touch, and with a body so sexy, so beautiful, he couldn't imagine ever being sated. He was so hard for her it almost hurt. Kissing and fondling wasn't nearly enough. He needed to be inside of her. Backing her up against the small antique dresser set against the wall, he watched through lust-hooded eyes as she lifted herself up onto it and pulled him between her legs. Yes, this would do.

The small piece of furniture held her weight well while he quickly retrieved a condom from his pocket and let his jeans fall past his knees. She leaned back slightly onto her hands, waiting for him to roll it on. He only got as far as pushing down his boxer briefs before he lost his concentration on the task, however. The look on her face threw him off balance.

It was a look of pure sex.

Her cheeks were flushed, her mouth slightly open, her eyes bright with desire. Her small nipples were rigid and he moaned when she toyed with one for his benefit. But it also compelled him to get the condom in place.

As he leaned in to kiss her, he pulled aside her panties and trailed his fingers along her wetness, making her suck in a breath. That turned into a whimper when he slid a finger deep inside her. She was warm and slick and he wanted to drop to his knees to lick every bit of her, but Jesus, he'd be lucky to last more than a minute if he did.

Instead, he told himself there was time for all that later. Right now, he required the pure pleasure of fucking her.

But, first, a little teasing was in order. He played the tip of his dick against her clit until she couldn't take it and pulled him inside her. The intense sensation of her taking him made him break away from their kiss so he could catch his breath.

"Jesus, darlin'," he breathed into her neck.

The only sound in the room, besides their increasingly short breaths and their skin-on-skin contact, was the weathered attached mirror and metal drawer pulls of the dresser rattling to their rhythm.

Pulling away to look at her, he found she still had that heated expression. But it was more than sexual desire, he realized. It also conveyed the trust and intimacy of their connection. A connection he had feared was lost. And it almost sent him over the edge when she met his eyes. With his fingers to her jaw, he directed her to see in the mirror what he did.

"Look at how beautiful you are," he told her.

After a moment of watching herself, she turned back to him and squeezed her legs tighter around his waist, bringing him even deeper inside her.

"Hold on to me," he said and she wrapped her arms around his neck as if she knew his plan.

Grabbing her backside, he lifted her to him and made small steps toward the bed, careful not to trip over the jeans still around his ankles. Once he had her on the bed, he kicked off his shoes and managed to free himself of his clothes.

Now, he could concentrate on grinding his hips against hers, pushing deep enough to make her gasp. Raising himself up on his hands, he worked a rhythm that he could see was bringing her close. He watched her half-closed eyes as she lost focus, saw the way her hips bucked up against his in just the right way to please herself.

"Darlin', touch yourself for me. Like you do. The way that drives me insane."

She met his eyes then, playing with her nipples once more. Seeing that little extra touch got him moving faster, chasing his orgasm.

But she cried out first, trembling beneath him as she rode a wave of ecstasy and he kept pumping until he was sure she'd gotten everything she could out of it. When he saw her small, pleased smile, he allowed himself to let go.

It was the longest, most intense orgasm he could remember.

He collapsed onto her and she squeezed him with both her arms and legs, pulling him to her so that they felt like one being.

Kissing her neck, earlobe, cheek, and lips, he murmured, "I don't want to let you go." There was no use in pretending at how he felt or holding back.

She placed her hand over his where he had been toying with her nipple. "Then don't."

16

GAVIN

The night passed in a dreamlike daze as they alternated between making love, talking about the events they had missed in each other's lives, and sleeping for brief periods. Gavin couldn't bear to bring up the real world and whether they would exist together in it. For the time being, he was content that their reality was contained in his small room at the Chateau Marmont.

They got hungry at four in the morning and Gavin charmed room service into providing a random and indulgent assortment of things: French fries, pancakes, and buttermilk fried chicken. They made a picnic out of it on the bed, and as the sun was beginning to rise they ate and talked.

"You remember right before you left we heard a bootleg of 'Day's Done' on the radio?" he asked as he pulled the crispy skin off a chicken leg.

"Yes! Did you ever figure out how that happened? Did they play you again?"

He smiled at her excitement. It was as if the band was still hoping for their big break and Sophie thought this could be it. She was right back in the moment.

"Well, Conor and I went down to the radio station, is what we did. But after waiting for over an hour to see the station manager, the first thing he told us was that we were just one of dozens of U2 wannabes out there."

"But, wait—had even heard Rogue? Didn't he know you have a totally different sound? That you're harder rock and with more soul?"

"He admitted that he'd never listen to our demo. But I told him all about our sound. And that we don't go on about religion and politics like U2. I told him that my songwriting is about exploring the beauty and cruelty of the heart."

"I love your lyrics because of that. You explore people and relationships so honestly. It's raw and complex. Just like life."

The way she understood him, even after these years apart, made him catch his breath. To cover for it, he leaned over the spread of food and kissed her, pulling away just as she reached for him.

"Tease," she said with a laugh.

He cocked his head, examining her. "Me? A tease?"

"You know the effect you have on girls." She bit the bottom corner of her lip, letting it release slowly as she watched him.

"What kind of effect is that, darlin'? As I recall, *you're* the one who had an effect on me from day one."

When she smiled, he knew she was remembering him telling her that very thing the first day of school.

"All the girls at school wanted you, you know?"

"What did they matter when I had you?"

"See? Tease."

He laughed. "It's not a tease if it's the truth. When I'm with you, nothing and no one else matters. You're my whole universe."

"Gavin," she whispered, her cheeks going pink.

He'd worshipped her when they were together, spending every possible second with her. And if he wasn't with her, he was writing lines of lyrics or poetry to her on scraps of paper. She was both his escape and his home. He invested everything he had into her. In return, she'd made him her life, supporting his musical ambitions and providing a safe place to land when he would run out of his house after fighting with his father. He had big dreams and visions for the future, but she was a grounding influence that he needed just as much. So, he wasn't exaggerating when he said she was his universe.

"Well, the way you do that—make someone feel like they're the center of your universe? You bring that energy to the stage, too. You're . . . magnetic. You must know that. With all those screaming girls in the audience?"

There was a bit of jealousy in her voice and for the first time, he thought about their two worlds colliding and what it might mean for the future. But he didn't want to give over to examining that. Not right now.

"Ah, it's all part of the live show experience. Clapping, shouting."

She arched a skeptical brow but let it go. "So, then what happened at the radio station?"

"Oh, em, we basically got thrown out of the guy's office with no hope about being played."

"Oh, that sucks."

"Yeah, it did. But on our way out, we ran into Sean Reynolds—the very same fella who played our bootleg to begin with. We introduced ourselves and he was shocked to see how young we were. We gave him the demo and basically begged him to play it."

"Did he?"

"No," he said with a laugh. "Not even after he said he was impressed with our confidence and that if we were as good as we claimed, he'd want to be able to one day claim to have discovered us."

"His loss."

"Well, the thing is, he's been trying to act as if he had some hand in our success. When we hooked up with James—our manager—and got signed, Reynolds made the biggest noise over our album. He's fucking obsessed with trying to say he discovered us. Of course, playing a bootleg one time on a whim doesn't make it true. Still, he's our biggest fan to this day."

"As long as it works in your favor, right?" she said. She dipped a French fry in ranch dressing before taking a bite.

She wore nothing but the white bathrobe provided by the hotel. Her hair was tousled and her makeup was smudged. He had never seen a sexier woman in his life. The look in his eye must have given him away as she returned his gaze with her own open desire.

He leaned toward her and the trays of food slid to the center of the bed. Rather than take the time to clear it away, he took her hand and pulled her with him to the aqua-tiled bathroom. As she watched, he adjusted the hot and cold tub faucets to get the right temperature.

She opened the mirrored medicine cabinet and found a bottle of

Kiehl's bath and shower gel. She poured a stream of it into the water and bubbles quickly multiplied.

"Bring the shampoo," he told her. "I got you dirty. Time to clean you up."

She smiled and did as he said.

The tub was small but they fitted themselves together, her back to his front. With inordinate care, he wet her hair with a washcloth and proceeded to lather it with the shampoo. Ensuring that no soap got into her eyes, he rinsed her hair and then conditioned it as well. He massaged her scalp and the base of her neck as he went.

"That was another first," she said, leaning back into him when he was done.

"What's that, darlin'?"

"Having my hair washed that way. That felt so nice."

He wrapped his arm around her and gave her a squeeze. "It all feels so fucking good, being with you again."

She looked back at him with a smile and he leaned forward to kiss her.

"What did you mean by 'another' first?" he asked as he trailed a soapy washcloth over her belly and between her breasts.

"Just, you know, because you're my first. And only."

That took a moment to register in his sleep-deprived mind. When he looked at her, she averted her eyes. He touched her chin to turn her face up to his.

"Really?"

She nodded and he couldn't hide his confusion.

"What?"

"I just, em, I don't understand how you couldn't have been with anyone else. You're the most beautiful girl I've ever seen."

"Well, it's not because no one wanted me," she said with mock incredulity and he laughed. "I just never found the right connection."

"Interesting."

It had taken ages for her to go all the way with him when they were at school, but he still remembered well the way she had undressed herself for him without any first-time nervousness. The thought that no one else had touched her with this kind of intimacy was enormously satisfying to his male ego. And though he didn't say it out loud, he was overcome with the desire to be not just her first, but her last.

17

SOPHIE

It was after ten o'clock when a repetitive knock at the door woke Sophie. She and Gavin were tangled together in bed, too tired and comfortable to respond.

"Gavin, get your arse up. We need to get going."

She recognized Conor's voice behind the door. The steady knock continued and it didn't appear that Conor had any intention of stopping until he got an answer. His persistence worked because Gavin finally stirred.

"Leave it!" Gavin called.

"Let me in, ya fucker. What'd you get so busy chasing skirt last night, you forgot us lads?"

"Go ahead," Sophie said quietly. She slipped on the hotel robe and went into the bathroom, leaving the door partially open.

She watched Gavin pull on his boxer briefs and go to the door, opening it three inches.

"It's early yet, isn't it?" Gavin asked.

There was impatience in Conor's voice when he replied, "It's half bloody ten. We're meant to be in the car on the way to the venue at eleven."

"I didn't realize the time."

"She that good?"

She ducked behind the bathroom door when Conor looked over

Gavin's shoulder in an effort to see who had been keeping his friend so busy.

"Better than you can even imagine," Gavin said and Sophie could hear the smile in his voice.

"Congratulations. Now, let's fucking go."

"I'll meet you down in the lobby."

"Don't keep us waiting."

Sophie emerged from the bathroom as Gavin closed the door. She knew the exchange she just heard meant their time was over. What a night it had been, though. It had been a delicious taste of what a real reunion might be like. They had amazing chemistry, of course, but the familiarity that came with knowing and understanding each other was even more exciting. There was an ache in her chest now that they had to say goodbye all over again.

"Looks like we need to be down in the lobby in less than a half hour," he said, pulling her into his arms.

"I heard. I know you have to go."

"*We* need to go, darlin'. You're coming with us. With me. Right?"

She knew that to spend the day with him was only prolonging the inevitable. He would soon be moving on to the next city. That didn't stop her from wanting to be with him every second before then, though.

"Yeah, sure. I have VIP tickets, anyway, don't I?" she said and he smiled.

———

Sophie knew this wasn't the best way to ingratiate herself with the other boys of Rogue all over again. Though she had done what she could to clean herself up, it would be obvious she had spent the night with Gavin. Her unbrushed hair was tied into a messy bun. Her makeup was mostly gone, leaving her with only the lip-gloss from her purse. And she wore no panties beneath her sundress, though only Gavin was privy to that.

Gavin led the way, holding her hand as she trailed behind him into the lobby. The large space had high ceilings with dark wood beams, arched entryways, and elegant Mission Oak furniture. There was a buzz of activity as other guests organized their excursions for the day. A couple decked out in matching denim shorts and tank tops scanned the room in a transparent celebrity sighting effort but they looked right past Gavin.

Conor saw his friend straightaway, though, because she heard him call out. "Let's go, lover boy."

His raised voice made some of the other guests turn his way, but it was his striking good looks that earned him a second glance. He was impeccably groomed, with his short black hair styled into a fauxhawk and his face cleanly shaven. He wore dark jeans, folded precisely at the cuff two times, and a soft gray cotton tee shirt that clung to his muscled chest, showcasing his devotion to fitness. A silver pocket chain that had become his signature, made a loop from his front pocket to his back jeans belt loop.

Sophie recognized in his good looks and careful style the epitome of a rock star. He was made for this.

She placed her other hand on Gavin's forearm and her appearance seemed to trigger in Conor a wild mixture of emotions. First it was surprise, but that turned into a sweet smile before fading into what she had seen at the Palladium: lust. Finally, frustration took over.

She had to blink to clear all that away. It was a lot to take in when she was already apprehensive about seeing them all.

"Isn't this brilliant?" Gavin asked as they got to Conor. "She came round last night to see me before the show today."

Conor raised his eyebrows and stared at her for a beat too long. "Good to see you again, Soph."

"You too!" She gave him a quick hug.

"Em, and you're coming with us, then?"

She looked to Gavin with renewed hesitation.

"Yes, she is," Gavin said with a note of finality in his voice.

Conor turned and started out to the hotel driveway, mumbling "fuck me" under his breath.

"Is this a bad idea?" Sophie said. "I don't want to interfere."

"It's fine, darlin'. Relax."

She nodded and followed him to the black Suburban idling at the curb. Conor disappeared inside and Gavin wrapped his arm around her neck, pulling her so they could both look into the car.

"Lads, look who I've got," Gavin said with a grin.

"Sophie!" Martin said. "Why amn't I surprised to see you?"

She laughed.

"Because it's the natural fit, isn't it?" Shay said and winked at her.

"Good to see you guys," she said. It felt better than good to see them. Shay was right. Being back in the company of these boys felt like returning home.

"After you, darlin'," Gavin said, gesturing for her to get into the car. He slid in after her, sitting to her right while Conor was on her left. Martin and Shay were in the third row. Gavin made the introduction to their manager, James Kelly, who sat in the front passenger seat opposite their driver for the day.

"It's nice to meet you," Sophie said, offering him her hand.

"You're the one, are you?" he asked in return. He gave her hand a brisk shake.

She wasn't sure how to take that greeting. "Um, I guess?"

"We've got plenty of time to get acquainted. I hear Irvine is a bit of a drive."

"WELL, then, I guess it's good you're here," Conor told Sophie.

As if orchestrated, James then handed him the entertainment section of the *Los Angeles Times*. He, in turn, held it up for her to see.

The headline read "Mystery Girl Rocks Rogue Singer on KROQ." It was a short article on the inside pages, detailing the phone conversation Gavin had had with Sophie live on the radio the day before. The angle was that the call had generated so much interest that an informal campaign had formed to discover who "Sophie" was and whether she would give Gavin another chance. The article said the station had been inundated with calls asking for more information on what was behind the episode. The only official comment from the station was that they, too, hoped to learn the answer when Sophie showed up at the Weenie Roast.

Sophie was stunned, but saw that Gavin was bemused.

Conor was barely able to contain his irritation, saying, "This isn't what we're about, this, this—"

"What?" Gavin asked with a lazy smile.

"'Spectacle' is the word I'm after," Conor said. "James and I agree on this, you know."

"That so, Jamie?" Gavin asked.

"It's not exactly the focus we need," James said. "We had some momentum going and this feels like a huge distraction. No offense, sweetheart."

Sophie raised her chin and maintained eye contact with the band manager. A small piece of her feared that if she let herself be defined as a distraction, Gavin might agree and their time would be cut even shorter. It was that instinct that led her to speak up, replying, "None taken, *sweetheart*."

It got very quiet in the car.

Conor raised his eyebrows and she was about to apologize when she saw Gavin grinning. His reaction was a reminder that he had always liked when she came back at him.

"It's really good to see you, Sophie," Shay said, dispelling the tension. He had always been the peacemaker of the group.

Turning in her seat, Sophie smiled at him and returned the sentiment. Talk for the rest of the drive turned to more benign subjects. They fell into their old easy banter with one another as Sophie apologized to Martin for revealing the origin of the band's name. He took it in stride and playfully made her promise she would never speak of it again. Even Conor loosened up and joined in, admitting that Martin had actually gotten off easy, as all anyone cared about was Gavin's mysterious love story, not Martin's moment of dumb luck in landing on the band name.

She should have known better than to be nervous about being a part of this group of boys again. They were all sweethearts.

The Irvine Meadows Amphitheatre's main stage capacity was 16,000, but Rogue performed their soundcheck to the few dozen festival crew members going about their jobs and ignoring them. Sophie was the lone voice of support and Gavin played to her, much to Conor's annoyance.

71

Afterward, they crammed into the backstage tents. For an area that was supposed to be exclusive, it was overrun with musicians, techies, PR people for the bands performing, PR people for the radio station, radio station personnel, and catering crews, as well as the odd groupie who slipped through.

Rogue had time to kill since they were performing as the third-to-last act for the evening, with just The White Stripes and Foo Fighters after them. It was a heady atmosphere with so many big names mingling.

Though Gavin and the others readily accepted both the free-flowing alcohol and marijuana going around, they declined the offers of harder substances. Sophie hoped that was due to more than the fact that they would be performing that day.

While Gavin was careful to keep Sophie with him as he chatted with the other artists, she purposely took a passive role rather than engaging. It was an overwhelming but enlightening introduction to what had become his world. She loved how familiar he was with the other bands, using nicknames and easily slipping in and out of conversations with dozens of people. She also loved that nobody had anything but music on their minds. The intrigue of who she was had been lost on them.

Once they got word that Interpol was playing at one of the side stages, they braved the sun and the crush of the crowd, squeezing their way to the rail. When Conor saw that Sophie was using her hand as a shield against the bright afternoon light, he handed her his sunglasses.

"I want them back," he said.

They were classic black Oliver Spencer sunglasses with a distinctive red tip on one arm. Sophie knew they were expensive and it was fitting that Conor was indulging in a higher-end style. He'd always been the one most concerned with his image.

"But they look so cute on me," she said playfully.

Conor raised his eyebrows and tried to hide a small smile. "Not better than on me."

"No offense, darlin', but he might be right. He is a pretty bastard!" Gavin said and the three of them laughed.

Once the band started, the crowd rushed forward and Gavin pulled Sophie in front of him so that his arms were on either side of her, his hands on the barrier rail as he leaned his body into hers. She loved the posture as it was at once protective and possessive. Turning slightly, she looked back at him and touched his cheek. When he grinned back at her, she knew she had never stopped loving him. This, being here in his world, in his arms, was exactly where she wanted to be.

18

SOPHIE

The first thing Sophie noticed when she got home was the stillness. Her parents were due back from their latest excursion sometime that afternoon. The previous year, they had sold their tech company for a small fortune and relocated permanently to this Malibu beach house. They had a non-compete clause with the sale of the business and had been enjoying their forced relaxation time by traveling extensively—this time to Namibia. The solitude this gave her was exactly what she needed after the whirlwind of the last forty-eight hours. God, had it only been forty-eight hours?

She had nearly lost her voice screaming for Rogue during their performance at the Weenie Roast. The intense energy from the crowd heightened hers, and she ended up having the time of her life.

The boys had performed aggressively, with crisp playing that popped in the electricity of the evening. Gavin was in good spirits and enjoying their set so much that it carried over to the audience. He was skilled at keeping a connection going with them, whether through guiding a call and response during their songs or with chatter between songs that went beyond the usual "thank you" most bandleaders automatically employed.

"The sun's gone down," Gavin said at one point and the crowd cheered blindly, apparently agreeing that it had gone dark. "So why the fuck is it still so hot?" He took off his black tee shirt and used it to wipe his face.

The screams at his show of skin were ear-piercing and Gavin laughed into the microphone. "You like what you see, yeah?" he asked playfully, and was rewarded with more cheers. "Scream a little louder, maybe you'll get Conor to strip down."

Conor raised his eyebrows as he looked at Gavin disapprovingly. When the crowd began to shout "Conor! Conor! Conor!" he responded by beginning the next song, whether his bandmates were ready or not.

"Sorry, ladies and gents," Gavin said. He held his arms open wide for a moment, striking a pose. "You'll have to settle for this." He threw his sweaty tee shirt down by Shay's drum kit and found his timing with the song.

After the show, they stayed on and watched the headliners. The first after-party took place at the venue and Sophie watched with increasing unease as Conor pursued—and was pursued by—various groupies. Seeing how comfortable he was with girls he just met, how quickly he progressed to pressing his body against theirs as he chatted them up, was a too-intimate view into what Gavin had very likely spent the last few years doing as well.

The party eventually moved back to the Chateau Marmont where a large group that included several young actors put on an impromptu ping-pong tournament in the courtyard. The hotly competitive, obnoxiously drunk group was still going when Sophie suggested she and Gavin leave at four in the morning. They spent the rest of the morning in bed together before James retrieved Gavin to prepare for an interview he and Conor would be doing with *Rolling Stone* magazine. Sophie and Gavin agreed to meet later that afternoon at the CBS studios in Los Angeles for Rogue's taping of a performance on the Craig Kilborn Late Show. The free time meant she could go home to Malibu to clean up and get a change of clothes.

Now, she kicked off her sandals and padded across the gleaming hardwood floors of her parents' house toward the marble and stainless-steel kitchen. She pulled a bottle of sparkling water from the Sub-Zero and took it with her through the wall of glass doors and out onto the deck.

The house was situated on the sand in exclusive Carbon Beach, an area that stretched a mile and a half from the Malibu Pier south toward Santa Monica. It was the least spectacular home in the wealthy enclave, but it was enviable nevertheless. Both of its stories had fourteen-foot ceilings and an abundance of windows to take advantage of the ocean views. Minimally but comfortably furnished, the style inside had a classic and clean feel, with sheer cream curtains at the windows that flowed with the salty breeze.

At times like this when there was no one else home, Sophie liked to settle onto one of the padded teak lounge chairs on the deck and let her mind drift. There was a thin layer of fog hugging the ocean, but the sun's heat beat through it. She shaded her eyes with her hand against the glare, looking up and down the coastline, unsurprised to find the sand empty. Though all California beaches from the water line up to the high tide line are technically public land, the seventy-odd homeowners of this area had never been particularly inclined to provide access.

Closing her eyes, she let the sun warm her through. She was running on too little sleep, but it put her in a mellow, happy state rather than one of exhaustion. Being with Gavin these last two days was the happiest she had ever been, despite the fact that their time was running out. The band was scheduled to leave the day after next. They had five more music festivals, all scattered around the East coast. They then headed to New York City to attend MTV's Video Music Awards show as both nominees and performers. After that they were scheduled to get back home to Dublin to start work on their second album even though Gavin had confessed they didn't have any material for it. The band had toured the hell out of their first album, expending all their energy on the performances. They might have kept playing gigs had their label not insisted they start to make efforts toward new music.

Gavin was still in a state of semi-disbelief about the band's success and current position of being under the gun to make a new album. It was, he'd admitted, both thrilling and terrifying. He confessed that he worried that the success of the first album could well be a fluke. Then what? Sophie had fallen into her old role of biggest supporter, assuring him that he only had to trust himself for it all to flow and watched as he nodded in agreement. He had been gratefully, willfully convinced.

They hadn't discussed, however, any kind of future together. Sophie tried to steel herself against the inevitable heartache she would feel once he was gone from her life again. The conversation she'd had with her friend Felicity back in their school days came to mind. Felicity had known with an old soul's confidence that this would be the typical scenario for anyone trying to date one of the boys from Rogue, and she had preemptively guarded against it. It had been smart, Sophie knew. But at the same time, she knew herself. She didn't have that kind of strength and willpower when it came to matters of the heart. Especially not matters of the heart that involved Gavin.

She'd lost all self-control that moment in his hotel room when he'd declared he'd been heartbroken when she'd walked away from him. Because the unspoken implication was that she had repeated what his mother had done. From the moment she had her first real conversation with him back in school, she saw that a deep part of him was wounded. He did his best to hide the hurt with boisterous confidence and a preternatural drive toward music. He had only opened the door of his hurt a sliver with her at first. Then, in his own way, he had thrown it wide open and essentially begged her to enter. He didn't want her to know him, he *needed* it.

In return, he'd worshipped at her feet and fulfilled the unrealistic romantic visions of love instilled in her by the princess paradigm movies she had grown up with, including the illusion of having a unique power to heal her tragic true love.

They had fallen right back into the same dynamic in the last couple of days, Sophie realized. It was so easy being with him. They were simply *good* together. The love they'd found in school had been genuine and more mature than it should have been given their ages. But it had been *real*. And it still existed.

None of which mattered now, Sophie knew. She opened her eyes and with the brightness of the sun came the sting of tears. Gavin was soon moving on. To the next city. To the next girl. Just as he had told her at the Palladium gig.

If that was to be the case, she resolved to make the rest of their time as memorable as possible. She knew she would be feeding off the memories for years to come, after all.

19

C onor was so frustrated he could barely sit still. He and Gavin had been speaking with John Riley from *Rolling Stone* magazine for close to an hour and nearly every question was focused on chipping away at the Sophie "mystery." That *Los Angeles Times* article had only been the beginning of the publicity their reunion had garnered. The photos of them from the Weenie Roast were plastered everywhere. One particular photo of them gazing at each other as if they were the only ones in the crowd at the Interpol show had struck a nerve. And just like that, they had gone from being an up and coming band to some sort of tabloid fodder. In Conor's mind, it was a disastrous turn of events because he feared this meant their music would get lost in the frenzy.

For this interview, he had deferred to Gavin, but his friend had uncharacteristically ducked straight answers, which only seemed to pique the reporter's interest all the more.

"And how old is she?" Riley asked, sending Conor to his feet with a plaintive look directed at James.

"Is something wrong?" Riley turned his tape recorder off.

"No problem," James said. "Conor's just the restless sort."

Conor reluctantly retook his seat but threw his head back against the overstuffed chair. They had convened in the living area of the Chateau Marmont's penthouse suite. French doors opened onto a tan and brown striped awning that partially covered a balcony overlooking greater Los Angeles. The midday May sun, combined with a layer of smog, made the sprawling buildings appear to be a mere suggestion of a city as the edges went soft.

He looked out at the view, longing to escape out into it. This interview was a big deal, but James was being too patient with letting Gavin skirt around the issue. As their manager, he should have stepped in to redirect the reporter to the point—the music. But he hadn't stepped in, and instead had now sent a signal that he wanted Conor to keep waiting things out as well.

The reporter had waited patiently for an answer to his question and now Gavin picked up the tape recorder and turned it over in his hands.

"The thing is, Johnny," he said familiarly, "Rogue is of the mind that the focus should be on the music. We all have personal lives, and playing up mine seems trivial and irrelevant when we figure our music offers actual substance. Now, you're a journalist. I understand you have to ask the questions, but in order to get answers, you'll have to tell me how the readers of a music magazine like yours will be served to know details about the girl I'm with."

With that, Gavin put down the recorder and emptied his bottle of Stella Artois. They had all picked at the buffet lunch, happier to indulge in the array of beers on ice.

Riley eyed Gavin while biting on the end of his pen thoughtfully. Conor imagined the reporter was confused by Gavin's reticence. Gavin had begun the interview as his usual self—charming, open, and bright. But that disappeared with the questions about Sophie.

"You have to admit," Riley said, "you're playing naïve about the whole thing. This girl calling into the radio station—if it wasn't a publicity stunt, well then, it was brilliant luck."

"It was not a stunt," Gavin said adamantly.

"Okay, I'll take your word. But maybe you should hear a playback of the call, because what has sparked this intense interest, what got you and this girl in the LA Times and all over the internet, is the sound in your voice. The way I'd write about it is this: the desperation in your voice to connect with this girl was so strong, so naked, that you instantly won over every girl who has ever wanted to be wanted by a boy. So, yeah, Rogue is going to get more attention now than it ever has. It may not be precisely for the reasons you'd like, but it makes your band a household name." Riley paused for effect. "That's something hard to come by, and I'd argue that you take this story for all it's worth because you do seem to be the real deal. You've got the music to back up the extra attention."

"You'll forgive me if I'm reluctant to whore myself out," Gavin said, and Riley laughed.

"Fuck it, Gav," Conor said. He was done waiting this out. If James wasn't going to step in, he would. "Go ahead—tell the story, the whole bloody thing. It's all going to come out anyway. At least this way, initially, we'll have some control."

Riley looked to Conor as he switched on his recorder. "Why don't you tell me your version of the story, Conor?"

Conor looked at Gavin, and when his friend didn't object, he realized Gavin was purposely stepping back so that he could shape this the way he wanted. It was a concession he appreciated.

"I'll give you the quick and dirty version. It's not all that complicated. Sophie came to Dublin when she was sixteen. We all met her in school. She was there for the school year. She and Gav fell in love. She had to go home. Hearts were broken. She finished school here, and we worked on our band. We came to America on tour, saw Sophie last September at our Palladium show, but then had to move on to the next gig. Next thing we know, we get a call at the radio station. The two are reunited and everyone's happy. End of story."

"Except everyone doesn't quite seem happy," Riley said.

"Meaning?"

"Well, I'm sensing a bit of attitude, is all."

"Oh, I'm only *delighted*. I'm just one of those who believe in focusing on the music."

"Okay, Conor, tell me about the music. Tell me about the writing process."

Conor took a deep breath and was happy to launch into a detailed description of how the band worked together to create their music. Gavin joined in and the two inadvertently demonstrated the fluid way they played off each other. It was a display of how their childhood bond had developed over the years into an indispensable music partnership.

They were so involved in the conversation that they were startled when Gavin's cell phone rang.

"Really, Gav?" Conor said. "You should have switched it off."

"I'll do it now," Gavin said. But when he took the phone out of his pocket no one in the room, least of all Riley, could mistake the change that came over him. His posture straightened, his shoulders pulled back, and an excited gleam came to his eyes as a broad smile lit up his face.

"It's Sophie," Gavin said. "Just—"

"Don't you even think about it," Conor said. "We're in the middle of a fucking interview."

Gavin visibly struggled with what he would do next.

"I'll be just a second," he said, and got up.

Conor wasn't used to Gavin putting the band in second place, and he seethed as he watched him walk out onto the balcony. He could just imagine the impression Riley had now and how the article would be written. It would be all about the whipped singer of the up-and-coming Irish band that could have made it to the big time, if only their Yoko hadn't taken over.

"So, Conor," Riley said, "do you get along with Sophie?"

It wasn't easy, but he thought he did a good job of hiding his temper over the question.

"Sure. She's grand."

"Gavin is notorious for being . . . *generous* in interviews, happy to pontificate on any given subject. Why do you suppose he's holding back now?"

It was a good question. Not that Conor wanted to focus on Sophie, but he was just as surprised as the reporter was by Gavin's lack of candor. Maybe it was because Gavin wasn't really sure how to define this fling with Sophie.

But he simply raised his eyebrows and offered nothing more than a shrug. Whatever was going on with Gavin, he wasn't about to throw him under the bus.

"Sorry about that," Gavin said as he returned.

"Anything wrong?" Riley asked.

"Hmm? Oh, no. Thanks."

"So, Sophie lives in Los Angeles. You live in Dublin. How does that work?"

"We'll figure it out. It'll work."

"How?"

"Love conquers all, doesn't it?" Gavin said with a wink.

Love? Conor had to summon all his strength to keep from questioning Gavin on that one. He didn't want to provoke a bigger reaction out of Riley than he already had. But with that one word, Gavin had just revealed he'd been keeping quiet about Sophie, not because he wasn't sure what they meant, but because he thought they meant something too special to share.

Just what the fuck was happening here? It was ridiculous to think Sophie was going to play a part in Gavin's—in the *band's*—future. They were too focused. They were having too much fun touring and partying and bedding a different girl every night.

Thankfully, James stepped in before he could go any farther down this rabbit hole of worry to suggest they end the interview so the band could get ready to go to the Craig Kilborn taping.

20

GAVIN

"Are you sure you know where you're going?" Gavin asked.

He was blindly following Sophie up a dirt trail in the Hollywood Hills. They had caught the last remnants of a warm orange sunset and were rapidly losing light as night came on. The buzz he had from the sake at their sushi dinner was beginning to wear off as he heard creatures scurry in the brush.

After the taping of the Craig Kilborn show, Sophie had insisted on taking everyone—including John Riley—to the acclaimed Japanese restaurant Matsuhisa in Beverly Hills for an early dinner. It was the first time any of the Irishmen had tried sashimi and, with the exception of Martin, they enjoyed the exotic offerings. The sake had been especially well received and served to make for a round of lively conversation as the group forgot about the reporter's presence and reminisced about the "old days" with Sophie.

They had all playfully teased Sophie when she used a black American Express card to pay for the meal, even though she explained that the bills went straight to her parents. For reasons Gavin couldn't quite understand, he was uneasy at this nonchalant display of wealth, but he took pains to dismiss it.

After Sophie settled the check, Gavin was willingly taken away by her, even as the boys responded with good-natured whistles and knowing grins. He was happy to see the easy familiarity she had regained within the group, though he suspected it came in part from the fact that she was once again only a temporary player. Just as when they were in school together, the underlying understanding that she wouldn't always be there lent a confessional nature to their interactions. They could safely share of themselves without worrying that it would somehow come back to haunt them.

Gavin had been too busy talking, hyped up from the band's television performance and the dinner, to take note of where Sophie was driving them in her sporty white BMW 325i. She had wound around the narrow, densely populated streets up into the hills before parking in front of an upscale home toward the end of Beachwood Drive.

"What's this? Don't you live at the beach?" he asked, even though the street name contradicted the fact that the ocean wasn't anywhere in view.

"This isn't my house, silly. We're going on an adventure. Come with me," she said, and pulled a backpack out of the backseat.

Now he was following her past the hum of caged electrical equipment and a red and white radio tower as her flashlight bobbed along the path.

"We're almost there," she told him.

The wind picked up as they approached the peak but it was a warm evening. She had promised that the trek would be worth it, and he had seen glimpses of city lights beginning to burn bright in the deepening darkness that confirmed this. As they went, she told him about her classes at USC and the fact that she had taken her last final the same day as calling into the radio station. The summer break was upon her and the only plans she had were to possibly travel with her parents. He had been about to interrupt her careful talk about the future when she stopped walking.

"You go first," she told him, and pointed with the flashlight up a steep dirt hill.

Now he knew why she had changed out of her strappy sandals and into running shoes at the car. His own lace-up boots were covered in dirt and he had had several near misses with horse manure.

"Come with me, then," he said and pulled her hand.

As he came to the top of the hill, he was astounded by the view. They were directly above the huge white letters of the iconic Hollywood sign, with the entire city spread out and lit up before them. The downtown buildings to the left stood tall amongst the sprawl. To their right, a reservoir glittered under the moonlight. He tried in vain to see where the lights ended, and the enormity and beauty of the golden glow brought a smile to his face.

Sophie put her arm around his waist and leaned into him as he held her in return.

"What do you think?"

"It's brilliant," he murmured.

It was hard to wrap his head around the view. They were alone, with only the sound of crickets and the odd rustling of small animals. The warm air smelled of the pleasantly pungent combination of earthy shrubs and cooling dirt. It was peaceful and invigorating at the same time. He couldn't imagine a better way to see Los Angeles.

"I've never been here at night," she said. "I'm pretty sure we're trespassing. But I wanted to do something memorable for one of your last nights."

He turned to her and kissed her, long and softly. The ache in his chest soon spread throughout his whole body as he held her to him. The effort she had made was not lost on him. It reinforced what he had believed during their time together before, that she was an extraordinary girl, unlike any he would ever find again. The fact that she had planned out this adventure, as she called it, to create a unique memory for them to share, was all he needed to confirm what he had felt the moment he saw her at his hotel room doorstep. She was the one.

"I'm glad you like it," she said in a whisper.

He knew without looking that there were tears in her eyes. She was feeling the same thing he was of not wanting to say goodbye.

Pulling away, he took her face into his hands and made eye contact. "I never loved a girl before you, and I haven't loved anyone since. I still love you something desperate. There's no way I want this to be one of our last nights."

She nodded and blinked away the tears.

"You didn't take me seriously the first time. Take me seriously now." He took a deep breath. "Marry me. I want you to marry me."

He couldn't read her in the long, cruel thirty seconds of silence that followed as her eyes left his and focused beyond his shoulder.

The sensation he felt of sinking was either his heart or his suddenly unstable knees.

"Gavin—"

Before she could refuse him, he pressed his lips to hers once more. He closed his eyes tightly, not sure whether he wanted her to feel the disappointment in his kiss or not.

"Baby," she said as she pulled away.

"Darlin', I'm not able to hear you say no or laugh it off. So, don't say anything, okay? We'll just enjoy the view." He turned back to gaze upon the lights.

"But the answer is yes," she said.

He was slow to understand and turned to her with a look he knew expressed his disbelief. "For definite?" he asked.

She nodded and smiled, tears once again filling her eyes.

Their next kiss was filled with a mixture of giddiness and awe at the audacity of what they had done.

21

I t was the distinctly noticeable noise one makes when trying to be quiet that woke Sophie the next morning. Gavin was dressing while on his cell phone as he looked out the hotel window, his voice hushed but insistent.

Staying as still as she could, Sophie wondered if this meant he had taken to heart the out she'd tried to give him before they fell asleep. After returning to the Chateau Marmont, he had ordered champagne through room service. It was yet another example of how easily they were able to drink despite being underage—a nice benefit of Gavin's fame, she supposed. They had enjoyed the entire bottle together in celebration of their engagement.

But as they lay together on the verge of sleep, Sophie's more prudent nature finally came to the forefront. She knew that agreeing to marry Gavin was reckless. She would be twenty in July, but that didn't mean she was ready for marriage. Marriage to a rock star, no less. Her more fantastical side wanted to dive deep into the sheer romance of the evening they had shared overlooking the city lights. But she also feared that he had been giving into that good feeling too, and that the practicalities of what he was proposing hadn't been even remotely considered.

"Gavin," she had said softly. Her head was nestled into the crook of his arm, her naked body pressed against his.

"Hmm?"

"I know that this—us—feels good. But it doesn't have to be marriage. I mean, I'm not going to hold you to that. Everything has happened so fast. I understand if you want to just see how things go."

He shifted slightly but didn't respond.

"Baby?"

"Let's talk later, darlin'," he said in a sleepy mumble.

Now he was busy making some sort of plan and she realized she had better get up. But doing so seemed like waking herself up from the best dream she had ever had, and so she stayed curled up in bed instead.

"Darlin'? Wake up for me," Gavin said.

She reluctantly opened her eyes and saw him crouched down by the bed, watching her. His face was covered in stubble from the last few days, giving his usual disheveled appearance an even sexier edge.

"I need your help with something." He held up a piece of paper with scribbled notes. "Will you drive me?"

Sophie was preoccupied as she followed Gavin's directions, driving through West Hollywood and along Santa Monica Boulevard. As they neared Beverly Hills, palm trees began to neatly line the streets against the backdrop of the clear morning sky.

Meanwhile, Gavin toyed with the radio and when he heard "Last Night" followed by "All My Life," and "Fell In Love With A Girl," he regaled Sophie with his theory that they were experiencing a rich period in music with the likes of The Strokes, Foo Fighters, and The White Stripes, respectively, making their mark. "Clocks" by Coldplay came on and that sent him off on a rant about how close Chris Martin was to being a good front man but that he was clearly lacking confidence. He declared "Toxicity" by System of a Down too heavy-handed, but thought Chris Cornell's effort with Audioslave was one of the better transitions of a singer into a new band that he had seen.

As Gavin's commentary went on, Sophie's doubts about his commitment to her grew. He hadn't mentioned their engagement once, and seemed more interested in this random errand than making the most of their last full day together.

"Here. Turn here," he told her.

When she realized that he was taking her down Rodeo Drive, she rolled her eyes. When had he become the kind of person who wanted to do this kind of sightseeing?

"Park around here. Any spot is good."

It was still early, not yet ten in the morning, and only a handful of people were on the sidewalk. She found a vacant metered spot and pulled over.

"You know, nothing's going to be open yet," she said as he took her hand and led her down the street.

"Guess what? Turns out my limited celebrity actually has some perks."

"What does that mean?" She knew there was an edge of irritation in her voice that came off as petulance. The romance of last night had been an incredible high and now it was like crash-landing into banal reality.

"I was on the phone earlier, before you got up, with our business manager. She's helping me sort this out."

Sophie stopped walking, now completely confused. "What are you even talking about, Gavin?"

He laughed. "Listen, darlin', I'm told this is the place to get what we need. And they're willing to open up early for us."

She looked at the gray stone building in front of them on this manicured street. The fact that it was Tiffany & Co. didn't register. Had he really dragged her out here to get a gift for his business manager?

"I don't—"

"We are here, sweet girl," he said slowly, emphatically, "to pick a ring."

She took in a quick breath, feeling both thrilled and stupid. How had she managed to mangle this incredible gesture?

Gavin stroked her cheek with the back of his fingers. "I heard what you said last night, Sophie," he said. "And I know what you mean. I know how scary this all seems. You and I have spent years apart and it's fair to worry that we don't know each other anymore. The thing is, I have no doubt that I love you. I love you for what you were and I know I'll love you for what you've become. I absolutely want to marry you. What do you say?"

Wiping at the tear escaping her eye, Sophie smiled. "You sure know how to sweep a girl off her feet."

Gavin laughed and kissed her. Pressing his forehead to hers, he whispered, "Will you marry me, Sophie?"

"Yes," she whispered back.

———

INSIDE THE STORE, there were four employees and they all had their eyes trained on them. Sophie smiled and said hello but the enormity of their task—finding that one ring to last a lifetime—was daunting.

"Just breathe," Gavin murmured to her, squeezing her hand.

She looked at him, relieved that he could read her. His hand was warm and reassuring.

A lovely saleswoman with a calm way about her took control then, showing them the various bands, settings, and cuts to choose from while also casually questioning Sophie about her own personal style.

Though the glittering jewelry was mesmerizing and she adored admiring all the options, Sophie quickly realized that the one setting that most pleased her was the classic Tiffany.

"Let's size you, then," the saleswoman said. She quickly established Sophie's ring size and pulled a solitaire diamond set on platinum out of a glass case. "Gavin, why don't you help Sophie with this?" She handed him the engagement ring.

Sophie looked at him and smiled, tickled by the fact that he was about to put a ring on her finger that held so much promise for their future.

"Shall I make a speech?" he asked with a smile.

"You've already made a couple of amazing speeches," she said.

He toyed with the ring for a moment before dropping down on one knee.

"Sophie Michelle Kavanaugh," he said and tears instantly sprang to her eyes. "I've broken your heart in the past. I never want to do that again. But if I do, I promise you that I will *always* mend it. I will be the *one* for you, just as you are the *one* for me. I love you fiercely, desperately, absolutely. Marry me, sweet girl, and make me whole."

"I'll marry you again and again and again," she said, smiling through her tears.

90

He slid the ring onto her finger and kissed the back of her hand before standing.

As they kissed, the store employees applauded softly.

"Will we always have an audience for special moments like this?" she whispered.

"Welcome to my world, darlin'. It's a wild ride, but we'll be okay."

She had no doubt about it.

22

GAVIN

"You've got to be kidding," Gavin said as Sophie led him inside her family's Malibu home.

A clear view of the ocean was visible through the entry hallway. The large sliding glass doors were open and the sheer curtains fluttered softly in the breeze. The sound of the waves crashing filled both his ears and his chest.

"You like?" Sophie said, smiling.

"It's amazing," he replied.

He turned to admire the colorful modern abstract artwork on the walls. They were real pieces, not prints, and the first paintings he had ever seen in someone's home. He had always known her parents were wealthy, but knowing and seeing was a different story. As he took in the warm, elegant front room with the plush living area to the right and pristine dining area to the left, he thought of how shocking Ireland must have been for Sophie. Not that his country had been in bad shape then. It had been on the cusp of the prosperous economic Celtic Tiger era, and none of the boys had come from impoverished or rough backgrounds. They'd grown up middle-class on the tame Southside of Dublin. But she had apparently come from a kind of wealth he hadn't even come close to fathoming. And yet, she had never presented herself as "better than" despite his insecure jabs at her when they first met. Instead, he was the one to feel that he wasn't worthy of her, always fearing in the back of his mind that he didn't deserve someone so refined.

"Is that you, Sophie?" a female voice called.

"Yes, we're here," Sophie replied, and pulled Gavin deeper into the house.

The hardwood floors carried through to the kitchen where they found an older, if less striking, version of Sophie.

"Mom, this is Gavin," Sophie said. She couldn't contain a big smile. "Baby, this is my mom."

"You can call me Maggie," she said, and offered her hand.

Gavin took her hand into both of his and shook it with warmth. "I'm so pleased to meet you," he said, keeping eye contact.

Her eyes were also hazel, but didn't quite have the spark Sophie's did. Tall, with blonde hair and high cheekbones, she was a natural beauty, but it was clear that her appearance wasn't a priority. She was dressed casually in shapeless khakis and a cotton top, her hair pulled into a hasty ponytail. She had been working on a laptop set in a nook in the kitchen and her reading glasses were now hanging from her neck on a beaded chain.

"Well, it is certainly nice to meet you! After all this time of hearing your name, and now here you are!" Maggie said with a smile.

"Yes, it seems the timing has worked in our favor. Didn't you just get back from a trip to Namibia, was it?"

"We did! Well, by way of London for a few days upon our return. The jet lag is phenomenal. But we're glad to be home now, and to have you over."

"I appreciate it as well, but I have to apologize for it being a short visit. I'm due back with the band for a photo shoot soon."

"Well, that sounds exciting."

They all turned to see a man joining them. With dirty blond hair and wearing cargo shorts and a polo shirt, along with glasses perched over a hawkish nose, he had "dad" written all over him.

"Hey, Dad," Sophie said, and gave him a hug.

"Good to see you, kid." As he pulled away, he held Sophie's hand and naturally looked down at the ring on her finger. It was a thin band of platinum with a round cut three-karat solitaire diamond. "And what is this?"

Gavin hoped his efforts at charming Maggie would allow for a favorable response from her now that their news was out.

"Surprise!" Sophie said with a smile. "We are engaged. And I'm so happy. We're so happy."

Steve looked at Maggie. "They're so happy, Mags," he said sardonically.

———

GAVIN WATCHED the concern color Sophie's face as she strained to hear her parents' conversation. They had retreated to the kitchen immediately after the engagement news with the excuse of getting them all something to drink. Their voices couldn't be heard clearly but it was obvious they were trying to process how to respond.

"It'll be okay," Gavin whispered. "Parents tend to love me."

She laughed nervously and he wished he had the chance to say something more to calm her, but Maggie and Steve returned with drinks.

The best he could do is squeeze her hand once they were seated and coupled off in the living room.

"So, em, I'm sure you're very surprised by all that's happened in such a short period," Gavin started.

"Surprised is probably a bit of an understatement," Steve replied, but with an affable smile.

"And you don't need me to tell you how special your daughter is —you've had her a lot longer than me. But I really aim to prove to you both how much I love her. She is the most important thing in the world to me."

Sophie leaned into him and smiled.

"That's nice to hear," Steve said. "In fact, I wouldn't expect to hear you say anything else."

It was hard for Gavin to read his future father-in-law. He wasn't sure what lay beneath his incongruously casual, pleasant manner, and it put him on guard.

Before he had a chance to go on the offensive, however, Maggie interrupted. "How much longer will you be in town, then?" she asked.

"I, em, I leave with the band tomorrow, actually."

"I see. So you must be planning a long engagement, so that you two can get to know each other again. That is, in between all this traveling."

"We actually have five more gigs, then an awards show. After that we'll be back in Dublin to work on our new album. We talked about Sophie spending the next few weeks sorting out how to transfer her university studies there and get her things ready in order to move. Because, though we have indeed agreed to a long engagement, we want to be together," Gavin said.

Steve and Maggie shared a silent glance before refocusing.

"So, this big move," Steve said. "You think this will happen, what, in time to start the new school year?"

"Yes," Sophie said with as much confidence as she could muster. "I'll have USC help me with transferring to a university there. I could attend Trinity, Dad. It's an amazing school. And being in Europe, in the heart of so much art history, it'll be an even better education."

"Well, Gavin," Steve said, "you've certainly convinced our daughter this is plausible. But why don't we cross this bridge when we come to it? We'll see how it all hashes out, won't we?"

It dawned on Gavin that Sophie's parents were counting on this being some sort of passing phase, something that would fade away when they were separated. This belief seemed to free them up to simply enjoy a nice visit with their daughter's guest.

Deciding it was most prudent to let her parents accept all this in their own fashion, Gavin nodded slowly. "Sure, you're right. We'll take it a step at a time."

A brief silence ensued.

"So, what's this whole rock star thing like?" Maggie asked, surprising Gavin so that he laughed quietly.

"It's amazing, actually. It's all I ever wanted to do with my life. And now I'm getting paid for it. The places I've seen, the people I've met along the way, though, that's more than anything I ever imagined. I love it," he told her. "But, please, tell me about your trip. It must have been fascinating."

"It is the land of dust and wind. I think I'm still cleaning remnants of red dirt out of my ears," Steve said with a laugh. "But it was truly beautiful. Out in the desert, it's absolutely devoid of people. Just animals and silence. The silence was the most intense thing I've ever experienced."

"Really?" Gavin edged forward in his seat.

Sophie's parents proceeded to tag-team in detailing their experiences and Gavin was fully engaged, peppering them with questions. Their rapport was smooth and comfortable. Except for the fact that they held no stock in him being a part of their family, it was a very pleasant first meeting.

When Sophie and her mother went to the kitchen to piece together a simple lunch, Steve took the opportunity to show Gavin some of his photographs. Conversation over sandwiches continued to flow in an easy manner, and afterward Sophie pulled Gavin away for a quick walk on the beach before they had to head back to Los Angeles.

They took off their shoes and held hands as they walked toward the water.

"Does it bother you that they think this is a joke?" Gavin asked.

Sophie looked at him, silent for a moment. "No. I guess I can't blame them. When we were getting lunch my mom asked me some questions that made sense. I can see where they're coming from."

"And where's that?"

"She asked me if we've agreed on having children and when. If I had enough trust in you to basically live alone while you're out on the road, living it up. If I've had enough experience with relationships to know that this is the one I want for the rest of my life. If I've even lived my own life long enough to know who I am and what I really want before I attach myself to you. If I was okay with all the media attention you get, and always being known as the girl who happens to be your girlfriend or wife."

He took a deep breath. "Shite. All that, aye?" he said with a laugh.

She gave him a small smile.

"Well, look, some of that I can help you with right now. Kids, I vote yes. Down the line, of course, but definitely yes. I think you'll be an amazing mother."

He knew telling her this would resonate deeply. Because she, of all people, knew how hard it was for him to have gone without a mother, so his confidence that she would make a good one wasn't something he came to lightly.

"As for the other stuff, all I can say is that I will give you whatever you need to explore those questions. But I think if we commit to it, we can figure it all out together."

Sophie watched him for a long moment, then smiled. "Wow," she said softly.

"What?"

"You made everything okay. Just like that."

Gavin smiled. "I do my best, darlin'. Now," he said, looking up and down the spotless coast, "it's a lovely day. Where is everyone?"

"Um, well, this is sort of unofficially a private beach for the home-owners. Public access isn't actually very accessible."

He shook his head in disgust. "What a waste. That's really a horrible show of elitist bullshit."

"Hey, it's not my doing, you know?" she said with a laugh.

"Yeah, sorry. But capitalism at its finest is not always pretty, is it?"

Taking his hand, she led him closer to the water. "No, but that doesn't mean you shouldn't take advantage of your access. Come, feel how nice the water is." With a firm shove, she sent him knee-deep into the water, soaking his jeans.

"You are in so much trouble," he growled playfully, and ran after her as she screamed.

23

Sophie and Gavin were more than thirty minutes late getting to the studio for the *Rolling Stone* magazine photo shoot. The guys didn't bother to mention the tardiness, though, once they saw Gavin's decidedly *un*-rock star clothes. Instead, they mercilessly mocked him for the oversized khaki cargo shorts and yellow polo shirt borrowed from Sophie's father after having taken an unexpected swim in the Pacific Ocean. He had enjoyed the warm water so much that they ran too late to do anything about his wet clothes. Steve's gear had done well enough in a pinch.

Gavin went along with the jokes and even made some at his own expense, all while the reporter John Riley watched from the back of the room. But as Sophie raised her hand to push back her hair, she glanced over at Conor and caught him staring daggers at her.

He raised his eyebrows and directed his gaze to her ring finger as a question and she smiled with a small acknowledging nod.

"Hang on, hang on." Conor held up his hands and got all their attention. "Gavin, are you serious with this?"

Gavin looked from Conor to Sophie and back again. "What's that?"

Conor reached out and took Sophie's left hand, holding it up to showcase the ring. "What the fuck is this all about? Tell me you are not getting married."

"Yeah, that is the plan." Gavin shrugged.

"You're not even twenty-one yet."

Gavin looked at his friend for a long moment. "Con, that's got nothing to do with it. All you need to know is that this is the real thing." He pulled Sophie to him, wrapping his arm around her shoulders.

"You've just fucked over the band. You know that?"

Sophie cringed at this declaration. It meant Conor was no fan of hers, that, in fact, he would blame her for anything negative that happened to the band. She also cringed at the fact that the Rolling Stone journalist was witness to all this.

"How do you figure that?" Gavin asked.

"A married lead singer? You've got to be joking."

"It'll be fine."

"It's a right fucking selfish move," Conor grumbled.

"Listen, Rogue can't be undone by this." Gavin's voice had been confident, insistent, but he searched Conor's eyes. "Right?"

The energy shifted in the room as Conor hesitated. Sophie recognized the need in Gavin's eyes. He needed Conor to not just accept this but support it. Gavin had always looked to Conor for approval, but this was something more. It was clear that if Conor didn't validate the engagement, the dynamics of the band would be irrevocably changed.

"Yeah, sure, you're right," Conor finally said. "Congratulations are due, I suppose."

Gavin smiled and released Sophie so he could embrace Conor.

"Congratulations, Sophie," Shay said. He gave her a hug. "You're good for him."

"Thanks," she said.

"Welcome to the club, then!" Martin said. He kissed Sophie on the cheek.

"Wait, what does that mean?"

"I'm getting married myself. Celia is her name. She's planning it all out for spring next year."

"That's fantastic!" Sophie hugged him.

"Yeah. Guess a married bass player doesn't rate the way it would for your man," Martin said with a laugh. There was no malice in his observation. He said it as a simple fact. "Anyway, I think you'll love my Celia."

"I can't wait to meet her."

WHILE GAVIN LOOKED for a wardrobe change with the magazine's stylist, Sophie sought out Conor. She found him in a chair in front of a large mirror, flirting with the makeup artist. Or rather, the makeup artist was flirting with him as she leaned against a narrow table filled with her supplies.

"What I wouldn't give to have those eyelashes," she told him. She was petite and her brown eyes were a stark contrast to her bleached white hair.

"You're doing just fine," he told her. "More than fine, actually."

She tried to hold back a smile. "What are you guys doing after this?"

"I'm not busy now," he told her with a smile so suggestive there was no mistaking it.

Sophie saw the color rise to the girl's cheeks. But rather than retreat demurely, she seemed ready to jump into Conor's lap there and then. Sophie understood the girl's impulse. Conor was model-handsome—and the guitar player in an up-and-coming rock band.

But allowing these two to follow their hormonal instincts would disrupt Sophie's plans of having a private talk with Conor, so she cleared her throat.

Conor glanced at her with irritation, but his expression quickly relaxed.

"Can I talk to you for a second?" Sophie asked, moving closer.

He watched her, his eyes lingering on hers before doing a quick scan over the rest of her body. She wore a denim miniskirt with an embroidered maroon boho top. Her blonde hair was loose and she wore large, thin gold hoop earrings. Platform sandals accentuated her long legs. Though she didn't think the outfit particularly sexy, the way he examined her almost predatory. She'd always known he was attracted to her, but after that first day at school, he'd backed off. At the Palladium, however, he didn't try to hide his desire. And this was a continuation of that openly *hungry* way of drinking her in.

"Stop looking at me like that," she said.

"What?" He straightened up in his chair, startled by being called out.

"So, is it okay to interrupt for a minute?" She gave the makeup artist a small smile.

"Em, yeah, sure." Conor looked at the girl. "Don't go too far, okay, honey?"

The girl wasn't happy at being dismissed but she obliged them and wandered away. Sophie went to the makeup table and toyed with some of the brushes.

"So, we'll practically be related," she said as she opened a MAC lipstick and tested the deep plum color on the back of her hand.

"What?"

"You know, with you and Gavin as close as brothers."

"Oh."

She put the lipstick down and wiped absently at the mark she had made. Taking a deep breath, she said, "I hope you can be happy for us."

"Soph, it's grand. Okay?" He shifted in his chair, and something about the way he looked away revealed more than his words.

"You're hurt," she said, her eyes widening as she understood where his anger was coming from. He and Gavin had been friends since they were seven years old. That was the same year Gavin lost his mother, and while he had never specified that this had been a factor in cementing their friendship, she suspected it had. Gavin had an older brother he had never been close with. He liked to say that the only reason he had any ties to his brother Ian was to filch his music collection. Conor had no siblings but had always acted as if Gavin was his brother. It was natural that he would feel possessive of their friendship.

He raised his eyebrows. "Em, not sure what you're talking about."

She touched his forearm and he looked down at her hand. "Nothing will change with the band, you know."

He scoffed and pulled his arm from her. "It's already fucking changed, hasn't it? Instead of running with a lead for a song—three in the morning or whenever—instead of getting to our gigs on time, instead of hanging with us after the show, he's with you. And that's all well and good, but don't go telling me nothing's changed."

Sophie nodded. "No, I get it. You're right."

"I know I am."

"But—"

"But what?"

"I think I can make him happy. Truly happy. And we both know he needs that." She pointedly skirted around saying what they both knew about Gavin—that a part of him was broken and would never be mended. But she could be—wanted desperately to be—of use in lessening his hurt.

Conor looked away from her as he took this in. He fixed his eyes on some middle distance for a long moment. At last, he released a heavy sigh. "I think you're right," he said softly. "At least I hope so."

Sophie smiled and nodded, quickly blinking back the tears that came with her relief. She had bet right. They were united in wanting to take care of Gavin. She had known instinctively that this was important to assert, that it would make them into allies rather than adversaries.

There was an outburst of laughter from the other side of the floor and it served to instantly lighten the mood between the two of them.

Sophie smiled. "Thank you, Connie."

"Don't start that again." He stood up.

She had naturally used Connie as a nickname for him when they were in school together but was the only one to do so. Everyone else knew how much he hated it. He vehemently shut down any attempt to call him that. But he'd always let Sophie have her way, his protests mild at best.

"Anyway, sorry to interrupt your little . . ." she said, gesturing to the makeup counter and back to him suggestively.

"Little what?" he asked, amused.

She laughed. "Whatever it was you two were about to do."

"Ah, you saw that, did you?"

"Just a bit."

"Well, do you think I have a chance?"

"I don't think there's any doubt about it."

He put his arm around her neck familiarly as they started toward the backdrop for photos. Leaning down, he whispered conspiratorially in her ear, "I don't either."

"CONGRATULATIONS ON YOUR ENGAGEMENT," John Riley said as he took a seat next to Sophie.

She had been watching the boys for the last forty-five minutes as they were photographed. The outburst she and Conor had heard earlier was Shay and Martin's reaction to seeing Gavin wearing dark brown leather pants with a softly draping white long-sleeve shirt. The style was perfect for a rock star singer but not one Gavin had ever tried on. He had always been a jeans and T-shirt guy. But despite his bandmates' jokes, he took to the ensemble well. The trousers were made of the softest calfskin and molded to his body. The shirt was tucked in front, showcasing a silver belt buckle low and tight across his hips. The unmistakable effect was that he exuded sex.

The others looked exactly like themselves: casual yet cool in well-worn jeans or work pants and distinctive tee shirts. Shay wore an old Clash shirt, while Martin wore a brand-new baseball-style shirt with Mickey Mouse holding up what seemed to be a middle finger. Conor's military-style black short-sleeve shirt with gray striped epaulets, combined with his black jeans and silver pocket chain, served to make him even more darkly handsome.

They stood together, varying their positions now and again, and Sophie thought they made a striking group. Each brought so much to the band and their personalities came through as they stood staring into the lens of the camera. As the photographer grunted his approval and gave minor directions, she imagined the impact this cover would have. The sudden rise their career had already taken was merely the beginning, and she knew she wasn't the only one to sense this.

"That's the one," she murmured.

"What's that?" Riley asked.

"That's your cover shot." She pointed to the boys. Gavin had his arms around Conor and Shay's neck and was leaning forward slightly, a taunting smile playing at his sensual mouth as he focused intently on the camera. Martin was to Conor's right, but Gavin drew all the focus.

"Yeah, maybe. Listen, it would be fantastic to hear how Gavin popped the question. I can use it to wrap up the story neatly."

Sophie was slow to look at the reporter. "Um, no, I don't think so."

"No?"

"It's something that should be kept private. You understand, don't you?"

"Well," he said with a laugh, "not exactly. Maybe you can give me just one detail? Like, where you were when he asked?"

Sophie thought about that. It didn't seem terribly harmful, even if it meant admitting to trespassing. "I wanted Gavin to see the city at night. We hiked up behind the 'Hollywood' sign. Alone up there, with the lights spread out before us, it was . . . perfect."

Riley scribbled in his notepad for a moment. When he was done, he looked at her and asked, "So, in this very short period of time, you reunited with your ex-boyfriend, got engaged, and now he's leaving to go on tour. He'll be on stage every night in front of screaming girls. And you'll be here in LA?"

"For a little while, yes."

"You're not worried that this big romantic gesture will turn out to be a fairytale?"

The question wasn't as unkind as it seemed. Sophie knew she was making a huge leap. But she'd rather take that leap, hoping she could fly, than never know what heights she might reach with Gavin.

"Actually, I already think it is a fairytale," she said with a smile. "But I'm okay with it not being a predictable one."

"Why's that?"

Just then, Gavin looked away from the camera and made eye contact with her. The stoic rock star gaze he had been using for the photographs faded and was replaced by a wide smile. He placed his hand over his heart and winked at her before turning his attention back to the photo shoot.

Sophie felt her insides go liquid. She knew she'd never be able to get enough of him. The sentiment overwhelmed her and she told Riley more than she probably should have.

"Gavin's all I need. No matter what happens now, I know I'll always choose him. And that everything will be okay."

24

When Gavin and the band left Los Angeles to fulfill the rest of their commitments, Sophie realized that her declaration to the *Rolling Stone* reporter about everything being okay would be tested immediately. Their separation meant that though they had just made the ultimate commitment to each other, they were also in a long-distance relationship. It was jarring. One minute, she was basking in the attention of her fiancé, and the next she was craving a text or random phone calls from him.

It was late one night a few weeks after Gavin left that she asked about his history with groupies and the continuing temptation they would be. It was uncomfortable to acknowledge the fact that her fiancé had been with a slew of women over the last two years. But she also knew that asking a twenty-year-old rock singer to give up being with anyone else was a ridiculous expectation and wanted to acknowledge it.

"I want no one but you," Gavin told her. "I think of no one but you. Darlin', I'm absolutely obsessed with you."

"That's easy to say when it's only been a few weeks since you've gone without—"

"Listen, I understand there are consequences to this commitment. I know it's not always going to be easy, but it's going to be okay. I promise you, sweet girl."

She smiled, but the ache for him was only slightly tempered.

"I miss you, baby," she said quietly.

"I miss you something desperate, too. Which is why, I think it'd be a very good idea for you to jump on a plane and meet me."

"Meet you? When? Where?" She sat up straighter. Because of his busy schedule and her needing to work out her school transfer, they hadn't planned to see each other again until her move to Dublin.

"This weekend. We'll be in New York City for the MTV Awards show. I told you about that, didn't I?"

He had. He'd been giddy with the news that they'd be both performers and nominees. It was their first awards show and a big deal.

"I can have Jamie arrange a plane ticket for you, yeah? Come see me, darlin'. I need you."

Her eyes teared up at the prospect of seeing him again. She nodded and smiled. "I can't wait."

WHEN GAVIN GREETED Sophie in the lobby of his Manhattan hotel, he held her so tightly she felt dizzy. And when he released her it was only slightly so that he could kiss her.

"I can't tell you how much I missed you, darlin'," he breathed into her neck.

"Oh, tell me, tell me!" she said with a laugh.

He looked into her eyes, a smile playing at his lips. "You're it, Sophie. You're the one."

His simple declaration revealed his unwavering and absolute certainty about their reunion, and it mirrored her feelings as well. It sent relief and joy coursing through her body. But instead of letting herself be overcome by the emotion of the moment, she changed the subject to something she knew he would have no trouble resisting.

With a mischievous smile, she grabbed his hips and said, "You'd better take me somewhere private—and quick. I've had five hours on that plane to think about naughty things."

"Good Christ," he murmured, shaking his head. "I do love you."

"Show me how much," she whispered into his ear as they stepped into the elevator.

He responded by dropping her bag to the floor, pulling her body hard against his with a hand around her waist, cupping her cheek with his other hand, and kissing her deeply.

"Oh, uh, maybe—"

They broke apart to find a woman with her young son hesitating to join them in the elevator.

"Apologies," Gavin said. He waved an arm to indicate they should step in.

Once they had and the doors closed, the woman turned her back to them. But the boy, about six years old, kept facing them, looking up at Sophie with a slightly opened mouth.

"I know what you mean," Gavin said to the kid. "She's the most beautiful woman I've ever seen, too." He gave him a wink and the kid broke out into a grin.

"Is she your girlfriend?"

"Nathan, leave them be," the woman said curtly.

"Even better, lad. She's my fiancée. That means I'm going to marry her and make her mine forever."

"Wow," the boy breathed.

"Let's go, Nathan," the woman said as the doors opened on their floor.

The kid had to be tugged out while he kept his eyes on Sophie. She smiled and waved at him.

When the doors closed, Gavin pulled her close again. "That kid is going to fantasize about blondes in lifts for the rest of his life," he said before pressing his lips to hers once more.

"All I want is to be your fantasy," she told him.

He moaned and bit her bottom lip. "You have no fucking idea, darlin'."

The doors opened on their floor and he reluctantly pulled away so he could retrieve her bag. Grabbing her hand, he pulled her so quickly to his room that she giggled at his impatience.

Not that she didn't feel the very same need to be with him. Their time in Los Angeles had been so brief. They'd barely gotten reacquainted and definitely hadn't been sated.

As soon as they were inside his room, they reached for each other, pulling at clothes, lips and tongues desperately exploring, and hands roaming feverishly.

"Wait," Sophie said breathlessly. "Maybe I should take a quick shower. I've been on a plane for—"

"After. I need you now."

They were stripped down to their underwear and it was clear by the sizable bulge straining against his boxer briefs that he had no desire to wait a second longer. To press the point, he grabbed her around the waist and lifted her up so that she wrapped both her arms and legs around him.

She didn't notice he had carried her past the bed until she felt cool glass against her bare back. Glancing over her shoulder, she could see traffic moving like a miniature display some twenty-six floors below. And then there were the other skyscrapers crowding the view.

Could there be someone looking into their room at this very moment? Someone getting an unexpected sexy show?She wasn't sure about continuing, even though Gavin was tempting her with kisses along the hollow of her neck. Then it occurred to her that he may have been eager for this very scenario.

"Was this one of your fantasies?" she asked.

He released her gently so that she stood and looked into her eyes. But instead of saying anything, he slowly dragged his thumb across her bottom lip until she opened her mouth and took it in.

There was no question what he wanted, what his fantasy was. She turned them so they were in profile to the window and dropped to her knees, pulling his boxer briefs down with her.

His erection sprang free and she spent a minute using both hands to stroke him from his swollen tip to his tight balls. She looked up at him while licking his pre-cum.

"Fuck," he moaned.

The look on his face of ecstasy bordering on agony made her smile because she hadn't even started yet. She quickly removed her bra and then guided his throbbing cock over the hard ridges of her nipples before taking him deep into her mouth.

He grabbed a handful of her hair, twisting slightly. It was enough to send a tingle down her neck, but not enough to hurt. She knew that wasn't what this was about with him. He would never hurt her. And all she wanted was to fulfill everything he needed. Every emotional need. Every sexual desire. Everything.

She watched his face go slack as she sucked him, rhythmically working her tongue over his tip as she pulled him almost all the way out before fitting him into the back of her throat as she took him in as far as she could. He was incredibly vulnerable in this position, so dependent on her movements. It completely turned her on and she moaned in pleasure with each thrust, with his increasing helplessness under her touch, his dependence on the heat and pressure of her mouth.

It was mostly instinct on her part. She wasn't especially experienced with this, but she was in tune with him and soon she had him tensing, groaning in pleasure, and then she was swallowing him down.

He pressed a hand to the glass, leaning hard against it for a moment before recovering enough to take her hand and stagger over to the bed. Pushing her down, he buried his face between her legs. His tongue did wondrous things to her, alternating between teasing her clit and pushing deep into her.

"Gavin," she whimpered as she neared her peak.

That only made him moan and focus more intently on her clit. She felt heat break and spread throughout her core as she came. The waves hadn't faded yet when he pulled away and rummaged for something at the nightstand. A moment later, he was leaning over her again, sliding into her, ready to make this reunion last in the best way possible. And she was ready for it.

25

SOPHIE

Sophie tried to keep her head down as she moved through the crowd at Radio City Music Hall, but she heard her name repeatedly as the boys were asked by reporters where she was.

She was, of course, moving in parallel with them but not on the red carpet. Gavin had told her it was for the best that she not join them and instead meet at their seats inside the venue, but she suspected that Conor was directed that decision.

Though she had dressed to kill, she didn't mind the separation. She didn't need the attention. Making Gavin's jaw drop when he saw her all done up was enough.

Her dress was form fitting and a nude shade that blended so well with her skin tone it would have been scandalous if not for the shimmering bead embellishments on it. Falling to upper-thigh, with just one shoulder strap and a draped back that fell away to reveal smooth bare skin, it had the perfect amount of sex appeal without going too far. The nude Jimmy Choo stilettos she wore were the perfect match. Her drop-down earrings were multi-colored gems that turned her hazel eyes deep green. She had set her hair so that it fell past her shoulders in soft, loose curls, and done her make-up in delicate shades. The overall look was incredibly sexy and ultra-feminine—and she fit the part for this event.

Still, it was a surreal being there.

The whole experience of being at Rogue's first MTV Awards was surreal, in fact. The response to the band's appearance was huge. Though they had built up popular and critical respect, there was no denying that the well-chronicled Gavin and Sophie romance had been publicity gold.

James remained on the sidelines to see that the boys gave each media group enough time, leaving Sophie to find her seat and wait by herself. The situation was made even more awkward when the show started and she was still alone.

Within a few minutes, however, they all filed into their seats. Doing so hurriedly and in the dark meant that Conor ended up sitting next to Sophie.

The opening act began with Britney Spears doing a cover of Madonna's "Like a Virgin," complete with the white veil and a short wedding dress. Christina Aguilera soon joined her in the duet. When Madonna herself appeared as the "groom" all in black, she brought the house down. The only thing that topped her initial appearance was when she and Britney had an open-mouth kiss. Her kiss with Christina was chaste in comparison.

When Gavin turned to Shay to get his opinion on whether any tongue had been used, Conor took the opportunity to talk to Sophie.

"You look amazing tonight, honey."

"Thanks," she said.

Conor looked at her with exasperation, reading more into her short reply than she had intended. "Look, you didn't miss anything out there. You've got to understand that this band, it's a job. We were *working*, and if you were there, it would have become the Sophie and Gavin show and nothing about Rogue. Understand that, please."

"I do. It's okay."

Though she had been sincere, he seemed to hear the opposite and was instantly annoyed. "It's a phenomenal skill you women have, to say the exact opposite of what you really mean."

Before she could respond, Gavin interrupted by telling Conor to switch seats with him.

THE SHOW FLEW by and Sophie thought herself incredibly unbiased when she found Rogue to be the best performers of the night. And when Gavin and the boys took the stage to accept their award for Breakthrough Video, they made the most of it. Gavin quickly thanked the producers of the video, James, and MTV and then shifted gears.

"This show opened with an amazing performance by three lovely ladies," Gavin said and the audience cheered wildly. "I must say, I felt a little left out. But then again . . . ." He looked to Conor and before his friend could understand his intentions, he grabbed him by the back of his neck and kissed him hard on the lips as the crowd laughed, screamed, and whistled.

"He's been looking for the perfect excuse to do that," Martin told Shay with a laugh and the microphone picked it up.

Conor finally pushed Gavin off of him and wiped at his mouth.

"Well, he is a pretty bastard," Gavin said with a grin. "No, seriously, one more thing. Thanks also to my sweet girl, my love, my Sophie."

IN THE LIMO on their way to *Blender* magazine's after party at Tao, Sophie remarked to Gavin that they were all handling their entry into this industry incredibly smoothly. They'd been besieged by press as they left who shouted questions about Rogue's first win, the sensation caused by Gavin kissing Conor, and Gavin's relationship with Sophie. All of the guys seemed to take it in stride.

Gavin replied, "Sure we are, because, you see, none of this is real. This vibe about who's hot and what's on is manufactured by ordinary people, and that doesn't impress us. Only bands that have created quality music consistently and stood the test of time get in that category—which, I guess, means I can't be impressed by Rogue yet. Even though I am!"

"The exception to the rule," Shay added.

"Exactly, mate. Thanks."

Conor helped himself to the mini bar, pouring a tumbler full of Jack Daniel's and taking a drink. "Aye, Gav, did you see that little actress who was chatting me up backstage after we performed?"

"No, I didn't catch that," Gavin said, glancing at Sophie.

"You sure? The reason I ask is 'cause she said she would find me at the party and that she had a friend who was interested as well."

"So, take Shay along," Gavin replied.

"Thing is," he said in between taking another drink, "she's interested in you in particular, so I thought—"

"For fuck's sake, Con, you've never needed me to get yourself laid. What are you going on about?"

"He's trying to annoy me since my being here seems to annoy him," Sophie said. The progress she thought she had made with getting on Conor's good side back in Los Angeles had clearly dissipated with her surprise arrival. It was obvious he saw her as intruding.

"No, this is normal tour life, honey," Conor told her, smiling. "You think your man wasn't taking every advantage before you came back?"

"Enough of that," Gavin said curtly.

Conor shrugged. "It's the truth now, isn't it? If she's to be a part of all this, glued to your side and all, then she'll have to deal with it." He raised his glass in a mock toast to her.

"Ignore him—he's drunk," Gavin told Sophie.

"I'm just enjoying myself, don't everyone panic," Conor said before taking a prolonged swig.

"He's not drunk. But do you think he's taken something?" Sophie asked. If Conor was going to make her uncomfortable by suggesting that Gavin help him chase groupies while she was right there, then she would go ahead and push back against his game-playing.

"Why, you want what I got, Sophie?" Conor asked with a suggestive leer.

In a rush, Gavin leaned forward so that he and his friend were inches apart. "Knock it the fuck off," he said.

"Piss off, Gavin. You know what your problem is? You're no bleeding fun anymore. You're tired and boring me to death."

Sophie winced at the look of hurt on Gavin's face. Before he could recover and respond, the limo drew to a stop and the door was opened for them. A waiting crowd of paparazzi and gawkers drowned out any effort Gavin could have made to reply. Conor jumped out first and didn't wait for the rest of them. He ignored the red carpet screams of photographers for him to stop at the step-and-repeat background for photographs and went straight into the restaurant-turned-event-space.

"Let him be, Gav," Shay said. "He's bound to get it out of his system first girl he finds."

"Yeah, sure."

Sophie expected to navigate around the media like at the awards show but Gavin held her close, his arm around her waist as he slowly moved them along the red carpet entryway. The flash of the dozens of cameras blinded Sophie but Gavin held his own, doing his best rock star stare.

"Conor is going to really freak out about this," she said.

"He needs to shut his gob and worry about himself."

She hated the idea that she was creating a rift between Gavin and his best friend. She wasn't quite sure why Conor felt so threatened by her. There had been none of this adversarial attitude back in school. In fact, Conor had quickly stood down from flirting with her once it was clear she and Gavin had a connection. Their friendship had been easy after that. But she realized now that might have been at least partly due to her temporary status with the group.

"He'll come around," she said, and they inched forward.

Gavin was oblivious to the fact that Martin was mimicking them by trying to hold Shay in the same intimate way that Gavin was holding Sophie, but she saw it from the corner of her eye and tried not to laugh. Gavin needed her attention at the moment.

"Fuck him," Gavin grunted.

"Oh, don't say that," she said reproachfully. When he didn't turn to look at her, she playfully bit his earlobe, pulling on the tender skin with her teeth and making him laugh.

She knew the increase in the camera flashes meant the moment would be well documented the following day. She was quickly learning what the paparazzi responded to. Anytime she and Gavin appeared relaxed with each other, they pounced—just like now. Gavin was so comfortable with the attention that she took his lead and tried not to second-guess it.

26

GAVIN

The *Blender* magazine party was a sexy, splashy affair, with go-go dancers performing on a stage backed by a giant bronze Buddha statue. Oversized lanterns hung from the thirty-foot-high ceilings. Amber and blue lighting washed against the expansive brick walls. Alcohol was offered everywhere, including from a specially crafted Jägermeister shot slide carved out of ice. The magazine's latest edition featured Radiohead's Thom Yorke, and versions of the cover were displayed throughout the space, both as hanging posters and embedded within ice carvings. Popular DJ Junior Senior had the crowded room on their feet, and the first floor was a mass of sweaty bodies.

Gavin thought he saw Conor talking to Carmen Electra, and briefly wondered if he'd have to jump into the fray if her man, Dave Navarro, took issue with it. Before he could sort out the odds of this, he heard his name being called.

It was easy to put the voice to the person, as Christian Hale stood taller than most. They greeted each other with a familiar hug.

"How the hell have you been, mate?" Christian asked, his hearty Australian accent a welcome sound. "And more importantly, why didn't you invite me to the bloody wedding?"

Gavin laughed. Tabloids had been running with a story saying he and Sophie had secretly married in advance of her soon giving birth. "Ah, you know it hasn't happened yet—not without you there, man.

Listen," he said and pulled Sophie closer to him, "meet my girl, Sophie. Sophie, this is my mentor, my great friend, Christian Hale."

Gavin watched as Sophie smiled up at the singer of Australia's most respected pop-punk band, Scandal. At 6'4" and with a white-blond crew cut and full-sleeve tattoos on his arms, Christian could be an imposing figure. But his smile was welcoming and boyish, belying his thirty years. It clearly set Sophie at ease.

"It's nice to meet you," Sophie said.

Christian surprised her by pulling her into a quick hug. "Bloody marvelous to meet you, love. I don't know why I had to learn about you through the rags, though." He gave Gavin a scowl.

"For fuck's sake, Hale, I was going to tell you if you gave me a minute," Gavin said with a laugh.

"Yeah, yeah. You've been busy winning awards and playing the festival circuit, I get it. Don't forget that I knew you back in the day, mate."

"Yeah, I know. Sophie, remember I told you we did a mini-tour opening for Scandal right after we got our album deal? Well, that's when I met this bastard. He took me under his considerable wing and taught me a massive amount about the music industry—"

"Look what it got me, too—now we'll have to fucking support Rogue next tour. And we'd be lucky to get the gig!"

Gavin laughed before launching into more good-natured trash-talk. They went back and forth at each other, both ignoring the women who tried to join them, despite Sophie's presence. They weren't subtle, either, as they slid between him and Christian, but both men ignored the intrusions.

"I need to hit the jacks," Gavin said after a while. "Be right back, darlin'."

While Christian occupied Sophie with entreaties to visit him and his wife at their beachside home, Gavin sought out Conor. He found him standing at the base of a wide staircase, leaning on the railing as he surveyed the scene. Surprisingly, he had only a bottle of beer for company.

"Aye, Con," Gavin said, "what's going on?"

"Nothing. You?"

"Christian's here. You should come over."

"Yeah," he said, and fell silent.

Gavin looked out at the crush of people, spotting Christina Aguilera despite her diminutive height. The crowd around her had expanded to give her space as she and a couple friends danced.

"I was a dick before," Conor said.

"That's cool," Gavin said quickly, to put the matter to rest. He and Conor were not in the habit of fighting. Or apologizing to each other. He wanted to bury whatever had happened and move forward.

"It's just . . . are you sure she's it? I mean, you've barely begun this whole thing again with her. Are you sure you know?"

"I know it's sudden. But I am absolutely sure."

"And her?" Conor asked, gesturing to Sophie. She was looking up at Christian with a smile. "You know for sure she's ready for it to be just you?"

Gavin nodded without hesitation. "I am. See, she's only ever had me love her, if you take my meaning."

Conor eyed his friend for a moment. "You're joking me."

"Almost too good to be true, aye? She's still my pure girl."

Conor shook his head and laughed. "But still, marriage? Why don't you just live together?"

"Because I don't want just that. I need her to be my wife. She's . . . she's my one. The one that makes everything bearable when I'm running empty, you know?"

Conor took this in before saying, "Guess it's meant to be then."

"Yeah." Gavin exhaled and his body relaxed. They could move on now and establish the new norm, one with Sophie in it. "So, I've gotta take a piss. Then I'm getting us both a shot, okay?"

"Bring the fucking bottle, why don't you," Conor returned with a smile.

27

SOPHIE

"There you are," Sophie said as she came upon Shay. She'd been searching for him in vain before finding him here on the third floor of the club where a private dining space had been set up as a lounge. It was quieter here as everyone seemed to be down on the first level, dancing and drinking with abandon.

"Em, hi Sophie," he said, removing his headphones.

"Can I keep you company?" she asked.

"Don't you want to be with Gavin, though?"

"He's making nice with Conor."

"I'm sorry he was so rude earlier."

Sophie turned her eyes away from the party below them to look at Shay. He had always had a level of sensitivity the other boys lacked.

"You don't have to apologize for him."

"Still—"

"He's testing me. Testing Gavin. I'm guessing he doesn't even know that he's doing it. But he's threatened by me, worried that I'm going to change everything."

Shay nodded. "And will you?"

The directness of the question surprised her, but she gave it thought. "I hope not. That's not what I want."

He appraised her for a long moment. "It'll be grand."

She knew his use of the word "grand" meant "fine" and appreciated this vote of confidence so much that she wanted to hug him for the support. But she knew he would be uncomfortable with that.

"So," she said, changing directions, "don't you take advantage of the girls, Shay?"

He laughed. "You want the truth?"

"Of course."

"I do, on occasion. Usually when I've had some drink in me."

She saw him blush. "You're still shy?"

"A bit, but it's talking about sex with you more than anything."

"I suppose we are practically strangers now."

"No, it's not that. What's weird is seeing you again. It feels like school was yesterday. It's more about admitting to you that I do the rock star thing—it's such a cliché."

"Yeah, I suppose it is. But I know you're not one of those guys that got into this for the girls. I know you do it for the love and art of making music."

Shay smiled and shook his head. "God, you can still do that."

"Do what?"

"You have a way about you. Your focus on the one you're with . . . you can make someone feel like the most special thing there is."

She laughed. "I can do that?"

Before he could reply, Gavin joined them. "There's my girl! Won't this be a story—'band's drummer steals singer's fiancée.'"

"Hey, at least I'll follow in Clapton's footsteps of stealing George Harrison's wife, yeah?" Shay asked with a sheepish grin.

"Yeah, if you could manage the impossible." Gavin smiled as he wrapped his arm around Sophie.

THE PARTY WAS STILL GOING strong at four o'clock, as Gavin and Christian held court on a set of sofas, a crowd around them, including some of the members of The Strokes, as they exchanged tour stories.

Sophie, not yet used to keeping these late hours, found herself close to nodding off so she wound her way past the third level and out onto the roof. The cool early-morning air was a welcome relief. She felt refreshed and enjoyed the sense of expectation that came with the darkness softening as the sun began to edge its way up. Looking over the railing, she was surprised by the amount of foot and street traffic. Tilting her head up in the opposite direction, she saw dozens of stories up to the top of the nearby Four Seasons Hotel.

"This is a nice hideout," Conor said, coming up behind her. He held a joint in one hand and a bottle of water in the other.

She glanced at him before looking up again, this time trying unsuccessfully to find any hint of stars. Both the city lights and the brightening sky blotted out whatever was up there.

"What are you escaping from, then?" he asked.

She looked at him again, wary. "Maybe *you*, depending on what you've got to say to me now," she replied with a laugh.

His smile was tight, contrite. He shook his head. "Care for some of this?" He held out the joint.

"No, I'm good."

They shared in the burgeoning city noises together for a couple of minutes as he smoked.

"Listen," he finally said, "drink got the better of me. Forgive me?"

The explanation he was giving her—that he'd been rude because he was drunk—didn't jibe. He hadn't had that much to drink. He'd just been in a really bad mood and took it out on her. Still, when she looked at him again, he seemed embarrassed. That was enough to let it go. "Sure. No harm—as long as you'll admit that I'm not the enemy."

"Ah, I know you're not, Soph."

She examined him and saw that he was sincere. Nodding to put an end to the awkward apology, she then focused on the slices of brightening sky between the surrounding buildings.

"Do you guys usually stay out until dawn?" she asked, stifling a yawn.

He finished the joint, drained his water bottle, and followed her gaze.

"More often than not." He paused. "Are you going to ask about groupies and all that temptation?"

"No."

"No?"

She laughed wearliy. "I can imagine what it's like, thanks."

"I have the feeling you can't scratch the surface of what it's really like, Sophie. Not without having some . . . *experience*."

Though she could feel him watching her, she didn't meet his eyes. She didn't want to indulge whatever it was he was getting at. But when a breeze picked up and left her skin with goosebumps, she rubbed her arms and glanced at him. He didn't stop his gaze. It was the same kind of heated look she had seen from him before.

"Connie, be a gentleman and give me your jacket." She wasn't that cold but she wanted to disrupt whatever lascivious thoughts he was having.

Blinking, he set the empty water bottle on the roof ledge before pulling his leather jacket off.

She looked back at the street in anticipation of the warmth of Conor's jacket. Instead, she was tickled as he trailed his fingers along the bare skin of her back. Before she could pull away, he had his mouth to her ear.

"Shame you've never known another man's touch," he said, and rested his warm palm against the cool skin at the small of her back, his fingertips inside the fabric of her dress. "You'd like it." He removed his hand, but at the same time leaned into her as he gently pressed his lips to her bare neck for just a moment before placing his jacket over her shoulders.

The eroticism of his touch paralyzed her. She felt herself being seduced. The fact that he could have this effect on her was confusing. She didn't want to admit she could be attracted to him, and forced herself to shake it off. Taking in a deep, sharp breath, she pulled away from him and walked several feet toward the other side of the rooftop.

She was bewildered, both by what his statement implied—that he knew Gavin was the only man she had been with—and by her response to his advance. It took a few seconds to convince herself that she hadn't done anything wrong, that it was Conor who had crossed the line. She would have to revise her earlier declaration to Shay that Conor didn't realize he was acting out. Because it now seemed to her he knew exactly what he was doing.

When she turned back around to tell him as much, she found he had disappeared. The incident—or should she call it the test?—was clearly over for him.

28

SOPHIE

"The city lights from the Hollywood sign have nothing on this," Sophie murmured to Gavin as they looked out through the floor-to-ceiling windows at a mesmerizing evening view of Manhattan across the Hudson River. They were at the Boom Boom Room at the top of the Standard Hotel High Line in New York's Meatpacking District and the Empire State Building was clear among the glittering cluster of buildings in Midtown. The pleasure of this unique view came in second for Sophie, however, to watching Gavin taking it all in. He was truly amazed, and she was reminded once more that he was on sensory overload. The band had taken off much more quickly than even he had anticipated and their success had opened up an overwhelming number of experiences.

"Ah, but that is the view that is burned into my heart and soul, darlin'," he said. "I'll never forget being there with you and hearing you say 'yes.'"

She smiled, charmed.

Surveying the interior of the nightclub, she marveled at how many people were squeezed into the space for the party put on by Rogue's label. The guests had to slither past each other like snakes, most drawn toward the enormous, circular, Art Deco showpiece bar. She saw Conor at the far side of it, his arm around the waist of a stunning brunette who was gazing up at him adoringly.

She had last seen Shay and Martin on the open-air part of the club one floor up. Shay's excuse for lingering there was so he could smoke, but she teased him that he really wanted to eye the bikini-clad girls taking a dip in the communal hot tub.

They had left the previous night's party not long after her encounter with Conor on the rooftop of Tao. She had told herself to disregard Conor's attempt to toy with her, and he had obviously done the same, as he gave no sign of it when they all shared a late lunch together the next day.

She and Gavin had this evening and the next day together before another separation. Her official move to Dublin would take place in two weeks.

She would be living with Gavin in the house he had purchased in the suburb of Sandymount, an area she didn't know well. When she lived in Dublin before, she was younger and directed in where to go and how to get things done. Now she would be making a life for herself. They would be making a life together. The prospect was both thrilling and terrifying.

Gavin soon took her mind off such things, pulling her with him to get another drink.

29

GAVIN

Gavin had been having a good time at the party, regaling a group of new "friends" with the story of how Rogue had come in dead last in a battle-of-the-bands-style contest the same week they were signed. But then someone mentioned a recent Yoko Ono sighting and that sent him off thinking about John Lennon. Whenever he thought of Lennon, the line "I wanted you but you didn't want me" from his song "Mother" came to mind. After that, there was no stopping the flood of thoughts that came with it, and something shifted inside him. It was a darkening of mood he couldn't shake off.

He'd had the same sort of spells back in school, where everything seemed fine one second and in the next he was on edge and prone to push everyone away. Conor had called it "The Clash," as in their lyric, "One day it's fine and next it's black." Even Sophie, who was so adept at handling him, always opted to steer clear when he was afflicted this way.

She had nowhere to go at the moment, however, as she was wedged between him and Conor in the back of a taxicab. Conor had dropped the girl he'd been chatting up and volunteered to leave with them when Sophie hurriedly explained they were going. Gavin knew Conor had read his mood and decided to assume the role he had long played, one of subtle caretaker. It was a role Gavin had relied on for years.

Now, he leaned forward and spoke to the driver. "Aye, mate, change of plan. Take us to the Dakota. You know where that is?"

The driver, a middle-aged Asian man, nodded shortly. "Yeah, yeah," he grunted. "West 72nd Street and Central Park West."

"Why are we going there, Gavin?" Sophie asked, and exchanged a quick glance with Conor.

He was quiet for a long moment, gazing forward. The streetlights illuminated the windshield off and on rhythmically as the taxi moved along.

"Do you know that I was destined for this?" he finally asked.

"Gav," Conor said, "don't do this to yourself."

Gavin knew his friend was right. Knew he should shut his mouth, shut down these thoughts. But he couldn't. He needed to purge them. To vent. To rage.

"The moment my Ma walked out the door I had no other choice. I mean, it's almost fucking funny."

"How does this help?" Conor asked with frustration.

"Let him talk," Sophie said quietly.

"Look at all the musicians who were fucked up by their mother dying or some abuse. Hendrix, McCartney, Lennon, Bono, Geldof—their mothers all died early on. The list is laughably endless. And me . . . I don't even know if my mother is alive. What do you think is worse? Knowing or not knowing?"

"You know I can't begin to imagine," Conor said.

Gavin knew the list of musicians he had referenced wasn't unfamiliar to Sophie. He had shared with her his studies of their stories back in their school days when he finally confessed the truth of his mother's absence. The truth was, contrary to what he led most people to believe, his mother wasn't dead. The truth was, she had abandoned her family after the car accident that killed his baby sister, Nora. He had explained to Sophie that after his mother unexpectedly checked herself out of the hospital, they never saw her again. They were in shock about it, making excuses for her until it became clear that it wasn't going to be temporary. None of her family or friends had any explanation. His father gave up, talked about her as if she were dead. His brother Ian simply stopped talking about her at all.

But Gavin had always chosen to believe his mother just needed time. Time to heal before her eventual return. He still remembered the conflicted sympathy on Sophie's face as he told her this. At that point, it had been nine years since his mother had left. It was preposterous to still have hope that she would come back, but Sophie had allowed him his denial.

"It's great fucking company to be in. At least there's that," Gavin said now, still unable to let go the tortured thoughts that had overtaken him at the party. And now they were in this cab, and he couldn't stop from launching into his often-repeated claim that he shared a cruel commonality with amazing singer-songwriters who had lost, or been rejected by, their mothers.

He continued to rant even as Sophie attempted to soothe him with the ritual of intimate touch they had established years ago, taking his hand and gently stroking the sensitive skin on the inside of his wrist. It didn't work.

He spoke of the history of music being littered with the absence of the mother, either by death or some sort of neglect, and how it served as the catalyst for artistic ambitions among so many. He told them about Paul McCartney's mother dying of cancer when he was barely in his teens; Bob Geldof's mother dying of a cerebral hemorrhage when he was six or seven, and a teenaged Bono's mother dying of the same affliction after suffering an attack at her own father's funeral.

"Do you think I don't know these stories backwards and front already?" Conor asked. "I'm just as fascinated by what it all means but I don't see any reason to go over and over it."

Gavin didn't want to stop, though. He was on a roll, and quickly segued into Eric Clapton's story. Clapton had had his mother in his life, only he didn't know it for far too long as his grandparents acted as his parents and his mother acted as an older sister. Both Jimi Hendrix's and Louis Armstrong's mothers were neglectful and absent, leaving them in the care of family or friends.

"Then there's John Lennon," he continued. Lennon's mother had been removed from caring for him when he was five years old. Though they still had a relationship with regular visits and she was even the one to buy him his first guitar, full amends for his erratic upbringing were thwarted when she was killed in an automobile accident. He had been seventeen at the time.

"Ah, perfect. Here we are," Gavin said with forced brightness as the cab slowed to a stop.

He quickly got out and beckoned Sophie and Conor to join him. They stood across the street from the ten-story brick and sandstone apartment building known as the Dakota. A dry moat encircling the building was surrounded by a low cast-iron fence. Behind them leafy Central Park was a peaceful contrast to the four lanes of traffic still humming by at almost two in the morning.

"I always wanted to see the spot. Morbid, I guess," Gavin mused.

"And why are we here?" Sophie asked.

"This is where John Lennon was murdered," Conor replied flatly.

"Oh," Sophie said, brow furrowed.

Gavin gazed at the features of the building. Its protruding dormers, dark brown corner masonry, oriel windows, and intricate niches lent it a gothic feeling. In truth, it was a prestigious home to multimillionaires. The doorman at the main arched entrance eyed them with suspicion, and in return Gavin gave him a mock salute.

"And yes, it is morbid. Let's go, Gav. You need to get some sleep. You'll feel better in the morning," Conor said.

Gavin laughed. "Con, if this feeling ever left me, even for a minute, I'd be only delighted. But it doesn't and that's why I'm a great fucking musician. So, I guess I should thank my ma for that, shouldn't I?"

"Stop giving into this," Conor said. "You work yourself up into misery and—"

"I'd thank her if only I fucking knew where she was," Gavin continued.

Before Conor could try some other argument, Sophie went to Gavin and held his face in her hands. She looked intently into his eyes and whispered, "It's okay."

He reached up to take her hands from him. "Don't—"

"It's all going to be okay," she insisted.

Gavin froze as this declaration washed over him. Conor's entreaties for him to let go this rant had fallen on deaf ears. But Sophie's loving, dare he say it, *maternal* approach made all the difference. She had witnessed him coming apart and, rather than fleeing, she had given him the kind of assurance he so desperately needed. It made him feel both seen and accepted. In response, he crumbled gratefully into her embrace.

They stayed there on the street for a while longer, Gavin and Sophie holding each other tightly while Conor paced.

THE SHEER CURTAINS that made the hotel suite so elegant also failed to block the morning sun and woke Gavin well before he was willing. He tossed and turned, too tired to get up to draw the heavier curtains and darken the room. Finally, he pressed his body against Sophie's backside and squeezed her waist.

"Sophie, wake up. I have something to tell you," he whispered.

"Hmm?" she moaned.

She turned around and her hair fell over her face as she leaned into him.

"I'm going to miss this," he said. "Waking up with you. You're so beautiful."

"Is that what you wanted to tell me?" she asked, and looked at him sleepily.

He smiled and brushed the hair from her face. "No. I wanted to tell you that last night, well, I didn't plan on letting you know how fucked up I was until after we were married. Now I'm afraid you'll run back to California and I'll never see you again."

"No such luck, baby. I'm hooked on you and that's for good."

"You're more than I deserve, darlin'."

"We deserve each other, Gavin."

"I don't ever want to let you go."

"So don't," she whispered, and kissed him.

PART II

30

SOPHIE

Sophie exited Trinity College's academic registry offices, her vision unfocused as young men and women passed her by in a blur. As registered students for the upcoming term, they all had someplace to be. Sophie would not be joining them in loading up on course materials. She wouldn't be angling for a good seat in lecture halls either. She wouldn't be a student at all.

The bold pronouncement she had made to her parents about transferring to Trinity from USC had been all bluff—though she hadn't known it at the time. The idea had been legitimate, but ultimately unrealistic given the short timeframe for her relocation. Sophie told no one about having missed—by more than six months—the deadline to request a transfer, and forged ahead with the plan to move. She wanted so badly for the fairy tale of her reunion with Gavin to work out, complete with a seamless university transition to please her parents, that she convinced herself she would be able to talk her way into school once she was in Dublin.

The polite, but firm, admissions clerk had just put an end to that fanciful idea. She would need to wait until the following year to apply for the transfer. This not only changed the timeline of her studies but endangered the student visa she had planned to use to stay in the country.

THE WOMEN'S restroom was crowded and Sophie had to squeeze her way into a place at the mirror so she could check her hair and makeup. Gavin and a dozen others had taken over a large part of this pub's beer garden, and it looked to be another long night.

This was only her fourth day in Dublin and each evening had been spent at a pub, club, or someone's house party. The pattern of drinking into the early morning hours with large groups of friends, followed by sleeping late, meant she hadn't really absorbed the fact that she had moved to another country and was living with her fiancé.

As she looked into the mirror and reapplied lipstick, the day's disappointment filled her again. She hadn't yet told Gavin about the problem with school, partly out of denial and partly because she knew he wasn't exactly one to champion her education. He would rather have her all to himself.

Adjusting the deep cowl neckline of her gray Helmut Lang pullover, she saw out of the corner of her eye other girls watching her. Maybe they had seen her with Gavin, the local celebrity, and were curious about her. Or maybe they just didn't like the look of her. Her blonde hair was slicked back at the sides with the top pulled up high in a style emulating what she had seen in photos from Paris fashion runway shows. It was becoming clear after these nights out that she tended to overdress in comparison to the other girls. It was one of the many things she would have to adjust to now that this was her new home.

The route back to the outdoor area was a maze, requiring a trek through the dark, wood-paneled old-fashioned pub and out to the alleyway, but Sophie found her way. Gavin, however, was not where she had left him. His chair was empty, and in the crush of people she couldn't spot him for several seconds. And then he was there, in the far corner, where the overhead hanging string of lights faded. But the glow of the ample heaters lit him, along with the woman he was speaking with. The distraught woman. The expression on her face could only be described as incredulous.

A sudden warm, intimate pressure at the small of her back startled her. It was Conor. His touches were never casual, always lingering a bit too long.

"Sorry, just passing by," he said and started to move on.

"Wait. Who's that?" she asked.

He stopped and followed her stare. "Em, maybe you should ask Gavin that one," he said.

That response wasn't exactly comforting. Sophie lingered by herself as Conor quickly joined their group at the center of the garden. She watched Gavin and the woman from her distance. They were standing too closely together for this to be a casual encounter. She was pretty, with shiny raven-colored hair that fell short and wavy around her face. When Sophie realized that the girl's blue eyes were watery, she started toward them.

"Hi," Sophie said, touching Gavin's elbow as she joined him.

"Oh, hey." He replied a bit too quickly at the sound of her voice.

Sophie watched the woman expectantly and the three of them stood there silently for a long minute. "I'm Sophie Kavanaugh," she finally said, offering her hand.

"Sorry," Gavin said. "Sophie, this is Jules—Julia O'Flaherty."

"Nice to meet you," Sophie said.

"And you," Julia replied and shook Sophie's hand. "Ciggies always make me tear up," she explained, waving away imaginary smoke.

Sophie nodded slowly. The number of cigarette smokers in the garden had been mercifully few that evening.

"Well, I better get going. We'll talk later, Gav?"

"Sure. I'll ring you, Jules."

Julia nodded and quickly walked away.

"Who was that, Gavin?" Sophie asked.

"Just a friend."

"Why was she crying?"

He was lost in watching Julia walk away.

"Gavin?"

"Hmm?" He blinked and shook his head. "The smoke, she said, yeah?"

With an arm around her shoulders, he steered them back to their tables, and Sophie opted not to further question him. A nagging feeling that Julia represented something destructive kept her from pushing the issue and risking finding out something she didn't really want to know.

31

SOPHIE

The house Gavin had purchased at Conor's urging was on a tree-lined street in Sandymount, a town less than six miles south of Dublin City. With a brick exterior, the detached three-bedroom home had been remodeled in recent years to add numerous skylights as well as a modern kitchen. The layout was European, however, as the reception room, study, and combined kitchen and dining room were all closed off rather than part of an open layout. Sophie thought its best feature was the large windows in the kitchen that overlooked a lovely, leafy garden.

It was a few minutes' walk from pubs, shops, and restaurants, but Gavin took pains to point out to Sophie that it was also very near the Strand. The wide sandbar leading to a seemingly perpetually low tide was better suited to runners and walkers than sunbathing or swimming, but it was definitely a selling point for living in the area. So was the fact that it was a reminder of the intensely romantic sunrise they had shared at the Strand back when they were in school and had stayed out all night.

Upon arriving at the house from the airport, Sophie had been struck by its emptiness. Gavin had only stayed in it once before getting back on the road to tour, so all the amenities that made a house a home were missing. Gavin had acquired the essentials, which in his case included a large-screen television, a robust sound system, and a bed in the master bedroom.

Sensing Sophie's disappointment in the vacant feeling of her new home, Gavin had suggested she be the one to decorate it, and she readily agreed. Up until this day, however, she hadn't had the time to do the shopping required for such a project as Gavin kept her busy either in the bedroom or out on the town.

Now, as Gavin slept, she dressed and quietly let herself out of the house. She took the DART into the city, as she dared not try to drive on the "wrong" side of the road. If all went according to plan, she would be placing orders for delivery of furniture and the like rather than carrying much home, so taking the rail system was the perfect option.

SOPHIE FELT EXCEPTIONALLY ACCOMPLISHED by the time she got home in the middle of the afternoon. She had found what she was looking for at the shops in Dublin and had placed orders for a sofa and loveseat combo, an entertainment center, a dining table and chairs, area rugs for the hardwood floors, a bed frame, lamps, curtains, and various sets of pots and pans. She was further loaded down with bags containing supple throw blankets, ridiculously high thread-count sheets, plush bath towels, bath rugs, and sweet-smelling soaps. As a bonus, she'd even picked up a few colorful scarves to make bundling up in the cooling temperatures as fashionable as she could.

The endeavor had made her feel very grown up and she couldn't wait to see it all come together. After finding out that her admission to school would be delayed due to her impetuous decision to move to be with Gavin, she needed to establish as much stability as she could, and the act of creating a home that was theirs seemed an important step in solidifying the commitment they had made so quickly.

She had dropped everything just inside the front door that Gavin could never seem to remember to lock when she heard voices coming from deep in the house. Moving toward the kitchen, she heard a woman's voice along with Gavin's through the open door leading to the garden.

Hesitating at the outer dining area, Sophie felt an uneasy sense of déjà vu. Gavin stood with Julia O'Flaherty. And once more, she looked upset.

"This just isn't making sense. Are you trying to say we experienced two completely different things?" Julia said, verging on tears.

"I don't know what else to tell you, Jules. I feel terrible. I do," Gavin replied.

Sophie hesitated, torn between wanting to continue to listen in and doing what was right. She took a deep breath and moved through the kitchen, stepping outside with them and forcing a bright smile.

"Hi, guys," she said.

The tension was obvious. Julia looked down and let the growing ash of her cigarette fall to the ground. Sophie almost laughed out loud when she saw Julia was smoking. That excuse of hers last night about smoke bothering her eyes really was as bogus as it had sounded.

Gavin turned to Sophie stiffly. "Where did you get off to, then?"

"Oh, I did some epic shopping," she said. "This place is going to look like someone actually lives in it really soon."

He nodded distractedly. "That's great, thanks."

The silence stretched out as they stood there, and Sophie could not have felt more out of place. "I'm going to let you two talk. Nice to see you again, Julia," she said, and Julia nodded.

"Thanks," Gavin said again.

The tone of dismissal stung Sophie and conjured up the not-so-long-ago moment in the backstage room of the Palladium where Gavin had rejected her. She turned and quickly moved back inside the house.

32

GAVIN

avin watched Sophie until she was inside and out of view before turning back to Julia. "Look, I don't know what else you want from me here. All this is doing is making Sophie uncomfortable."

Julia closed her eyes briefly and shook her head. "And we wouldn't want that," she said.

"I don't see the point—"

"You never could be alone. When we were just friends I could see that easy enough with the constant stream of girls you'd go through. I knew that and that's why I said to go on and do whatever while you're on tour. But I didn't think you'd get so desperate you'd get engaged."

God, he had really fucked up. Not purposely, of course. But here it was. His fiancée was inside while his ex was out here haranguing him on relationship etiquette. The thing was, he didn't really think he had done anything wrong.

"Jules, you don't understand. I just never thought we were serious. You were on tour yourself and I had no expectations of anything once we were both back."

"This revisionist depiction of things is rather convenient for you, isn't it?"

Tears shimmered in her eyes once more and it felt like manipulation. He was weary of it. "Cut the crap. You didn't once reach out to me in all these months. Why the drama now?" He saw her indignation waver under this truth. But then she dug deep to reveal the real source of her anger with him.

"You said you loved me," she told him.

"I didn't—"

"What? You didn't say you loved me, or you didn't love me?"

Gavin looked at her for a long moment before deciding that being brutally honest was the way to end this conversation. "Both."

"Then I guess the word had a different meaning when you were fucking me, didn't it?"

There was no reply he could make that would help matters so he kept silent.

"You're a selfish bastard," she said, and swiftly moved passed him.

He waited until he heard the front door slamming before going inside. The house was still and he wondered if Sophie had gone out again. He went upstairs and found her in the bedroom admiring several scarves laid out on the bed.

"Hey," he said.

"Hey. What do you think? Aren't they cool?"

He went to her and wrapped his arm around her waist. He was acutely aware of the fact that she did not put her arm around him in return.

"Yeah, lovely."

They stood there for a moment, staring at the bright colors of the scarves.

"Is she okay? She seemed upset again," Sophie finally said.

"Ah, she'll be fine. Did I tell you she's a singer? We all met her a few years ago. Her first album was put out on a small label and she just got back from a European tour. Anyway, you know how singers can be, what with the mood swings and reckless emotions," he said with a laugh.

She turned to him, slipping from his arm, and he saw a struggle work its way over her face. It was clear she was concerned about what this all meant. Her doubts were the last thing he wanted. But he thought going into the details of things with Julia would do more harm than good.

A change in direction seemed the best course of action. "Were you running away from me today, Sophie?"

"What?"

"You left without waking me. You stayed away all day."

"No, not at all, baby. I went to shop and the time flew. And, I figured we probably need to ease into all of this, that you need your space."

"I don't want space. I want you," he told her urgently, hoping she'd understand what he really meant was that she was the *only* one he wanted.

There was a moment before she smiled in return, her face and body relaxing. "You got me," she said, and kissed him.

33

A t home and with yet another day's purchases unloaded, Sophie grew restless in the quiet house. Gavin had left her a voicemail saying he was at Conor's, and she decided to join him there. She figured she might arrive in time for them all to have dinner together.

Conor had purchased a modern home in Blackrock, a town near the coastline less than three miles south of Sandymount. As Sophie slowed the car to a stop in his pebble driveway, she admired Conor's sensible approach of investing his earnings in real estate. He'd been the one to persuade Gavin to do the same, hoping the base it created would stem Gavin's tendency to wander.

Conor answered after a short delay and didn't hide his surprise to find Sophie at his doorstep.

"Hi, Soph. What are you doing here?" he asked.

"That's not a very warm welcome!" she said with a laugh.

"Apologies, honey. Come in, please." He offered her his hand and when she took it he leaned in to kiss her on the cheek.

He led her inside and down a short hall to an unadorned foyer.

"I thought I'd see if you and Gavin want to have dinner."

"Sure, but where's Gav?"

Sophie looked around his empty living area. "He's not here?" Her heart suddenly felt heavy, each beat a thud.

"When I talked to him today he didn't mention coming by," Conor told her carefully.

"And where was he when you talked to him?"

Conor hesitated. He ran his hand through his short-cropped hair and then rested both hands on his hips. "I don't think I should get in the middle."

"Just tell me."

"He was," he said hesitantly, "at Julia's."

"Oh." The blood drained from her face as the image of Gavin and Julia standing closely together and talking came to mind.

"Nothing's going on with them anymore, though. You don't have to worry."

Sophie blinked against the tears stinging her eyes. She needed answers. Information was the only way to feel any kind of control at the moment.

"Nothing's going on *anymore*?" she asked.

Realizing his mistake, Conor closed his eyes and muttered, "Fuck me."

"How long were they together?" she asked.

"A year or thereabouts."

"And they broke up when?"

"I dunno."

This confirmed her fear that Gavin was still involved with Julia. She had been their fool. His fool. Leaving home, school, her life, on a mere whim. Agreeing to marry someone she didn't even really know anymore. Someone who had another lover. Maybe even someone he loved. She suddenly felt incredibly young. Young and naïve. She longed for her mother, longed for a protective embrace and assurances that everything would be okay. It was a false desire, though, as she knew her mother would only suggest she had made her own mistakes and had to fix them herself.

She had suppressed her usual common sense when she agreed to marry Gavin and move to another country. It had been denial and living in a fantasy to rush into all of this. And now the truth of how reckless she had been came crashing down around her and left her short of breath.

She raised a shaky hand to her mouth. "What have I done?" she whispered, her eyes filling with tears.

"What have you—no, Sophie. It's not what you think. It's certainly nothing to weep about."

"I have changed my whole life for him. For nothing."

"That's not true. Jesus, don't you know that he chose you? That's what this all means? You have been the only thing on his mind since that Palladium gig. It's right fucking annoying, to be honest."

"You don't understand."

"Listen, Julia's just a friend now."

"Then why is he lying to me about where he is?"

"Probably so you wouldn't think the things you are now."

She could see in this answer how Gavin would manipulate things as well. He would twist it so that his deceptions were somehow her fault.

"I should go. I'm sorry to drop in on you like this."

"Wait. Stay for a cuppa. Just 'til you calm down."

Tea was the last thing she wanted. It wouldn't replace the over-whelming feeling of betrayal nor would it bring back the hope she'd had for a future with Gavin.

Shaking her head, she turned to go. But he grabbed her hand and pulled her into his arms before she could move away. After a moment's hesitation, she relaxed and let his warmth envelop her.

"It's all right," he whispered and stroked her hair.

He held her closely and his arms were strong. And when he kissed the top of her head she felt safe.

But he wasn't Gavin.

She began to really cry then, although quietly, and her whole body trembled.

"Shh, now," he told her, pressing his lips to her temple.

He was being sweet to her. The tenderness was too much, though, veering on intimacy. The sudden need to see Gavin overwhelmed her. She pulled away from Conor and wiped at her eyes, careful to keep from smudging her makeup.

"Thanks, Connie. I really need to go."

This time there was no stopping her.

34

SOPHIE

Though she desperately wanted to see Gavin, she didn't know what she would say to him. The lights were on in the house and she stared at the front windows from inside the parked car until her vision lost focus. She was nauseous and opened the car door to force air into her lungs.

After a silent count to ten, she went to the house and let herself in. Gavin was in the front room, crouching down by the sound system as he sorted through CDs. He was in bare feet and had a bottle of Smithwick's Ale in one hand.

"Hey, darlin'," he said breezily. "That must've been another epic shopping session."

She wondered if he would continue to lie, so she baited him. "It was. How's Conor?"

"Good," he said shortly, and set down his beer. "You all right?"

So Conor hadn't called to warn his friend that he'd better work on his story. That was interesting.

"How's Julia?" she asked. "Did you make up with her?"

Recognition flooded his face as he realized his misstep. He stood up and moved toward her. "Listen—"

"To what? More lies? No, forget it. I don't want to hear it."

She started to move toward the stairs but he quickly blocked her way.

"Come on, darlin', don't overreact," he tried.

"Let me by."

"Talk to me. You can't just run off without talking to me. Give me a chance."

Her anger rose and she looked at him, wanting him to see the hurt in her eyes. And the fury. "I gave you every opportunity to tell me the truth. I didn't get jealous and demand to know why this girl kept crying to you. And you *still* chose to lie to me. And before you tell me that you didn't lie, stop and think about the fact that you didn't tell me the truth either."

"You're right," he said, surprising her. "I didn't. Because I didn't—"

"Everything is wrong here. Everything," she said. "I need to go home."

"You are home, Sophie. Don't be rash."

"All I've ever done is be rash when it comes to you. I spent my whole year in school here devoted to you. I left everything I had in LA for you. I didn't once question whether you already had a goddamn girlfriend. And now look what I've gotten myself into. I'm in another country, playing house with someone who isn't really there."

"That's not true."

She laughed bitterly as she finally pushed her way past him. Hurrying up the stairs to their bedroom, she pulled the diamond engagement ring off her finger. It was a dramatic gesture but she wasn't interested in being reasonable at the moment.

"Here," she said as he joined her, "this doesn't belong with me." She held the ring out to him.

He looked stricken. "Yes, it does. Of course it does."

They stood staring at each other, both refusing to move.

"You've got to believe me, darlin', nothing is going on with Julia. I fucked up, but it wasn't about cheating on you. I swear to you."

"Then why lie to me?"

"I . . . I'm an idiot is why. A complete fucking idiot." His face was pained, the regret and disappointment in himself easy to read.

"You're right about that," she muttered, and he laughed with relief.

She hadn't meant to give him an out but realized that was exactly what she had done. She had gone from feeling betrayed and hurt to almost flippant about it all. What was it about him that made her want to forgive him?

"Here's the absolute truth: the other night at the pub was the first time I've even thought about her since we left for the tour. Once I saw her, I realized what a dick I was and I certainly didn't want to confess that to you. I mean, from my perspective, what she and I had was casual. There were no promises made. I hadn't been with her or even spoken with her in months. But that still doesn't mean I shouldn't have thought to explain things to her, especially after you and I got engaged. I took the easy way out, I guess, and convinced myself I didn't owe her anything. I was a royal bastard to her."

Sophie nodded and looked away from him.

"Put the ring back on, Sophie. Please."

She closed the ring in her fist and sat on the edge of the bed. "I don't know if that's the right thing to do."

"I was never in love with her. It was a friendship that slipped into a sexual thing. And it's all over. It's been over."

She closed her eyes tight, trying to think. Trying to be logical and not be assuaged so easily by his dismissal of it all. "How long were you together?"

He thought for a moment. "About a year."

This time he passed her test and she looked at him. "Don't you ever lie to me, Gavin. I don't deserve that kind of disrespect."

He sat next to her and kissed her cheek. "I know and I don't ever want to make you feel like this. You are the absolute love of my life. When I saw you in Los Angeles, I knew you were the only one for me. Literally, everything and everyone else fell away. There is no one I could love more."

She fought against the instinct to give in to his sweet words. "What happened today?"

"I wanted to explain to Jules—"

"Before you talked to me?"

"I . . . yeah. It was another wrong move on my part, I know. I told her I was sorry, that I wanted her friendship, and that you and I were for real. Then, after giving me hassle, she tells me she's involved with a forty-year-old Frenchman. So, really, she wasn't exactly pining away for me. She was just hurt by how I went about things."

"That makes two of us."

Gavin hung his head for a moment and then dropped to his knees in front of her. "I am so sorry, darlin'. I can only imagine what it made you think of me. But please know that I love you and I don't want to hurt you."

"Gavin, what else haven't you told me?" she asked. "What else am I going to find out about?"

"Nothing. There's nothing, Sophie. What can I say? There are no dark secrets you have to worry about. I'll tell you the truth, I've slept with a lot of girls, but I don't have any diseases and I don't have any babies out there. You are the only one I want. Now that I have you, I can't tell you how much I need you. I swear to you, I've *never* let anyone as close to me as you. No one knows me, knows what makes me who I am, the way that you do. I can't lose you again." He cupped her cheek in his hand and whispered, "Please."

The look in his eyes was sincere, bordering on desperation. She knew he was saying she was the only woman who understood his pain, knew where it came from. That, of course, triggered her desire to be his savior. To be the one person who could in some small way fix him. This was why she forgave him so easily. Because he was broken inside and made sure she felt like she was the only one who could come to his aid.

She opened her hand and exposed the ring to him as an offering. He took it quickly, sliding it onto her finger before she might change her mind.

Then he took her face into his hands and kissed her. "You won't regret this."

"I know," she replied in between more kisses. "I might need to marry you to stay in the country, anyway."

He pulled away and looked at her in surprise.

"I messed up with school. I can't start until next year."

"More time for us," he said with a grin and pushed her back onto the bed.

"My parents are going to kill me," she said.

"Nah, I won't allow that." He pressed his body to hers, slipping between her legs and kissing her neck. Winding his kisses to her ear, he sang softly, his voice raspy with modified Bowie lyrics: "Pretty girl, you know you drive your Mama and Papa insane."

"You'll save me, too?" she asked, and then closed her eyes tightly in embarrassment at her vulnerability and neediness.

But he didn't respond, instead kissing her on the mouth deeply, grazing her body with his hands, and pressing his hips against hers. She was glad he was going to brush past her asking him to be her savior. It was easy for her to ignore it, too, as anytime he sang to her she lost all sense. Combine that with his touches and she was defenseless against him.

But then he stopped, held her face in his hands and met her eyes. "I'll save you," he whispered.

The relief that flooded through her at his reassurance should have been an indication that they were headed down a tangled path. But she chose to dismiss the nagging feeling that this exchange was setting up an unhealthy reliance on each other in favor of moving forward with the man she loved.

35

2004

The Swiss Suvretta House hotel was one of the dozen-plus resorts in the greater Engadin St. Moritz area. It offered modern luxury and access to world-class skiing, and was where Sophie's parents had arranged for them all to stay for their post-Christmas get-together.

Gavin and Sophie flew from Dublin to London and on to Zurich, followed by a train ride with a change in the city of Chur to a smaller rail service. From there, the experience became something exceptional as they moved in their train car over a hundred-year-old limestone viaduct and through switchback tunnels among the spectacular glacial mountains. Some two hundred feet below the smoothly rocking train were frozen lakes surrounded by trees freshly dusted with snow, adding to the mesmerizing landscape. It was scenery Gavin had never experienced and he was captivated. The wonder he felt helped to ease the discomfort he'd been harboring at the idea of Sophie's parents paying for the vacation.

Once they finally made it to the hotel, a picturesque, supersized chalet a couple miles from the town proper, checked into a posh Junior Suite with frozen lake and mountain views, and were fully immersed in the stunning wealth that defined this playground for the mega-rich, Gavin's qualms returned.

"Is this how you grew up? Apart from your time in Dublin?" he asked from his position lounging atop the plush bed. He absently thought that he should probably take off his Dr. Marten boots. They were still damp from the snow.

Sophie laughed. She was unpacking their bags and putting their clothing in the fine wood wardrobe. "No, baby, I didn't. This is a whole other level, believe me."

He watched her as she moved fluidly about the room, settling their things into the space. She had always possessed uncommon poise and maturity, especially in contrast to the girls in school. As a result, she had seemed grown up from the start, as if she was born knowing the proper way to navigate life. She projected an expectation that her path was assured one way or another, and Gavin attributed this to her having been brought up to assume she would succeed. It was a quintessentially American trait, but one she carried with grace.

And it was also the opposite of what he had grown up with. The Irish were much more likely to knock you down than build you up. His brother and father had always promoted the idea of lowering expectations, especially when it came to his musical ambitions. Though he prided himself on defying both the odds and the lack of confidence of his own family to make it in the music world, being in this extravagantly wealthy environment brought forth a deeply ingrained sense that he wasn't good enough to be there. Rather than acknowledge this, he found himself deflecting and going on the offensive.

"But this is where your parents brought us," he said. "To this outrageously expensive spot that only the lucky few get a chance to see. What are they trying to prove?"

Sophie closed the door to the wardrobe and went to the foot of the bed. He watched her with interest as she peeled off first her sweater, then her jeans. She stood before him in a matching moss green and pink lingerie set for a moment, letting him look at her. Though thin, her body was feminine with soft skin, a narrow waist, and shapely hips. There was a pale brown birthmark above her left hip and he envisioned pressing his lips to it.

Before he could make a move, she climbed onto the bed and up the length of his body, straddling his waist. Leaning down, she kissed him long and slow.

"Stop overthinking it," she told him softly. "It's just a vacation." She kissed him again, deeper this time.

He grabbed her backside and stopped thinking at all, happily giving himself over to pure sensation.

―――――――

GAVIN'S SUSPICIONS of Sophie's parents' motives were dispelled at dinner, where they all fell into easy conversation and drank too much. Steve and Maggie readily admitted that the location of their vacation was chosen primarily for the opportunity to be spectators to the kind of sports only the obscenely wealthy indulged in.

"Where else can you see snow polo?" Steve asked with wonder. "As if regular polo wasn't enough of a rich person's sport, let's go ahead and transport these world-class animals to high altitude cold and snow and put them through their paces on a frozen lake!"

Gavin laughed appreciatively. It was exactly what he had thought when Sophie mentioned their trip was timed so that they could watch the snow polo tournament.

"And not to mention the 'White Turf' horse race later next month," Maggie added.

"Or the skijoring!" Steve said enthusiastically. He went on to explain that skijoring was a sort of human chariot race. The horses ran up to fifty miles per hour while the "rider" trailed behind on skis, holding tight to long reins.

"It really is fascinating," Maggie said.

"I imagine it's quite the spectacle," Gavin said. "Too bad we'll miss it." Their trip was only for four days since Sophie's parents had managed to use their influence as former business owners in Dublin to get her admitted to the university. Rogue was also supposed to start working on new material. Their label had recently gone from encouraging them to produce demos to using more forceful language.

"We'll tell you all about it," Steve said. "Listen, Gavin, do you golf?"

Gavin tried not to laugh as he wondered how drunk Steve was. It was a frozen, though beautiful, world out there. What would golf have to do with anything?

"No, can't say that I do, Steve."

"Tomorrow you will. Snow golf." The amusement shone in his eyes.

"Seriously?"

Steve and Maggie glanced at each other and laughed. "That's just what they do here," he said.

Gavin nodded. "Okay then. My first time golfing will be in the Swiss Alps. On snow, no less."

Sophie gave Gavin's hand a quick squeeze. "It'll be his first time skiing, too."

"I thought I'd give snowboarding a chance, actually."

"Ugh, I tried last winter," Maggie said, "and I fell so hard that my tailbone was bruised for a solid month!"

"Your record label has insurance on you, right, Gavin?" Steve asked with mock seriousness.

"Dad," Sophie said in a reproachful singsong.

Dinner gave way to fireside drinks in a separate, cozy lounge area of the hotel, and Gavin found he was enjoying his future in-laws. They had adopted a much more accepting attitude toward his and Sophie's engagement since the first time he met them. And they were keen on having a good time while treating him and Sophie as equals.

As the conversation moved on, however, it became clear that this relating as equals stance wasn't a recent byproduct of Sophie now being a grown-up. They mentioned in off-handed ways how they had raised Sophie to be independent from the start—due to both their demanding work schedule and their general parenting philosophy—and that they wanted her to feel responsible for and in charge of her own life.

Gavin saw how this had created an odd distance between Sophie and her parents. They were respectful and caring with each other, but with a layer of removal. It reminded him of Shay's emotionally vacant parents in a way, though to a far lesser degree. He guessed Sophie recognized something of a kindred spirit in Shay, which explained her fondness for him.

And Gavin understood on a different level why she had committed herself so deeply to him. She was desperate to hang on to the one person in her life who had shown her she was needed.

36

Money was on display everywhere at the Snow Polo World Cup. It was obvious in the fur hats of the trophy (and aspiring trophy) wives mingling under crystal chandeliers in the white VIP tents, the free-flowing top-tier champagne, the lunch prepared by renowned chefs, and the branding done by BMW, Cartier, Maserati, and more. The social aspect of it, with guests milling about on AstroTurf-covered platforms and chatting rather than watching the match, was such an annoyance to Gavin that he finally grabbed Sophie's hand and pulled her away. He kept moving until he had reached the free general public grandstand seating. Instead of finding a spot on one of the benches, he went to the waist-high barrier at the edge of the field of play and stared intently at the action.

This allowed them a measure of relief, too, from the running commentary being broadcast over loudspeakers. The random facts thrown in among the play-by-play, such as why the ponies' tails were braided—to keep them from being caught in the player's swinging mallet—were interesting but also distracting.

The "field" for the polo tournament was a frozen lake centered between snow-capped, tree-lined mountains rising high and craggily into the sky on one side and the sand-colored resorts and other buildings of St. Moritz on the other side. Under clear skies and bright sun, the polo ponies raced the length of the stark white field, urged on by their riders who wore vivid blue or red jerseys, creating a stunning vista. The two teams of four players chased a red ball, swinging their mallets with concentrated grace.

Gavin watched the way the horses' breath came out of flaring nostrils in huge puffs, their exertion manifested in clouds of steam in the low temperature. The chukka, or period, would be over soon and these ponies would be given a rest, swapped out for different world-class horses.

The action came their way and they watched as two opposing players strained for the red ball. Their horses were exceptionally well-trained, forging ahead at the command of their riders in a "ride-off." It was a move Gavin had learned about earlier from the announcer where one player attempted to push the other away from the line of the ball, even as that meant their horses' flanks collided at high speed. The impact was quick and the riders expertly righted themselves without ever losing balance or focus on the two neon-yellow and black striped goal posts.

The dexterity the riders showed in manipulating the ponies was impressive, and Gavin couldn't deny that they were genuine athletes. He was even more amazed when one player was thrown from his horse and obviously sustained some sort of injury to his elbow, but almost immediately returned to his saddle. That same rider went on to score with much fanfare, as a referee on foot waved an orange and yellow flag to signal the play amidst whistle and air horn blows.

"You're loving this," Sophie told him with a playful nudge.

"I'm not ashamed to admit it." The halftime was called and he watched as the players guided the horses off the field for the short break. The loudspeaker commentary was replaced by upbeat music to keep the crowd rallied, though the hip hop selection was oddly dated.

"My parents love you, you know?"

He glanced at her. She wore a fitted white North Face jacket that had a bright teal zipper, the color of which matched the wide cotton headband that pulled her hair back while warming her ears. He knew that behind her sunglasses her hazel eyes would have turned a brilliant green. Her smile for him lingered and he wanted to appease her, but he couldn't stop from saying what he really thought.

"Your parents are full of contradictions, aren't they?"

A look of confusion replaced her smile. "What do you mean?"

"Ah, you know. They're as rich as all these people but they were trying to set themselves apart by making fun of it at dinner the other night. But it's bullshit, isn't it? They're just joining in with a wink and a bloody nod."

"Where is this coming from?"

"It's just, I mean, look at their place in Malibu. Look at that excess and exclusivity."

"They worked to get what they have. They didn't start out with that kind of money. It's not generational wealth like all of this." She gestured to the tents and the luxury hotels nestled into the hills behind them.

"Okay, fine. But they're still so phony with things."

"Just because they are amused by all of this?"

Her question was reasonable, but he ignored it, too fired up—even if he was about to quickly go off track. "It's like a game to them, isn't it? This pretense that they're apart from things. Is that how they make you feel? Apart from them?"

"What—"

"Is that why your worry over having messed up your school admission turned so quickly to relief? Because you got their attention when they pulled connections to guarantee you got in this term?"

"I needed the help," she said sullenly.

He saw in the way she turned away from him that she felt stung. But he wasn't done. "You could have sorted it out on your own, but you were so pleased to feel important to them for a minute, weren't you?" He took a deep breath and suddenly realized pointing out that he could see what she had been missing, and that her parents were to blame for it, wasn't really what she wanted to hear. He hadn't meant to go at her like this.

They had spent the last two days playing snow golf, snowboarding, bobsledding down the oldest naturally refrigerated bobsleigh track in the world, going on horse-drawn carriage rides, eating gourmet meals, and generally living the life of Riley. Which was all well and good, but under the surface he had been absorbing the way her parents tried to act as if they weren't buying into it all, and that had combined with an unacknowledged anxiety he had been harboring about his own status changing so rapidly. He and Rogue had become a sensation, flush with cash and fame. He knew it was only going to get more intense, making him nervous for a future that would turn him into what he and Conor often described as one of "them." That is, once a threshold of success and money was attained, artists could no longer really identify with who they had been at the start of their career. He dreaded this change, fearing it would take hold before he ever really got a chance to create the kind of music and art he knew he could. All of that conspired to this point where he unleashed on Sophie, the one who didn't deserve it at all.

She spoke before he could backpedal and apologize. "What about you?" she asked, a challenge in her voice as she turned to him. "What about you just breezing by the truth of your mother? You tell my parents you 'lost' her as if she were dead and leave it at that. You're not exactly being honest, are you?"

His mother being gone from his life had come up during one of their outings and, as was his habit, he had glossed over it. Sophie bringing it up now sent him on the defensive.

"It was the truth and you know it. I lost any mother I had at age seven. The reason for that, whether she left me or died, doesn't fucking matter much in the grand scheme of things, does it? So don't you question me on how I tell my story. You don't get a say in it."

The effect of his rebuke was immediate. She seemed to deflate, her usual brightness diminished. He recognized his hypocrisy as a bitter taste in the back of his mouth. Hadn't he repeatedly pulled her close to him precisely because she knew and understood his story? And here he was trying to claim she had no right to what he had begged her to be a part of. But he didn't see any way to fix it now. Christ, this had all started because he couldn't keep his mouth shut.

"Let's just leave it—" he started.

"No," she said.

He waited for more but the only thing to break up the silence between them was the signal sounding the start of the next chukka. The crowd in the grandstands behind them came to life as the players rode out onto the ice on fresh ponies.

"No, you don't get to silence me," she finally said. Her manner had changed again, her back straighter now, a determined set to her face. "I know up until now this has been your burden to bear, and that it's torn you to pieces," she said. "But you don't get to tell me I don't have a say."

He looked away, uncomfortable with how clearly she could see him. At the same time, he was grateful for the fact that she was pushing back. Taking a deep breath, he turned back to her with resolve to fix this somehow.

"I'm sorry I went after you, after your parents." he said. He pushed his sunglasses up into his hair and pulled her glasses away so he could see her eyes. "I just love you so much and want the world for you. I want you to always have everything you need out of this life. I hate to see how you've been let down."

"I know that, Gavin. I do. But don't change the subject. We're talking about you. Let me be part of your story. Because I'm in this with you. Let me help with the weight of it all."

The simple plea hit him hard and he wished he hadn't removed his mirrored sunglasses. Damn if she didn't know once again how to handle him, how to give him what he needed when he didn't even realize it. He had lost his faith in religion, but all he could think was that she was a true godsend.

"Fuck me if I ever let you go, darlin'," he said, and pulled her into his arms. He sighed with relief when she held him tightly in return.

37

SOPHIE

On the day of Martin's wedding, Sophie was delighted to see Gavin looking more put together than he ever had. He showered, used some mild product to tame his unruly hair, shaved, and put on a finely tailored suit. She wore a long, form-fitting pale pink sheath that was suitably subtle so as not to take attention away from the bride, though she had to admit that it was very flattering to her figure.

"We're fucking gorgeous," Gavin said with a mischievous smile as he wrapped his arms around her from behind while she checked herself in their bedroom's full-length mirror.

She laughed and reflexively leaned into him as she turned to kiss him. His body reacted to the pressure of her backside against him and he moaned.

"We have time?" he asked.

"You're the best man, baby. We should have already left."

"Ah, I'm sure Marty can use some extra time to recover from last night." He pulled her around to fully face him and wrapped his arms around her waist.

"Do I even want to know what kind of trouble you got him into?" she asked.

"Probably not. Let's just say, he got a taste of what he'll finally get from Celia after the wedding."

"You're not saying that Celia is going to go from being a pious virgin to a stripper for him, are you?" she said with a laugh.

"That would be amazing," he said with a laugh. "But no. Just that he's revved up."

"I hope he didn't tell her what you orchestrated for his bachelor party. It will only make her judge you more."

Celia had planned a traditional Catholic ceremony in a nineteenth-century stone and stained-glass church on the Southside of Dublin. The nearly ninety-minute service would include a full choir, multiple Bible readings, and communion for those who would take it. Gavin wasn't actively anti-religion, but he had lost all comfort from it when his mother left, and he had made it clear for the last six months that he had no intention of taking communion. This conflict had resulted in Celia casting aspersions on the idea that Gavin was fit to be Martin's best man, but there was no changing either side's position on the matter.

"I will not be judged by Celia Rogers, of all people," he said with a scoff. "She's got her man, that's all she needs to worry about."

"And I've got mine," she said with a sexy smile as she grabbed him over the fly of his suit pants.

"We have time. I know we do," he said, backing her up against the bed.

———

THEY CAUSED a stir when they arrived at the church as it was surrounded by eager photographers from various tabloids and legitimate papers. As usual, Sophie took Gavin's lead and smiled as he chatted amiably with the paparazzi and posed before they made their way inside.

Sophie spotted Shay first and told him, "Shay, you look so handsome."

"Thanks," he replied, his cheeks coloring. "You're lovely as ever."

"You two taking notes for your own wedding, then?" Conor asked as he approached them.

Looking at Conor, who also wore a smart suit that fell beautifully on his frame, a wave of emotion passed through Sophie. She realized that these boys who she had grown to love back in school were all men now. It was a wonderful thing to see.

"We'll not be doing a church wedding, that's for sure," Gavin replied with a grin.

"Ah, he says this in the house of the Lord." Conor laughed but also crossed himself for good measure.

A woman giggled with them and Sophie saw that a petite blonde was standing partially behind Conor. It was Conor's girlfriend, Sondra Delaney. She was an actress on Fair City, the long-running Irish soap opera and Sophie recognized Sondra as the notorious man-eating home-wrecker of the show. She was also at least five years older than Conor, and Sophie wondered how that affected their relationship.

He pulled her fully into their circle and they all greeted each other.

"We'll sit together, love," Sondra told Sophie, "since the lads have their thing."

Sophie smiled. "Sure."

"Darlin', I better go find the groom," Gavin said. "I'll see you after." He kissed her quickly before moving off.

CELIA ROGERS KEPT her eyes focused on Martin and she slowly walked down the aisle wearing an appropriately virginal white gown. Sophie watched her, smiling at the way she gripped her father's arm tightly with one hand and how the bouquet of Stephanotis flowers trembled in the other hand.

Sophie thought the service was beautiful, though it also made her think of her own wedding and what she would do differently. Apparently, Sondra had the same thoughts, as she occasionally nudged Sophie and whispered criticisms of certain music selections or the length of the bride's veil.

After several of these comments, Sophie looked down at Sondra's left hand to see if she had an engagement ring, since she surely was acting as if she and Conor were to be next down the aisle. When she saw that Sondra's hand was bare, she knew Conor was in a world of trouble, especially since she knew the two were "temporarily" living together. When she and Gavin were in Switzerland, Sondra's apartment had become unlivable due to a massive renovation, so she took the opportunity to move in with Conor. And her designs on Conor were clear.

―――――――

THE RECEPTION WAS HELD at a nearby hotel ballroom to accommodate the large guest list. The atmosphere was wild as waiters dodged the young children who were let loose from parents ready to have a good time. But mostly, it was a joyous occasion with a lively mix of contemporary and traditional Irish music, and enough free-flowing Guinness to please everyone.

Sophie finally got some time with Celia well after dinner had been served and once again marveled at how the sweet woman was so completely unprepared for the rock 'n' roll world her husband was devoted to. There was something naïve in the way she went on about the bizarre feeling of having press around her, especially given the fact that she had confessed upon their first meeting to being positively obsessed with the tabloid version of Sophie and Gavin's story. This suggested to Sophie that as long as the focus was not on her, Celia was only too happy to indulge in the gossip scene, and that made her slightly wary.

With Gavin in full social mode, Sophie was left to observe the party, but she didn't mind. She enjoyed watching the little ones form their own dance routines, the older folks drink a bit too much and show off dance moves that should never otherwise be seen, and the utter contentment on Martin's face at it all. Not even seeing Gavin chatting briefly with Julia bothered Sophie.

Gavin soon disengaged from his conversation with Julia, and Sophie watched as he scanned the room. He soon located Shay who had retreated to a table at the far corner of the room and looked miserable on his own. Sophie saw Shay brighten when Gavin pulled him toward the bar.

She had early on recognized the dynamics in the band— Gavin looked up to Conor, Conor tried to appear like he needed no one, Shay worshipped Gavin, and Martin was just happy to be in the mix. All of that was on display here.

Turning her attention to Conor, she watched as he danced with

Sondra, and intuitively knew there was something missing with their pairing. They had made a splash with the local tabloids, as they were a gorgeous couple. The contrast of his height and dark hair with her curvaceous but petite frame, combined with their own areas of fame, was appealing. But there was something needy in the way she clung to him, and Sophie knew he wouldn't tolerate it for long.

The two separated on the dance floor and Sophie lost track of them. She was sitting at a table with the boyfriends of Celia's sisters, who were also part of the wedding party. Her thoughts drifted to Felicity, their old school friend. Felicity had hoped to come to the wedding but ultimately had to decline in deference to her university obligations in Toronto, where she had moved a couple years back. Sophie imagined the good time they would have had, and was sad that they wouldn't have the chance to catch up.

"Dance with me."

She looked up to find Conor holding his hand out to her.

"Sondra's gone off for a ciggie. I need a partner," he explained.

When she hesitated, he took her hand and made the decision for her by pulling her to the feet. On the dance floor, he held her close and led her in slow movements.

"So, what do you think of my girl?" he asked.

"You two seem pretty serious."

"In what way?"

Sophie smiled and eyed him for a moment. "Well, I guess because you're living together. And she talks as if having a future with you is a forgone conclusion."

"She wants to marry me," he said.

"Does she know you're not going to?"

Conor raised his eyebrows with a small smile. "And how do you know that?"

"It's obvious looking in from the outside. She's not the one."

The smile left his face. "And who says there is just one, anyway?"

"I do," she replied matter of factly. "And you will too, one day. When you find her."

"You and Gavin are really something with your romance and drama. Not everyone operates the way you two do, you know? It doesn't have to be the be-all and end-all with another person."

Sophie shook her head a little as she looked at him. "Don't you know, Connie, that love is all there is?"

He was struck dumb for a moment, then scoffed. "You're drunk, honey."

"I'm not," she replied, though she probably was. The champagne had been delicious.

"Drunk on love if nothing else, then."

"Yes, definitely that."

"The lyric is 'All you need is love' anyway."

"Now you're talking."

With her heels on they were at eye level and he met her gaze with a small smile again. But there was something more than amusement in it now. It was obvious he was charmed by her, and that fleeting moment from the New York rooftop came to mind. He had teased her with his touch then, and she knew he'd been playing games with her. This was different, though. There was such warmth in his eyes. Then the expression faded as the music abruptly segued into something fast-paced, and he excused himself to go find Sondra.

38

CONOR

onor had an unattached studio in the back garden of his house
that had once been a large gardening shed. He had remodeled
and expanded it to make it into a space where he and the band could
work on music. The rustic wood floors remained but were covered
with tattered Oriental rugs and an old sofa. There was enough space
to house a drum kit and electric, bass, and acoustic guitars, along
with a set of microphones. A basic recording system allowed for rudi-
mentary demos, but he hoped to upgrade to a full-scale soundboard
and other, better, equipment in the near future.

The year was slipping into early summer, and the band didn't
have much to show for their efforts toward their second album. Gavin
was so wrapped up in Sophie that it had been hard for Conor to get
his attention to write music. Martin had returned from his honey-
moon but still seemed absent as he settled happily into married life.
Shay had been the one most eager to start working on things, but they
still hadn't been able to gather everyone other than for the odd
night out.

Truth be told, Conor had enjoyed the down time. He had always
shied away from being part of a big circle of friends, as much as
people increasingly vied for his attention as the band made a name
for itself. Gavin, Shay, and Martin were his closest friends, so if they
weren't available, he was happy to be on his own. He'd spend days
hiking the lush greenery of the Wicklow Way with a backpack filled

with water, protein bars, fruit, and a book. The mountain lakes, steep glacial valleys, flowing streams, and ruined buildings along the way were enough company to satisfy his loner tendencies and love of the natural landscape. Sondra would lure him out of too much extended time away, though, and they had a good time out on the town with dinners with her actor friends.

But this day was a confirmed band day as they had all agreed to meet at Conor's place to put in serious work. He had left his front door unlocked for the others and was sitting on a stool, freestyling on a Gibson Les Paul electric guitar.

"Ooh, is that new?"

He looked up to find Sophie letting herself in. She wore jeans and a pale green short-sleeve cardigan held together at the bodice by a jeweled broach, and the color made her eyes shine a deep emerald. He saw a flash of bare skin at the lower open end of her top and fixated on the fact that she wore nothing under the sweater.

"What you were playing, I meant. Is that something new?" she asked and moved closer to him. "It sounds so different."

"It's the open tuning on the guitar."

"Like Keef!"

He stared at her in surprise. How did she know Keith Richards used open tuning, let alone his nickname? Richards had created his signature sounds for "Honky Tonk Woman," "Brown Sugar," and "Start Me Up" by tuning his guitar the same way a banjo is tuned. The five-string open G tuning created three notes with different octaves and a "ghost" note formed by the two other notes harmonizing.

"Don't be so shocked," she said with a laugh. "I actually pay attention when you guys talk music, you know?"

"Oh. Yes," he mumbled and sat up straighter. "Where's Gav?"

"He had to run back home. Forgot his book with all his notes, if you can believe that."

Of course he had. Gavin could either be exceptionally focused or . . . not. It didn't seem to bode well for their session today. Neither did Sophie being here. Not that he wasn't pleased to see her, but she could be a distraction.

"I won't stay long," she said as if reading his mind. "I've got summer term to sort out at uni."

"I see." He hadn't seen much of her or Gavin since Martin's wedding a couple months ago. That's when she had declared his relationship with Sondra hopeless. He'd thought a lot about that since then, wondering why she even cared to make such a judgement.

"Let me hear that piece again," she said, gesturing to the guitar he held.

He did as she asked and ran through what little he had put together. Watching her as he played, he saw the notes resonating as she tilted her head just so.

"How do you do that? Play without looking at the strings?"

He could have taken the opportunity to share with her that as a child he had shown a prodigy-level talent for music, and had, in fact, taken violin and piano lessons starting at age three. It was likely he could have had a successful career in classical music had his friendship with Gavin not steered him toward rock 'n' roll.

Instead, he said, "I've given the guitar more hand jobs than I've given myself." Because it amused him to see her blush.

"More than I needed to know, Connie."

"You want to give it a try?"

"Give *what* a try?"

He raised his eyebrows and stared at her for a moment, feeling the heat between them and enjoying it. Then he pulled the guitar strap over his head and offered the instrument to her.

"Um, yeah, okay."

He lowered the strap over her shoulder, holding steady to the neck of the guitar until it was in place. When he let it go, she staggered.

"Oh my god, it's so heavy!" she said, astonished.

He laughed. It was a solid piece of equipment, one that he was accustomed to manipulating for hours on end. But seeing her surprise at the weight of it, and the look of admiration for him in her eyes, he viewed it anew. And he saw her anew. She was beautiful and sexy and fun—and Jesus, he was smitten.

"Give me a pick," she said.

He handed her one, though he feared what was to come next. The sound she made with her indiscriminate plucking at the strings was horrible. It made him cringe to see his exquisite maple wood and cherry-red Sunburst-designed guitar played that way. But then he saw the unfettered joy she had in playing. She knew it was awful, but she was enjoying it anyway. Her laughter rang out.

"Wait, how about this? Remind you of anyone?" She set about imitating the way he strutted across the stage during a live show, somehow capturing the confidence bordering on showmanship he knew he projected.

He watched her with a small smile, unable to look away. This attraction wasn't exactly new. He had been drawn to her from the first day she arrived at school, all legs and blonde hair, tanned skin, and extraordinary eyes.

"Got a new band member, then?"

Sondra stood at the door, her eyes trained on them. Conor blinked to clear his memories. Sondra being here felt incongruous and he wondered how long she'd been watching.

Sophie laughed again and shook her head. "No way. I'm just messing around. Here, take this thing before I fall over. I still can't believe you make it look so easy."

Conor took the guitar from her and placed it in its stand.

"Can I have a quick word, Conor?" Sondra asked, and gestured toward the door.

"Sure," he said, but groaned inwardly. Sondra's hints about wanting to be more serious had become less subtle lately, and he imagined she wanted to take this inopportune time to press the issue once more.

They walked out into the garden, closer to the main house but not inside. The air felt wet but rain hadn't fallen in a few hours.

"What on earth was that?" she asked, her face flushed.

Conor was taken aback by her sudden anger. "What are you talking about?"

"You and Sophie—what is that?"

"Just now? She was just messing, like she said. What are you on about?"

"Is there something going on with you and her?"

"She's Gavin's fiancée—you know that."

"The way you look at her . . . it's not right."

"What does that even mean?"

"Did you ever have something with her?"

Conor sighed. "No. She's always been Gavin's."

"Don't sound so *disappointed*, Conor."

"What do you want, Sondra? You want me to tell you that I'm after my best friend's girl?"

"Are you?"

He took a deep breath and shook his head on the exhale. "No, of course not." He knew this delayed response was too telling but he tried to keep his face impassive.

"Where is it going with us?"

"Don't let's do this again," he said.

"You owe me the truth."

"That's all I've ever given you. Fuck's sake, can't we leave it be? It's been grand with us the way it is. Isn't that enough?"

"I'm not sure," she said quietly.

"Well—"

"Conor Quinn! I've got a lead! Something good. Really good."

Conor watched Gavin make his way to them through the house, oblivious to what he was interrupting. Conor was especially glad to see his friend now.

"What is it?" Conor asked.

"It's dead romantic like, but you'll have to trust me."

Gavin's excitement was obvious. And contagious. Conor felt his blood start to pump in anticipation of new creative efforts. Efforts that had been long delayed because of Sophie. It was time to make something happen.

"Let's get to it, then," Conor said. He gave Sondra as apologetic of a look as he could conjure up before heading to the studio with Gavin.

"My heart, that feral bird, has found the sky in your eyes," Gavin said.

Conor took a moment to absorb the words. They were good. Romantic, like Gavin had confessed. But also poetic.

"Whose lines are they?" he asked.

Gavin was staring at his journal. "It's a deviation from something by a poet named Rabindranath Thakur."

Nodding, Conor was reminded once more of Gavin's tendency to use bits of poetry like this as a springboard to provoke and frame his own writing. It had actually become a problem in school when he was tasked with writing an essay on a given poem and he would instead turn in a paper that veered off into his own creations. Some of those poorly graded papers had found their way to the tabloids.

"And the title?" Conor asked.

"'You're My One.'"

A love song for Sophie, then. Conor sighed with the realization that this next album would be an ode to Gavin's fiancée. There would be no use in fighting it. Instead, he'd have to find his own meaning in it all. And after the moment he'd had with Sophie earlier, he was suddenly confident he could not just go along for the ride in this endeavor but enhance it.

"Lads, we're all here!" Martin said as he and Shay joined them. "What's the craic, then?"

Conor reached for his guitar. "You two need to hurry and catch up, because we've got a lead on something. A fucking good one."

Shay nodded. "Let's get to it, then."

They spent the rest of that day and several more days working on the song built around the premise of Gavin finding his true place with Sophie. He and Conor worked together to perfect the lyrics and melody. The first part of the song detailed the buried ache and longing Gavin had for Sophie when they were separated. Conor found the emotion in his guitar playing, perfectly mirroring Gavin's singing. The chorus was a passionate declaration:

> This thing we have, it's fearless darlin
> Because you're my one

The tone changed near the end as Gavin pleaded, "Don't let me chase you away, suffer the weight" before rising with release and optimism to an ecstatic close.

Gavin's voice had a depth and richness born out of new confidence. The result was that it, combined with the heartfelt lyrics and the stirring music, created three minutes and forty-one seconds of something utterly compelling.

39

The atmosphere was noticeably tense when Sophie and Celia arrived at the studio where the members of Rogue had been holed up for the last several weeks. The women had lunched together and decided on the spur of the moment to bring the boys food as well, but just about everyone seemed irritated by their unexpected presence.

Celia paid no mind to their annoyance. Instead, she walked down the hallway with bags of sandwiches, coleslaw, and brownies, chirping merrily about how exciting it was to see them at work.

"Celia, babe, you should've checked with me," Martin said as he followed after her helplessly. "This isn't a good time."

"But it's lunchtime, sweetheart. You need to eat, don't you?"

Sophie waited for Gavin to come greet her and introduce her to their team of producers, engineers, and other crew who suddenly seemed inspired to take a break due to the interruption. But Gavin and Conor were sitting on wood stools in an isolation booth at the far end of the studios, working intently on the rhythm of a guitar line and oblivious to their arrival.

Even though the studio was near Trinity on the Southside of Dublin, Gavin had never suggested she visit him there before. She was surprised by how small the studio was, even with its separate spaces for recording with either carpeted or hardwood floors. An enormous angled soundboard filled the front room, and its dozens upon dozens of knobs and switches and tangle of wires overwhelmed the space. Large speakers were both built into the wood paneled walls and set atop the soundboard. The equipment was complex, requiring more than one engineer to manipulate it and included a colorful keyboard and computer monitor resting in the middle of it all.

She knew the facility had a kitchen and a shower, but the air was stagnant with a lingering mixture of old takeaway food, stale alcohol, cigarettes, marijuana, and body odor. She sensed that the closeness of the space could easily lead to irritation.

Julia O'Flaherty sat sleeping in one of the battered leather chairs pressed against the wall opposite the soundboard. Sophie had seen Julia at various parties and nights out, but both women used Gavin as a buffer, keeping their distance from one another. They had come to an unspoken agreement that they wouldn't be friends.

Shay sat at the soundboard, listening to a playback a song. He leaned back and smiled at Sophie.

"Hey," he said softly. "Come here." He patted the empty chair next to him and she sat down. "Truth is, we're desperate for a break. But we're all too fucking stubborn to admit it. We've hit a wall here and it hurts."

"Is it bad?" She saw the circles under his eyes and knew out of all the band members he would take this kind of creative roadblock the hardest. The band was absolutely everything in his life.

"The record company is on our arses. We get reminders from them of how expensive studio time is everyday—sometimes twice a day," he said with a weary, bitter laugh. "And it's just not coming. We've got the lyrics and we've got some of the music, but for the life of us, we can't bring it all together."

"Oh, Shay," she said softly, and hugged him impulsively.

She was at fault for at least part of this. The publicity around her reunion with Gavin had helped to almost double the band's album sales to six million. The record label had made it clear they wanted to capitalize on the interest in the band—and their relationship. They had become tabloid staples since that radio phone call in Los Angeles, though the near-daily stories tended to be mundane. They'd mostly publish photos of Gavin when he was on his own or with Conor, and gleefully suggest there was "trouble in paradise!" since Sophie wasn't with him. Alternatively, they'd make innuendos out of innocent photos of Sophie with her male schoolmates. As baseless as all this was, it still caught Celia's attention, as she had just that day begged for details about several of that week's stories. Sophie and Gavin found it silly and didn't let it affect their routines, but she knew the fact that they were still garnering attention only stoked anticipation— and pressure—for Rogue's next album.

Shay was stiff in her arms for a moment and she could feel how tense the whole process had made him. But soon he exhaled and returned her embrace.

"Enjoying yourself?"

Sophie and Shay pulled apart at the sound of Gavin's voice. He stood with hands on hips as he glared at them. Sophie saw Julia stir, open her eyes, blink at them, and then pretend sleep again.

"Hi, baby," Sophie said, and stood up. She knew they were all on edge and figured it was best to ignore his attempt to start a fight. "We brought sustenance. You ready for a break?"

"I'm not in the mood for this, Sophie. And this isn't the kind of thing where you can just drop by. We're under a fucking deadline," he told her.

"Wow, you really are in a bad mood," she said with a smile, trying to lighten him up.

"He's been like this for the last two weeks," Shay said.

"Fuck off, Shay," Gavin told him.

Sophie shook her head, both at Gavin's cruel reaction and at his use of "Shay" rather than "Seamus." That was almost the bigger insult after Gavin had made such a big point of using the full name for his friend for so many years. To revert back to the shorter name, the one his parents had so carelessly bestowed upon him, was a true slight. But even though Shay looked wounded, remained silent.

"Gavin, don't be such a jerk," she said.

Gavin's annoyance was clear as he stared at her but she didn't back down, maintaining eye contact. "Don't do this to me now," he said stiffly. "I'm under enough fucking pressure as it is."

"Bit of a domestic, is it?" Conor asked as he approached them. He waited in vain for a response and finally slapped Gavin forcefully on the back a few times. "Be nice to your girl. She's the best thing about you, you know?"

Sophie watched the stubbornness drain out of Gavin at his friend's semi-playful words.

"Right as usual, Con," Gavin said. "I need some air. Come with me, darlin'."

He grabbed her hand and she let herself be taken out of the building through a rear door. It opened into a narrow, paved brick alleyway and they had it to themselves. They stood together, mirroring each other with arms crossed over their chests in defensive poses. The silence grew but Sophie wasn't going to be the first to speak.

"I fucked up," he finally stated.

"It's okay, Gavin."

"Thanks, but it's not. I'm at a loss and I don't see any change coming. It's more than frustrating. I'm sorry for taking it out on you."

Sophie took the few steps to close the gap between them and leaned her head against his shoulder. He wrapped his arms around her and kissed her forehead.

"I'm sorry to show up like this. I really didn't think it through. I only even suggested it because I didn't know what to say when Celia told me she doesn't like to have sex with Martin."

Gavin laughed and pulled away. "What now?"

Sophie raised her eyebrows. "Seems she's not that into it. Says it's a lot of 'fuss' over nothing much."

"Oh, poor Marty!" he groaned. "And he's completely fucked 'cause he's so in love with her."

"And she's in love with him, too. But she's just not into sex. It's too sweaty," she said, her nose crinkled with distaste.

"God, what else did she say?" he asked and they giggled together.

Gossiping about their friend's unsatisfactory sex life and agreeing they had no such worries was just the thing to alleviate their earlier tension.

"I've missed you, Gavin," Sophie said. She wrapped one arm around his neck and tried to tame his wavy hair with her other hand.

It had been months now of the band working together tirelessly, first at Conor's and now in the studio. Gavin had been keeping opposite hours from her, meeting with the guys in the afternoon and returning home at four or five in the morning, while she was committed to early classes and daytime study groups. Despite the lack of quality time together, they had stayed connected in bed. Once home, Gavin would strip naked and coax Sophie into lovemaking that began each morning with him trailing kisses and gentle bites over every exposed part of her body. She began to sleep nude in tingling anticipation of his arrival. They established a delicious routine where he would kiss, lick, and touch her while she feigned sleep. When he'd brought her close to the edge, and she could no longer maintain normal breathing, he would whisper in her ear, "now I'm going to fuck you" and she would reach for him. The extended foreplay combined with his forceful confidence always led to an intense experience.

Wrapping his arms around her waist, Gavin examined her. "We have been a bit off these last few weeks."

"Try months."

"Yeah, suppose so. It's been hard to keep up with you in school and me working on the album, right?"

She nodded. "I don't want to lose you."

"Never gonna happen. You're my girl."

"That's true," she agreed with a smile. "But do you think there's going to be an end to these studio sessions?"

"Yes. We're mostly there. Just need the final push. Be patient for me."

"I can do that." She kissed him.

"We have our Christmas trip to look forward to, don't we?"

Christian Hale had invited them all to his Sunshine Beach home near Brisbane for the Christmas holiday. Martin had opted out to spend his first Christmas at home with his wife, but Conor, Shay, Gavin, and Sophie had accepted the offer. Both Conor and Shay would be going solo. Conor had ended things with Sondra, suggesting maybe they could get together again after the band finished the album, but both knew the truth about his lack of commitment to her.

"We do! I'm so excited about having a summertime Christmas." The Australian seasons were opposite of theirs, so they would be arriving in time for a warm celebration.

"Look, we'll wrap this up with plenty of time to go shopping for togs."

She laughed. "Togs," she mocked. "Doesn't bikini have a nicer ring to it?"

"When I'm picturing you in one, it does." He pressed his lips to hers for a long, slow kiss.

"Okay, I've distracted you long enough," she said reluctantly. "Time for you to go back in and apologize to Shay."

"Apologize? Guys don't apologize to other guys, darlin'."

She rolled her eyes. "Okay, then do whatever you do to make it right."

"That I will. Let's go in."

40

SOPHIE

Their vacation began with the flight from Dublin to Brisbane, as even though it took almost twenty-four hours, including one stop in Dubai, they had splurged on first-class suite tickets and were rewarded with a luxurious journey. Flying on an Emirates Airlines Airbus A380 for the fourteen-hour flight from Dubai to Brisbane, they each had a private "suite" with a remote-controlled door that closed for privacy and chairs that relaxed back to full sleeping position. When the cabin lights dimmed, the ceiling of the plane sparkled with faux stars. The meals offered along the way were exceptional and included caviar and the finest collection of spirits and wine.

Gavin and Sophie's suites were next to each other, separated with a wall that could be lowered to waist height but wouldn't allow them to combine their spaces, so she spent a lot of the flight in his seat with him. They took advantage of the time to reconnect after having been apart for a week prior to the trip. Rogue's final task for their second album, *That Need*, was to take it to London for the record label to hear it.

The label's response to the album was so enthusiastic that Rogue ended up staying in London for several more days than initially planned so that the marketing department could jump on how they would roll out the new music. They also used the opportunity to celebrate, and while out partying at a club one night they met Jackson Armstrong, Britain's leading romantic-comedy actor and renowned bachelor playboy. He delighted in showing his new friends all of London's hotspots and made sure Conor and Shay had plenty of women to choose from. While they were living the high life, Sophie was in Dublin, taking her end-of-term exams. The demands of Trinity were greater than that of USC, and she had struggled with the workload for the whole year. Gavin's frequent and unapologetic ways of distracting her from her studies hadn't helped, but in the end, she felt like she did well.

Now, as she and Gavin squeezed themselves together in his reclined seat, they were well fed, bordering on drunk from the bottle of Dom Pérignon they'd shared, and content to cuddle with the door closed. Conor and Shay had gone to the lounge and bar and hadn't been seen for more than an hour.

Sophie pressed her face into Gavin's neck and smelled a foreign scent on his skin.

"You're wearing cologne?" she asked lazily.

"It was in the WC. Had to give it a try. There's women's perfume in there too," he replied. "You can always wash it off in the shower room if you don't like it." He laughed softly, unable to hide his incredulity at the lavishness of this experience.

Before she could lose her nerve, she asked him as casually as possible, "So, when you guys were in London . . . did anything happen?"

"Lots of things happened," he said, and kissed the top of her head. "We got rave reviews from the record company on the album, we talked preliminary tour and video plans, we met celebrities like the actor Jackson Armstrong and saw the posh nightlife. And during all that, there was not one time that I so much as looked at another girl."

Sophie laughed because he saw right through her attempt to check up on him. "Not even a glance?"

"No," he said. "Marty, he was another story."

"What does that mean? Did he cheat on her?"

"No. Absolutely not. He did not and he would not."

"But?"

"But, he's got an eye for the ladies. And I don't blame him much. He said that Celia has even less sex drive since she's got pregnant."

That revelation went right by her in her champagne haze before sinking in. She pulled away from him and pressed her hand to his chest. "Pregnant? Is she really?"

Gavin laughed. "Seems so."

"Oh my god. That's so exciting!"

"You mean petrifying. They're only kids themselves."

"I know, but it will be so much fun to have a baby in the group!"

"Sure, yes. It'll be great—for them."

Sophie smiled and touched his cheek. "Don't worry, Gavin, this doesn't make me want to have a baby."

He relaxed. "There's plenty of time for all that. Let's be young ourselves first, yeah?"

"Yeah, for sure."

41

Sophie knew that Christian, as the founding member and lead singer of the pop-punk band Scandal, had a solid career, including a rabid hometown fan base. But Gavin shared with her that the real reason he could afford to have his own home built on the sands of Sunshine Beach wasn't due to respectable band earnings, but rather the gifting of the land to him from beloved grandparents. Christian preferred to let his fans think he had poured everything he had into the land instead of telling the truth, though, since admitting to having had a comfortable and easy childhood with a generous and wealthy family would have conflicted with the punk ideals he otherwise preached and lived.

Sophie had found it interesting that the two men had this sort of thing in common. Both chose to manipulate the public version of their pasts for their own reasons, though she wasn't sure Gavin had revealed his own secrets to Christian.

As soon as they arrived to the house, Christian introduced his wife Patsy, a willowy blond with a warm smile.

"It's lovely to meet you," Patsy said. "Now, I want to show you all to your rooms so you can have a bit of a rest, because I hear we've got a special treat this evening."

The plan was to have all of Christian's bandmates over, grill dinner on the deck, and then listen to the newly completed Rogue album.

"Screw the rest bit," Christian said with a big smile. "The best cure for jetlag is ocean water. Get your togs on and let's go for a swim!"

Sophie took this as a good sign that Christian wasn't suffering from one of his "moods" as Gavin called them. That was another thing the two men had in common—the tendency to give into the darkness pulling at them. Gavin had mentioned it in passing, wanting to assure Sophie that no matter what state their host was in, they'd still be able to enjoy the visit.

They all agreed with Christian's suggestion and soon were diving into seventy-five-degree ocean that was just a short walk from the house. It was the perfect way to start their vacation.

———

THE THREE-STORY WHITEWASHED house had been lovingly co-designed by Christian and Patsy with the focus being on open spaces and ocean views. As impressive as it was, Sophie got the feeling that the most-used area of the house was the deck, as it had all the amenities of the indoors, including a built-in grill and stocked bar, a large seating area encircling a fire pit, and, of course, the prized ocean views. The large wooden pergola had a crisp linen canopy to provide some welcome shade in the daytime.

By the time they all finished dinner, it was dark and the air was mercifully cool. The evening had been filled with beer, fresh grilled fish and veggies, as well as overlapping and excited talk. Sophie mostly watched as the five members of Scandal and three of Rogue's members went after each other with good-natured barbs. Even Shay was out of his shell and in the mix. They had toured together briefly before Rogue could claim many fans for themselves, and it was obvious they had all come out of it as good friends. Patsy graciously included Sophie in the conversation with the wives and girlfriends of the guys of Scandal, but she was mostly content to just to observe the rambunctious goings-on.

Finally, Christian stood up and told everyone to shut up. This was met with boos and "fuck offs" from several guys before everyone quieted down.

"It's time now, mates," Christian said, "for a very special treat. Let's have a listen to Rogue's second album. It's called what?"

"*That Need,*" Gavin said, and was met with a chorus of "oohs" and howls.

Christian manipulated the sound system and the first song filled the night air at high volume through the outdoor speakers.

Sophie leaned into Gavin as "Return To You" began. She knew the subject matter was obvious enough—their reunion—but she thought Conor's sharp guitar and Shay's crisp drumming kept it from being too sentimental.

The following three songs, however, expressed darker themes relating to love. One was a brutally honest account of being the one to disappoint a lover. Sophie read this as a combination of Gavin's guilt toward Julia and Conor's guilt toward Sondra. Another explored the idea of love withheld as a byproduct of neglect, a song that obviously took from Shay's experiences. Still another song was a bitter depiction of unreturned love, which she knew reflected Gavin's ongoing struggle with his feelings about his mother's abandonment.

Despite the band's success in the past few years, Gavin had gotten away with his stock answer about his mother, saying he had "lost" her at a young age. If pressed, he admitted it was a car accident but then cut off any further prying. Reporters seemed to take the tragic story at face value and no one had delved deeper to find the truth.

Sophie wondered if Gavin was trying to call out to his mother with this album. She was either the subject or referenced several times, enough to be a key element in the unifying theme of pained love. His pride and insistence that she heal in her own time had kept him from hiring a private detective to search her out. But with this album, Sophie could see that this self-imposed restraint was eating away at him. His anger at what he had lost when his mother chose to leave her family was testing his life-long coping mechanisms.

The title song "That Need" lightened the mood. All of Scandal howled when Gavin sang the line "That need is deep inside of you/Exactly where I wanna be" with a sexy, husky intonation.

"Aw, what a fantastic pickup line, McManus!" Kerry, Scandal's guitarist, shouted above the throbbing combination of Shay's drums and Martin's bass line. The pulsating rhythm was seductive and a perfect match for the sexually charged lyrics.

"The world needed another song to fuck to," Gavin said unapologetically, and they roared with laughter.

Gavin was letting them think of the song in terms of the surface level, but Sophie knew he had really been acknowledging her need to be the one to save him, and his need to lean on her. They met perfectly in that place of need, each seeking and finding the other there.

Sophie watched the reactions of the others as the album continued and was happy to see that they all seemed to genuinely like the new material, making specific, positive comments about melody, guitar lines, drumming, or lyrics, and applauding after each song.

Finally, the closing song, "You're My One," started. The previous freewheeling chatter during the other songs ceased as everyone stilled. It was obvious upon first listen there was something special about this song. The air seemed to change as they absorbed the way Conor's guitar evoked romantic longing. Then Gavin's passionate, confident singing took over.

They all sat mute and motionless for thirty-seconds after the song ended with Gavin's entreaty for his lover not to leave him, "to suffer the weight" of all he put upon her. Listening to the album, and especially the last song, had been an intense experience and they needed a way to come down from it.

"What a bleeding-heart romantic you are, McManus," Christian finally yelled, to the delight of everyone else.

"Aw, I think it's sweet. If only you'd stop shouting long enough to sing me a proper love song," Patsy said with a wink to her husband.

"But sweetheart, I write love songs all the time. It's my mates here who won't have it."

Christian's bandmates all objected at once, claiming that they adored romantic love songs.

The next couple of hours passed in the same high-spirited way, with plenty of alcohol fueling loud talk. The two bands traded tour stories and took every opportunity to harass each other. Scandal mocked Rogue for their instant fame, and Rogue mocked Scandal for their legion of incredibly intense fans.

It was late in the evening when Sophie noticed that Conor was no longer among them on the deck. She had come to see that he had loner tendencies, as he often disappeared from gatherings, but it didn't seem right that he would leave like this on their first night together.

42

SOPHIE

Getting up, Sophie went to the railing and could just make out his figure down at the beach. He was standing ankle deep in the water, smoking what she knew was not a cigarette.

It was futile to wait for a break in the rapid-fire conversation to tell Gavin she was going to take a walk, so she simply slipped away unnoticed.

"Hey," she said as she came upon Conor.

He was slow to respond, his eyes trained on the water. "Hey."

"What are you doing?"

"Em, well," he said, and then laughed. "I don't know if I'm higher than I've ever fucking been or what, but I could swear I saw bits of neon blue sparkles in the water out there."

Sophie was tempted to tease him but then decided to be nice.

"You did see it. It's bioluminescent phytoplankton."

"What are you on about?" he asked with a laugh.

She laughed too. "No, really. Christian was just telling us that they had a swarm of it a couple days ago. Apparently, they're tiny plants and they bloom if a colder current gets pushed up to the surface in warm climates. We missed the best of it. He said the whole surface of the water was glowing bright blue, and he even went surfing in it and came out looking like Tron."

"Fuck me. What a trip."

"Yeah." She watched the ebb and flow of the water for a few quiet minutes. It seemed the marijuana didn't make him chatty. "Hey, let's see if we can find the spark."

"What's that?"

She hiked up her sundress and fell to her knees. "The spark. Christian said the phytoplankton can live for up to a day in the sand and that if you dig in the wet part you might see a spark of light. That's them."

Digging with both hands, she stared into the small hole she was making. When a tiny spark flashed, she laughed out loud. It lasted less than a second but was a thrill nonetheless.

"That's madness," Conor said and moved to his knees beside her.

Soon they were both digging and pointing out sparks to each other and laughing excitedly. After a time, they stopped digging and worked to catch their breath.

Sophie moved toward the drier sand and started pushing it into a small, slightly inclined mound. Then she made another next to it. She stretched out, using the mound as a sort of pillow, and gestured for him to do the same.

Conor settled next to her and they looked up at the sky. The moon was a sliver and the stars shone brightly without nearby city lights to dim them.

"It's amazing here," she said with a sigh.

"You know any constellations?"

"Hmm . . . Big Dipper?"

"Can't quite see all of it in this hemisphere," he said softly.

"Oh, yes. Of course, you're right."

"Look there," he said, and pointed.

She followed his direction but wasn't sure what he was indicating.

"See those four?" He pointed at four spots and the pattern of a giant square became visible to her eye. "It's part of Pegasus. The winged horse."

"I see it!"

"The story goes Pegasus was formed when a few drops of Medusa's blood fell into the sea and mixed with the foam."

"I never knew that." She glanced at him, but he was still looking upward. "What else do you see?"

"How about that one there, the very bright blue one?"

"God, you can't miss it, can you? Not once you've actually focused on it."

"It's called Vega, and it's that bright because it burns something like six or seven times hotter than the sun."

"Amazing."

"That intensity means it'll burn out that much faster, though."

"And then what?"

"It'll die."

"No, don't die Vega!" she pleaded, only half joking. "I'd miss it."

"Well, when stars die, they don't really go away. They sort of reincarnate. Their material creates other space formations."

Sophie turned on her side, resting on an elbow so she could look at him. "How do you know so much about this stuff?"

He glanced at her, then back at the sky. "I can be clever."

"You're more than clever, and you know it. I wish you wouldn't hide this part of you so often."

Now he moved so he mirrored her pose and watched her with eyebrows raised.

"It's like you pretend to be just the 'rock star' always chasing girls, but there's so much more to you."

"But I am a rock star and I absolutely adore chasing girls."

"You're also smart and thoughtful and caring."

"Ah, Gavin's the sensitive one in the band. There's only room for one," he said with a smirk.

"Be serious," she said and touched his arm.

She saw him look down at her hand and linger on the connection. Before she could process what he was doing, he leaned toward her and pressed his lips to hers. She was stunned motionless but aware enough to think his kiss surprisingly sweet and gentle.

It only lasted two-seconds before he moved away and jumped up, pulling her with him in a rush.

"Feel like a dip?" he asked.

"What?" She was confused. Confused that *she* hadn't been the one to pull away from his kiss. And confused by his sudden change of mood. After sensually, albeit briefly, kissing her, he was now . . . playful?

"Water's warm—even now," he told her and without warning, he scooped her up and over his shoulder.

Sophie screamed in protest, at first with real anger, but quickly collapsed into a fit of laughter as he swung her around teasingly, going knee-high into the water.

"You throw me in and I swear to God you're coming with me!" she said.

"We'll see about that," he replied.

As he attempted to hurl her back over his shoulder and into the water, she wrapped her foot around the back of his knee, buckling his leg so that he came crashing down on top of her. He ended up pressed between her legs and they both laughed for a moment. When they grew quiet, he met her eyes and she saw the desire there.

Locked into his gaze, she felt the heat between them. For the first time, it wasn't just him wanting her.

He was gorgeous and sexy as hell. There was no denying that she was attracted to him.

And there was no denying that he could see she felt that way. He was watching her with a small, knowing smile.

When he moved to kiss her again, he only got as far as brushing his lips against hers before she put a hand to his chest to stop him.

What was going on here? So what if they were attracted to each other? That didn't mean something would actually happen between them. She knew that. Didn't he?

"Whatever attraction you have for me—it's not going to happen," she said. This declaration was as much to herself as to him but she couldn't admit that to him. "Okay?"

His laugh was dismissive as he stood up. "Honey, relax. I was just messing. Too much drink. Too much weed. You know, you were chatting me up, so I acted like I was falling for it. Didn't know you'd take it so serious."

That flustered her, made her unsure what to think. Had she read too much into the situation? She stood up and glanced at him. His white cotton v-neck shirt was wet and stuck to his skin, molding to the defined muscles of his pecs and abs. With a quick glance down at herself, she realized her wet sundress was plastered to her body in the same provocative way. The difference between them was that he was sporting a noticeable bulge at the crotch of his blue and white board shorts.

"Yeah, sure," she said, and let him know with her eyes what she had discovered. "Just—no more. Okay?"

He moved toward her and said softly, "I'm really sorry, Sophie."

He seemed sincerely embarrassed, and she just wanted it to be over.

"Don't worry about it," she told him quickly. "Let's go back to the house."

He agreed and they walked silently together. But when they got close enough to hear the music and the voices straining to rise above it on the deck, he steered them toward the front entrance. After a moment's thought, Sophie realized he was right to want to hide the fact that they had jumped into the ocean together at three in the morning.

Inside, they separated and went to their own bedrooms. Sophie showered and crawled into bed, her head swimming. She tried to think about everything rationally.

Okay, so what if she was attracted to Conor? And a little curious about what might be different in being with another man. Wasn't it normal to feel these things? Especially at her age and with no other relationship experience?

The bottom line was that the sexual attraction she and Conor apparently shared was inconsequential compared to the reality she had with Gavin. Her commitment and true desire was for Gavin and Gavin alone. He was a skilled and attentive lover, and could leave her body trembling from the intensity of her orgasms. He was all she needed. Her confidence in this was complete by the time she drifted off to sleep.

But, when she woke an hour later as Gavin climbed into bed, she immediately reached for him, eager to prove her devotion.

43

Christian's excitement was contagious as he took everyone to a surfing beach in nearby Noosa National Park the next day. On the way over, he admitted he had been addicted to surfing all his life and that he loved to share the joy he got out of riding the perfect wave.

This beach was much more populated than where their hosts lived and featured an exposed point break that had fairly consistent and somewhat gentle surf perfect for newbies.

"Just look out for the sharks, jellyfish, and rocks, okay, mates?" Christian said with a wicked grin.

Sophie exchanged a look with Gavin, hoping he'd be careful. But he was too caught up in the moment and didn't stop to reassure her. He and the others followed Christian to the blue-green water, while she and Patsy set out a couple of large, thin blankets on the sand.

Sophie found Patsy to be both a wonderful host and a genuinely nice person. She and Christian had also met while young, and Sophie took comfort in the fact that their marriage had survived over the last eleven years with them still seeming to be very much in love. Tall, with sandy hair and a laid-back demeanor, Patsy was the perfect complement to her rangy and intense husband.

"So, Sophie," Patsy said as she pulled her sundress over her head, "will you go on tour with Gavin?"

Sophie piled her hair on top of her head in a messy bun as she replied. "No, I can't. I'm still in school."

"Hmm . . . ."

"Uh-oh. What does that mean?" Sophie asked with a nervous laugh. She pulled off her tee shirt and shorts and adjusted her black bikini.

"Nothing really. Just seems like you two shouldn't be parted again so soon. You know, I have to confess, I followed all of your tabloid stories!"

Sophie laughed. "I hope you don't believe everything you read in those."

"No, I know better, believe me. But . . . ." She hesitated as she watched her husband gracefully ride a glassine wave.

"What is it?"

"Watch out for the story about you and Conor."

Sophie's chest tightened. "What do you mean?" she asked as calmly as she could. Had Patsy seen what happened last night?

"Or Shay or Martin. One of those rags will come up with a story that you're about to run off with another member of Rogue. Happened to us, so it's bound to happen to you."

Looking out to the ocean, Sophie saw Gavin sitting on his borrowed surfboard, bobbing in the water next to Shay and Conor. The three of them seemed happy to simply watch their more experienced friend take on the challenge of the waves.

"I don't think any of us take those magazines seriously," Sophie said carefully, still trying to discern whether Patsy was intimating anything more than the obvious.

"Ah, you think that now. Wait until they hit a nerve, hit on something that's a little too close."

"Is there something you're trying to tell me?" Sophie asked, unable to skirt the issue any longer.

Patsy looked taken aback. "No, no. I'm sorry, I hope you didn't think I was getting at anything about you. I guess I was really talking about myself and the troubles Christian and I have had."

"Oh . . . I'm sorry to hear that," Sophie said, and gave her a small smile.

"It's in the past now," Patsy said.

Sophie waited for her to continue. When it was clear that they would instead share silence, she turned her attention to watching Gavin flop about in the waves. He was a hopeless surfer, and Shay wasn't much better, although they both seemed to be enjoying their attempts. Conor, on the other hand, was a natural athlete and succeeded in getting up on his board a few times.

Eventually both women settled on their bellies as they watched the water. Sophie untied her bikini top and relaxed as the heat drew beads of sweat along the small of her back. She was close to dozing when Patsy startled her by speaking again.

"It was a story that said I had an affair with Scandal's manager, actually," she said, her voice flat.

Sophie pulled herself to her elbows so she could look at Patsy. "I don't understand where they come up with some of these things," she said with a shake of her head.

"Thing is, there was some truth to it." Patsy saw Sophie's look of surprise and laughed. "Oh, not that I had an affair, but I was close friends with him. When the band is in the thick of things, with touring and publicity and everything that goes along with it, sometimes the manager is your connection to your man. So, we got to be friends. We had an . . . emotional bond, you could say."

Sophie didn't know how to respond. She let the silence grow between them.

"It was a little too close to the line, really. And the tabloids picked up on that and ran with it. It challenged our marriage."

It was hard for Sophie to imagine how a person could let that happen to their marriage. But then her attraction to Conor—and his to her—came to mind and she felt renewed guilt. It hadn't been anything more than a passing moment, though, and she knew that in the end she would always choose Gavin.

"I can't imagine how awful it must have been," she told Patsy, for want of anything else to say.

Patsy blinked away the tears in her eyes and forced a smile. "But we made it through. And we're great now. Again."

"It's so nice to see the way you two are together. You're a very sweet couple."

"Thanks. I can say the same about you and Gavin, too."

"I think it's Gavin and Christian who make a great couple,"

Sophie said, and Patsy laughed. "No, I mean it in a way. Christian is a good mentor for him."

"Yeah. He really is fond of your man. Which is why it'll break his heart that Gavin can't surf to save his life!"

Sophie looked up in time to see Gavin slip backward off his surfboard. "Oh, I hope he doesn't hurt himself!"

"Nah, he's fine. Christian's got his eye on him."

Sophie hoped that was true—not just in the water, but as a friend, too. Gavin had countless "friends" but there were only a few who he had really let close to him. And she knew he could use all the real friends he could get.

44

GAVIN

Gavin sat mesmerized by the show Sophie was putting on. She and Patsy, emboldened by liquid courage, had jumped up to do a karaoke version of Blondie's "One Way or Another." They danced together, giggling as they sang with abandon. Sophie's hair was loose and her short white sundress showcased her long, tanned legs. The smiles both women wore as they improvised dance moves were contagious.

The whole gang had assembled at the Noosa Heads Surf Club Bar to catch the sunset on the covered deck. The club was one story up from the beach and offered a lively spot to drink and enjoy the local scene. They had pushed together four tables and had been there for hours when it was announced that it was karaoke night.

"This is the girl for you. Don't fuck it up," Christian said.

"Thanks for the vote of confidence," Gavin replied with a laugh, though he didn't pull his eyes away from Sophie.

"Gav, I'm telling you as a friend is all. Rogue is about to fucking explode. You think you've seen mayhem? You ain't seen nothing yet. This album is the real deal. I'm telling you this is what is going to send you guys so far over the top you won't remember what life was like before it."

Gavin felt a shiver run up his spine at the bold proclamation, though he couldn't accept it so easily. "Jesus, I appreciate the support," he said with a glance to Christian, "but think you might be exaggerating a bit?"

"Mate, I've been around long enough to know what I'm talking about. You're going to need something to keep you grounded. And from what I can see, Sophie is it for you."

Pulling his eyes off Sophie, Gavin finally turned to Christian. "Don't think for a minute that I don't know that about her. As much as everyone thinks that last song on the album is romantic bullshit, what she and I have is real."

"Good," Christian replied. "And look, no one thinks it's romantic bullshit, okay?"

Gavin laughed and lifted his pint glass to his friend. "Listen, what do you want to bet Con ends up with not only the blonde there, but her friend as well?" he asked with a sly grin, and nodded to where Conor stood in a corner chatting up two women.

"As long as he takes it to their place and not mine, he can have at it."

As the song ended, Sophie and Patsy bowed in response to the raucous applause and whistles they received. Sophie then hugged Patsy before begging off.

Gavin watched as she walked away, and soon noticed that she turned quite a few heads along the way. He had always known she was a beautiful girl, but he was now realizing she was truly exceptional and would naturally get the attention that went along with that. Understanding this, however, did not make it any easier to accept. As a man, his pride told him not to share her in any way, shape, or form. And so it was a battle between that instinct and his rational intellect over how possessive he could truly be.

45

Sophie frowned at her reflection in the mirror. Out there with the karaoke machine, she had felt free and sexy. But now, under the fluorescent lighting in the restroom, she just felt drunk.

The chilled Cosmopolitans were so refreshing in the heat of the late afternoon. But now that she thought about it, she realized her cocktail had been replenished the moment she'd drained it by some enterprising waitstaff who was catering to their local celebrity, Christian. And so it was far too easy to just keep drinking.

She was well past buzzed and teetering on her feet. Patting her cheeks to try to snap out of it, she then refreshed her lipstick, ran her hand through her hair, and bumped right into Conor as soon as she stepped out of the restroom. He had been deep into putting the moves on a blonde, having backed her up against the wall in the dimly lit hallway.

"Sorry," Sophie told him with an amused smile. Of course, Conor would be with some random girl. It was entirely typical.

He pulled away from the girl. "You all right?"

"Yep," she said and laughed. "I'm just a little, little, little drunk."

"Come here, let me get you some water," he said, and took her arm to steady her.

"Um, hello?" Conor's new friend protested.

"Oh, listen, eh . . . ."

"Natalie," she replied with a forced smile.

193

"Just give me a minute, Natalie. My friend needs some attention."

Sophie slung her arm around Conor's neck and leaned heavily on him. He wrapped his arm around her waist in return, holding her up more than she liked to admit. Holding her up effortlessly with a strength she couldn't ignore. That, combined with the trace scent of his intoxicating aftershave made her realize why it was so easy for him to hook up with any woman he wanted.

But that wasn't something she should be dwelling on. Instead, she said, "Don't worry, Natalie. Conor is guaranteed to give you a good time—he's a sure thing!"

"All right, chatty," he said, fighting a smile as he pulled her toward the far end of the bar.

In no time, he got the bartender's attention and was handed a bottle of cold water. He then wrapped his arm around her shoulders and steered her outside of the bar and down onto the cool sand.

"Drink up, honey. You've done a number on yourself."

She took the water and drank half the bottle greedily.

"I don't know what happened," she said with awe, and wiped her mouth with the back of her hand. "I only had a few drinks."

"A few being how many?" he asked.

"Um, four, no, five? Maybe?"

"Sophie Kavanaugh, what were you thinking?"

"I don't know," she said simply, wide-eyed.

He laughed. "You're a hell of a cute drunk."

The look in his eyes as he watched her . . . it wasn't exactly desire. Or, it wasn't *only* desire. There was adoration, too. It reminded her a whole lot of the way he looked at her last night, under the stars and on the wet sand.

"Are you going to kiss me now?"

He took a step away from her. "No. You didn't say anything to Gavin, did you?"

"No, silly. I'm not stupid, you know." She looked wistfully at the bar, thinking of her fiancé now, just as she should have earlier. "I love him so much. Do you know that? He is the sweetest, most wonderful man and I never, ever want to hurt him."

He nodded. "Drink your water. Sober up a bit so I can go back inside."

"Oh, yeah. You've got Natalie to fuck," she said and laughed.

"Yes, I've got Natalie to fuck. And whoever else I feel like. No guilt-trips from you, miss can't-hold-her-liquor."

She grabbed the finger he had playfully shaken at her as he spoke. "Tell me something," she said. "Do you want me?"

The question had just spilled out of her. Damn those Cosmopolitans.

"Stop it, Sophie," he said without conviction.

Still, she wanted to know. So, instead of obeying his weak command, she wrapped her arms around his neck and looked up at him. "I was wondering if you're attracted to me, or if you were just lonely and I was convenient."

He watched her for a long, silent moment before taking her hands and pushing her away from him. He seemed to waver briefly before finding his answer. "You were just a convenience for a lonely man, honey," he said softly. "Now I'll go find a more suitable form of release."

"Oh. Okay. Go ahead." She suddenly sobered. She wasn't sure what her motives were or what she was expecting, but his response was like being doused by a bucket of cold water.

"You'll be okay?"

"I am fine. Thanks, Connie."

He nodded and left her to go back inside the bar.

She downed the rest of the water, took a deep breath, and made her way back inside as well. She found Gavin standing at the bar, surrounded by half a dozen young women. He was chatting amiably with them as he waited for the bartender to refill a tray full of pint glasses.

Winding her way through the women, she wrapped her arms around Gavin's waist and pressed her face to his shoulder.

"Where've you been, darlin'?" he asked, holding her to him.

"Aye, leave off, then, girlie. We were here first," a woman whined, and got the others complaining as well.

"Come, ladies," Gavin said, his voice raised. "This here is my lovely fiancée. You wouldn't stand between a man and his true love, would you?"

With reluctance, the crowd broke up.

"Gavin, will you take me home?" Sophie asked quietly.

"What's wrong, sweet girl?"

"I got drunk."

"Is that why you made that spectacle of yourself?" he asked.

She pulled away and looked at him. "What do you mean?"

"Dancing with Patsy like that. You know, you turned on half the men in here with that."

Relaxing, she smiled. "Only half?"

"Funny. Do you really want to go? You seem okay now."

"Hmm . . . how about we stay for a while, but only if you promise to take me for a swim later. We've never been skinny dipping."

"I do love you, Sophie," he replied with a grin.

46

CONOR

Conor took pains to quietly let himself into Christian's house through the deck. It was after eight in the morning and he had ended up going home not with Natalie, but with a young woman named Sienna. She had been fun, eager, and just the distraction he needed. Now he hoped to slip into his room to sleep it all off.

But as he started past the kitchen, he noticed Sophie peering into the refrigerator. She had plugged in a waffle maker and had an assortment of breakfast ingredients out on the counter.

"Morning," he said.

She turned quickly and then smiled at him. "Hi. Have a good night, then?"

He raised his eyebrows. "I did, actually. You going to lecture me on chasing girls again?"

"Nope. Hungry?"

He smiled. "Starved," he told her.

"If I can get this thing to work," she said, and gestured to the waffle maker, "you'll be all set."

He sat down in the corner of the breakfast nook and leaned his head against the window behind him with a yawn. In a half-daze, he watched as she squeezed oranges for fresh juice, sliced strawberries, scrambled eggs, fried bacon, and pressed waffles out of the iron.

"Coffee?" she asked as she placed a full plate and juice before him.

"No, I'm headed straight to bed after this. Thanks, though."

He piled the eggs, bacon, and strawberries onto the waffle, covered the whole thing with maple syrup, and folded it like a taco. He devoured it in three bites and drained his glass of juice.

"I'm sorry I was a jerk to you last night," she said.

The apology took him by surprise. "No, you were fine. A bit drunk, but no harm in that," he said with a smile.

He wouldn't have changed a thing about the night before. Watching her karaoke performance had been thoroughly enjoyable, as was the flirty way she acknowledged the attraction he felt for her. Even if she did make the point that she was in love with Gavin. Of course she was. He knew that. And that was why he took the out she had offered by suggesting he had kissed her just because she was convenient.

But Sophie Kavanaugh was not a girl one wanted simply out of convenience. She was the kind of girl you willingly followed into all kinds of inconvenient situations, as he was only beginning to understand.

"I shouldn't have said what I did, though. I don't want you to think I'm playing games."

Sitting up, he examined her more closely. There was a little line in between her eyebrows, revealing her worry. It occurred to him then that she was feeling guilty over the fact that his attraction to her wasn't one-sided. That she was beating herself up over being drawn to him.

As flattering as that was, he suddenly didn't want to toy with her. Not if it meant she would be beating herself up over it. No, he'd rather help her rationalize it away. To help her understand that attraction could be seen as just a basic physical response. It didn't equate to love or any kind of betrayal—not necessarily, at least. Because surely the nervous way she played with her glass of juice meant she was worried she'd done something really wrong.

"So, em," he started, "I know you don't care to see me hook up with girls like I do—"

"You can do whatever you want."

"Yeah, you're right. I just mean to say that it's all harmless. You know, these . . . connections I make, they're surface-level. It doesn't really go beyond that. But finding and indulging in that attraction, that's definitely a rush. Sometimes, I'll admit, that rush overtakes me, sweeps me away. But, in the end, I'm content to let it go. You know what I mean?"

She met his eyes and kept his gaze for a long moment. In the silence between them, he thought they shared an understanding. Their attraction and whatever flirting or line-crossing they'd done, it wouldn't lead to anything more.

When she gave an almost imperceptible nod, he released a breath, only now aware of his need to put all of this into perspective. He'd made a mistake on the beach that night. It was reckless and entirely unlike him to lose control. But now, they could move forward and put all that behind them.

He finally noticed that she was sitting opposite him with nothing but coffee and juice in front of her. "You're not eating?"

The change of topic made her blink and sit up straight. "No. I couldn't sleep, so I thought I'd get things ready for later. I'll wait until everyone gets up."

There it was: they could carry on without anything hanging between them now. They could return to their roles. She as his best friend's girl. And he as the guy on the prowl—for other women.

He ate the slices of strawberries that had fallen out of his waffle taco, then took his time wiping his mouth and hands with his napkin.

Finally, he sighed and hoped it didn't sound as wistful to her as it felt to him. "This domesticity suits you. And me, for that matter. Thanks for the trouble of this. Very sweet of you."

She smiled in response as she arranged her glass and mug on the placemat just so.

He stood and stretched. "Gavin's a lucky man indeed," he said, before leaning down to quickly kiss her on the cheek.

Shuffling off to his bedroom, he shook his head at his predicament. He was infatuated with his best friend's fiancée. Despite what he had just tried to tell her, it wasn't just physical attraction—not for him, at least. No, she had hooked his heart, too. And there was nothing he could do about it.

47

SOPHIE

S ophie woke Gavin early on Christmas morning, anxious for him to unwrap the gift she had sent ahead of time.

But it was Gavin who convinced Sophie to open hers first. She sat in bed, a light blue silk robe loose around her otherwise naked body, and excitedly ripped through the Santa-themed paper on the large, heavy present. It was an exquisitely framed color aquatint by Fauve-era artist Georges Rouault, depicting Sainte-Femme kneeling before Christ during The Passion. Sophie was speechless for a moment.

"Do you like it?" Gavin asked. "I know you did a paper on this guy, so I thought you'd like it."

Tears rushed to her eyes. He had been paying more attention to her studies than she thought. This wasn't something he could have easily purchased. He must have spent time and money tracking it down. And the fact that he put aside his own aversion to religion to gift her with this was not lost on her.

"Gavin, this is so perfect. I love it, and I love that you even thought of this for me," she said, and kissed him.

"Seemed appropriate for the holiday, as well," he said with another laugh.

She smiled and turned her eyes back to the artwork.

"Do you know what his intent was in this? In all of his work?" she asked.

"Tell me, darlin'."

"He said he wanted to show passion mirrored upon the human face. He painted in the early 1900s, at a time when the world seemed corrupt. But he always believed in spiritual renewal through Catholic faith. So you're right. It is a perfect Christmas present."

"Glad you like it."

"Now you have to open your present."

She smiled as she handed the gift to him. It was in a large and meticulously wrapped box.

After a brief struggle to get through the red silk ribbons, he tore the wrapping off and pulled apart the box to reveal a framed piece of sheet music with the original lyrics to "Heroes."

"Are you fucking with me?" he asked, nearly breathless upon seeing the hand-addressed note in red marker at the top.

It read, "Gavin McManus: make it happen." And was signed by David Bowie.

He hastily set the frame against the pillows and got out of bed, pacing a small circle with hands on hips.

"Don't you like it, baby?" Sophie asked, playing innocent to his incredulous joy.

"How did you do this?"

"Don't worry, I didn't actually get to meet him—in person, that is. James helped me. I tried to contact his so-called 'people' to do this but didn't get very far. Then James got me the number of the recording studio where he was, though he figured that wouldn't do much good. I called anyway and got lucky."

"What do you mean?"

"After a couple tries, he came on the line. It was weird because I thought he'd be so removed and hard to convince. But as soon as I mentioned Rogue and you, he said he knew the band. That's when I turned on the charm," she said with a self-satisfied smile. "I told him how much his music meant to you, that it still inspires you. But you know what really got him?"

"What?" he asked, still flabbergasted. He ran his hands through his hair as he shifted his eyes from her to the scrawled personalized note and back again.

"I told him about you listening to 'Heroes' over and over again and how it made you think of trying to still time."

"Sophie, you didn't."

"It really interested him though. And he finally agreed to send me this and said to have you give him a call for an invite to the next show."

"I can't believe it. Jesus, this is amazing." He looked at her and really focused on her for the first time since he saw the signature. "You're the best, darlin'. The absolute best."

"You like it?" she asked coyly.

He went to her and pulled her into his arms, kissing her hard.

"Marry me, darlin'," he whispered in between kisses.

"Okay," she replied, pressing her body to his.

He pulled away and held her face in his hands as he looked into her eyes. "Before the tour. Marry me before we go out again."

"That's . . . soon."

He laughed. "Yeah, it would be. But, Sophie, I don't want to wait. I love you more than anything in the world. I want you to be my wife."

"Wow. I guess we'll have to invite Bowie to the wedding, then," she said with a smile, and Gavin laughed.

The fact that the idea wasn't that far fetched given Gavin's fame reminded her once more that she was living her own version of a fairytale.

48

SOPHIE

2005

Sophie stretched, waking with the slow, tingling realization of what the day held. Rolling over to the empty side of the bed, she grabbed her cell phone and dialed Gavin. The line rang four times before his voicemail picked up. She disconnected and tried again.

"Darlin'?" Gavin answered hoarsely.

"Hi, baby. I wanted to hear your voice before everything got too crazy. Sounds like you had fun last night."

"Yeah, sure. Got drunk with half of Dublin."

"Did you cuddle with Conor last night?" she teased.

He laughed. "I didn't get that drunk. He's in his room and I'm in the guest room."

"The fans who 'ship' you two will be so disappointed."

"They'll survive," he said.

"Are you going to be able to meet me this afternoon?"

"I'll do my best. You'll be the one in the white gown?"

"Yes, that'll be me."

"Guess who Conor's date today is."

"Who?"

"Sondra."

"Really? Are they back together? When did this happen?"

Gavin laughed. "I don't know. I think he gets romantic notions in his head now and again. He doesn't really want to be with her the way she wants. Hopefully she's going in with her eyes open."

"You never know. Weddings are awfully romantic."

"Especially for the two getting hitched."

"Are you nervous?" she asked.

"Just worried you'll change your mind and won't show."

"Keep you on your toes."

"Give me a little hope, won't you?"

"Well . . . I do have this really nice dress and nowhere else to be today, so I think I will be there."

"Brilliant. I can't wait to see you, Sophie."

"Me too, baby. But I better go now. I've only got seven hours to get beautiful for you."

"More beautiful? Didn't think it was possible."

"Keep that up and I just might marry you, mister."

"I love you, sweet girl."

"I love you, Gavin."

49

There was no going to sleep after that call. Not when his thoughts bounced from one thing to another the way they did. Everything was happening at once—the new album had been holding tight to the top of the charts for three months, the world tour would begin the following month, and he was about to get married.

That Need had immediately garnered excellent reviews both in Europe and America. It debuted in the top five in over a dozen countries, thanks to the massive success of "You're My One." The song had been released as the first single at the insistence of the record label, along with a subtle marketing campaign that put the Gavin and Sophie reunion story back in the news.

James was in a near frenzy every time he talked to the band, as the demands of his management duties had exponentially escalated and drained his capabilities. Hiring an extensive staff was the only way to relieve the burden, and so he now had a complicated organization supporting Rogue. He had even assigned one staffer the duty of dealing with media requests concerning Gavin and Sophie's wedding.

Gavin got up and padded across the hardwood floors of Conor's guest room to the bathroom. The vision in the mirror plainly revealed a hung-over young man. There were faint dark circles underneath his bloodshot eyes, his face had gone unshaven for several days, and his hair was a tangled mess.

"Who'd want to marry you?" he said softly, and then laughed.

Turning on the countertop radio, he raised the volume to be heard above the stream of shower water, and heard his own voice singing "You're My One." Groaning, he turned to another station and heard "That Need."

Giving in, he sang along with himself as he showered.

Afterward, with towel around his waist, he wiped the steamed mirror to see if he looked any better. His wet hair, detangled with the help of conditioner, now dripped down his back but his eyes still needed help. He quickly dressed in jeans and a tee shirt before going to Conor's room.

"Wake up, wanker," Gavin told him, sitting heavily on the bed.

Conor groaned and pulled a pillow over his face.

"Come on, you're supposed to be my best man."

"What do you want, Gav?"

Gavin snatched the pillow from his friend's face. "Look at me, Con. I'm getting married today and I look like shite."

"Yes. Yes, you do. Now go away."

Gavin watched as Conor turned on his side and away from him. He thought about letting him sleep but couldn't dismiss his anxiety.

"Question?" he said.

Conor was motionless for a few seconds before replying, "I've got an answer." Rubbing his face as he yawned, he sat up and leaned against the headboard.

This question and answer repartee had begun when they were kids and was used as code to start a serious conversation. The question could be specific or general and the person who had "an answer" wasn't claiming it would be the right answer, but that he would at least try to offer something of value.

"What if Christian was right?"

"About what?"

"Over holiday he said Rogue was about to explode. He said we'd get more attention than we could handle."

"Sounds like a good thing to me."

"It'll mean more scrutiny on us. On me."

Gavin watched as Conor silently understood then that his greatest fear really had to do with his mother. Rogue was a successful band on its own merits, but all the publicity about Gavin and Sophie's romance had further driven Gavin into the spotlight. Now, with the intense popularity of this album, it was like time was running out. Soon, the story would come out that Gavin McManus had been abandoned by his own mother.

"You worry too much, Declan," Conor said gently. The use of Gavin's middle name, "Declan," was intentional. Conor and Gavin had discovered the music of Elvis Costello together and got a kick out of the fact that the artist's real name—Declan MacManus—was so similar to Gavin's—Gavin Declan McManus. Conor used the name sparingly, in moments like this where he was trying to get through to his friend. "Let it happen. Just let it out of your grip. Because, you know what?"

"What?"

"It's not yours to hold onto anyway."

"I know you're right." Gavin nodded slightly and forced a weak grin.

"How's about we get some breakfast? Get on with the day?"

"Yeah, sure."

Gavin knew he had to shake off the anxiety he was feeling. He had an amazing day to look forward, too, after all.

50

CONOR

Conor had many regrets at Gavin's wedding. He regretted that watching Sophie walk down the aisle toward him—or rather, toward *Gavin*—in her body-hugging white lace dress spurred lustful thoughts he knew he shouldn't indulge. He regretted he could only really get away with dancing with her once. To try more than that would be too obvious. He regretted he wasn't able to spend much time with Felicity, who had made the trip from Toronto to be Sophie's maid of honor. But most of all, he regretted ever thinking that bringing Sondra as his date would be a good idea.

He hadn't thought it through. That was especially clear after he made his toast, in which he spoke glowingly of the singular love Sophie and Gavin had, and how he could only hope to one day find his own version of that. Sondra had turned hostile after the speech, refusing his offer to get her a drink or to dance. It was only when he got the chance to dance with Sophie that he understood what had caused Sondra to sour.

"That was a beautiful speech," Sophie told him. "Well, the last part, anyway."

He laughed. He had joked at the start about the fact that Sophie had been the one to pursue Gavin when they were in school, even though it should have been the other way around.

"I was only trying to find some words at the end that might match your beauty."

"You are such a good flirt."

"You make it easy, Soph."

She tilted her head and eyed him. "In what way?"

He had meant because she was everything he wanted in a woman: gorgeous, sexy, smart, fun. But he couldn't say that, not with this being her wedding, after all, so he scrambled for another response.

"I dunno. Just because we're friends. We have an easy way, don't we? I feel like we can talk about things. We can joke, flirt, whatever. It's harmless."

She nodded, seeming to accept this as a way to dismiss the attraction he was certain they *both* felt for each other. There was no way she could really focus on him, anyway, not with over a hundred guests in the room, all clamoring for her attention.

The outdoor, nondenominational ceremony had been simple but sweet. The venue was a private estate just over the border in Northern Ireland, and they had lucked out with mild weather. Sophie had chosen a dress that was perfectly her—elegant, but with a neckline low enough to have some sex appeal. She'd placed an emerald brooch at the base of it, near her breastbone, ensuring that her hazel eyes turned vivid green and making it even harder than usual for him to look away from her. In fact, he had barely taken his eyes off her the whole afternoon, and now into the evening here in the banquet reception room. It was a restored Victorian-era space with brick walls, iron-framed windows, and gorgeous crystal chandeliers with soft amber lighting that set the party aglow. There was a live band consisting of a female singer and all male musicians. Fittingly, the singer was American and her band was Irish. She had a soulful voice and had been finding the right mix of mellow and more upbeat songs all night.

"You know that thing you said about wanting to find for yourself the kind of love Gavin and I have?" Sophie asked.

"Yeah?"

"I really hope you do find it."

"Well—"

"But you can't play games with the one you're with if she isn't it."

He sighed and cast an eye around for Sondra. She was at the far end of the hall, demonstrating drunkenly with one arm as she steadied herself with the other around the neck of Kevin, an old friend from school who was just as drunk.

"That was a bit of a mistake, wasn't it?" he said.

"The speech? Or bringing her?"

"I think we both know the answer to that."

"Be sweet to her, if only for tonight."

He watched Sophie for a moment. They were dancing to a slow song, their bodies close together. He felt the warmth of her hand in his, and the same warmth where her other hand rested delicately on his shoulder. In fact, the heat of her skin on his was almost enough to expose exactly how he felt about her if he wasn't careful. Forcing himself to digest her last comment, he nodded.

"Of course. Whatever you think of me, I'm always a gentleman."

The song ended and within seconds a faster-paced one replaced it.

"I know that. You're one of the best, Connie," she said, and smiled before kissing him on the cheek.

He watched her move away. She was engulfed by the crowd on the dance floor, with everyone who saw her wanting to stop her, to have just a piece of her.

He knew how they felt. Any little piece would do, even if it was fleeting. He'd soak it up and funnel the longing and ache she left behind into music. The inspiration would have to be his solace.

51

SOPHIE

"Your mother knows how to dance!" Gavin said with a laugh.

Sophie raised her eyebrows, caught between admiration and embarrassment. Her mother had definitely been enjoying herself, dancing with anyone—or no one—for most of the night. She couldn't remember ever seeing her mother dance before, but it couldn't be a sudden, new passion.

The accepting attitude her parents had adopted in St. Moritz had disappeared once Sophie informed them a wedding date was set. They made it clear then that they believed marrying a rock star after such a short engagement was a recipe for disaster. They thought she was being too short-sighted. They would have loved for her to stay engaged indefinitely, or at least for as long as it would take to show that their instincts were right. They insisted that she needed more time to develop and keep her own identity. Sophie's promise to them that she was still going to get her college degree didn't help.

Still, they had both showed up with enough goodwill to be a part of making the day special. In the moment before walking Sophie down the aisle, her father told her something she knew she would always remember.

"Your mother and I, we were always so concerned with granting you your autonomy that we may have erred in not always treating you like the child you were. But we did the best we could. And I just," he said, "I just want you to know that we do love you and we trust that you'll find your way. You'll have a husband after this. But you'll always have us, too."

It was the most emotional her father had ever been with her. But rather than affecting her to the point of tears, it set her mind at ease. It was such a reassuring moment that when she met Gavin to say their vows, she was never more sure of what she was doing. She didn't have any nervousness, didn't waver. Her father's words had set her free to simply be. And what she wanted to *be* was Gavin's wife.

That's what she was now and had been for the last four and a half hours. Now she and her husband—she tingled just thinking that word—were standing near the cake, waiting for the band's song to end so they could do the traditional cake cutting. Her mother, having exhausted her father, was dancing with Christian, and both were having a blast. Everyone at the wedding, in fact, had been in good spirits from the start and they showed no sign of slowing down. It was wonderful to be surrounded by such positive energy.

"What are you thinking?" Gavin asked. He wrapped his arm around her waist and pulled her to him.

"That this has been the most amazing day of my life," she said. "It almost feels like it can't get much better than this."

"I know. But it will. You and I are only just beginning, darlin'."

She turned and took his face into her hands, meeting his eyes. "My heart will always be yours," she said, playing off the vow he had made during their ceremony: "My heart will always search for yours."

He smiled and started to speak, but she interrupted him.

"Except, that is, if you smear cake all over my face."

He laughed and then kissed her. "There is nothing so delicious as you are, my sweet girl. No need for frosting on top." Before she could speak, he continued, "You can trust me, in everything."

"I know, baby. And I do."

"Good. So you won't have any concerns when I get up on that stage in a few minutes and take the mic, right? 'Cause I'm ready to kick this party up a notch."

She laughed. "I wouldn't expect anything less. Go ahead and show my parents what a real rock star looks like."

"Their first Rogue concert will be at their daughter's wedding. I like the sound of that!"

THE WEDDING HAD INCLUDED ALL the traditions Sophie had grown up wanting: a long white dress, walking down the aisle with her father, beautiful flowers, the heartfelt exchange of vows, the formal pronouncement of becoming husband and wife, and the various toasts and dances, along with cake-cutting at the reception.

So, when all of that had been fulfilled, she was happy to leave the customs behind and see the reception turn into a full-fledged concert.

Gavin brought Christian to the stage with him and the boys of Rogue soon displaced the hired band at their instruments. Shay and Martin had discarded their suit coats and ties. Conor still wore his full suit and looked impossibly put together after such a long day. Gavin had never been more handsome to Sophie as he stood at the microphone in his finely tailored navy blue suit, his tie undone and hanging around his neck, his shirt halfway unbuttoned.

"That's my husband," Sophie giddily told Felicity as the band started their first song.

"And that's the song he wrote for you in school. Talk about full circle," Felicity mused.

Sophie's eyes widened as she recognized the song he had titled "Exotic Creature."

"This is the first song I ever wrote for my wife," Gavin said, and the gathered crowd screamed and applauded. "Conor was right in that toast when he said I was a little slow on the uptake when it came to Sophie. But I think I made up for it with this. Falling for her was the best thing I ever did. I'll never stop falling. 'Cause as the song goes, I *like* this dizzy feeling."

The room shifted their focus from Gavin to Sophie, and she blushed. Not because of the hundred-plus people staring at her, but because of the way Gavin was looking at her. It was love and lust and the certainty that she was his one.

What this man could do to her.

She was ready for the rest of her life to begin.

PART III

52

2006

"I'm going to jump in. Come with me, darlin'," Gavin said, his eyes bright and mischievous.

This energy was exactly the same kind he had when he was on stage. He was obviously looking for a similar high now that Rogue was on a short break after a solid year of touring.

They had started married life on that tour. At first, Sophie was just as taken with the excitement of it all as Gavin and the boys were. It was a thrill to feel the energy of the crowds, to experience a sliver of what it was like to be on stage in front of thousands of people. Gavin would come off stage after a two-and-a-half-hour concert so hyped that it would take him conscious effort to come down. She could see why. He had spent all that time, after all, being not only validated by the audience, but also worshipped. Their outstretched hands straining to get his attention, the way they would shift en masse based on where he moved on stage, the absolute obedience they showed when he directed a call-and-response were an undeniable ego-boost. And after each show, Sophie would watch Gavin's disappointment as normalcy returned.

The alcohol-soaked after-parties helped to revive rush of the stage, and the tour became a cycle of traveling to the next gig, sound check, gig, and after-party. Sophie had thought there would be more time along the way to explore the cities they were in, but it all went by in a blur

But, after twelve months of living the life of a band member, Sophie craved an identity of her own. She hated to admit it, but her mother had been right when she questioned if she was ready to be married to a famous person who might overshadow her. Being Gavin's wife made her happy, but she realized she needed the personal reward of something that was *hers*.

At this point, going back to college even though her husband was one of the biggest rock stars in the world, seemed absurd. How could she reestablish that kind of normalcy? She didn't know if it was possible, but she figured it was her only option and started the paperwork to reenroll at Trinity.

Since her re-enrollment hadn't yet come through, they decided to use this free time to go to the Italian island of Capri. The holiday was meant as a way to "detox" from the maddening pace of the tour, to slow things down and enjoy being together before separating for the first time in over a year.

Instead of keeping a low profile, though, Gavin brought his rock star persona to a guided rowboat tour through the Grotta Azzurra. And now he was threatening to jump into the cool water, an act they had been emphatically warned in both Italian and English was illegal.

"Baby, they told us we can't," Sophie told him.

Gavin tore his eyes away from the otherworldly crystalline blue waters and grinned at her.

Their guide's voice echoed against the rock walls as he sang an ancient Neapolitan song.

"Can't you just enjoy this?" she asked, gesturing to their surreal surroundings. But she knew it was a futile effort. He was too hyped.

"Gotta seize the moment," he said. He pulled her to him and kissed her fiercely on the mouth. And then he jumped into the heavenly-colored sea.

The splash he created was accompanied by gasps from the other tourists. Their guide let out a rapid-fire stream of Italian that Sophie was pretty sure had something to do with calling the police.

Sophie watched Gavin as he swam deep into the water, fascinated by how pure it was. He only came up for air when he absolutely had to. Floating on his back, he waved at the irate guide.

"It's fucking fantastic. You should come in," he said.

"I can't," she said with another shake of her head.

"Why not?"

She laughed and said, only half-kidding, "I need to be able to bail you out when you get arrested."

In the end, he didn't get arrested. Instead, he "paid" for his crime with an impromptu performance of "You're My One" within the cave, eliciting wild applause from the other tourists.

———

SOPHIE GOT Gavin to promise that he would keep a lower profile the next day for their excursion to the summit of Monte Solaro via single-rider chairlifts. At almost six hundred meters above sea level, they had a panoramic view of the island, as well as the surrounding Bay of Naples and the Amalfi Coast. The bright yellow patches of wildflowers on the bush-covered hills led to views of deep azure waters so stunning that they sat under a tree for hours gazing upon it. The only thing to lure them away from relaxing in each other's arms with one of the best views in the world was their hunger. On advice from a local, they took advantage of the shuttle bus run by Ristorante da Gelsomina to find their way to a late lunch.

Settled comfortably on the outside patio with a bamboo cover shading them from the sun, they again enjoyed a high-altitude view of the majestic waters below—this time with copious wine, olives, and bruschetta to start.

They were disturbed from the romantic setting when a middle-aged Frenchman approached their table. He was neatly dressed in white trousers, a pale pink Oxford shirt, and a fine blue blazer. His dark, receding hair was slicked back and he smelled of cigarettes and aftershave. Begging their pardon for the intrusion, he nonetheless proceeded to seat himself next to Sophie and compliment Gavin on how beautiful his wife was.

"Yes, I know," Gavin replied with an amused smile.

"Have you ever modeled?"

"You're not giving me the classic 'you could be a model' line, are you?" Sophie asked with a laugh.

The Frenchman looked confused for a moment. "No, no. Allow me to introduce myself. My name is Henri de Chavannes and—"

"De Chavannes? Like the painter?" Sophie asked.

Henri smiled. "*Oui*, very good!"

"My wife is very smart, Henri," Gavin said.

"So I see. And so very striking a woman, too. I am a modeling agent, so I see beautiful women all the time. *Oui*, there are many beautiful women, but very few who have such a striking look. Your eyes are magnificent." He reached out to stroke her cheek, studying her bone structure.

"Watch it there, *Henry*," Gavin said as he leaned forward.

"My apologies. I forget myself," Henri said quickly.

"My eyes only get that deep green color when I'm wearing something green. Otherwise, they're just plain hazel," Sophie said.

"No, I do not think plain at all. Listen, I would love for you to come to Paris, take some test shots. I think you could find work very easily."

Sophie watched the man for a moment, trying to sort him out. "You don't know who my husband is, do you?" she asked.

Henri looked at Gavin, straining for recognition that did not come. "No. I should?"

"I guess you should know me for that matter. I've been photographed a lot already. You see, my husband is Gavin McManus and he's the singer of the band Rogue. They've sold millions of albums. And in the last few years, we've sort of become a bit of a big deal as a couple in the tabloids."

"Oh. Interesting."

Gavin laughed. "What I think she's saying is we're not buying what you're selling. Thanks for stopping by, Henri."

"Gavin, be nice," Sophie said.

"You're not interested in this rubbish, are you?" Gavin asked.

"Should I be, Mr. de Chavannes?" she asked.

"Well, of course, I think so. There are great opportunities to be had with modeling. Traveling, wonderful people in the industry, money, fame. It is a very exciting way to make a living."

"She already has all of those things," Gavin said flatly.

Henri nodded and smiled, the corners of his eyes crinkling. "Yes, but that is in connection with *you*, no? If she were to try modeling and become good at it, the success and all that comes with it would be entirely of her own doing."

This struck a chord with Sophie she couldn't deny. Unlike the mundane university studies she was planning, modeling had the potential to set her up on a level similar to Gavin's. "I'll think about it," she said.

"That is all I ask. Please, take my card," Henri said, and handed it to her. "I beg your pardon, once more, for interrupting."

Gavin shook his head as he watched the Frenchman walk away. "You were just being kind to the man, right?"

"I don't know," she said. "It might be fun."

"What—being a clothes hanger? Come on, darlin'. You're better than that. What about your studies?"

"I can always go back to school, no matter how old I am. But if I want to be with you at a moment's notice, or even try something fun like modeling, I have to take advantage now."

"You don't *have* to do anything."

"Except seize the moment."

He shook his head but smiled. "You could stay on tour with us if you're not going to go back to school."

"Gavin, I think . . . this is something I just need to explore, you know? I need to see if it's something that feels right."

He looked out at the deep blue sea. The sunshine glittered on the water like fallen stars. It was breathtaking. But she knew he wasn't really taking in the view. She could see him struggling. He didn't like being without her. But more than that, he didn't like sharing her with anyone else. He had made that clear ever since they got back together. She was proposing that she do both things.

When he finally spoke, she was relieved by what he said because it meant that though he had his misgivings, he was willing to trust her.

"Okay, darlin'," he said resignedly, "do what you will. I want you to be happy." He leaned over the table and kissed her.

53

SOPHIE

2010

Joining Gavin in São Paulo, where Rogue was to play Lollapalooza, had been planned as a way for Sophie to spend time with her husband. They often had to carve out solutions like this where she came to him on tour since in the last several years both of their careers kept them busy and traveling all over the world.

The band was currently riding high on the success of their third album, *Dream State*. The single "Slip Away" had been a hit, due in large part to its familiarly confessional tone. In it, Gavin admitted his fear of losing the connection he had with his wife since she seemed to "slip away" into her separate life of modeling. He also admitted his jealousy and anxiety over having to share her with the world.

Fans ate up his romantic vulnerability and filled increasingly larger venues. The Lollapalooza show would be massive. It also required Gavin to do media appearances and kept him away just as Sophie arrived and was ready to be with him.

It was par for the course, really. Even if she did manage to find time to join him, they still often had to accept less time together than they wanted. But, they had a longstanding agreement that they wouldn't go more than three weeks apart, so she would make the best of this trip.

With São Paulo being the densely populated financial center of the country, and not near beaches, she decided a trip to the Museum of Art would be a good distraction. The concierge of the hotel they were staying in let her know that it was possible to walk to the museum and was giving her directions when Conor joined them. He had just come back from a run, the sweat still dripping down his temples in the humid weather.

"Where are you off to?" he asked, and she told him her plan. "And you're walking? By yourself?"

Sophie laughed. "Yes. I tend to do that quite often and am pretty successful at it. You know, renowned fashion designers even pay me to do it down a runway at times?"

He ignored her attempt to joke. "Give me twenty minutes to clean up and I'll join you, yeah?"

"Sure."

It wasn't unusual for them to—platonically—spend time together. Over the years, they had developed a genuine friendship based on mutual interests like art and literature. They were familiar and easy with one another.

Conor still spent a lot of his energy chasing after women and making a paparazzi spectacle out of himself when his girlfriend du jour was a well-known model or actress, but a long-term relationship never seemed to stick. He also continued to flirt shamelessly with Sophie when they were alone but they had gotten to the point where it was almost like a harmless inside joke.

There had only been one incident that made Sophie question the real depth of Conor's feelings, and it wasn't even anything that he had done. Rather, it was the mild "scandal" of a photograph widely circulated in the tabloids along with the speculation that the way Conor was looking at Sophie in it was suggestive of a previously well-hidden love for her. Gavin had dismissed it out of hand, Conor had laughed it off, but Sophie wasn't so quick.

In the photo, they were at an after-party and Sophie was leaning against the end of a sofa, a smile on her face as she looked at something that had been cropped out of the shot. Conor was seated not far in the background, surrounded by several women vying for his attention. But his eyes were firmly fixed on Sophie, with an expression of such naked longing and adoration it was impossible to deny. She'd realized she was all too familiar with the expression captured on his face. Whereas once he had been charmed by her, he had for quite a while looked at her with something more. She chose, however, to push this understanding to the back of her mind rather than address it.

Now they wandered the museum, examining the Renoir, Chagall, van Gogh, and Modigliani pieces in companionable silence.

That is, until Conor leaned close to Sophie and asked in a hushed tone, "Where are all the nudes?"

Sophie slapped his arm and he laughed. "Speaking of nudes," she started.

"You've got my attention."

She sat on one of the benches in front of Modigliani's less-than-flattering portrait of Diego Rivera, and he joined her. This could have been her alternative life, studying art like this. But with her modeling career doing so well, it was highly unlikely that she'd return to school.

"I got some news earlier," she said.

"I'm intrigued."

"I got the cover of *Sports Illustrated Swimsuit Edition*."

"Really?" he asked with obvious delight for her. "That's fantastic, Sophie. That is big, isn't it?"

She smiled. "Yeah, it is. It's huge. I'll get a look at what photo they chose tomorrow. And the magazine will be out in a couple weeks."

"Good for you, honey. I know you've been working like crazy."

"Yeah, and it feels especially good because now no one can say I got it because I'm married to Gavin. I've been working too hard."

"What, people would tell you that? Give you a bad time of it?"

"Sometimes. Especially in the beginning. But not as much anymore."

"Good," he said protectively.

She stood and nodded toward the far exhibit hall, and they continued to walk through.

"I met a model last week. Her name was . . . Astrid something," he said.

"Astrid Ekdahl?"

"Yeah, that's the one."

"She's pretty young, isn't she?"

"Twenty-two, in fact."

"Good in bed?"

"Not bad," he answered automatically. After a second, he smiled sheepishly.

"And you don't even know her last name," Sophie said with a teasing tsk.

"It was a one-time thing. No need for formalities."

She shook her head. "That's still all you want?"

"Sophie, you're a sweet, smart girl, but you have no clue about men. Having a ride with a girl like Astrid is exactly what I want. No complications, no expectations, no hassles."

"Whatever. I do know that Gavin is going to hate this *SI* cover."

"Trust me, he'll love the photograph."

"You know what I mean. He will hate that the rest of the world gets to see it."

"Jesus, you've been doing this for more than three years already, yeah? He'll have to learn to appreciate your work at some point."

She knew that was true, she just didn't think it would ever really happen. The more she thought about this cover, the more she tried to convince herself that making a point to tell Gavin about it beforehand might be giving it too much importance. She hadn't told him when she got her first *Vogue* cover. Maybe it would be better to treat it like just another job.

Wrapping her arm through Conor's, she told him, "Thanks for your support, Connie."

"You know I'm your biggest fan, honey."

54

CONOR

Conor was the first to enter the room, throwing himself onto one of the couches and examining a cut on his finger that had bothered him during the last song they did for sound check. He'd have to tape it to prepare for another enthusiastic South American crowd here in Buenos Aires—their latest stop on the Lollapalooza festival circuit. After a moment, he pulled a magazine out from under his feet. The photograph on the cover stopped him cold. Then he got uncomfortably hot.

The magazine was the *Sports Illustrated Swimsuit Edition*. On the cover, Sophie was standing ankle-deep in the clear turquoise waters of the Maldives, wearing white bikini bottoms that matched the pristine sand. She was bent over at the waist, with one hand and forearm barely covering both breasts while she reached for her "fallen" bikini top with the other hand. At the same time, her hair was blowing in the wind and a few strands covered one eye. Droplets of water clung to her skin.

It was the sexiest she had ever looked, and his buried desire for her was quickly rising to the surface all over again. He had tried to place Sophie in the "friend-zone" for years now. Longing for his best friend's wife was a hopeless endeavor. It went against the precision and control he required in the other aspects of his life. But the ache she caused in him had never really gone away, not since that moment in the studio at his house. Since then, he had bedded gorgeous women, even had fleeting relationships, but it was always Sophie that he wanted.

"Jesus," Martin said, looking over his shoulder. "That's one hot girl."

The intrusion into his thoughts made Conor jump, but he tried to cover it by replying with a sly grin, "All grown up, aye?"

"Look there, is that her—"

"Nah, they wouldn't show nipples on the cover of this," Conor told him, but the thought that it might be there was enough to make him study the photo all that much more closely.

"What's this, then?" Shay asked, putting a hand on Martin's shoulder as he trained his eyes to the magazine in Conor's hands.

"Our supermodel," Conor said.

"Fuck me," Shay said.

"Say that again," Martin whispered.

"What's the craic, lads?" Gavin asked, the last to file in.

Conor simultaneously sat up and rolled the magazine up, grasping it with both hands. "Oh, nothing. Nothing at all."

"Come on, give us a look," Gavin said, snatching at the magazine.

"Get off," Conor said and pulled away from him.

But Gavin was too quick. He grabbed the magazine and let it unfurl. Recognition filled his face over the fact that his three best friends had been ogling his wife as if she were some sort of men's magazine centerfold.

"We were just having a laugh," Shay said. "You know, saying she's all grown up, is all."

"Yeah, sure yous were. Bet you were off to have a wank while you're at it," Gavin said.

Conor stood up. "Relax, Gav. She's a pretty girl, but she's yours. No reason to let this bother you."

But Conor saw that his entreaty was going nowhere. Gavin had always been possessive with Sophie, so Conor could see how this would bother him. But at the same time, it was just a photograph. She wasn't giving her actual self to anyone else. He knew that all too well.

Sophie entered the room then, unaware of what she was walking into as she chatted with Randy, Conor's guitar tech. What timing. Not just coming into the room now, but having just rejoined them on tour once more in time for a copy of this magazine to come out. He knew she'd been nervous for Gavin to see it. Now, he could see trouble was coming but was powerless to stop it.

"Sophie," Gavin called, motioning curtly for her to join him.

"I'm being beckoned," Sophie told Randy with a laugh and went to Gavin.

There were a dozen or so people in the room, and they all seemed aware of the tension in the air and kept their conversations low.

"Hey, baby," Sophie said, smiling at Gavin.

"What the fuck is this?" he asked, holding up the magazine.

She took in the photo as well as Gavin's attitude. Conor watched her inhale a deep, bracing breath.

"That's me," she said lightly. "Guess someone got an early copy?"

"You didn't tell me you're doing this kind of shit."

The whole of the room was now an uncomfortable audience to their conversation. Conor shook his head and silently urged Gavin to get a grip before he went too far.

"Let's go somewhere else to talk," Sophie said.

"Why, are you suddenly shy about this?" He held up the magazine again so all could see the cover. "A little late for that."

"No, I'm not shy about the photograph, Gavin," she said. "But unlike you, I don't want an audience right now." She gestured to the people in the room but Gavin didn't quit his intense stare at her. "This is why I didn't tell you before," she continued, "because I knew you'd have a bad reaction."

"What do you expect, when this is the way I find out? I just walked in on my so-called friends having at it, because you've decided stripping down to nothing is part of your job."

"Stop this right now," Sophie told him urgently.

"It's disgusting, this."

Conor saw tears fill Sophie's eyes at the rebuke. "Gavin, that's enough," he said sharply. He couldn't stop himself.

"Stay the fuck out of it," Gavin returned with a glare.

"I'm done," Sophie said, turning to go.

"Yeah, you are."

"You're a fucking gobshite, Gavin," Conor said as Sophie hurriedly left the room.

"Can you all get your own fucking lives?" Gavin shouted. He grabbed a bottle of beer from the nearby bar and took it to an adjacent room.

55

Conor had been the one come after her, letting her cry on his shoulder outside of the stadium. He was always there when she needed someone to lean on or vent to. This time, he'd tried to dismiss Gavin's bad behavior as a return of "The Clash," the mood swings Gavin would get when they were younger, but she sensed there was more to it. Gavin had been anxious lately but repeatedly denied anything was bothering him.

She hadn't stayed to watch the show. Instead, she'd retreated to their hotel room, wanting to be alone. Gavin's reaction had been even worse than she had feared, and it left her angry and confused. He had never fully supported her modeling, but for him to act out like that, in front of an audience no less, was inexcusable.

It was after two in the morning when she heard him letting himself in to their suite. She was lying in bed with her back to the doorway, starring through the open drapes at the leaves in the trees rustling with the breeze. She didn't react to him, even when the bed shifted under his weight as he joined her.

When he stroked her bare arm with something velvety, she took in a quick breath. It had to be the petals of a rose. She could smell the sweet, rich aroma of the flower. He continued to slowly drag the rose over her skin, then followed the trail with soft kisses.

Turning to face him, she saw that her husband was studying her intently. He cupped her cheek with his hand and stroked her skin with his thumb. "I'm an idiot," he told her. "But I don't mean it."

"That doesn't excuse—"

"You're art to me, Sophie," he said. "You're beauty and light. I don't want to share you."

"I share you all the time."

He put the flower aside and settled so he was propped up by his elbow and leaning close to her. "How's that?"

"The songs you write, baby. They're so personal. And not only are they out there forever, but you give so much of yourself when you perform them."

"Darlin', people may think they know me from the songs but it's just their interpretation. They'll never know the real me, not like you do."

She looked into his eyes for a long moment. "Sort of like how people might see me in a photo but they'll never have me?"

That registered with him and he looked contrite, but she wasn't ready to let him off the hook.

"You hurt me. That's not okay."

"I know, and I'm sorry I did that to you. I've no right to behave that way—"

"Why were you so agitated? What else is bothering you?"

He met her eyes and started to speak but then closed his mouth. She waited him out until he told her, "I'm fine. I really am."

"I don't think you are," she said softly. "Please tell me what's going on."

His eyes left hers but she waited him out until finally he sighed. "Jamie says he's had inquiries about my mother."

"Inquiries?"

"Some enterprising young reporter taking it upon herself to dig at my history. Anyway, I guess she was keen to get into the details of my mother's 'death.'"

His face was a mask of anguish. He'd never accepted his mother's abandonment of him, nor had he ever plotted out how he might answer such questions from the media.

"So, maybe it's time to talk about it?" she suggested.

He shook his head curtly. "No. I won't. I can't."

"But—"

"Jamie dealt with it. The story is dead." He laughed and it came out forced and bitter. "But likely as dead as my mother."

"Meaning you're worried it's going to come up again?"

"It's bound to, right? Isn't that what I've set myself up for?"

Her husband, whose life was so profoundly altered by the loss of his mother, was still in so much pain over it. She had always thought she could be the one to help heal him, but after all these years, it was clear there was little she could do.

"Just hold on to me, baby," she whispered. "I'm here."

He watched her for a long moment before gently kissing her on the lips, lingering until she returned the pressure. "I love you with all that I am," he told her, "even when that's not good enough."

She touched his face. "You're always enough, Gavin."

56

GAVIN

2012

Rogue's fourth studio album, *Gone*, received middling reviews and earned a decent place in the charts, but at five million albums sold, would rank the lowest of all their efforts. The single "The Truest Thing" was the biggest hit of the album, once again because fans ate up the confessional nature of Gavin's lyrics and insight into his relationship with Sophie. Gavin posed the question, "What do you do when everything you ever wanted isn't enough?" in the song and alluded to the fact that though Rogue was an enormous success in every conceivable way, he still felt empty. Though he didn't explicitly state it in the song, his mother was still the big hole in his life and her lack of contact with him was getting harder to bear. His fame felt hollow given he had pursued it in part so that his mother might have an easier time reaching out to him. He turned even more to Sophie to fill the void, and this song claimed she was the only true thing in his life, while everything else was artifice.

With other songs, Gavin vented his frustrations. In "Lies (Baby, They're All Lies)," he wrote about the lies we tell ourselves to get through the day, and was especially hard on himself. And with "Do It (Til It Hurts)," he employed a familiar tactic of allowing his lyrics to have two meanings—the surface level that appeared sexual in nature, and the deeper level that had nothing to do with such things. In this song he goaded himself to keep doing what he was, which was basically beating his head against a wall. He was increasingly numb to the riches and adulation and fame they had achieved because it didn't change the aching loss he felt from never having a resolution with his mother. But yet, he was paralyzed from doing anything about it, no matter how Sophie tried to convince him to be proactive in finding her.

With the response to *Gone* not as enthusiastic as the previous three albums had been, the tour was scaled back in comparison to previous years. They played arenas again, drawing primarily their dedicated fans rather than attracting new or casual ones. They ended the tour in Dublin and held the after-party at the Rogue organization's new offices in the Docklands where Sophie had worked with event planners to transform the raw industrial space with lounge furniture, specialty lighting, and plentiful bars.

Gavin sensed everyone's relief to be done supporting an album that even he had to admit was a downer. But he gamely played his expected role as the life of the party, keeping multiple conversations going and interacting with both friends and strangers in the animated, engaging way he had become known for.

It was still early in the evening when things took a turn. He had just stepped out of the restroom when a man cornered him, introducing himself as Gary Paulson, a writer for the American magazine *Vanity Fair*.

"Good to see you," Gavin said, wondering how the journalist got in. "But I'm not doing any press just now."

"Just a quick question. I'm doing a piece on the tenth anniversary of Rogue's first album and need a little backstory," Paulson said.

"What is it?" Gavin asked.

"Can you tell me whether your mother is dead or alive?"

"What?" The air got thin and the lights bright, as if he had been sucker-punched.

"See, there's no death record. So we're looking into the details," Paulson said. "Care to help me out?"

Gavin didn't respond. Instead, he headed back to his group of friends in a daze.

"Aye, Gav," Martin said, "tell these guys what you were saying about them songs. You know, the length of the lyrics."

Gavin heard Martin's entreaty but was slow to respond. Everything around him felt off. It seemed to take a massive effort just to blink and clear his throat. Then Paulson came into his line of sight and he needed the distraction that Martin had offered.

"The thing is," Gavin said, and the group collectively leaned forward to hear what he would say, "your average rock or pop song is around two to three hundred words. Then there's Bob Dylan's 'Desolation Row.' That one goes on for six hundred and fifty words. That's huge, right?" He was enjoying the telling of this now, the reporter gone from his thoughts. "And the bleedin' song is over eleven minutes long!"

"I'll murder you if you're after a song that long," Conor said, and the group laughed.

"No, but here's the interesting thing. There's another song—a better song if you ask me—that is four hundred and seventy-three words. Here's the catch: it's only four minutes, thirty-eight seconds."

"Less than half as long, then," Martin said.

"Well less. Done by The Killers with their brilliant song 'This River is Wild.' Imagine the lungs on that singer—Brandon Flowers is his name—to write a fucking novel as a rock song. Seriously, I never knew that many words could work in one song. But it does."

The group went off trying to think of other lengthy songs, and Gavin saw that Paulson was still watching him.

"Is that guy a problem?" Shay asked, following Gavin's gaze.

Instead of answering, Gavin heard a line from that Killers song in his head about always holding your head up high, "because it's a long, long, long way down." He got up and went to the bar, ordering a whiskey before locating one of Rogue's security staff to have Paulson removed as an uninvited guest.

57

CONOR

Though it was well past eight in the evening, Conor kept his sunglasses on to withstand the bright flashes coming from dozens of photographers crowding the red-carpet premiere of his friend Jackson Armstrong's latest splashy romantic comedy. He obliged the frantic paparazzi for several minutes, turning ever so slightly from one side to another as they shouted his name familiarly.

Coming to London for this event had been a last-minute decision, one born out of post-tour restlessness. Rogue had been home less than a month and he had yet to make the transition from the touring routine to quiet home life. They had performed better than they ever had, turning each show into a thrilling display of their cohesion as a band. And he ached for the adrenaline rush of performing before a rowdy audience on a near nightly basis. Going to pubs and parties once home was no substitution. He needed a distraction and he wasn't going to get it by working with his bandmates on a new album.

Gavin was sullenly lost in his own head, overcome by worries of when and how the story of his mother's abandonment might surface. Ever since the end of the tour, he had been on edge, waiting for the bomb to drop. And with each passing day that nothing happened, his fear seemed only to grow rather than subside. There was little Conor could do to pull him out of his funk, and besides, he knew that if it was anyone's job to do that, it was Sophie's.

Martin was dedicated to making up for lost time with his wife and sons. Donal was now a rambunctious five-year-old and his baby brother Colm was almost three. Martin had arranged for the family to go away for a month to live in a cottage in a small town outside of Burgundy, France.

An opportunity had come up for Shay to score an independent movie soundtrack, which he promptly accepted, and was thus spending all his free time in New York.

All of which meant Conor was now attending a movie premiere in London where he would be lucky to get five minutes of the star's time. The media crush was intense, and he was beginning to regret his decision to make a spectacle of himself when he felt a hand on his arm.

He turned with the expectation that it was a publicity person urging him along and was delighted to instead find himself face to face with Colette Devereaux.

She was as stunning as the last time he saw her some six months ago when she'd tagged along with Sophie to Rogue's New York gig. They had shared one fiery night together and left it at that, partly because she was living with her photographer boyfriend at the time. She was also very young. Barely twenty-one, if he remembered correctly. Now twenty-nine, he was beginning to feel age differences like that more acutely.

Tonight, she was wearing a filmy cream dress with black lace trim that fell short against her thighs and strappy heels that made her slightly taller than him. With olive skin, rich brown eyes, and a wild mane of chestnut hair, she was a knockout. The addition of long legs, slim waist, and large breasts explained her rapid rise in modeling.

"Aren't you a vision," Conor murmured to her as he leaned in and gave her cheek a tender, lingering kiss.

"Good to see you, too," she said with a smile.

They had inadvertently set off a vigorous round of new photographs that would catch their revealing body language as they stood close together, her hand still on his forearm.

"Are you going inside or straight to the party?" she asked.

"That depends."

"On?"

"You," he said, as he pulled his sunglasses off to look her in the eye.

Colette watched him for a moment, and he knew she was prolonging this to tease him.

"That simple, is it?" she finally asked with a small smile.

"It is," he replied matter-of-factly.

They stood staring into each other's eyes for a moment longer, ignoring the cries of their names and the continued clicking of cameras.

"Then take me out of here," she finally said, and Conor smiled in return.

"MATE, you missed a great party last night. Where'd you go?" Jackson asked.

"I, em, ran into a friend," Conor said softly, eyeing Colette as she slept soundly next to him. They had spent a good part of the night exploring each other's bodies, leaving little room for talk. Their chemistry was phenomenal. He had forgotten how much fun she was, and it made him wonder if she still had a boyfriend.

"I take it by the whisper that the girl is still there," Jackson said with an amiable laugh. "Well, anyway, you weren't the only no-show. I was expecting a girl—a woman—to come but, alas, I was disappointed."

"I didn't know movie stars got stood up," Conor said with a laugh.

"No, you wouldn't think so, would you? I'll track her down yet."

"So, who is the lovely?"

"She's a model I've seen once or twice. Sophie probably knows her —Colette Devereaux."

"Fuck me," Conor muttered.

"What?"

"Seems we have a mutual friend."

There was an uncomfortable silence on the line.

"I see. Well, there it is. No use getting upset about it," Jackson finally said.

"I really had no idea, Jack. I guess I should have sorted it out, though."

"No, there wasn't anything to be sorted out. She's slippery, Conor. At least with me she was. She couldn't stand to think five minutes into the future. So I didn't really lose much."

"Still . . . ."

"Fuck it, you know? There's plenty more out there and it's not like I went without last night."

Conor laughed. "Well, you free tonight? Let's grab a drink."

"Perfect. Come 'round about nine. Oh, and give Colette my regards," Jackson said before hanging up.

Conor looked at Colette again. She lay on her side, facing him. Her thick hair fell like a blanket over her bare shoulder. There was no doubt that she was vibrant and beautiful, but Jackson's call made Conor wonder what he was in for with her.

AFTER A LAZY, sex-fueled morning, Conor suggested he and Colette come up for air. Though their time together had been ridiculously satisfying, he realized they would have to leave the hotel room to actually have a conversation. They reluctantly separated so she could go to her hotel room to clean up while he did the same in his.

When they met up again, they wandered around Covent Garden, content to mingle with the tourists and admire the disparate mix of architecture of the Market Hall and Royal Opera House. As they window-shopped at Burberry, Sandro, and Paul Smith, conversation was easy, and Conor enjoyed the feel of Colette holding onto his arm.

Late in the afternoon, they stopped at Champagne & Fromage on Wellington Street. The immaculate wine and cheese cafe looked like something out of a Hollywood set with its chalk-written menu on blackboards and contrasting olive-colored walls. Perfectly weathered wood tables were paired with rustic red metal chairs, and an enormous stainless-steel wine-glass rack hung from the ceiling. Conor felt like they could have been in the middle of Paris, especially with Colette's perfect pronunciation of the Gallic offerings. The daughter of a Greek father and a French mother, she had been raised in Quebec before beginning to model at age fifteen. She was not only fluent in

French, but preferred to play up that part of her heritage, even taking her mother's surname.

They were well into their bottle of champagne when she asked about his history with women.

"What about them?"

"I know—everyone knows—all about the models and actresses you've dated."

He laughed. "Why do you say 'dated' with such suspicion?"

"You do have a reputation for liking, let's call it, volume and variety."

Sipping his champagne, he gave that thought. "I enjoy women," he conceded.

"What was your most serious relationship?"

He smiled at her bluntness. "I suppose that was with a woman I lived with for a short time."

"Were you in love?"

He didn't need to think about it but he hesitated as if he did. "No. I wasn't very fair to her in that sense."

Colette shrugged and took a bite of a crostini topped with figs and melted Fourme d'Ambert cheese.

"It happens," she said. "Most of the time people come together wanting different things and pretending that's not the case."

This declaration struck him as something relatively deep, especially coming from a twenty-one-year-old model. "You're probably right."

"So, have you ever been in love?"

"Yes," he replied, this time without hesitation and regretted it.

"Who with?" she asked, intrigued.

"Someone who was unavailable to me."

"You were never with her?"

"No."

"But yet you fell in love? That's sort of sad."

Now, he was the one to shrug. "It happens."

She watched him for a moment, seeing something he couldn't hide. "Oh, you poor thing," she said. "You're still in love with her, aren't you?"

"No, not at all," he said quickly.

A knowing smile came to her lips. "Then you and I are a good match—we both don't want anything serious and we both could use some fun and distraction," she declared.

He shook off the thoughts of Sophie this conversation had raised and focused on the beautiful young woman before him. "A good match. So that means we'll be seeing each other again?"

She shrugged, feigning nonchalance. It wouldn't do to seem too eager. "We can be friends. I'm not interested in anything more."

He recognized this as a bit of game playing. The paparazzi attention they had already garnered was on a Gavin and Sophie level. He could foresee it only getting more intense if they continued on. Normally, he'd try to minimize the kind of drama being involved with someone like Colette seemed to promise, but both the timing of being between albums and the desire for simple "fun and distraction," as she called it, was hard to resist.

"I would love your friendship, honey," he told her.

58

CONOR

It was less than a week later that Conor, still restless, made another trip. This time, it was to New York City, with the goal of seeing Colette. They'd spoken once and texted a lot since their time in London, and though she tried to play coy and keep up the pretense of them just being "friends," he thought she'd welcome his visit.

She lived in a brownstone on Barrow Street where just enough sunlight filtered through trees to warm the back of his neck as he waited on the stoop for an answer to his knock.

She couldn't conceal her delight when she finally opened the door. Wearing distressed cut-off jeans and a plain white tank top with several contrasting bead necklaces, she was a casual, but still striking, beauty.

"Conor! Are you're really here? she asked with a laugh.

"Surprise. Happy to see me?"

"I am, but you should have warned me. I have plans in a little while."

It was the risk he took, he realized. He'd gone as far as having someone in the Rogue organization track down her home address and contact her modeling agency to see if she was out on a booking before showing up here. But he knew that didn't guarantee she'd be available. Though he wasn't usually someone who settled, right now, he'd take what he could get. That meant starting this visit off right.

She was looking at him expectantly, so he dropped the small

canvas weekend bag he had brought, wrapped his arm around her slim waist, pulled her body to his and kissed her deeply. In return, she grabbed his backside and pressed her chest to his. This was going exactly as he had envisioned during the taxi ride over.

"We'd better go in," she said after they traded several more increasingly passionate kisses.

Inside, she led him straight to her bedroom but he got a quick glance around on the way. It was enough to see that it was sparsely furnished with a red fabric sofa, a black leather chair, and a black lacquered coffee table sitting on bare white oak floors. Artwork leaned unhung at the base of the white walls, a testament to the nomadic lifestyle she led as an up-and-coming model.

The bedroom was just as spare, but they had all they needed.

"I CAN'T BELIEVE you're tossing me out," Conor said with a bemused smile.

He was sitting on Colette's sofa, watching as she transferred the contents of one purse into another that would better match the short black floral-patterned dress she wore with black suede high-heeled boots that came up to her knees. She had given him an hour of electric lovemaking before looking at the clock and telling him she had to go meet her friend for shopping. It was quite a change to have a woman use him for sex without wanting anything more.

"Oh, come on, Conor. I told you I had plans this afternoon," she said distractedly.

"Can't you cancel? I mean, I'm just here from Ireland, for fuck's sake."

"But I didn't ask you to come. You planned this all by yourself," she said.

"Colette, I didn't plan anything. I'm here to see Shay."

That wasn't exactly true. But the fact that Shay was in town working on a movie soundtrack was a neat excuse he could leverage. It wouldn't do for *him* to seem too eager.

"So go see him. I really have to get going now."

Conor glanced down at the coffee table where there was a *Cosmopolitan* magazine with Sophie on the cover. Without thinking, he picked it up and studied the sexy photo. She wore a low-cut red dress and her hair was down and full of body as an unseen fan blew it back. Her hazel eyes were focused on the camera, conveying a compelling mixture of playfulness and sensuality. He was reminded of all the times he had stared into those eyes, desiring her body and soul. She had long ago become the ideal woman in his mind. Perfect . . . and unattainable.

"Well?"

The sound of Colette's impatient voice pulled him from his brief reverie. "Hmm?"

"You're going to make me late. Time to go."

Standing, he said, "You're a cool one, aren't you?"

"What? Are you in love with me or something, Connie?" she asked.

Conor met her eyes and said flatly, "No." He paused. "And don't call me 'Connie.' I fucking hate it."

"Okay, fine. Look, we have fun together. Just now, that was fun, right?" she asked, but didn't wait for him to respond. "But that's all it was. So, I have to go now because I have a date."

"Oh, it's a date, is it?"

"So what if it is?"

He was being sucked into her games. Pursuing a woman was fun, a challenge. But this was something different, this was pure game playing for its own sake. She had slept with him knowing full well she was shortly to meet with another man, and that didn't sit well with him.

"Never mind," he said with a sigh. "You're right. It was a good time. I'll be going."

She met his eyes for a moment before dropping her gaze to the magazine he still held in one hand. She took it from him and looked at the cover of Sophie.

"Who is the unavailable woman you're in love with?" she asked.

"What? What has that to do with anything?"

"I . . . I don't know at this point."

"Right. Because we're just friends, yeah? What does anyone else matter, anyway?"

She tossed the magazine face down on the coffee table and put on a determined smile. Placing her arms around his neck, she kissed him long and sweetly on the mouth.

"Call me tomorrow," she said softly.

———————

Left to his own devices for the rest of the day, Conor realized he really should get in touch with Shay since they were in the same city. His friend sounded stressed and hurriedly gave Conor directions to the recording studio where he was working.

It was something of a surprise for Conor to walk into the studio and see Shay in such a position of authority as he gave orders to the sound engineers at the mixing board.

"Aye, Shay," Conor said. "Aren't you the man?"

Shay was startled by the intrusion but quickly smiled. "Good to see a friendly face, mate," he said.

"I thought you were almost done with this project." Conor put down his bag and took the chair beside Shay, leaning back and stretching.

"There are a few things I'm still working on. There's a bit where I'd love to have some acoustic guitar but I can't seem to communicate to the session musicians exactly what it is I want."

"You want me to play with it?"

"You're a lifesaver!" Shay said.

Conor watched as Shay got up and retrieved a guitar. Though he was energized by the work he was doing, Conor could tell that Shay was exhausted underneath it all. His perfectionist tendencies had clearly left him with little sleep.

"Jesus, man, you need to get laid," Conor told him.

"Don't I know it," he replied with a laugh.

———————

Working together, Conor and Shay composed a delicate, Spanish-infused acoustic guitar melody that was perfect for the love scene in the movie. It was after nine that evening when they stepped out of the studio and thought about food and relaxation.

And it wasn't until they were seated in a nearby sushi restaurant that Shay thought to ask what Conor was doing in New York.

"Thought you'd get curious at some point," Conor said with a laugh.

"You can see how wrapped up in this project I've been."

"Don't worry about it."

The waitress appeared then and lingered at their table as she poured Ichiban beer from large bottles into frosty glasses.

"How are you today, then?" Conor asked her.

She was petite, with a mixture of African American and Asian heritage. Her hair was slicked back, showcasing beautiful mocha skin and ebony eyes. Her form fitting, high-collared black dress was long but had a dramatic slit up both sides to reveal smooth, shapely legs.

"Good, thanks. Can I make any recommendations?" she asked, clearly not recognizing them.

"Sure. What's the best way for my friend here to get to take you out for a drink later tonight?" Conor asked casually.

The waitress glanced at Shay, saw his embarrassment and smiled. "He could ask himself," she replied. "I'll give you a minute with the menu and be right back."

"Conor Quinn, you bastard," Shay said mildly.

"Well, she's a good-looking girl. Why not?"

"What about you, then?"

"Me? Me, I'm in trouble. I've only got one girl on my mind these days and that's why I'm here in New York."

"The model you were in all the papers with?"

"That'd be the one."

"Rock stars and models—what a fucking cliché."

They laughed and then made a toast to the lovely absurdity of it.

59

CONOR

This time, the sun was warm on Conor's face as he leaned against Colette's front door, his eyes closed behind his dark sunglasses. It was just after nine and he had been waiting on her front steps for ten minutes, having gotten no response to his phone call or knock on her door. He didn't know how long he would wait, but he was content to sunbathe for the moment.

"Conor?"

He opened his eyes to find Colette standing before him, a paper cup of coffee and a small brown bag in her hand. There were two things he noticed that pleased him: she was bringing home coffee for one, and she wore jeans and a threadbare tee shirt, meaning she had changed clothes and wasn't doing some sort of walk of shame from having stayed overnight at another man's place.

"Morning, honey," he said as he stood. He tried to kiss her on the lips but she turned her cheek to him, though he caught a hint of her pleased smile before she covered it.

"What are you doing here?" she asked. "One surprise was nice, I'll admit. But two times in as many days is a little pushy, no?"

Ah, so she was back to trying to play hard to get. What game was this, anyway? She'd pushed him away yesterday . . . until that weird thing of asking who the "unavailable woman" he'd been in love with was. That had come out of nowhere, but it did seem to spur her interest. Or, was it jealousy? She'd kissed him like she never wanted it to end.

"You did say to ring you," he told her. "You know, yesterday? When you were kicking me out only moments after I'd given you more than one toe-curling orgasm, that is?"

She tried and failed to hold back a smile. "So, I did."

Leaning toward her, he brushed his lips against hers but didn't kiss her. Instead, he moved his mouth to her ear and said, "Invite me in. We can try for a new record."

She pulled away to meet his eyes. He imagined she saw her own desire reflected there because she nodded and turned to unlock the door.

As he followed her inside, his cell rang and he automatically checked it. It was Gavin. He hadn't spoken to him in over two weeks, a rarity. But he figured a day or two longer wouldn't hurt, and let the call go to voicemail. There were other things on his mind at the moment.

THEY DIDN'T MAKE it to the bedroom this time. Instead, he bent her over the back of the sofa and took her forcefully, talking dirty to her as he coaxed the first orgasm out of her with expert fingers massaging her clit. Afterward, she collapsed, folding over the sofa, and the sight of her luscious bare ass made him drop to his knees so he could taste and tongue her even as she claimed she couldn't handle anymore. He soon proved her wrong, bringing her to another explosive peak. By then, she was left even more undone and he pulled her limp body into his arms and carried her into the bedroom. Gently placing her on the bed, he spooned her from behind, holding her generous breasts and planting slow kisses along the side of her neck. A teasing pinch of her nipples had her arching her back, her ass grinding into his ready cock. That would end in orgasm number three for her, one more than the day before, but still just the start, he thought.

He was still catching his breath from the last effort when his cell rang again.

"Let me see who it is," he said as he reached over her to grab the phone.

The readout said it was James, and as Colette trailed her fingertips over his chest and down his abdomen, he again let it go to voicemail. But within a few minutes the phone rang again.

"Fuck's sake," he groaned.

"Ignore it," Colette said, kissing his neck.

This time it was Shay. And now he began to worry. He answered the call.

"What's up, Shay?"

"Turn on the tele. Wherever you are, find a tele and watch MTV or CNN," Shay said quickly.

"Tell me what the fuck it is," Conor said as he gestured to Colette to turn on the television.

Her expression quickly changed to one of concern and she scrambled to turn on the TV before handing him the remote control.

"Gavin's talking to the press about his mother," Shay said.

The screen came to life, showing the surreal vision of Gavin standing in front of his home surrounded by a dozen photographers and journalists.

"Fuck me," Conor said softly.

"From what I can tell," Shay said, "all this started 'cause there's an article coming out in *Vanity Fair* this week about his Ma. Christ, look at Sophie there."

Conor focused on Sophie. She was standing next to Gavin with an expression that clearly showed her heart breaking for her husband.

"I can't believe the madness of this," Conor said.

"I guess Gav didn't really intend on doing this, but MTV says all these reporters have been at their house since early this morning trying to get a response."

"What's going on?" Colette asked.

"Watch," Conor said.

He stayed on the phone with Shay while his eyes were fixed on the screen.

The camera had a dead-on angle, focusing on a tight shot of Gavin as he ran his hand through his hair and prepared to speak.

"I'll just say a few words," Gavin said, and the reporters suddenly hushed while the camera clicks sped up. "You're all here because there's been a terrible intrusion into my family's privacy," he continued. "An article is due out concerning my mother, the premise being that I have lied to the press and misled fans for the past few years regarding whether she is alive or dead. The article rightly says she is alive." Here he paused and looked down for a long moment before returning his hard stare at the cameras. "At least to the best of my knowledge she is. I have been one hundred percent honest in the past when I've said anything at all about her. I never claimed she was dead, only that I had lost her. I would like to now ask for my privacy back. This is no one's concern but my own family's. Please do as we have done and let her live the life of her choosing."

With that said, he then stepped back from the mass of microphones that had been thrust toward him. He looked exhausted, and as Sophie took his hand he leaned into her slightly.

The station stayed with the scene as the reporters shouted questions at Gavin.

"Why did she abandon her family?"

"Have you ever heard from her?"

"Was she being abused—is that it?"

"What would you like to say to her?"

Conor winced as he imagined the turmoil Gavin was going through. And then he smiled when he could clearly read Gavin's lips as he muttered "fuck off" in response.

"I can't get out of here until tomorrow," Shay said.

"I'll leave today," Conor told him.

"Good of you. Then I'll see you back in Dublin in a few days."

"Plan on it," Conor said before ending the call.

"I don't understand any of this," Colette said as she pulled on her T-shirt.

"It's complicated. Let me try to get in touch with Gavin, then I'll tell you some of it."

He tried Gavin's home phone and immediately got the answering machine. Then he tried Gavin's cell and went straight to voicemail.

"Fuck, he won't answer his lines."

"Do you want Sophie's cell number?" Colette offered.

"Good idea. I have it," he said and tried her next.

"Why do you have Sophie's number?" she asked.

"Why wouldn't I?" he asked absently.

"Because she's your friend's wife."

He ignored her as Sophie answered. "I just saw it on the tele, Sophie. What's going on there?"

"Oh, Connie, it's awful. Gavin is ready to break down," Sophie said, her voice trembling with a mixture of anger, sadness, and hurt.

"Shh, now, honey. You know he needs you strong," Conor told her. "Can you put him on the line?"

"Yeah. Where are you, anyway?"

"I'm in New York, visiting Shay. I'll get a flight back today, though, and come straight there."

"That would be great, Conor. Hang on."

He waited while she took the phone to Gavin, who after a few moments said a hoarse hello.

"You okay, Declan?"

"Been better, Con. I have the feeling once I finish off this whiskey I'll be right numb enough," Gavin said with a laugh.

"Save some for me. I'll be there late tonight."

"Where are you now?"

"In New York. Shay's coming back tomorrow."

"Marty offered to come back from France. I told him no. I'm not even sure why you should rush back, man. There's nothing to be done at this point. They're a pack of rabid fucking dogs, the press is."

"I can see that. Nice touch, by the way, as you went inside."

Gavin laughed softly. "I couldn't resist. The fuckers. Here I am asking ever so goddamn nicely to be left alone and they're suddenly hard of hearing."

"Least if I'm there we can tell 'em to fuck off together," he suggested.

There was a long silence and Conor looked to see if he might have lost the connection on his cell phone, but he hadn't.

"Gav?"

When Gavin spoke again his voice was seething with hurt and betrayal. "Con, it was my own fucking brother who gave 'em the best quotes. He's the one who suggested a *reinterpretation* of my lyrics. I could kill him."

"Jesus Christ," Conor muttered. Conor liked Gavin's brother about as much as Gavin did, which wasn't saying a lot. Gavin and his older brother, Ian, had never gotten along. They were born with an incompatibility that seemed to carry over with Gavin's friends. Ian had always taken the Irish tendency to be skeptical of someone's ambitions and raised it to the level of contempt for Gavin daring to dream of something as fantastic as being in a band. Despite all their success, Ian had always dismissed Gavin's part in things, categorizing it as luck rather than talent and hard work.

"Yeah. And I only know it 'cause the magazine sent me the article asking me to comment on it before they went to press. Bastards knew I would give them nothing."

"When did you read it?"

"About a week ago."

"A week? Why didn't you say anything?"

"I dunno. I guess I didn't know how the fuck to respond at first. Now it's gotten all out of control."

"It'll die down," Conor reassured him. "You gave them enough. Now just shut it out and they'll have nowhere to go with it and it'll be done."

Gavin was quiet again. "I hope you're right, Con. 'Cause I honestly don't know if I can handle this."

"You can, Gav. You can. Look, I'll be there soon enough. Now, put Sophie back on for a second, okay?"

"Sure."

While he waited for Sophie, Conor noticed Colette was watching the continued "news" report on the true story of Gavin's mother. A ripple of irritation coursed through him at seeing her so captivated.

"Gavin seems a little better for talking to you," Sophie said as she got on the line.

"Thing is, it won't last," he replied. "Do me a favor, honey?"

Colette now turned and watched him as he spoke on the phone.

"Sure, what?"

"Cancel whatever modeling gigs you have for a bit. He shouldn't be alone."

"Wait a minute, what makes you say that?" she asked with alarm.

"No, I don't mean it like that. He's about to slip into some serious depression here—you said it yourself."

"I know. I'll do whatever I can. You know that, Conor."

"I know, Soph. Thank God for you. And hey, do your best to . . . distract him from all this 'til I get there."

Sophie laughed. "Are you suggesting what I think you are?"

Conor smiled. "You know me—always comes back to sex."

"We'll see you soon. Have a safe trip."

After ending the call, Conor fell back against the bed, already exhausted.

"So you're leaving?" Colette asked as she sat with him.

"Yeah. I gotta get back. Not sure how to get the fastest flight—"

"I texted my agent—she's booking it for you. She'll call back in a few minutes to tell you which airline."

He sat up and smiled at her. "Thank you, Colette. That was awfully sweet."

"That's where you belong, isn't it? With Sophie?"

"And Gavin," he said, showing his annoyance.

"I just thought with you calling her *honey* and talking about sex, she'd be the one you'd need to rush back to."

Conor got up and started dressing. He knew Colette had a weird thing with Sophie, both admiring what she had accomplished in the modeling industry and yet feeling competitive with her, but this was something else.

"You don't understand what you saw with Gavin, 'cause if you did, you'd know you have no fucking right to pull some jealousy trip right now."

"What I understand is that Sophie is the unavailable woman you're in love with and—"

"Stop this. You sound like a child trying to speak of adult things of which you have no understanding," he said sternly. But his entire body was tense over the idea that he was that transparent. "And fuck your agent getting me a flight, too," he said and strode out.

He was at the front door when she grabbed his arm.

"Don't go like this. I'm sorry. I don't mean to be jealous. I don't. Please."

"I don't have time for your games," he said, pulling away from her.

"Please, Conor," she said, and the naked pleading in her voice made him stop and look at her.

"Please what?"

"I don't want this—*us*—to end."

He met her eyes for a moment. "I'll ring you later, honey. Okay?"

She nodded eagerly. "Just do me a favor," she said, wrapping her arm around his neck and pressing her breasts against him.

"What?"

"Don't call any other girl honey. Let me be your honey," she purred.

"You, honey, are a total mind-fuck," he told her, and she smiled as if it were a compliment.

60

CONOR

At half past one in the morning, Conor quietly let himself in through the McManus' front door. There were no lights on inside, though he saw a glow coming from the back garden. He put his bag down and walked toward the open door that led to the well-manicured yard.

Gavin was lying in a chaise lounge with his head in Sophie's lap. The hanging lanterns and outdoor fire pit provided soft, romantic lighting.

"My whole family," Gavin said with a pronounced slur. "I don't understand why my whole family has betrayed me."

"Shh," Sophie said softly before leaning down and pressing her lips to his forehead for a long moment. "Just hold on to me."

Conor watched the scene for longer than he knew he should. It was a view into an intensely private and intimate part of their marriage.

"Well, I've made it," he finally announced, forcing a smile. "Shall we start the real drinking, then?" He held up the bottle of whiskey he had brought.

Gavin sat up and struggled to his feet. Sophie stood with him and put her arm around his waist to steady him.

"Aye, Con," Gavin said slowly. He went to him and wrapped his arms around Conor in a tight hug. "You are my brother, right? You, I can trust with my fucking life."

"That's right, Gav. That's right," Conor said.

"Fuck 'em," Gavin said and released Conor. He turned his eyes heavenward and shouted, "Fuck you all! I don't need yous anyway!"

Conor winced and then looked at Sophie. Her eyes were filled with tears. She looked helpless.

"I mean," Gavin continued, this time mumbling to himself, "I never had me ma in all these years. So what have I lost? Nothing. And Ian—we may be related, but that means nothing. He's been waiting for this day, waiting to tell the world what he really thinks of me."

"You ready for another drink?" Conor asked. "I know I could use one."

"Sure, yeah. Why not?" Gavin replied and led the way back inside.

"You okay, honey?" Conor asked Sophie, taking her hand.

"Yeah. It's just hard knowing you can't do anything to help," she said.

"You're doing everything you can, and that's enough," he replied, and received a quick hug of thanks in return.

They found Gavin in the living room, passed out on the sofa. He was lying on his back, breathing heavily through his open mouth.

"Let's at least turn him on his side," Conor said, ever conscious of the cliché of a rock musician choking on his own vomit while passed out.

"YOU MUST BE EXHAUSTED," Sophie said.

They were sitting at the kitchen table together in the near dark, having left the lights off and with only the outside lanterns for illumination.

Conor tipped the Redbreast 15-year-old whiskey over one of the tumblers Sophie had brought out, filling it halfway. He then filled the other a quarter full and pushed it toward her.

"A bit tired, yeah," he admitted, and knocked his glass against hers before downing the contents. He should have savored the drink but he craved the warm buzz he knew it would provide.

Sophie sipped hers and stifled a cough.

Conor smiled at her. Though the liquor was of the highest quality, it still went down harshly for her, reminding him that she was a woman of intriguing contradictions, at once sophisticated and innocent. Even when he thought he knew her, she could still surprise him, and that kept him wanting more.

"Colette wanted you to call her when you got in," Sophie said.

"Fuck's sake," he muttered as he refilled his glass. "She called you?"

Sophie laughed, amused. "Yeah, right after you left for the airport. She told me quite pointedly that you two are together."

He tossed back his second glass, trying to buy time to sort out how he felt about all of this.

"She seemed happy, Conor. You think you really like her?"

"I do, indeed," he replied honestly. "Though, she's different than what I'm used to. A bit of a challenge."

Sophie nodded and sat back. She absently swirled the remaining whiskey in her tumbler, sinking into her chair.

"Thanks for coming back so quickly," she said. "Gavin thinks the world of you for good reason."

"I wish he hadn't said that thing about trusting me so much."

Sophie looked up at him. "Why?"

He looked at her with eyebrows raised for a long moment, hoping he wouldn't have to say aloud what they had skirted around for years.

"Oh, you mean . . . ."

"Yes, that."

"The thing is," she said, trying to keep her tone light, "it's just a sexual attraction. So, it's really pretty harmless."

He started to grimace in denial of this characterization before catching himself and acquiescing with a small nod. She had always been quick to accept his attraction to her as nothing more than surface-level. How could he be disappointed by that, though? He'd set it up for her to rationalize it that way years ago, after all.

"Yeah," he said as he helped himself to more whiskey. "That's all it is."

"And even then, it's really probably just your defense mechanism to keep from getting close with anyone else."

He laughed. "You're saying I have intimacy issues?"

She touched his hand and smiled at him playfully. "It's okay. I hear a lot of men have that problem."

He would gladly let her tease him all night long, especially if it meant she would touch him while doing it.

"I mean, you do have a pretty terrible record with relationships."

"You're judging me based on the wrong criteria. I've had the relationships I've wanted."

"So that means all you've ever wanted is short-term flings with beautiful but vapid girls?"

"Ouch," he said, and laughed. "They haven't all been vapid."

"But they have been short-term. What's keeping you from being serious with someone? Afraid you'll end up compromising your cool, controlled image?"

"Honey, the whiskey has gone to your head," he said, and she laughed.

"Probably," she said.

He studied her for a moment. It was no wonder, after the day she'd had propping up her devastated husband, that she looked disheveled and tired. Her blonde hair was pulled up into a ponytail, but several strands had fallen loose. Her eyes lacked their usual shine. At the same time, his heart ached with how beautiful he found her. Then he almost laughed out loud, thinking of the fact that he was starting to feel something for Colette and yet still couldn't shake what he had for Sophie.

They sat in easy silence for a good five minutes.

"Conor?" Sophie said at length.

"Hmm?"

"How on earth is he going to get through this?"

"He'll just have to, Sophie. What other choice does he have?"

She nodded reluctantly, unconvinced. "You'll stay here tonight? I can make up the guest bedroom for you."

"Sure. I'm ready to pass out myself."

They went upstairs together and he helped her put fresh sheets on the guest bed.

"Sleep well," she told him.

"You too, honey."

After hesitating a moment, she reached up and wrapped her arms around his neck, hugging him.

It was so easy for him to return her embrace, to close his eyes and take in her lovely, familiar scent. Just feeling the warmth of her body against his was so sweet he wished it could continue through the night. He had a vision of getting into bed together and holding her while they slept and he longed for it to be real. Though his fantasies for her were still sexual, he just as often desired her for the intimacy of companionship alone.

"See you in the morning," she said as she pulled away and left him by himself.

It took him a long while to surrender to sleep that night as his mind raced. He knew he wasn't doing himself any good by indulging his feelings for Sophie, especially when he now had Colette taking him seriously. In the end, he decided it was best to help Gavin as much as he could and then after that return to a single-minded pursuit of Colette. Because she had the potential to be more than just a distraction, he felt sure he would be doing the right thing.

61

SOPHIE

Breakfast was incongruously jovial. Gavin had, temporarily at least, gained a happy disposition, and he and Conor talked and joked and laughed as if nothing had happened the day before. It made Sophie wonder if the sex they'd had that morning had really been that good.

Waking early, she had found Gavin in the garden, gathering empty beer bottles from the previous day. Her simple kiss in greeting had ignited a passionate response from him. When she let her surprise show at the aggressive way he reached inside her robe, he told her he needed her, desperation in his voice. She knew he needed a release more than anything and suggested they go their room, but he was too eager. Despite her warning that Conor was upstairs, he backed her against the garden wall, pulled at her panties until they tore away, and fucked her. When he was done, he moved to his knees and pulled her leg over his shoulder to make sure she was satisfied as well.

It had apparently been exactly what he needed to push past the emotions of the previous day, as he was now enjoying Conor's story of how frazzled he'd found Shay in New York, and that he'd taken it upon himself to connect him with their pretty waitress at the sushi bar.

"Did he get the ride?" Gavin asked, suitably amused.

"He better have. We'll ask him when he gets here—embarrass the hell out of him," Conor said.

"Why don't you two leave him alone?" Sophie asked, smiling. "Just because he's not your typical lecherous Irishman doesn't mean you should harass him."

The men laughed.

"It's such a shame to see him miss out on all the advantages he has," Conor said. "I mean, not only is he a good-looking kid, but he's the fucking drummer in the best band in the world. Why wouldn't he be out every night with a girl or two?"

"Maybe because you do enough of that for the whole band!" Sophie said, and they laughed again.

"Nothing wrong with liking sex," Conor said.

"I'm with you on that one," Gavin added. "But I hear from my friends at the tabloids that you're committed to one girl in particular now."

Conor grinned. "Don't think I'd go that far with it, mate. But she has potential."

"Well, when I talked to her yesterday, she sounded positively in love," Sophie said.

"In that moment she may have been. She's a bit of a mind-fuck. Would you agree, Sophie?"

"She likes attention, that's for sure," she conceded.

"As long as you're getting fucked the other way, does it matter?" Gavin asked with a laugh.

"There is something to be said for knowing who you're dealing with and what they want. But it's fun enough for now."

"Oh, that reminds me!" Sophie said. "Did you ever call her last night?"

"Fuck. I forgot. I'll bet I'm in for it!" Conor said, smiling as he got up to go make the call.

Once alone, Sophie turned to Gavin and took his hand into hers.

"What do you want to do today, baby?" she asked.

"This. This is all I want—to be with my best friends. Okay, darlin'?"

She nodded before leaning over to kiss him.

THEY KEPT the television and phones off and spent most of the day in the back garden, soaking up the rare, warm sunshine. The boys stripped down to their shorts and Sophie put on a bikini. They lounged while drinking margaritas and chatting aimlessly.

The reporters kept themselves off the property lines after Sophie had called the police the first day to have them removed as trespassers. But they hadn't given up entirely, and instead set up camp in the street. Fortunately, they were unable to peer over the high back garden walls.

It was midday when they heard a commotion coming from the street, the paparazzi signaling the arrival of someone at their door with shouting and jostling for position.

"I'll get it, guys," Sophie said.

"More margaritas while you're at it, please," Conor said with a grin.

Sophie pulled on a sundress and headed to the front door where someone was knocking hard.

Expecting to find Shay, she swung the door open and was surprised to see Ian instead. He was shielding himself with a newspaper from the dozen or so photographers and camera crews still lingering in the nearby street. Ian was an older, heavier, and less attractive version of Gavin. Clothes were always ill-fitting on him and he attempted to tame his unruly hair with too much gel, leaving him looking greasy. Sophie had never bonded with him, in large part because he rarely accepted her invitations to dinner parties or other events. And when she did see him, she instinctively recoiled from the negative energy radiating from him. He was someone who could suck the life out of a room and was, therefore, the exact opposite of his brother.

Before she could say a word, he let himself in and shut the door.

"Jesus, I've never seen anything like it," he said, exasperated.

"What are you doing here, Ian?" she asked.

"I've come to see my brother, of course," he replied with a degree of casualness she found galling.

"You've got to be kidding," she said. "Look, he's in no shape to see you now. You have to understand that he's hurting and you being here will only make it worse."

"Nonsense, my dear. Just lead me to him."

Sophie appraised him for a moment. He had gained weight since she had seen him last and it had added to his usual disheveled appearance. At the same time, he returned her stare with a look of stubborn determination that told her it was no use in trying to dissuade him from seeing Gavin.

"Fine. I warned you though," she said, and started toward the back garden.

He followed closely behind her. As they stepped out into the sun, he held his hand to his brow in an effort to adjust to the light.

And in that moment, Gavin saw who his visitor was and jumped to his feet, his entire body tense with hostility.

"Look now, calm yourself," Ian said, holding up both hands.

"I'll tell you once," Gavin said. "Get out of my house."

"I knew it, I bloody well knew it," Ian said in disgust. "You're putting this whole thing on me, aren't you? As if you're not the very one who set this whole disaster up!"

"Fuck off, Ian. There's no way you're going to turn this around on me just so you can get by. You know damn well what you did was wrong."

"And what was it I did, anyway? I told the truth—something you should have tried from the beginning. You wouldn't have been in this mess if you had."

Gavin relaxed his posture and his shoulders sagged beneath the weight of his brother's words.

"What'd you come here for?" he asked quietly.

"To tell you to get this thing under control, if only for Da's sake. He's being humiliated by this."

"Funny, that. Since the focus seems to, in fact, be on me. And because of you, my band has to suffer even worse for it."

"What, the lyrics shite?" Ian asked with a smirk. "Give us a break. Like it was an original concept, or something to figure not every word was about Sophie. Yeah, like you're so bleedin' deep they needed me to clue them in!"

That raised the ire again in Gavin. All his brother had ever done was demean his abilities and choices. But before he could respond, Conor joined in.

"Why don't you go fuck yourself, Ian," he said.

"Stay out of it," Ian replied.

"Why don't *you* stay out of it?" Gavin returned. "You've done nothing to help the situation. Tell me how you justify saying one word to that reporter?"

"At least the world knows you're fucking human now, don't they?" Ian said, spitting his words. "Everyone knows now this fairy tale you've concocted for yourself is bullshit, that you're just some kid whose own mother couldn't even be *bothered*."

There wasn't a second's hesitation before Gavin raised his fist and punched his brother hard in the face, drawing blood instantly. Sophie cried out for him to stop but he kept swinging at his brother again and again.

"Conor, stop them!" Sophie said.

Conor clearly hesitated before finally pulling his friend away. Gavin had left Ian's nose bloody and most likely broken, his lip split, and his left cheek quickly bruising.

"You fucking arsehole," Ian moaned as he cradled his head in his hands.

Gavin was still seething as Conor finally forcibly moved him to the far side of the back garden and held him there by the shoulders.

"Come with me," Sophie told Ian, taking his arm.

"Show him the fucking door, Sophie!" Gavin shouted.

Sophie ignored him as she took Ian inside and sat him down at the kitchen bar. She quickly wet a towel and put ice into a plastic bag.

"You're a mess," she said softly as she gently wiped at the blood around his mouth.

"That's your fucking husband. A real prince, aye?" Ian said, shaking his head.

"You asked for this, Ian."

He was quiet for a long spell as she worked on cleaning him up. "Do you know," he finally said more calmly, "they made me redundant at work a month back? Do you know what that feels like? And to have your own brother have everything you don't? Don't you think that makes it worse?"

Sophie pulled the towel away from him and met his eyes. "I'm sorry you lost your job," she said. "I really am. But that's not Gavin's fault."

"Never said it was. But here he is living the life of luxury and it's all due to this false pretense—that he's some sort of long-suffering artist. I mean, it drives me to the edge to see the way he's created this persona of the tragically orphaned boy whose heart is still bleeding from it all."

"Wait a minute," she said. "Are you saying you don't think his feelings are genuine?"

"They were, sure. But you get the fuck over these things and grow up. Now he's just using it to make a spectacle of himself."

"You couldn't be more wrong, Ian. God, I wish you two would actually try to know each other instead of constantly tearing each other down. You're missing out on something so special."

"I think I'm fit enough to leave now," he said and stood up.

"Do you need help—with money?" she asked.

"I'd sooner live in the streets than take his money," he replied and moved toward the front door.

"The offer's always there," she said, though he ignored her.

When Sophie went back out to the yard, she found Gavin in need of aid as well. He had a cut above his left eyebrow and blood was smeared across his temple from having tried to wipe it away. Ian must have caught him with his ring.

He was obviously still irate, pacing back and forth even as Conor tried talking him down.

She went straight to him and wrapped her arms around his neck, and for the first time in years, he rejected her attempt to soothe him.

"Darlin', I'm in no mood," he said curtly, and walked inside without another word.

There was no hiding the disappointment she felt. Conor gave her a quick one-arm hug. "Give him some space, Soph. It's a lot to deal with right now."

She nodded and blinked back her tears, telling herself that in the end she and Gavin would find a way through this together.

62

GAVIN

E ven though everyone gave him space for the next several days, Gavin still sensed they all thought he'd bounce back from this and return to his old gregarious self before too long. He supposed he only had himself to blame for that expectation after so many years of funneling his emotional turmoil into his songwriting efforts.

Still, when Conor and the band pulled away from him with all good intentions, it was actually the opposite of what he wanted. But he couldn't bring himself to reach out, even though he needed them more than ever. So, when they retreated, he sank deeper into himself.

After the fight with Ian, he hid away in the house for ten days straight. He spent most of his time in the room he had fashioned as his writing space, with the door closed. But he wrote little and instead stared out the window gloomily at the back garden, ruminating on what had become of his family. He had spoken to his father only once and briefly at that. Brendan McManus had berated Gavin for the fight with Ian and expressed disappointment over this public spectacle. Though he didn't necessarily put the blame on Gavin for it all, like Ian had, his disapproval of Gavin seemed once again to be validated.

It all served to give him the agonizing feeling of reliving the emotional havoc he'd suffered as a child when it became clear that his mother had intentionally left her family. Then, he had gone mute for weeks after recognizing that the person most expected by cultural and familial norms to sacrifice all to care for her children had abdicated that responsibility. His father and brother barely noticed as they were concerned with their own survival. It was his imagination and interest in music that saved him. He lost himself to his brother's music collection, becoming obsessed with Bowie but also devouring countless others. And when his schoolmate Conor Quinn seemed to be the only one receptive to his constant talk of music, they became inseparable.

That friendship wouldn't be the salve this time around. He couldn't envision a way to move past the renewed sense of abandonment he was experiencing. To at the same time have his music called into question was both a public humiliation and a staggering blow. But worst of all was the cruel fact of his mother's continued silence. After all these years, years where he had generously excused her absence and convinced himself she was only trying to heal in her own time, he finally took things for what they were.

Ian was right: He was just some kid whose own mother couldn't be bothered.

63

Now and then Sophie would knock gently on Gavin's writing room door to see if he would spend time with her or take a call from a friend, but he rejected all entreaties. She was at a loss as how to help him.

Conor had stayed with them for three days before Gavin starting spending long stretches in his writing room, making it clear that his friend's presence was no longer helping. Sophie was sad to see him go, but she knew caring for Gavin wasn't his responsibility. She urged him to take Colette's calls since she was now in full pursuit-mode with him, obviously motivated by their roles being reversed since she now viewed him as the one playing hard to get.

The press was a constant on the rare outings she made, including a visit to the grocery store. A tabloid even featured a photo of her coming out of the store alongside a list of the items she had purchased.

While Gavin brooded, Sophie had to find ways to occupy herself since she had done what Conor suggested and canceled several modeling gigs. Some time ago, she and Gavin had casually discussed looking for a second home in the Los Angeles area, so she took it upon herself to now do some of the real estate research.

She had various materials spread out on the dining room table and was concentrating on the beach areas of Malibu when Gavin shuffled into the room.

Bedraggled was the word that came to mind when she saw him. He wore boxer briefs with an open robe and while his hair was pulled back into a short ponytail it clearly needed a good washing. His face was covered in an unkempt beard and his eyes were red.

"What are you up to?" he asked, leaning down to kiss her.

She reached for his hand but he pulled away, slipping from her grasp. Stifling her disappointment, she managed a smile instead.

"I'm looking at properties in LA."

"What for?" He took a chair and turned it around, straddling it as he sat down next to her.

"Remember we talked about buying a house there? I thought maybe we should go ahead and look now."

"Well, I'm not fucking buying a house in Malibu, that's for sure," he said as he pushed aside the listings she had for that exclusive area.

"Okay," she said slowly, put off. "If it helps any, I want to buy this house."

He looked at her with surprise. "What do you mean? With your parents' money?"

"No. With mine." She was trying to be patient with him and understanding of the fact that he was going through a rough time, but it was getting more difficult to keep in mind.

Glancing at the listings again, he saw the price range she was considering. "You're telling me you can buy a house that costs in the millions?"

"Yes. Baby, I've been modeling for six years and making good money. I can do this. I want to do it for us."

"Fucking hell," he said softly.

He sifted through the papers, coming to properties in Venice Beach, the eclectic beach town on the Westside of Los Angeles. There was a photo of a three-story, quasi-Mediterranean style house on Grand Canal, accompanied by a sales pitch boasting of an offbeat, artistic neighborhood. Canals fashioned after Italy's famous waterways had been dug at the turn of the twentieth century to drain the area's natural marshes, turning it into a tourist destination. After all these years, the beach still attracted gawkers for its eccentric Ocean Front Walk vendors, lively pickup basketball games, and Muscle Beach area for weightlifters in search of an audience, but the canals had been relegated to the wealthy few who could afford the real estate.

"How about this one?" he said, holding up the flyer for the Venice Beach house. "Sounds like this area would better suit us than Malibu."

"Looks good," Sophie agreed. "Okay. So, how about we take a trip? We can get away from here and look at some houses out there?"

"Yeah, let's do it. Let's go today."

She smiled, relieved. Maybe the worst was over. "I'll get us a flight right now."

"That can wait a bit," he said. He leaned toward her and kissed her.

"Baby, no," she said, pulling away from him. "You need a shower."

He laughed. "That bad, aye?" he asked, and she nodded with a small smile. "Ah, come on—you promised for better or worse, didn't you?"

She let out a playful scream and jumped up when he reached for her again. He chased her all the way upstairs and trapped her in the bathroom.

"How about a dip in the tub first?" she asked with a laugh.

"Don't you want to have dirty sex with me?"

It had been ten days since they'd had any kind of sex, so she decided it wasn't the best time to put conditions on him. She went to him and wrapped her arms around his neck, kissing him deeply, urgently.

64

GAVIN

Being in Los Angeles proved to be an inspired idea as Gavin was able to elude intense media attention for the most part while they went house hunting. He immediately fell in love with the Venice Beach area, especially after they took a stroll along the beach and he saw the street performers there. He was captivated, both with the diversity and the complete lack of recognition he got. Being able to engage in conversations with the guy who juggled knives, or the local graffiti artist, without having to talk about Rogue or his current debacle was utterly refreshing.

Though they were shown half a dozen houses by a local real estate agent, they agreed that the one Gavin first approved of back in Dublin was the one for them. Terracotta and stone on the outside, it had been gutted inside and remodeled with smooth lines and everything white except for dark wood floors and tasteful wrought iron work throughout the house. A top-of-the line kitchen with glass-front white cabinetry, white Caesarstone counters, and steel appliances opened to a formal dining room. The large step-down living room's French doors led to a patio overlooking the canal. It was elegant and clean and immediately felt like the fresh start they instinctively sought. They giddily put in an offer for the house and were assured it would be accepted and escrow would be short.

Their reprieve from media scrutiny ended when they returned to Shutters on the Beach hotel in nearby Santa Monica. There was a line of cars backed up to get into the short hotel driveway, and the valet had just relieved them of their keys with reverential apologies that they would have to walk the distance to the front entrance when they were confronted by a well-known paparazzo.

"Hey, Gavin," the heavyset man said, his camera flashing relentlessly. "Did you hear? They found your mother!"

Gavin did his best to keep his face a blank mask. He knew there was no truth to the jerk's taunt. His mother, wherever she was, had done an excellent job of staying hidden. If she had been located, he was sure he would hear about it from James before anyone else. James, who usually had such a tight grip on the band's media concerns, was working double-time to stay on top of this after failing to stop the *Vanity Fair* article. He had expressed profound regret over it, taking on all the blame, though Gavin didn't hold anything against him. The whole situation had been of his own making, just as Ian said.

Gavin put his arm around Sophie's shoulders to steer her around the man's stubborn presence. Technically, they were still on Pico Boulevard, and that meant it was public property. The photographer, as obnoxious as he was, was entitled to be there.

"Come on," the paparazzo groaned, "give me something. I'm doing a public service here. Think about all the other kids whose mothers abandoned them. Don't you have something to say for their sake?"

It wasn't the absurdity or the cruelty of this argument that bothered Gavin, it was the self-satisfied laugh added at the end that enraged him. And that rage immediately took form as he released Sophie from his protective half-embrace and lunged at the photographer. With one firm shove he sent the guy to his ass and earned a quick threat of a lawsuit in retaliation.

Gavin wanted to pounce on him, to unleash his fury on him, but Sophie pulled him forcefully toward the sanctuary of the hotel.

Once in their room, Sophie turned to him. "Gavin, what's going on? Where is this violence coming from? You're scaring me," she told him.

In reply, he took her into his arms and held her tightly, kissing her cheek gently.

"Baby," she murmured into his shoulder, "I'm so worried and I don't know how to help."

The way her whole body trembled against his added to the feeling that he was not only flailing but bringing her down with him. And he didn't want that. He didn't want to hurt her, but he knew he couldn't survive without her. Having her with him was beginning to feel like the best and worst thing, and even acknowledging that racked him with unbearable guilt.

"Shh, darlin'," he whispered to her as he stroked her hair. "Don't worry a bit. I'll sort it out and it'll be okay."

She pulled away to meet his eyes. "Will it? Will you?"

As he opened his mouth to reply, his cell rang. He chose to release her and answer it with a distracted hello.

"Mate! So, the rumors are true!" Jackson said with a grin in his voice.

"Aye, Jackie," Gavin replied, forcing himself to sound upbeat.

"Though I'm glad you're in town, I must say I'm a little dismayed to have learned so through TMZ, of all things."

"Sorry, didn't have a chance to call."

"No, not that, mate," Jackson said with a laugh. "I'm sorry to see that TMZ drivel actually gets it right sometimes!"

There was a silence as Gavin fought to get himself into a more jovial mood. He looked at Sophie. Her back was to him as she gazed out through the window at their picturesque view of the Santa Monica pier. It was starting to get dark and the lights of the Ferris wheel were growing brighter.

"Listen, Gavin," Jackson continued, "I should have called you before. I'm sorry to hear about your family troubles. It's a real kick in the balls, that."

"Thanks, man."

"So, here's the other reason I called. I'm having a fucking outrageous party tonight and you and your lady are coming. I'm up in the Hollywood Hills—just bought an insane nine-million-dollar house and I need to break it in! You'll come, right? You have to come. It'll take your mind off all this other crap."

Gavin relaxed into a smile. "Yeah, we'll be there, mate. Give me directions."

65

SOPHIE

As Sophie receded farther into the corner of the room, she watched all the beautiful people around her with detachment. It had taken Gavin a half-hour to convince her to go to Jackson's party with him, as she hadn't been remotely interested in a splashy social event after the altercation with the photographer. She had finally relented when Gavin explained that he desperately needed to have some pure and simple fun and that he was sure this party would be the perfect solution. And so they made their way up above Sunset Boulevard to Hillside Avenue, where Jackson's stunning mid-century modern home perched over greater Los Angeles.

And as soon as they arrived and were greeted by Jackson, Gavin's mood did lighten noticeably. He fell into his naturally sociable self and was quickly surrounded by a group of new friends. Watching him reminded her of the way he'd held court in the hallways of school. He was naturally charismatic, yet he never fully understood how engaging he was, how much people revered him. He always greeted the worshipful fans at their shows and the people who showed up at their house to get a glimpse of him with such openness, never putting himself on a different level. And Sophie knew that attitude made him all that more special of a person.

Jackson broke up the gathering to whisper into Gavin's ear. Gavin responded with a nod and excused himself, walking across the length of the open room toward the kitchen. Jackson then approached Sophie before she could see what Gavin was up to.

"What's the most beautiful girl in the room doing sitting so quietly?" he shouted to her over the thumping bass of the latest dance song being spun by the DJ.

Ignoring his typical flirting, she told him, "Great party."

"You're lying. For that, you owe me a dance," he insisted, and pulled her by the hand so she stood with him.

She laughed and allowed him to lead her to an open space outside on the patio. He pressed his body to hers, touching her with unnecessary intimacy before segueing into an uncoordinated freestyle excuse for a dance.

What he lacked in skill he made up for in enthusiasm, and she found herself laughing and having fun. After the song, he offered to get her a drink. The outdoor bar was out of the sparkling water she craved, though.

"Come with me to my enormous kitchen, love, and I'll get you a drink," he shouted to her as the pulsating music continued.

He led her by the hand and the crowds seemed to part reverentially for them. As they entered the large and airy kitchen, she saw Gavin sitting at the marble island bar. There were several other men with him, one of whom casually cleared something from the countertop before she could register what they were doing.

"So, my dear?" Jackson asked. "Don't you want something . . . *harder* than fizzy water?"

She laughed. "I'll take some red wine along with the water if you have it."

Gavin grabbed her hand and pulled her to him so that she stood between his legs.

"Where have you been, darlin'? It feels like it's been ages, you know?" He spoke rapidly, his words almost running together as he failed to take a breath. "God, I missed you. Don't leave me. You won't leave me again, will you?"

There was laughter from the group at Gavin's quick cadence, but it didn't seem funny to Sophie. She cupped his face in her hands and looked into his eyes, even as they darted around the room. His pupils weren't right. They had the same look she had seen in the eyes of certain models and other industry people.

"What have you been doing, baby?" she asked, her heart racing because she already knew the answer.

"Nothing. Nothing at all. Don't you worry. I got it all under control and I feel good for the first time in a long time," he replied.

She hesitated, wanting to believe him. But then he rubbed hard at his nose and she knew with complete certainty that everything wasn't "under control."

"Gavin, no," she said, and shook her head. "Don't do that. It'll only make things worse."

"No, Sophie. The only thing making it worse is me doing nothing but thinking about it. I've been paralyzed by all this shite. I need a fucking release from it or I swear to God I'll go mad," he said, speaking rapidly. "I need an escape. I know it's only temporary, I know that. But I feel so much fucking better right now, darlin'. I can't begin to describe how good I feel now. Can't you allow me that? Don't you want me to feel good?"

"That's not fair," she said quietly, aware they had an audience. "You can't ask me to say this is okay."

"Sophie," Jackson interrupted, "it really is pretty harmless. Don't panic about it."

She glared at him, now suspecting that he had danced with her as a distraction so that Gavin could get high on cocaine. Then she saw the large glass of wine he had set before her and she picked it up, taking several gulps to down it. She was furious and hurt and wanted to mirror Gavin's recklessness in the only way she could. With an empty stomach, the alcohol went almost immediately to her head and she regretted her childish act of defiance.

"So? We okay?" Gavin asked, oblivious.

"Just tell me it's a one-time thing. Okay?"

"Yeah, sure. Of course it is." He took her hand and kissed it.

She looked at the two guys who had gotten him high. "You better take care of him," she said as forcefully as she could, before turning on her heel and rushing to the nearest bathroom where the red wine came up.

As she sat on the cold tile floor of that small guest bathroom, she was shocked to think of what had happened. Gavin had experimented with cocaine—and other drugs—before, but it was obvious that he was playing with it in an entirely new way. She knew with a sinking certainty that him trying it now, amidst his depression and desperation, was exactly the wrong thing to do. But she had just given him permission.

66

SOPHIE

Though they didn't talk about that night for the rest of their weeklong stay in Los Angeles, Gavin's experimentation with cocaine gnawed at Sophie. She silently worried what it meant for his mental and emotional state that he would give in to something so dangerous as a means of "temporary" escape.

He seemed to be going through the motions, putting on a false bravado for her. He told her he was ready to shake off all this nonsense about his mother and that the constant harassment by the tabloids was of no matter to him any longer. But there was a clear disconnect between his words and what she knew to be true. He wasn't someone who would cast aside the devastation he felt so easily. For him to try to convince *her*, of all people, that he could do such a thing was unsettling. He had never faked his thoughts and emotions with her before, and it left her with the sickening feeling of waiting for the other shoe to drop.

At home in Dublin, Gavin read aloud some of the email messages from James he had ignored, including the news that the recent controversy had "paid off" with a spike in Rogue's album sales to the tune of 1.4 million copies. It seemed that buyers were taking Ian's advice to examine Gavin's lyrics in a whole new way now that the "truth" about their mother was out. Listeners had taken to dissecting the lyrics to categorize which songs were about Sophie and which were about his mother, determining the former correlated to references to "darling" and the latter was generally when an unnamed woman was the subject. Sophie knew this would only bolster the repeated accusations from Gavin's detractors that he was an emotional narcissist. They would gleefully seize the opportunity to claim Gavin had milked his angst for the precise purpose of generating material, and accuse him of calculating it all from the start to manipulate people's sympathies and therefore increase record sales. This was so far removed from the truth that it made Sophie sick to think Gavin would have to deal with this on top of everything else.

James also emailed to say that the band's record label had redoubled its efforts for them to produce their fifth album while they were "hot."

Sophie watched Gavin respond to that one with a mild smile and shake of his head. Again, his reactions were muted and unlike him.

He pulled a beer from the refrigerator and poured it into a glass before casually saying, "Probably is a good idea, as far as the marketing angle goes, isn't it?"

That response let her speechless and he took the opportunity to read the next email. It relayed the news that the offensive photographer from outside their hotel was indeed filing a civil suit against Gavin for damages in the amount of one million dollars, an absurd amount that was likely just a starting point.

"I'll call Jamie later and see if we can't negotiate our way out of this," Gavin said.

"You're . . . backing down?" Sophie asked, shocked. Though she knew he was in the wrong for going after the paparazzo, she never would have thought he'd admit as much, let alone agree to pay the man off.

"It's not worth the trouble. I shouldn't have gone off like that, but I did. I suppose I have to pay for it. And if we do it quickly, there will be one less story, right?"

"I guess so," she replied, still hesitant.

"Now, listen, darlin'," he said and took another gulp from his glass of Guinness. "Your babysitting days are done. You can go back to work now. Really, there's no need to worry about me."

"I know you've been doing better, baby, but I think I'd like to spend some more time with you."

"Really, Sophie," he said and looked into her eyes for a long moment. "I'm okay. And, truth be told, being on my own for a bit here and there is probably the best thing."

"Oh," she said quietly.

"Once you're back on schedule with all your jobs, maybe I'll come with you to a few of your shoots. How about that?"

She recognized his attempt to soften what he'd said, and it felt to her as forced as he had sounded.

"Okay," she finally said. "Whatever you want."

"Great. It's settled." He nodded and left here to go upstairs.

Though leaving Gavin to his own resources terrified her, she was partly relieved at the prospect of being away from him. The weight of his sadness had been so massive, it was more than he could bear on his own. She wanted to take it on for him, but it was clear that nothing could diminish his load. She would allow him his space and try to reclaim her career, and in doing so, maybe even a piece of herself.

67

When Sophie returned home from a day trip to Paris to where she had met with Henri to go over new bookings, it was early evening and the house was dark. Something told her she shouldn't be surprised that Gavin wasn't eagerly awaiting her arrival. He hadn't left a note or text to say where he'd be, and she ended up having to leave a voicemail when she called his cell.

When he called back nearly two hours later, she thought about letting him have to leave a message right back. But her need to know what he was doing and with whom was stronger than her desire for petty retribution.

He spoke in a rush, everything coming out in one breath. "Darlin', it's me. Are you home? I thought you were staying the night in Paris. Weren't you supposed to stay the night in Paris? Didn't you say something about the Four Seasons?" he asked quickly, his voice rising above the background din.

"Gavin," she said, and closed her eyes tightly in dismay. "Where are you?"

"I'm with some friends. We're hanging out and having a good time. You should come meet us. Do you want to come meet us? We'll have a great time. I can give you directions—let me just figure out where the hell I am." He laughed, clearly amusing himself.

"I don't want to meet you, not if you're doing what I think you are."

281

"What—having a good time? No, you wouldn't want any part of that, would you?" he snapped.

"What does that mean?" she asked, taken aback.

"I don't understand why you have to jump down my throat, Sophie. Why do you have to give me hassle when I'm finally having a good time?"

"Is that what I'm doing?"

"Aren't you?"

"I don't mean to," she said, despite herself. She was in the right to be short with him. It was obvious he was playing with cocaine again and she knew no other way to react than to be upset about it. But he had a way of turning things, making her feel she was being unduly harsh, especially if all he was getting out of his experimentation was a good time.

"So don't, darlin'. Just don't."

"Okay. Tell me where you are, baby. I want to be with you."

THE NEIGHBORHOOD WAS in a seedy area on the Northside of Dublin, and as Sophie locked her brand new E350 Mercedes she said a silent prayer it would remain unscathed. The street was lined with what looked to be abandoned warehouses and it was clear where the party was as only one of them had any kind of lighting. Making her way toward it, the throbbing beat of house music grew louder.

There was a line of three dozen people waiting to get in, and they grumbled when she went directly to the door and smiled at the large man blocking the entrance.

"Good evening to you, Mrs. McManus," the doorman said, ushering her inside.

She followed the instructions Gavin had given her on the phone and wound her way to the back. The club was packed full of twenty-something-aged kids, all grinding mindlessly to the DJ's mix.

The makeshift VIP section consisted of several tables pushed together in front of an abbreviated bar. Gavin was lounging there with a group of men and women, none of whom Sophie recognized. But they all greeted her familiarly and with great fondness.

Gavin made introductions hastily before pulling her onto his lap.

"Do you all want another round?" Gavin asked.

"Brilliant suggestion," a man named Jacob said with a pronounced Scottish accent. He was rail-thin, pale, and had shoulder-length dreadlocks. Sophie assumed he held some sort of leadership position within the group as he was the keeper of the bag of cocaine, pulling it out from his inside jacket pocket.

Sophie whispered to Gavin, "This is making me really uncomfortable."

"Sit next to me here, then," he said, deliberately misinterpreting her.

She slid off his lap and watched as Jacob carefully, almost lovingly, tapped out a good portion of the white powder. The excitement this rendered among those at their table was horrifying. Watching Gavin participate in this made her stomach queasy. They took turns snorting lines until everyone had had their share, whereupon they all stared at Sophie.

"Go on," Gavin said. "It's good stuff. Better than in Los Angeles even."

"No, thanks," she said, shaking her head.

Gavin wiped up a few grains of the coke with his index finger and then rubbed it into his gums greedily. "There's nothing to be afraid of, Sophie," he said.

"Yeah, just have one go," a woman with long jet-black hair told her.

"No fun being the only one sober," another man chimed in with a grin.

These people seemed, in appearance, normal enough. But their complete absorption in cocaine was obvious. Though she was inexperienced with this, Sophie knew enough to understand that they weren't casual partiers. There was something desperate about their urging and she realized that Gavin couldn't have found a worse group of new friends. She saw quite clearly that the only reason to befriend addicts was to become one of them.

"Here, love," Jacob said, "I'll set up a line just for you. Just a wee one is all it is."

Sophie looked at the thin line of cocaine that was now in front of her and tried to ignore the voices urging her on. The pressure to join in was palpable, though she was cognizant that Gavin was not saying anything else. It occurred to her how easy it would be to choose the route of escape, to forget, however temporarily, all her obligations and real-world ties. But it was only attractive for a split second because she knew it was a hollow choice—the real world was always waiting. And there wasn't anything so awful about it, anyway.

"No, thanks," she said again, and smiled when they claimed disappointment but then rejoiced in the extra that gave them.

Gavin kissed her cheek and gave her a quick squeeze. "You're an angel. A pure, sweet angel."

She had other words to describe herself: idiot, weak, pathetic. Co-dependent was probably the perfect description. But she preferred to tell herself she was just being a good wife, one who would do anything she could to help her husband—even if that meant enabling him in what must surely be some temporary self-destructive acts.

68

G avin did a good job of keeping his cocaine use to a minimum at first. He only used when he was out with his new friends a couple times a week. But then his occasional nights out became more frequent. He would leave the house by nine o'clock in the evening and return at seven the next morning, take a sleeping pill to come down from the high, and wake up at four in the afternoon.

As this behavior wore on, Gavin watched Sophie became resigned to their lack of time and intimacy together. When he wasn't high, he was irritable. It was difficult to have a meaningful discussion because he was so scattered.

He saw all this as clearly as she did, and yet he quickly dismissed her attempts to get him to stop or cut back. He ignored or mocked her suggestions that he talk to her, or even to a psychologist, about the depression he was suffering from, and the way he was using cocaine to medicate it. When she brought up the idea of being proactive, of finally tracking down his mother to get some kind of closure, he responded with cold resentment. His stance was that his mother had clearly chosen not to come forward after the article outed her and that her inaction could only be seen as confirmation of her rejection of him. He wouldn't be the one to chase after her. He was certain that his actions were not doing any harm, even as she argued that he was in denial.

And so, he did a poor job of hiding his relief when she let him know her itinerary for her extensive time away for work. Her first stop would be Los Angeles, where she was doing yet another *Vogue* cover. Then she would walk at New York Fashion Week, followed by designer Jeffrey Kalinsky's annual fundraiser. Added to that schedule was an assignment for the covers of *Elle* and W magazines that had been promised and scrapped when she unexpectedly took time off. Then came back-to-back fashion weeks in London, Milan, and Paris. Gavin had agreed to meet her in Paris, where he would watch some of her runway shows, and then they would stay a few more days for a mini-vacation. Their agreement to keep separations to no longer than three weeks went unmentioned by either of them.

Gavin took her to the airport for her flight to Los Angeles, as by now the constant press attention had waned. He was moving with more ease in his own city again, and that, coupled with the invulnerability cocaine gave him, made all the difference.

"Promise me I won't have to worry about you," Sophie said as he slowed the car at the departing flights curb.

"You don't need to worry, darlin'. I'm—"

His cell phone chimed with an incoming text. It was mounted to the dashboard, and a message from Julia O'Flaherty appeared. Julia had been a sporadic presence in his life over the years, but had become a near constant lately, having found her way into his group of cocaine buddies. He knew Sophie had always suspected Julia of trying to latch on to Rogue's success. There was probably some truth to that, as although he and Julia had produced a hit duet single for charity a few years back, she had never made it beyond indie status.

"Her again," Sophie muttered.

He quickly cleared the screen. "Never mind that. Listen, I'm going to see you in about a month in Paris, right? You still want me to come meet you?"

"Yes, of course I do, baby." She paused, clearly struggling with what she was going to say next. "Maybe you can try over these next few weeks to stop, you know?"

He dropped his eyes from hers and her shoulders sagged with disappointment. The pressure of being what she needed was more than he could bear lately. He knew she wanted him to bounce back from the public humiliation of his mother's abandonment and her subsequent crushing silence. He was expected to ignore the media attention that had lambasted him for "deceptive" lyrics, followed by fans rushing to support him with pity for what he had been through as a child. Their album sales had soared as a result, all while he had crashed. Cocaine was the only way he could force an imitation of his old self.

"Gavin?"

He met her eyes again. "Yeah, Sophie?"

"You don't need it. You're better than that. Please, please don't get caught up in that stuff."

The earnestness in her voice made him smile, then laugh. "Relax, pretty girl. I'm doing okay." He leaned toward her and held her face in his hands as he kissed her. "Now, you have a good flight and give ring me when you get in."

She nodded and took a deep breath. "I love you so much, baby. Know that."

"I do," he said, too quickly.

Resigned, she nodded again and opened the car door.

"Sophie," he said, stopping her, and she looked at him. "Just give me some time. I'll be okay."

"Of course you will," she replied, before giving him one last kiss.

69

SOPHIE

Sophie's travels started in Los Angeles, where she used the time before and after her Vogue shoot to meet with an interior designer to decide the style for the Venice Beach house, as well as visit with her parents. Steve and Maggie had tiptoed around the news of Gavin's mother since it had been revealed, clearly not wanting to impose, and other than general inquiries, seemed eager to believe that Sophie had everything handled. She didn't disabuse them of this notion, since she didn't want to share the details of Gavin's downward spiral with them. They never had the kind of relationship where she confided in them when things were bad. Why would she reach out to them when she knew their answer would be that she had to be strong and figure things out for herself?

The trip to New York was longer and included an offer by Colette to stay with her. The two women got a chance to play roommates and catch up in between work. As they relaxed with a glass a wine and a warm late-afternoon breeze found its way through half-opened windows, Sophie learned that while Colette and Conor were still together, they were currently having a bit of a spat regarding the fact that he was in Canada visiting an old school friend.

"What's wrong with that?" Sophie asked before taking another sip of her Chardonnay.

"The friend is a woman who just happens to have gotten divorced."

"No, not Felicity!"

"That's her name. And he hasn't told me much, but I think he still has feelings for her," Colette said.

Sophie took a moment to get over the shock and sadness of learning that her old friend's marriage had fallen apart. And it made her feel even more vulnerable in her own relationship.

"What makes you say that?"

"Because," Colette said excitedly, "I was thinking this whole time that you were the married woman he was once in love with. But now, it seems it was this Felicity all the while!"

"Wait a minute," Sophie said, nearly choking on her wine. "What are you talking about? Why on earth would you think Conor was ever in love with me?"

"Because he told me that the only woman he was ever in love with was someone who was unavailable to him. I guess he didn't even mean to say that much, since he'd never go into it again."

"But why would you think it was me? That seems like a really odd thing to assume."

"No, no, not really, Sophie. Don't you ever notice the way he looks at you? The way he . . . brightens up when you're around?" Colette got lost in thought, her face twisted in discomfort.

"That's not true," Sophie said, unwilling to acknowledge possibility. Lust, she could see. But, love? It was too much to even entertain. "I think you're worrying too much. And anyway, what did he tell you about Felicity? Because you have to remember that I was with them during one year of school."

That excited Colette again. "That's right! He said they were never boyfriend and girlfriend. He said they were just really good friends and that he wanted to go cheer her up now that she's having a hard time. What do you think?"

"He's telling you the truth, Colette. And he's being a good friend by going to see her now. That's all. I'm sure of it."

"Really?"

"Yes. God, you're all he can talk about anyway," Sophie said with a laugh.

"Good. Because I think I really love him, Sophie."

Sophie nodded and did her best to smile at the declaration. But at the same time, she felt an uneasiness she didn't want to examine.

A FEW DAYS LATER, Sophie had the house to herself for the remainder of her stay. Colette had been unable to keep from bickering with Conor when he called from Felicity's, and in a fit of immaturity, she flew to London early to meet up with friends.

Sophie was thinking of her own sporadic and unsatisfactory calls to Gavin when there was a knock on the door. As she padded barefoot to answer it, she tried unsuccessfully to ignore her certainty that Gavin was well beyond the mere partying stage when it came to cocaine use.

Opening the door, she was surprised to see Conor. And he was just as surprised to see her.

"Well, isn't this something," he said with a grin.

"Hey, Connie," Sophie replied, feeling unexpectedly happy to see his handsome face.

He stepped inside and dropped his bag familiarly in the corner. Looking beyond her, he seemed to take in the unusual quiet as he shook his head with a rueful smile.

"She's not here," Sophie said. "She flew out earlier today to London. She didn't tell you?"

"My girl, she has a flair for the dramatic."

"That's putting it kindly," she replied.

"And you're staying here for a while?"

"Just a couple more days. Then I'm off to London too."

"Well, hope you don't mind if I crash here, 'cause I'm not getting on another plane right away."

"Of course not. No, you should stay. Hey, we'll make a night out of it," she said, suddenly excited.

"What have you in mind?" he asked as he moved toward the kitchen to help himself to a beer.

"Be my date tonight at the Jeffrey Fashion Cares event?"

"What?"

"I have to make an appearance. But after that, you and I can go find our own fun. I heard there's a great new burlesque club—very sexy in a retro way. I've been wanting to check it out."

"How many ways are you trying to get me into trouble with Colette?" he asked with a laugh.

"What do you mean?" she asked.

"Well, first, she's not going to like me being your date. Second, she's really not going to like me going to check out mostly naked girls. And third . . . ."

"Third?"

"And third is, fuck it," he said, resolved. "It sounds like a great time, Sophie. You and me and no fucking drama. Yeah, let's do it."

She smiled because she was having fun for the first time in a long time.

SOPHIE GAVE Conor a ticket and instructed him to meet her at Manhattan's Intrepid Sea, Air & Space Museum for the Jeffrey Kalinsky fundraising event in support of LGBT causes. She then dressed to stun in a formfitting Dolce & Gabbana dress and went to her favorite New York salon to get her hair and makeup done. With sexy, just-rolled-out-of-bed hair and dark green smoky eye makeup, she was impossible to ignore.

When she met up with Conor the event, he looked at her with such naked desire that she felt a tingling in her core. And when chose to ignore Colette's calls, she knew he was going to have hell to pay later.

They stayed only as long as they had to, careful to mingle with others before stealing away together. They had a great time at the burlesque show. It was a performance by good-looking young women who were just as aware of their luscious bodies as they were of how to tempt men without any vulgarities. At one point, two of the dancers focused on their table, preying on Conor.

Sophie watched with amusement as he unabashedly enjoyed it when the women sat on his lap or playfully waved their breasts in his face. He then watched with pure joy as the women turned their attention to Sophie and treated her to the same bit of teasing.

When the show let out after midnight, they were still both wired. As they headed out to the street, they talked about going to a bar for another drink. But when a photographer unexpectedly blinded them with repeated camera flashes, they instinctively covered their faces.

Conor grabbed Sophie's hand and pulled her along at a sprint.

Luckily the lone paparazzo was not nearly in the shape they were and they soon left him behind. But being "caught" was a buzzkill to their good time, and they decided to go back to Colette's brownstone.

70

SOPHIE

Sophie pulled on a pair of thin sweatpants and a well-worn men's v-neck tee shirt before joining Conor in the living room. The fire he had built was the only light in the room, making for a romantic feel.

"Now that's a look," Conor said as he came from the kitchen with a bottle of champagne and two flutes. "No, really. I think that makeup looks perfect with that outfit. What were you doing with the whole designer dress thing?"

She laughed. "I should take it off but I suddenly feel completely lazy."

"Well then, have a seat before you drop."

There were large pillows near the fireplace for the exact purpose of cuddling up in front of it. She arranged a few and relaxed before the warmth of the glowing fire.

Conor set down the champagne and glasses and then joined her. He had taken off his shoes and socks but remained dressed in jeans and a crisp white button down shirt.

"What's with the champagne?" she asked as she accepted a full glass.

"That's all the alcohol there was. Sounded good, anyway."

"Yeah. Tastes good." She put her half-empty glass down and settled deeper into the pillows.

They were silent for a long moment, both staring into the fire.

"So, tell me about Felicity. Is she okay?"

"You know Felicity, she's a tough one. I think the hardest thing for her is that she honest-to-God thought it was going to be forever."

Sophie watched his profile. "I bet she was glad to see you."

"Well, I took her mind off things for a short time. Wasn't fucking easy with Colette calling at all hours, though."

"She thinks you were in love with Felicity once upon a time."

"I don't know where she gets her notions." He downed his champagne and settled into the pillows beside her.

"You told her you had only been in love once, with someone you couldn't have."

"What does it matter? Why should that matter to the person you're with now?"

She turned on her side and faced him. "I guess it only matters if the person you're with now thinks some part of your heart is still with someone else."

Now he turned on his side to face her too. After a moment of silence, he held up a finger to tell her to give him a minute. He then got up and disappeared briefly. When he returned, he had a dampened washcloth and a small bowl of warm soapy water.

"Sit up with me," he said softly.

She looked at him curiously but did as he said. And when he reached out and brushed her hair away from her face with his fingertips, his touch sent a thrill of expectation through her body.

In the next few minutes, he gently removed the makeup from her eyes and face, careful not to rub too hard or let water drip.

"There. Now I can have a proper conversation with you," he said with a small smile.

"I can't believe you did that," she said softly. The tenderness he had shown was something she hadn't seen from her own husband in too many weeks.

"Nothing to it." He patted the pillows and they resumed the position of lying on their sides and facing each other again.

"Conor," she said.

"Sophie," he returned, with mock seriousness that made her smile.

Undeterred, she said, "Tell me who you were in love with. Who would turn you away?"

"If I'm not telling Colette, I'm certainly not telling you."

"I guess that's fair," she said and suppressed a yawn.

He reached out and stroked her hair, letting his fingers fall all the way through the long silken strands.

"That feels good," she said sleepily as she closed her eyes.

"You," he said quietly. "You know it's you."

She opened her eyes with a start. "What did you say?"

"I was in love with you for a very long time, Sophie. You know that. You have to have known that."

The intensity of his deep blue eyes never wavered as he watched her response. For so long she had convinced herself that all he had felt for her was a basic sexual attraction. To think that it was anything more would have generated too many questions.

"No, I didn't . . . ." She trailed off.

"No?"

"I don't know what to say."

"Yeah," he agreed, and took his hand away from her hair. He closed his eyes.

She waited for more, waited for him to open his eyes and explain himself. But he didn't, and his breathing began to grow steady. What struck her most were the times he could have tried to seduce her, the times when she was vulnerable after a fight with Gavin and he had been there and let her cry on his shoulder. But he hadn't made a move since that kiss on the beach in Australia. That was almost ten years ago. He had always looked after her, let it be known that he cared for her. Now she moved closer to him, wanting to be as tender and sweet to him as he had been to her for so long.

He stirred then and wrapped his arm around her waist, folding her to him so that her face lay perfectly in between his neck and shoulder.

"Conor," she said in a whisper, "did I do something to lead you on?"

"You didn't have to, honey. All you had to do was be yourself," he replied easily.

She hesitated, struggling for the right words. "Did I hurt you?"

He resumed playing with her hair. "All the time. You broke my heart a million times, Sophie. But you made it whole a million times more."

"I'm sorry," she whispered. "You didn't deserve that."

He was quiet so long she wondered if he had fallen asleep, but his slowly moving hand in her hair told her he was still awake.

"No, I've gotten what I deserved. I'm not sorry."

"What does that mean?"

"Shh," he said, before kissing her gently on the lips.

She found herself returning his brief kiss, and when he pulled away and finally looked into her eyes again, she saw what he had been trying to hide. His eyes revealed pure adoration for her. She was the one to lean in and kiss him next.

The kiss was tentative and gentle on both their parts. It wasn't born out of passion, but of genuine love. But they both knew that if they went any farther the sentiment would quickly change and lust would overtake them.

Conor was the first to pull away. He got to his feet and held out his hand to her. "Time for sleep," he said.

She took his hand and stood with him. "Do you want to sleep with me? Just sleep? Or is that a really bad—"

"No, it sounds lovely," he said with a nod.

They held hands as they went to the guest bedroom she was using. Without turning on the lights, she pulled back the duvet and slid into bed. Conor didn't bother to take off his shirt or jeans as he followed her into bed, and they held each other in the same effortlessly comfortable manner as they had in front of the fireplace.

Lying there with his arms around her, Sophie felt safe and cared for. There was no denying that she was drawn to him, to his steadiness in contrast to Gavin's unpredictability. And to his genuine friendship. After all these years, she was also just as attracted to him as he seemed to be to her. Her mind raced until the steady rise and fall of his chest lulled her to sleep.

Sophie felt only warmth and comfort and security that night. And when she woke to find Conor beside her, she was happy.

He lay on his back, one arm thrown over his head and his shirt mostly unbuttoned. His breath was even as he slept.

She let her eyes fall over his bared skin, aware that her attraction for him was threatening to overwhelm her better judgment. She had always scoffed at the notion that a person could be in love with two people at once, but last night had made her re-think that. It made her think that in another world, she could have happily been with Conor.

He stirred then, turning on his side toward her. Opening his eyes, he smiled, and then closed them again. Wrapping his arm around her waist, he brought her close to him once more.

Being in his arms felt so nice that she snuggled into him, slipping her leg in between his to get closer. The position got her intimately acquainted with the hard bulge in his jeans.

She knew they were done sleeping. His fingers skimmed under her T-shirt, stroking the sensitive skin at her lower back. In return, she ran her hand over his tight abs, tracing the definition with her fingertips.

When he pressed his lips to the side of her neck, lingering in each small kiss as he moved up to her jawline, it was as if he wanted to take his time tasting her. He next teased his mouth around the corners of hers, never quite meeting her full on so that she was the one to lean in to him, anxious for the pressure of his lips.

The moment he finally took her mouth with his was unlike any other time they'd kissed. It certainly didn't have the sweetness and surprise of that time on the beach years ago. And it wasn't brief and tender like last night. No, this time, it was like a lifetime's restraint had been released. His lips were commanding, coaxing her into the most delicious surrender as he guided her onto her back and raised himself over her. That was all before he eased her mouth open with his tongue. He kissed her deeply, confidently, until she couldn't stop herself from pushing her hips against his, wanting so much more from him.

But he didn't take this cue. Instead, he pulled away and moved down the length of her body to her waist. She pushed her hands through his hair as he lifted her T-shirt. The feel of his mouth on her skin sent waves of desire through her body, making her ache for him to reach her breasts. When he did, he first caressed and kissed the whole of her breasts before flicking his tongue against her hard nipples. She moaned as he teasingly alternated between sucking and biting.

Pulling away, he quickly removed his shirt and she looked at through a haze of lust. His broad shoulders and well-developed but compact muscles were taut and his skin smelled good, and god he was sexy. There was a small smile playing at his mouth, a confirmation that he could see just how much she wanted him.

The way he moved his hands reverentially over her belly and up to her breasts again as he leaned down to kiss her only made her crave him all the more.

"I've never wanted someone so much in my life," he murmured between kisses.

She melted into him, losing all self-control under his sensual touch. But when he reached inside her sweatpants and placed his hand over her panties and between her legs, it all got too real. She was desperate to keep going, to have all of him. That desire, however, suddenly seemed as reckless and dangerous as Gavin's forays with cocaine.

"Conor, no. I'm sorry, no," she stammered as she pushed him away abruptly. She pulled her shirt into place and moved to the side of the bed.

"Sophie, don't do this to me," he said, half moaning.

She put her hands over her face and closed her eyes tightly, working to breathe evenly. At length, she looked at him and said in a voice just above a whisper, "We can't do this."

He moved to the foot of the bed and sat up, his back to her. "You wanted this a minute ago. I didn't imagine that."

"It's not about that. It's about Gavin and Colette and Rogue."

He nodded. Taking a deep breath, he looked around the room as if seeing it for the first time. Then he turned to her and asked, "Do you feel for me, Sophie? At all?"

She watched his anxious expression for a moment, trying to come up with an answer she could live with.

"I do. As much as I can feel for my husband's best friend," she said.

"Well that's a very well-crafted response," he muttered.

"Connie, I can't do this. It's too much." Her voice was shaky as tears came to her eyes.

He moved to her and wiped away her tears. "Don't cry, honey. It's okay." He kissed her cheeks, her closed eyes, her lips. "Listen, last night with you was the best I've ever spent with a woman. You don't have to say anything. None of this is perfect, but it's enough. Okay?"

Though she didn't quite understand what he meant, she nodded into his shoulder and let him continue to comfort her. It wasn't fair to him but she didn't know what else to do.

IT WAS, of course, awkward after that.

Conor offered her the shower, but she insisted he go first. After she had cleaned up, they went to breakfast, walking to a local café with several feet between them. They found a hundred things to talk about that didn't involve how they felt about each other or what they had almost done in bed together.

And as much as she trusted him, she still couldn't bring herself to tell him what she feared about Gavin and his drug use. For a reason she couldn't quite explain to herself, to do so seemed like the ultimate betrayal, worse even than nearly having sex with Conor.

"So I suppose I'll fly home today. Get back to Dublin and check in with the boys. Haven't seen any of 'em in a long while now," Conor told her as they waited for the check.

"The record company is still hounding James for you all to get in the studio," she said.

"Good luck with that. We're nowhere close to being studio ready. But it is time to get working. I think that's exactly what I need."

She nodded. "What do you suppose we should say about the photographs that came out from last night?" TMZ had already splashed photos of them all over the internet.

"The truth—that we found ourselves here and since we're friends we took advantage. Well, not took advantage. You know what I mean," he said with a laugh.

"What will Colette's reaction be?"

He shook his head with a small smile. "She'll break up with me."

"Do you want me to talk to her?"

He laughed again. "And say what? That I've never slept better than when I had *you* in my arms? That I came *this* close to being with the woman I've loved for more years than I care to admit?"

She had to look away from him, his confessions too bittersweet.

"No, she'll break up with me in her typically dramatic fashion. And I'll let her."

"Why, though? I know you have feelings for her. Wouldn't it help to . . . concentrate on her?"

"Is that what you'll do with Gavin? No, don't answer. Thing with Colette is that, despite all her games, she's loads of fun. I could see being serious with her."

That declaration made her sad, an emotion she knew she had no right to feel.

"She and I are very compatible—in and out of bed," he continued.

She recognized the game he was playing. He hadn't toyed with her in a long time, but that's what he was doing. She didn't blame him for being angry about how she'd led him on. But she also didn't want him to think he was succeeding at making her jealous.

"So why let her go?" she asked.

"I need to get my head together. Then we'll see. I mean, I'd be completely stupid to really let her go. But I need to be in a place where I can give her everything she deserves."

Sophie nodded. "You're right."

The confidence with which she said this left him with no response, effectively shutting down his game.

71

SOPHIE

The tabloid stories of Sophie and Conor's night out together featured photos of them running hand in hand down the street with big smiles, along with the provocative suggestion that the two had been up to no good. When Sophie finally got a hold of Gavin a day after the "news" broke, he hadn't exactly laughed it off, but he hadn't seemed very interested in it either.

"So, how have you been?" she asked him.

"Good. Doing fine. It's all been a blur, really. You'll have to call me when you get to Paris and remind me to come at the rate I'm going," he replied.

"That doesn't sound like you're missing me much," she said. He was so much more distant than the mere physical miles between them.

"Yeah, you know I do, Sophie. I've just been enjoying hanging out with Jacob and the gang. They're a good bunch of people."

"So, I guess that means you're doing that."

"Isn't it amazing you can nag me from thousands of miles away? Grand indeed of you to call."

"Gavin, don't do that."

"I haven't talked to you in going on four days now, you're running around with Conor at strip shows, and you're calling me on shite? I don't think so, darlin'."

Guilt washed over her. Not guilt over Conor, but guilt for having turned Gavin's mood sour. She didn't want to upset the delicate balance he had been walking.

"Baby, I miss you. Do you want to come see me in Paris earlier than we planned?" she asked.

"Oh, I can't. Jacob's opening his club in Temple Bar. I've got to be there, said I would, you know. I guess it helps with the publicity angle for him. So I don't think I can, darlin'. Just call me from Paris. Okay?" he asked, sounding in a hurry to end the call.

"Call you from Paris? Gavin, that's almost two weeks from now."

"Oh. Em, well, we'll talk at some point, yeah?"

Her chest ached at his disinterest. It felt like she wasn't just losing him. He was already gone.

"I love you," she said softly.

But he had spoken at the same time, saying, "Got to go. Take care."

Before she could reply, he'd ended the call.

THE RUNWAY SHOWS in London and Milan were a success, even though Sophie did her job in a daze. She missed her husband and she missed her home. And she found herself wishing she could step back to the time when she and Gavin had an unbreakable connection.

The connection they had now was mostly through their cell phone voicemail. He rarely answered her calls or texts and when he did, he invariably sounded irritated, as if she were interrupting.

But he had promised to join her this afternoon for the last two days of Paris shows. They would then stay in the city a few more days. The prospect of dedicated time together filled her with unwarranted optimism as she walked into the lobby of the Four Seasons Hotel George V. This was the hotel she always stayed in, and its marble floors and columns and grand crystal chandeliers were elegant and reassuring. Her eye was drawn almost immediately to Conor sitting in one of the plush gold and cream brocade chairs of the formal lobby. Even if she hadn't known it was him, he was the kind of strikingly handsome man who turned heads. Though she was surprised to see him there, she was even more surprised that he did not greet her with his usual bright smile and kiss as he stood.

"Hi, Conor," she said. "What's going on?"

"I'm so fucking upset with you, Sophie," he replied, his voice low but tight with anger.

She took a step backward and looked around. The lobby was half-filled with others she could call upon if needed. She hadn't in all these years experienced Conor's anger.

He grabbed her arm before she could move farther away. "I'm going out of my mind trying to understand why you didn't tell me Gavin's a fucking coke addict."

"Let me go," she said, struggling with his tight grip.

"No, you're going to stay right here and tell me what's happening with my best mate. See, I went home to Dublin, got the runaround from him, and then when I did see him, he's high as a fucking kite and offering to get me the same. And from what I've heard, this has been going on for months."

"I'm not going to tell you again to let me go," she said, her voice raised enough to be noticed by others.

He became aware of what he had been doing and quickly released her. "Don't you get it, Sophie? Don't you understand how bad this is?"

Her eyes filled with tears.

"And you're fucking facilitating him? He said you were fine with it. How could you be so goddamned stupid?"

"I didn't know what to do. I wanted so much to believe it wouldn't control him. He keeps saying it's harmless," she said quickly. "And I've been reading that William Styron book you gave me. You know, the one that talks about 'incomplete mourning' and how when someone isn't able to have the catharsis of grief, he's bound to suffer from rage and guilt, which could lead to self-destructive acts. And so maybe Gavin's just acting out and—"

"Stop this enabling shit right now."

"But you know he needs to mourn—"

"He can't mourn someone who isn't fucking dead. Goddamn it, what are you doing trying to justify this for him?"

She looked down and the tears that had been brimming in her eyes spilled down her cheeks. "I'm not trying to justify it for him. I'm trying to justify it to myself," she said, and covered her face with her hands.

"Oh, honey." He pulled her into his arms and rocked her slowly, his anger seeming to dissipate as she fell apart.

"I just want to believe he'll find his way out of this," she mumbled into his neck.

"Shh, now."

As he held her, she slowly regained a sense of calm. She took a deep breath and looked over his shoulder. What she saw made her pull abruptly away from him.

Gavin stood fifteen feet away, watching them. His expression was hard to read. It wasn't anger or jealousy. It was closer to curiosity, as if he couldn't comprehend the sight of his wife in his best friend's embrace.

"Gavin," she said, and Conor turned to see what she had.

She quickly went to her husband and hugged him tightly. "I'm so glad you're here," she said, trying not to fall into tears again.

He must have heard the shakiness in her voice and decided not to go down the predictable route of demanding to know what had been happening, because he told her, "I've missed you something desperate, darlin'."

Then he looked over Sophie's shoulder and eyed Conor. "And you're here. Why?" he asked.

"Don't be *paranoid*, Gav. I came to see Colette. But I ran into your fragile wife first thing," Conor replied.

"Let's go up to my room, Gavin," Sophie said, pulling at his arm.

"Yeah, let's. And why don't you go find your woman, Conor," Gavin said.

"Sure, I will. Hey, since we're both here, Gav, maybe we should work on writing the new album. What do you think?"

Sophie stared at Conor, hoping to convey a silent plea to stop provoking her husband.

"I'm not going to have a lot of free time. This trip is about Sophie and me. We'll meet back up in Dublin."

"Better count on that one," Conor replied, and Sophie saw him shake his head as he watched them walk away.

IN THE ELEVATOR, Sophie soaked up the sight of Gavin. The fact that he had lost weight and had slight dark circles under his eyes did nothing to subdue the delight she felt in seeing him again. She was suddenly full of hope that things would right themselves, that they would be okay again.

"You've been crying," he said, and gently stroked her cheek.

She leaned into his hand and closed her eyes briefly. The elevator stopped at their floor and she pulled him by the hand toward their room without replying.

They found a bottle of champagne on ice inside the room. She had forgotten about her request for it to be delivered in time for Gavin's arrival.

"Shall we open it?" she asked brightly.

"Come here, darlin'," he said.

She hesitated, but when she went to him and he wrapped his arms around her, she sighed from the pleasure of it. He had always told her they fit perfectly together and she knew it was true.

"Tell me why you were crying," he whispered to her as he held her.

She closed her eyes tightly. What could she tell him when she knew he would dismiss her concerns and deny his addiction once again? He didn't really want to know that her tears were because she was terrified that she'd lost her him. That she'd never get him back. That he no longer needed her.

"Let's not talk about it," she said, and kissed him.

This was the way she could feel close to him, if only temporarily. Passion was the easiest thing to share and she clung to it with unmasked desperation. Afterward, he held her in his arms and it was the only place she wanted to be.

"I think I want to stop modeling," she said.

He traced the curve of her breast with the back of his hand and waited for her to say more.

"It doesn't make me happy anymore."

"The modeling? Is that what's making you unhappy?"

She was quiet for a moment. "I just want to be at home, with you."

"I'll be back in studio soon, then tour, so . . . ."

His lack of enthusiasm for having her at home with him destroyed the hope she had felt earlier. She turned on her side away from him so he wouldn't see the tears that spilled from her eyes and onto the pillow.

"What's going on with you and Conor, then?" he asked.

"What do you mean? Nothing."

"Nothing?"

"He's been a good friend, is all. He lets me cry on his shoulder about you." She got up and went into the bathroom, closing the door behind her.

Looking into the mirror, she noted her red-rimmed eyes and wondered what she was doing. Her husband seemed to have little interest in their marriage. Conor was in love with her and seemed willing to suffer all consequences to be with her. Part of her knew her best course of action would be to go to Los Angeles to be by herself for some time, to grow strong in her own right. Not only could she do nothing to help Gavin with his troubles, but it was becoming increasingly obvious that he did not want her to even try anymore. She felt helpless, overwhelmed with the feeling that she was unable to make any meaningful change at this point.

Gavin's knock at the bathroom door pulled her from the downward spiral of her thoughts.

"Yeah?"

He opened the door and poked his head in. "You okay, darlin'?"

She gave him a weak smile. "I'm great. Should we go get dinner?"

"Sophie—"

"Really, I'm fine. I'm going to take a quick shower."

"No, Sophie, please," he said as he moved to her. He held her face in his hands and kissed her.

This familiar action brought a fresh round of tears to her eyes as she responded to his kisses.

"Please don't cry, sweet girl. Please. Those tears break my heart. And Christ knows I deserve that much, but I just can't take it," he told her.

"What do you want, Gavin? What do you want from me?"

"Give us a smile," he replied.

"Gavin—"

"Smile at me now like you did downstairs. God, that felt good— seeing you happy like that. You're so beautiful." He paused and considered her for a moment. "Does it mean anything to hear me say that to you, Sophie? Does it mean anything for me to say it?"

"Yes," she said, her voice a hoarse whisper. "It still means everything to me, baby. You still mean everything to me."

"And you're all that matters to me, darlin'. Don't think that's changed, okay? You're still the thing I love most in this world. No matter what else is going on, you're all that I hold dear."

"Really?"

"Really," he affirmed. "And I need you to not give up on me, on us. I know I'm fucking up. Believe me, I know I'm an insufferable bastard. But, please don't let go. *Please*."

She nodded. "I won't let go. I promise."

Gavin suggested they take their minds off things by going out for dinner. He told Sophie he would take her anywhere she wanted to go.

"Anywhere?" she asked with a smile.

"Anywhere."

"Okay, you might regret that. See, I've never, in all the times I've been to Paris, had a good look at the Eiffel Tower at night. Will you take me somewhere we can see it?"

"I'd do anything for you, darlin'," he said.

Sophie nodded and smiled weakly. In the past, she would have believed this unreservedly. Things were no longer so simple.

72

SOPHIE

G avin had told Sophie he was taking her on an adventure and that she'd better dress warm. She was glad for her DKNY gray wool and down-filled mid-length coat when they were let out of their car at the large open square of the Place du Trocadéro. She gasped as they were greeted with a breathtaking view of the Eiffel Tower. She had seen it in passing, of course, but seeing it unhurried now and with Gavin was exactly what she had wanted. This location on the north side of the Seine offered enough distance to get a full view of the iconic amber-hued structure and surrounding city lights. They weren't alone, as there were other tourists sprinkled across the square, but it still felt like the night was all theirs.

"Here, let's make a spot on the stairs," Gavin said, leading her to an unoccupied area.

He opened the large bag he'd carried with them and placed a blanket on the stairs. Next, he pulled out a still-warm baguette, a container of soft and hard cheeses, another with fresh and dried fruits, and one more with an assortment of olives. He also had a small box of dark chocolate truffles. The final but most essential item was the red wine and glasses.

Sitting there, she was mesmerized by the combination of the cool, fragrant air and the wondrous glow of the tower. "It's like magic," she whispered to him, and he smiled. "Have you ever seen anything more fantastic?"

"All the time," he replied, looking at her.

She smiled and squeezed his arm.

"This all right for dinner?" he asked as he set up their impromptu picnic.

She looked at the spread with delight. Her smile faded, however, when she looked back at him and saw the telltale sign of him rubbing at his nose.

"How did you even get it here?" she asked.

"I had the help of the hotel's amazing concierge, I have to admit."

"No, not the food. The cocaine. I can't believe you're high right now, Gavin." Though she was furious, her voice betrayed nothing more than mild disappointment.

"Don't let's ruin this, darlin'. Just relax and leave it be. Have some wine." He looked her in the eye for a long, silent moment. "It's okay. Really."

Finally, she nodded. "You are so incredibly lucky that I love you beyond all reason," she said. She didn't have the will to follow through on her disapproval. She would rather give him a pass so that the gesture he had made of taking her to this spot wasn't spoiled. It wasn't healthy to pick and choose what she would acknowledge, but it was part of her survival instincts in this unnatural new world.

"I am that indeed," he said. He took her hand and pressed his lips to it before putting his arm around her shoulders. "Now, do you want to hear something ridiculous about that beautiful thing there?" He gestured to the glittering tower.

"What?"

"It's illegal to publish photos of it taken at night. Technically it would be a copyright violation to do so."

She laughed at the absurdity. "Guess we'll have to stay for a while to get our fill of the view, then."

"We can stay here all night. Remember, like we did in Dublin when we were in school and we stayed out until sunrise?"

That night was burned into her memory, like so many other moments when he had seduced her out of her better judgment. She had always trusted him implicitly. Every time he implored her to do something she'd normally hesitate to do, it ended up being a time she treasured. In this instance, however, his cocaine high would keep him up through the night and she wouldn't be able to stay up with him.

Thinking of that left a bad taste in her mouth and a longing for those simpler times. If she could just hang on a little longer, she was sure he would find his way back to who he used to be.

73

onor hadn't intended to reunite with Colette like this. As he'd predicted, she had broken up with him in response to the tabloid news of his and Sophie's outing. He made a weak show of apologizing and then agreed they could use a break.

Finding out that Gavin was deep into cocaine was a huge shock. He and his friend had sampled a variety of drugs before, but they'd never taken it this far. Since he couldn't penetrate Gavin's denial about the level of his addiction, Conor's next instinct was to confront Sophie. Doing so in the public way he had, in the lobby of the hotel, meant he couldn't easily slink out of town. So he concocted the plan to reunite with Colette, turning his visit into a surprise to see her. She ate up the drama of his unexpected presence and quickly took him back.

It meant he was then committed to watching alongside Gavin as their women walked in various shows. The two of them garnered almost more media attention than the designers' work. Conor bristled under the relentless energy Gavin exuded as he had trouble sitting still. Conor recognized this as not something born out of drugs, but rather his friend's nervousness at his drug use being known. He also had to endure Gavin waxing poetic about Sophie and saying Conor deserved the same kind of ends-of-the-earth love. Gavin told him not to settle for Colette if she didn't give him that feeling.

The time together shuttling from the runway shows for Saint

Laurent to Valentino, then on to Miu Miu, and finally to Amaya Arzuaga was plenty for Conor, but Gavin insisted that the two couples share a late dinner that night.

They left the restaurant choice to Colette, and she chose the highly regarded Lapérouse. It offered exceptional service in an old-fashioned and traditional setting on the left bank of the Seine.

Once wine and starters were ordered, Colette sat back in her chair and openly examined Gavin. "You guys," she said, looking at Conor and Sophie with mock excitement, "how come you didn't tell me Gavin had this cute little coke habit?"

Gavin glanced at Sophie, who was in turn staring daggers at Colette.

"Oh, come, Colette," Conor said with an air of lightness he did not feel. "You know we're not one of those couples who tells each other everything."

"Is it funny to you, Sophie?" Colette asked.

"Why don't we change the subject," Gavin said.

Sophie couldn't meet her friend's eyes and instead played with the thick cotton napkin in her lap.

"So, how bad is it?" Colette continued, undaunted.

Gavin met her gaze and held it for a moment. "It's nothing more than recreational," he said with complete confidence.

The waiter approached the table then, addressing his comments to Colette in French, and they spoke rapidly as he gave her a taste of the wine for her approval. When she nodded, he filled all their glasses and stepped away from the obviously tense group.

An uncomfortable silence engulfed the table. Gavin loosely rested his arm around Sophie's shoulders and watched Colette defiantly, daring her to pursue her interrogation.

"It makes you impotent, you know," she finally said, smirking.

"Not in my experience," he returned.

"Keep doing it and it will. Its . . . charms do not last long."

"You seem to have firsthand knowledge, Colette," Gavin said. "How'd you come by that?"

"Oh, I've seen all kinds of things in this industry, including overdoses."

"I can take care of myself, thanks very much," he replied.

Conor had purposely kept quiet, curious to see where Colette would take the conversation, and thinking that, perhaps, as an outsider she would be able to get through to Gavin where he could not.

"Yeah, I can see that," she replied with a derisive laugh.

Gavin opened his mouth and then hesitated. Finally, he said, "Your man's done it himself. Why don't you worry about him?"

"You have?" both Sophie and Colette said in unison, turning their eyes on Conor.

"Thanks very much, Gav," Conor said. He locked eyes with Sophie, saw her mournful expression, and could guess she thought his confrontation of her the day before had been unfair. "Don't look at me like that," he told her. "I'm not a hypocrite. Yeah, I tried it. If we're all suddenly going to be honest here, I've tried just about everything there is. But I'm no fucking addict. That's the distinction and don't pretend you don't understand that."

"Aye, don't be getting the wrong idea," Gavin said. "I'm not an addict."

"Just stop," Sophie said. "All of you stop. Please."

The table went quiet. Conor watched Sophie as she looked out the window to the river. The dark water was softly illuminated by street lamps. All he wanted to do was make everything okay for her, to protect her. But it wasn't his place.

74

SOPHIE

"Feeling better now that you're nice and drunk, Soph?" Conor asked. They were several yards behind Gavin and Colette as they walked along the Seine back toward the hotel in opposite couplings after a particularly wine-heavy dinner. She couldn't imagine what those two had to say. They'd sniped at each other all night. But she was too drunk, as Conor just helpfully pointed out, to worry about them.

"Yes, I feel—"

Conor grabbed her arm to kept her from wavering. He steadied her and then put his arm around her to support her for the walk.

Sophie leaned her head into his shoulder, wrapping her arm around his waist. After a moment, she reached under his jacket for added warmth.

"You've got to sort yourself out, you know," he told her quietly and then kissed the top of her head quickly. "You need to find your own way, honey."

"What does that mean?" she mumbled.

"Just that it might be to your benefit to think about doing what's right for you. Take care of yourself. Gavin's a grown man—he can manage, you know?"

She pulled away from him then. "He's my husband and he needs me."

"Then you better run along and get him," he replied, removing his arm from her.

The wine had left her head swimming and her vision slightly blurred. Conor's anger at her was another rude awakening. It had never occurred to her that he would lose patience with her, that his adoration had limits.

They stopped on the street while Gavin and Colette walked on.

"Don't be angry with me, Connie," she whispered.

He took her hand into his and squeezed it. "I'm not, honey. I just . . . I want more for you. You deserve better."

"This is what I have right now. And anyway, it'll be better soon. Gavin promised me."

He nodded warily. "Okay, then. Let's walk. You need to get that alcohol out of your system if you're to do the shows tomorrow, aye?"

She thought about the day that lay ahead of her, of the absurdly high heels and breathtakingly tight-fitting clothing she'd have to strut in under hot, bright lights, and she grew dizzy. She leaned into Conor and was grateful once more when he didn't hesitate in holding her up.

75

Back in Dublin, Gavin tried to live up to his promise to Sophie to make things better. But it was all in vain. He was far too dependent on the escape cocaine gave him to pull back.

So, when things actually escalated for the worse and he spent two days away from home without explanation, he knew he'd face her anger. But when she glanced up at him through red-rimmed eyes, she was speechless.

It took him a moment, but then he registered what it was. She was too thrown by his changed appearance to fight with him.

His drug buddies, thinking it would be a hilarious prank, had sloppily shaved his head when he had passed out with the help of Ambien.

"How could they?" she whispered as she reached out to touch his buzzed hair.

He took her hand and kissed it. "Don't worry about that. It's not a big deal."

"It *is* a big deal. It means you've lost all control over this. You've—"

"I haven't lost control, darlin'. Truly. Because this is partly why I was gone so long. I had to do this. I had to. To show you that you're all I think about. Even when I fuck up."

Yanking up his shirt, he peeled away the clear bandage that was

316

on his chest. He proudly showed her the newly tattooed gold 'S' over his heart.

She took in the tattoo wordlessly. Her lack of enthusiasm was disappointing, but at least she wasn't angry with him. In fact, she seemed more interested in telling him about a house than swooning over his permanent body-art gesture.

She told him she had stumbled upon her dream house while out driving aimlessly to pass the time when he didn't come home. It was in the posh neighborhood of Dalkey, known as the Irish "Bay of Naples" for its sea views and cliffside villas. She had fallen in love with it for its location and promise of privacy with a gated driveway.

"Sounds fantastic," Gavin said. "Take me to see it."

"It's not for sale."

The disappointment on her face over this fact was more than he could bear. He was well aware of how badly he had been treating her, how fruitlessly she had been working to keep him together. He owed her so much. He should have promised to stop the coke, to fix things.

But he couldn't bring himself to do that. Instead, he latched onto the idea that if he could somehow purchase this dream home of Sophie's, all would right itself.

———

AFTER SOPHIE DID her best to even out his haircut, Gavin showered and dressed in clean jeans and an Aran wool sweater. The improved outer appearance, along with his self-imposed mission, gave him the confidence to charm the owner of Sophie's dream home when they dropped in on her later that afternoon. He deftly explained to Mrs. Smythe that Sophie had happened upon the area and instantly fallen in love with her home.

She believed his initial claim that they hoped to build their own home modeled after hers, and proudly gave them a tour, telling them in detail about the remodeling she had overseen. Despite its large size, the five-bedroom, six-bathroom, one-story house had a warm, inviting feel to it. The wall of south-facing windows along the living and dining areas flooded the space with natural light. The high ceilings with hand-carved beams that matched the dark walnut plank flooring made for an elegant great room. A two-sided gas fireplace was the only thing to break up the otherwise open floor plan.

It wasn't until the homeowner was showing them her daughter's room and was faced with poster-sized images of Gavin on the walls that she realized who he was. She giggled like a schoolgirl, covering her mouth with her hand.

"It's the haircut, I bet," he said as he admitted who he was.

"Yes, that's what's different," she replied, but eyed him as if trying to sort something more out.

He imagined that vague tabloid stories of his mother's abandonment, a bloody fight with his brother, and drug use played through her mind's eye as she finally recognized him. Above all, she seemed to understand they were there for more than a tour.

"It's a bit of a surprise, I know," Gavin said, his voice soothing, seductive even. They sat at the informal kitchen breakfast nook while Sophie stood on the deck, staring out at the panoramic sea view. "All I'm after is trying to make my wife happy. She has fallen madly in love with this house." He paused as he tried to understand the reasons himself. "She spent a lot of time on the beach as a kid, so maybe this place satisfies those cravings for childhood comforts we're never really able to re-create when we grow up," he said. "Or maybe it's the way the sea seems to promise a kind of renewal, a new start. I do know that the only real thing I'm capable of giving her is the hope something different brings. The thing is, I'd buy her a thousand houses if it meant she'd be happy again. Honest to God, she's an angel, but by being with me she has settled for less than she deserves. I can't bear to disappoint her, not again."

"I see," Mrs. Smythe said. "That's sweet, but—"

"It's a tremendous thing to ask of you and your family," Gavin continued. "But I'll do anything I can to make it as convenient as possible for you. And I will pay whatever price you ask. Whatever."

He wasn't being dramatic. The cost really didn't matter. He had chosen long ago not to rely on money and material things. He didn't care what car he had or where he lived, because he never wanted to feel beholden to a means of securing these things. It was a way of defending against—at least in his mind—becoming one of "them." If he didn't place any importance on his wealth, he would never operate out of fear of losing it. The idea was that he would be free to make artistic choices based on inspiration rather than economic need. That his career had been so successful as to never need to challenge this model wasn't something he gave much thought.

Tears flooded Mrs. Smythe's eyes, and Gavin sighed with relief. The sheer romance of what he was willing to do for his wife obviously resonated deeply with her.

"I can't promise anything, but I'll talk to my husband," she said, taking his hand in both of hers and giving it a squeeze.

And Gavin smiled because he knew he had just bought a new house.

"You look like shite," Conor said.

"Don't like the haircut? Thought I might be pretty like you now," Gavin replied, batting his eyelashes. He ran his hand over his short hair and grinned.

He had avoided Conor for weeks before finally agreeing to meet here at his house. Facing his best friends after giving them the runaround so he could fall in with drugs had been daunting. So, he got high before he came over. He knew when he was doing it that there was no denying he was an addict.

"Actually, it is an improvement," Shay said with a laugh.

Gavin had to agree. The shorter style had turned out to be a refreshing change after years of letting his wavy hair go longish. He noticed that the clean cut made his blue eyes pop, despite the circles beneath them.

"I gotta tell yous what happened to me this morning. I ran into a mate and we stopped to chat. This is a guy I've spent loads of time with over the past couple months, so I'm not expecting anything unusual. Then, suddenly, he fucking makes a play for me!"

The others laughed, amused by the scenario.

"You were asking for it, admit it!" Martin said.

"No, no," Gavin protested. "I had no clue Jacob was that way. But then today he's rubbing my leg all seductive like."

"What'd you do?" Shay asked.

"I was too put off to do anything really. Just told him he had the wrong man and to leave off that crap. Really odd, that."

"Maybe it's the new look you got going. How'd that come about?" Conor asked.

"Ah, I don't know."

Conor raised his eyebrows. "You don't know?"

"I was partying with some mates, and I guess I passed out and they cut it all off for a laugh," Gavin said.

"Good mates," Conor said sarcastically. "These your coke buddies?"

"Just don't you worry about all that," Gavin said quickly.

"It is all true, then?" Shay said, eyeing Gavin's gaunt face.

Gavin avoided looking at Shay. He had, in fact, avoided seeing Shay these past few months, aware of how his drug use would especially affect him. Shay had dealt with such things at far too young an age when his brother, Danny Boy, fell prey to heroin. Danny Boy had become an addict, disappearing for long stretches at a time before resurfacing when he bottomed out. He would seek Shay's emotional and financial help, get straight for a time, and eventually slip away again. The burden on Shay had been huge, but he never complained. Gavin, out of all of them, had been Shay's support when he needed it over the years.

"Thought we were here to work?" Gavin said now, unfolding a notebook stuffed with loose bits of paper.

"Haven't seen you in forever, Gav," Martin said. "You'll have to excuse us if seeing you all fucked up on drugs is a bit alarming."

"Well, get over it." Gavin smiled to temper the sharpness of his tone.

"And what's Sophie got to say about this?" Shay asked, looking at Conor.

"Why are you asking Conor that, Seamus?" Gavin asked. The already charged atmosphere in the room got even heavier.

"Maybe 'cause I'm the one she comes running to when things go bad," Conor replied.

"Here's an idea: stay out of my marriage," Gavin said, his voice steely.

"What am I supposed to do next time? Turn her away? You're

killing her with this coke shite. You know that? She used to be a beautiful, sweet girl. And you're tearing her apart," Conor said.

"You think you could make her happy, Con? Is that it? You think you'd be a better husband to her?" Gavin asked.

"I would never hurt her the way you are," Conor said cagily.

"Then maybe you should have married her."

"Maybe I should have." Conor closed his eyes and shook his head.

Gavin stared at his friend. He knew Conor didn't mean it like that. He was just looking out for Sophie, like he had for years. And Sophie needed caring for more than ever. Gavin wasn't deluded enough to not see how he was hurting her. But still. Hearing Conor, the friend he had revered since they were kids, voice his disapproval so bluntly while asserting himself as the better man was hard to take. Without another word, he headed for the door, feeling all their eyes on his back as he went.

77

SOPHIE

Checking herself in the foyer mirror one last time, Sophie smoothed her hair's sleek side part and headed for the front door. She wore a body hugging ivory pantsuit with alligator skin stilettos. The jacket was tight at the bust and cut wide and low around the neck and shoulders, revealing a sexy hint of an emerald-green lace bra.

When she opened the door to leave, she was surprised to see Conor about to knock.

"Sophie," he said. He stood straighter and took her in. "You look amazing."

She smiled her thanks.

"Is he home?"

"No . . . not yet," she said. "Listen, I have to run to the airport. I'm going to Paris for the day. Work."

"We should talk. There are things I need to tell you," he said. "I'll drive you to the airport. How about that?"

She agreed, knowing there was no time to protest, and they went to his car, a newly purchased silver Aston Martin DB9. Conor held the door open for her before going around to the driver's side.

"What's in Paris?" he asked as started the engine.

"My agent set up a meeting for us to talk to Lancôme. They're interested in me being their new representative. I thought it would be a good way to phase out of modeling."

"If you want to quit, why don't you just stop? Why keep hanging on?"

"It's what I do," she replied. "I hang on, even if it's not the best thing for me."

He looked over at her and they exchanged a lengthy moment of silent understanding.

"Listen," he said and hesitated.

"Yes?"

"Gav and I sort of had it out yesterday, and it got me to thinking about what I should be doing. You know, thinking about doing the right thing."

"I'm not sure what you—"

"I asked Colette to marry me last night. She said yes." He squinted at the road and shook his head. "Anyway, our plan right now is for me to move to New York. At least part of the time."

"But you can't," she said, unable to stop herself. She hadn't expected Conor and Colette to last, let alone see them get married. And now that he was telling her he would be moving away, she realized how much she had come to rely on him.

"I won't move until after we get the studio work done," he continued. "The trick is getting Gavin to calm down some and work with us."

All she could do was nod in agreement.

"So what did you mean when you said he wasn't home yet? He went out early this morning?"

"Um," she started, and had to stop to clear her throat. "No, he didn't come home last night. He might be back later this morning. Or he might be gone for a few days. I can't say for sure."

"Jesus Christ," he muttered. "This is the way you're living?"

She was silent, looking out the window. "When's the wedding?" she asked at length.

"Nothing's set. Tell the truth, this isn't something I've thought long and hard about. It just feels like the right thing. Colette's great. We'll be good together."

He sounded wooden, like he was trying to convince himself. Or maybe that's just what she wanted to believe. In either case, she knew she had no right to interfere.

"Yeah, I'm sure you will," Sophie said. "I'll have to call Colette to congratulate her. Will she be in Dublin long?"

"Nah, she's off again tomorrow." Conor pulled into the outer limits of the airport, following the signs to departures. "While you're making your congratulations, call Celia. She's pregnant again. Almost four months on."

Sophie felt an odd mixture of joy and jealousy for Celia and Martin at the news. They were a real family, much like she had envisioned for Gavin and herself so long ago.

"That's great. They are blessed." She stared out the window at the various airline terminals going by. "And Shay? How's he doing?"

"Good. Remember when I played matchmaker with him and a waitress at a sushi restaurant in New York?"

Sophie remembered the story only vaguely. It had occurred right before the *Vanity Fair* article came out about Gavin's mother.

"He's still seeing her. Seems quite madly in love, actually. Her name's Jessica and she's a student at uni there."

"That's great. I'm really happy for all of you," Sophie said.

Conor pulled to a stop in front of her airline. He put the car in park, taking off his sunglasses as he turned toward her. "Sophie, I want you to be happy, too. I want so much for you to be the girl I once knew."

She looked down and blinked away the tears in her eyes. "Am I that pathetic now?"

"You'll never be that to me, honey. But you can do better for yourself right now and you know it."

"Conor, I can't leave him," she said. "It's out of the question."

He sighed but said no more, so she reached for the door to get out.

"Wait a minute," he said. "Tell me where he goes with these so-called friends of his."

Sophie rattled off the few places she knew Gavin would go to get high and waste the night away.

"When you talk to him, know that he's still hurting so much from all that's happened. He's turned into something he hates, but that doesn't mean he knows how to make it stop."

Conor smiled ruefully and shook his head. "You're more than he deserves right now, Sophie."

"He tells me that all the time," she replied before getting out of the car.

78

SOPHIE

Three days later, Sophie was packing Gavin's extensive vinyl record collection in preparation for the move to their new home when there was a sharp rap on the door. Before she could go see who it was, Conor let himself in.

He looked grim and was holding several folded-up newspapers in his hands.

"Have you seen the papers?" he asked, without offering a hello.

"Um, no," she said. "But it looks like you have."

"I'm guessing you know that Gavin's in London with Jackson?"

"Yeah. He finally got around to calling to let me know." She sighed. "He told me he needed space. Guess you tracking him down the other night didn't go well?"

"You could say that."

Gavin had railed against her "selling him out" to Conor when he called, furious that she had told his friend where to find him. Of course, it was all her fault. And he used it to drive a deeper wedge between them. Whereas once he had needed her so desperately to help heal his wounds, he now seemed to enjoy telling her how she only made things worse for him. She was baffled by the change in the dynamic that had always worked for them. But at the same time, she stubbornly held to the belief that if she kept hanging on, Gavin would tire of this reckless behavior and then they could work on things together.

"Has no one contacted you about this?" Conor held up the papers.

Sophie sighed. Gavin's phone call had been followed by Henri's, letting her know that Lancôme had passed on her due to her "controversial" personal image. It seemed that Gavin's not-so-secret cocaine habit was reflecting on her. After that, she had silenced her cell phone and lost herself in the minutiae of packing.

"Just show it to me," she said, holding out her hand for the papers.

Conor reluctantly passed them to her and watched as she took in each of the three cover stories. They varied little from one another, all focusing on a photo of Gavin receiving a lap dance from a stripper. The redheaded woman had her g-stringed pelvis pressed to his and her very large bare breasts were clear even though her nipples had been censored by black bars. What was also clear was that Gavin was enjoying himself as he held her to him, his hands firmly cupping her ass. His face was animated, with raised eyebrows and a rakish smile.

The headlines all screamed the same kind of gleeful but tawdry accusation: "Gavin Caught Red-headed!" One of the papers claimed to have an interview with the stripper, who would detail her night with Gavin, including how he rated as a lover.

Sophie was detached as she took all this in. Her husband had indeed been caught doing something he shouldn't have. It was distasteful and disrespectful. But it didn't really mean anything more than that.

"So, he went to a strip club. But there's nothing more to it," she said, handing the papers back to Conor.

"You don't know that, honey," he said gently.

"Don't be ridiculous. Gavin doesn't cheat on me," she said. "And when did you start believing tabloids anyway? You know they're nothing but trash."

He looked at her for a moment before saying, "They weren't wrong about you and me."

"There is no you and me," she replied flatly.

"Yeah, you're right. That was all *nothing*, wasn't it?"

His anger fueled her own. "Why are you even mad? You're getting married. You don't want me."

"You don't know the first thing about me, do you?"

She turned away instead of answering him. She could have said that she could see quite clearly that he was marrying Colette out of some twisted attempt to do what he thought was the "right" thing. In his mind that meant doing whatever it took to stop being in love with her. It wouldn't work. She knew that, and she suspected he did too. But she didn't have the energy to spar with him.

"Forget it," he said. "I was trying to help, really. I thought you might want someone to talk to. But let's forget that. Just do me a favor?"

She looked back at him, her eyes hard. "What?"

"Make sure he uses a condom with you. Wouldn't want to catch anything from your husband."

"Don't say that. You're just being cruel now."

"I'm being a friend and you know it."

"What about being his friend?" she asked. "If he knew you were doing this, he'd—"

"Would you stop being so goddamn blind to all this?" he asked, incredulous.

"What do you want me to do?"

"Act like you've got some self-respect and leave!"

Sophie considered him for a moment and then she said the one thing she knew would push him away for good. "You're just mad because this isn't making me run into your arms."

The look of hurt on his face was undeniable. But it soon turned to anger. "You know what? I don't need this shite. Fuck off and don't come to me with your sad stories anymore."

Sophie returned his stare, silent, until he realized there was nothing more to say. He threw the papers on the floor, turned, and left her home.

When she was sure he was gone, she scooped up the papers, methodically spread them out on the carpeted floor, and devoured every word. When she read a quote from the stripper, Sammy, saying that her affair with Gavin was meant to be because he had a gold tattoo of the letter 'S,' she knew Gavin had betrayed her.

Conor telling her so hadn't been enough. It was too awful to believe, let alone hear from someone who knew exactly how much it would hurt.

But now she had no choice. And as she sat alone in the half-packed house, she realized she had no one left to hold on to.

79

GAVIN

"You're in for it with the wife," Jackson said.

He and Gavin were sitting at the kitchen counter of Jackson's penthouse apartment in London, trying to shake off hangovers with strong coffee and toast. Even with the skies overcast, light flooded into the space through the floor-to-ceiling windows and bounced off the predominately white and glass furniture. The bright light combined with their aching heads had him turning away from the spectacular view of the Thames.

"It'll be okay," Gavin said.

"Really? She doesn't mind that sort of thing, then?"

"The point is, she will never leave me. I know that much." This declaration didn't make him happy. He remembered a time not so long ago when his wife was more spirited, when she demanded more from him. It's what he had loved about her early on.

"What makes you worth it, do you suppose?" Jackson asked, his face a mask of curiosity.

"Not a goddamn thing. That's the crime of it," he said. "She's always seen some version of me that I don't think I ever really lived up to. But she keeps waiting for me to, even though I don't deserve it —or her."

Jackson considered this for a moment. "So why don't you try to?"

"Then I wouldn't be me, would I?" Gavin replied with a laugh.

"I'm not buying it," Jackson said.

"What?"

"You're not this guy, Gavin. It's so obvious you're trying on a role, like an actor would. You've been playing the cokehead—careless, selfish, fighting inner demons. That may be how you feel, but that's not who you are. The act is wearing thin and you're going to have to give it up."

"Jesus Christ, everyone's a shrink," Gavin said.

"Come on, you know you're going to give up this coke crap soon. It's not doing what you want anymore, right?"

Gavin looked into his coffee mug, hesitating. "No, I suppose not."

"This may sound absurd, but I want to help you quit."

Gavin gave him an incredulous look.

Jackson laughed. "I know, I'm the one who got you started. But I didn't think you'd go fucking crazy with it!"

"I didn't either. But it helps me get through the day."

"What's so fucking awful right now? That hysteria about your mum has gone away. Now all you've got is the press going on about you being a cokehead. Stop being a cokehead and it'll be done."

"Add to that adulterer."

"Isn't there a rule about how one time with a stripper doesn't count?" Jackson asked with a grin.

"Maybe there would be if it didn't have the bonus media coverage to go with it."

"Was she even worth it?"

"I didn't even fuck her, to be honest. I let it get too far, that's for sure. But I did come to my senses in the end and put a stop to it."

Jackson's eyebrows bounced up with intrigue. "You're saved, then!"

"After that photo, though, no one will believe the truth of it, let alone Sophie."

Gavin shook his head, wondering how he had gotten to this point. He never thought he'd sink this low, or hurt his wife this way. It was time to try to get back on track.

80

GAVIN

When Gavin returned to Dublin, he directed the taxi driver to the house that had just been vacated. It took him a moment to sort out what was going on, but then he flagged down the taxi before it left the driveway.

On the way to the new house in Dalkey, he asked the driver to stop at a flower shop. He quickly purchased two dozen long-stem red roses, hoping they would serve as a buffer.

Even the driver didn't buy it. He let out a smoker's cough of a laugh when Gavin climbed back into the car.

"Wishful thinking, aye, laddie?" he said.

"You mind your own there," Gavin said, but not unkindly.

When he was left off at the gates of his new home, Gavin lingered at the far end of the finely laid drive. The gates were open, and under the pale sunlight he saw a glorious view of the sea beyond the house. Taking a deep breath, he then trudged on and let himself in the front door.

Sophie was leaning against the deck railing, staring out at the water. He purposely crunched the plastic wrapping around the stems of the roses to announce his presence but she was slow to turn and look at him. When she finally did, he had partially covered himself with the flowers.

"Gavin," she said.

He lowered the flowers and attempted a charming smile.

"Don't be an ass," she told him, and he lost his smile.

He watched as she turned away from him again. Setting the roses down hastily, he joined her on the deck.

"So," he started, then faltered.

"I don't want to talk about it," she said.

"We need to, Sophie. In all seriousness, we need to. You need to know—"

"I don't want to hear lies or justifications or excuses."

"Hear me out for second. Look at me." He took a deep breath and waited for her to look at him before continuing. "I didn't have sex with her."

She watched him for a long moment, searching his eyes. "I don't believe you."

"You have to 'cause it's the truth. I swear to you. I got too close to doing something I shouldn't but in the end, it didn't happen."

This time when she examined him, she seemed to relent. The hardness in her eyes let up and her body relaxed a degree.

"I'm so very sorry for this," he said. "For everything."

"What do you want?"

He was taken aback by the question. "What do I want? I want you to forgive me."

"Do you want to be married to me?"

"Yes, of course I do. Sophie, you're all I want. I swear to you. I was so wasted at that club, I didn't know what I was doing."

"Just tell me—was she the only one? Or have there been more?"

"She wasn't *anything*. I swear to you, I didn't fuck her. And I've *never* messed around like that before." Over the years, there had been countless temptations from women eager to give themselves to him, ranging from young groupies to sophisticated women who attempted real seduction. But he'd never truly been tempted. He'd never been weak enough to do the wrong thing.

Until now.

Again, she searched his eyes for the truth. "Okay," she whispered.

It didn't make any sense to him, but he knew better than to question it. Instead, he followed her inside and sat with her on the sofa. They didn't speak, but little by little she let him pull her into his arms. They stayed there, quiet and entwined, for a long while.

As Gavin held her, he thought of all he had jeopardized and who he had become. It shamed him to know that he had treated his wife with such disrespect. There wasn't a doubt in his mind that he was less than a man.

At that moment, Sophie rested her head against his shoulder and sighed. The gesture brought him to tears for he knew that she had been pushed beyond her limits and yet she was still hanging on.

He held her tighter in return. "I'm going to stop. I'm all out and I won't get any more."

"Uh-huh," she said.

"Really, darlin'. It's time to give it up."

"Okay."

There was no faith or hope in her voice, and he hated himself all the more.

81

GAVIN

"So, what of all the rumors about drug use?" Sean Reynolds asked without preamble.

Gavin had braced himself for such a tack, so he wasn't surprised, even though the live audience seemed to be. They murmured collectively and then hushed. James had arranged his appearance on the acerbic presenter's show just the day before. James had been at the band's jam session and was delighted to see that Gavin was several days sober. The idea behind putting him on the show was to combat the cocaine and stripper stories that had dominated the tabloids. James had even begged Gavin to have Sophie join him, but Gavin was not only adamantly against drawing her into this, but also unable to as she was in Prague for work.

"Lots of rumors out there," Gavin agreed. Though he was too thin, he had cleaned up well for the show. A trip to a barber meant his short hair now had some style, with the sides and back at a close fade and the top a bit longer and tamed by gel. Even with jeans that were baggy on him, the rest of his ensemble—a dark blue fitted wool coat over a blue-green striped v-neck sweater, with a brown leather belt and boots—negated his recent sloppy tabloid images.

"Yes, let's talk about all those pesky cocaine rumors. Clear the air, if you will. Don't your fans deserve that much?" Reynolds asked with a salacious grin.

Reynolds had a reputation for putting his guests in uncomfortable positions, and now was no exception, especially since he had a personal stake in this. Gavin remembered that he'd been the radio DJ to play Rogue's first demo and gotten in trouble with the station for it. Though he failed to air the more polished demo Gavin and Conor later asked him to play, he had taken every opportunity to tell the world he had discovered Rogue. When the band hadn't backed him up on this claim, he'd grown bitter and traded his praise for barbs, especially as he gained his own platform with his chat show.

"What they deserve is to know that everything's fine with me, everything's fine with Rogue. In fact, we're working on our new album now and it's going really well."

"The artful dodger, aye?" Reynolds asked. "But we all know you're here for damage control, don't we? Let's talk about Sammy-the-stripper."

"Listen, that episode was not one of my proudest moments." Gavin paused to let the sincerity of that statement sink in. "But, to be honest, haven't we all at some point had a drink too many and gone a bit too far? Most go down to their local and only have a few witnesses, yeah? It can still be a bitch to get past all the good craic that comes out of making an arse out of yourself."

There was a ripple of knowing laughter in the audience.

"My fuckups, if you'll pardon the expression, are a bit more documented. But, really, aren't I tame compared to the likes of that Justin Bieber kid? All that underage drinking and public pissing in buckets," he said with a wink and a tsk.

Reynolds ignored the new round of laughter from the crowd and pressed on. "She claims you got on quite well, that you were intimate."

"You all saw what that intimacy entailed," Gavin said, alluding to the tabloid photo of the stripper on his lap. "Nothing more to it than that."

"Interesting. Then what's this about her claiming familiarity with a tattoo of yours?"

Gavin sensed a shift within the audience. There was a restlessness that suggested they were growing weary of Reynold's dogged pursuit of this angle even after Gavin had, for the most part, won them over with the comparison of the average guy making mistakes after too much drink.

Deciding to take a risk to shut this down, Gavin said, "What, are you of the mind that the tattoo is some sort of smoking gun?" He laughed. "Plenty of people have seen it."

"Why don't you give us a look, then?" Reynolds said and the audience cheered in response.

"Right here?" Gavin asked.

"Yes, here and now. Give the audience what it asks for," Reynolds said, and succeeded in getting the crowd to rally for this request.

Gavin shook his head slightly and then stood up. He removed the lavalier mic from his collar and then pulled off his coat, tossing it aside. He faced the camera and pulled his sweater and shirt up high for everyone to have a look. His torso was pale and thin, his ribs plain. And the tattoo on his chest now clearly read "Sophie." The tattoo was intricate and beautiful, without any of the raised redness that would indicate it had been recently drawn. There was a hum in the audience as they murmured to each other.

One of Jackson's friends had volunteered to touch up his original tattoo when Gavin was in London, and he had readily agreed as he had wanted to make the original, unremarkable, 'S' tattoo into something more befitting its extraordinary namesake. He hadn't known then that the final version would be the key to getting back into the public's good graces, as most people would infer that the stripper had not truly been intimate with him since she had incorrectly identified his tattoo. The tone of the interview changed after that. Reynolds knew he had lost the audience's will to interrogate Gavin, so he let Gavin dictate the topics. And besides Gavin's mildly controversial claim that Alex Turner of the Arctic Monkeys had an "aggressively unremarkable voice," he never strayed far from talking about Rogue, past, present, and future.

James congratulated him heartily afterwards, claiming he had never seen Sean Reynolds at such a loss of control over one of his guests.

Gavin knew it wasn't his doing. The audience, his fans, were much like Sophie. They just had no stomach to see him in a negative way.

82

SOPHIE

When Sophie returned home from Prague, she was surprised to find Gavin sitting behind his desk in the room he had made into a writing space. His MacBook Pro was aglow but he was using a leather-bound book to write. She watched him unnoticed for a minute, examining him for signs of drug use.

After he had returned from London with apologies and promises to quit cocaine, she was numb. They had spent the following days tiptoeing around each other as he dealt with the crash of his sudden lack of cocaine. He was exhausted but couldn't sleep, moody and anxious, all the while trying desperately to earn some forgiveness from her. Then work had taken her to Prague for two nights and she had been once again both relieved and worried to leave him.

But now he seemed clear-eyed and alert, and she didn't want to disrupt the focus he had on writing. It was something she hadn't seen him do in such a long time.

"Darlin', you're home," he said, stopping her as she turned to leave.

"I didn't want to interrupt you," she said.

He stood, held his hand out to her and she went to him. As he pulled her into his arms, she took in a deep, shaky breath. He smelled of soap and his skin was warm. She relaxed into his embrace, grateful to feel the kind of comfort and intimacy with him she had gone too long without.

—————

THAT GOOD FEELING was gone the instant she woke from a deep sleep at two forty-three in the morning with a feeling that something was wrong. Gavin was not in bed with her. They had gone to bed together having spent the afternoon and evening reconnecting, easing into the familiar, easy relationship they had always enjoyed.

Until now. The house was silent, still. She knew without exploring other rooms that he had gone.

—————

IT DIDN'T TAKE LONG to get to Jacob's club. It was well after hours, but there were still enough people inside that the sounds of a party spilled out into the street.

She pulled her jacket tighter around her, took a deep breath, and pushed the front door open. She was assaulted by blaring electronica and cigarette smoke. As she made her way to the back of the club, she struggled to identify Gavin in the crowd.

She naturally looked for him in the center of the largest group, but instead found him off to the side, sitting on top of a table. A dark-haired woman stood between his legs, entirely capturing his attention. He was leaning back on his hands as they talked, not the aggressor but not doing anything to dissuade Julia O'Flaherty from toying with the rip on the thigh of his jeans. The recognition of her husband's old lover came as the same reeling sensation she'd had all those years ago when she understood she had been made their fool. Then, it was because he had been clumsily trying to hide the fact that he had never really ended things with Julia, even as he had made Sophie his fiancée. Now, it was because he had apparently been lured by Julia out here in the middle of the night.

Sophie should have been devastated to find him like this, with her. They had been trying so hard to reestablish something real, something hopeful, only for him to casually destroy it all. What she felt instead of devastation was an odd kind of relief. Because now she—at last—had the final excuse she needed to give up on him.

Before she could assert herself, Julia glanced her way. Without missing a beat, she said, "Oh look, it's your wife come to fetch you."

Gavin's brows came together in confusion. But when he saw Sophie, he hurriedly sat up, got to his feet, and brushed past Julia.

"Sophie, I—"

"Thanks for making it easy in the end," she told him calmly.

"What? No, you don't mean that," he said, following her as she headed for the door.

Out in the street, it had started raining, and she had never been so cold. She stopped and turned on him, needing to confront him. "You left our bed to be with *her*?"

"No, that's not what happened. I didn't come here for her. She's just been around lately, hanging with this group."

"And I bet she doesn't make you feel guilty for doing drugs like I do, right?"

He looked away but didn't stop himself from saying, "She doesn't judge that."

She wanted to punch him. She wanted to unleash her anger, but all she could muster was, "That must be very attractive to you right now."

He turned his gaze back to her. "I've done nothing with her, I swear to you."

"I am done believing anything you say, Gavin. I have been a complete idiot for far too long." She laughed bitterly as she thought of her own behavior over the last few months. "I kept thinking if I just hung on, I could be the thing you need to get through all of this. I must have been delusional. But I'm done now. I don't want to beat my head against a wall anymore. I don't want to *do it 'til it hurts*."

He looked stricken. That was exactly the reaction she'd hoped for in mocking his song lyrics. But now she just wanted to get out of the rain and go home.

The stupid key fob wouldn't respond to her attempt to unlock the car door, however, even as she pressed it over and over again.

He put his hand on her wrist to stop her, then took the fob from her. With one push, he unlocked the door. She had been pressing the "lock" button in her attempt to leave, and she wanted to both cry and laugh at this bit of self-sabotage that so perfectly mirrored her life with Gavin.

They stood at the door of the car, the rain soaking them. Her body shook uncontrollably even as she hugged her arms tight around her chest.

"I'll let you go, if that's what you want," he said softly. "I'll give you a divorce. Whatever you want."

They had never spoken of divorce before. A life without each other had never been within the realm of possibilities.

"Is this what you've been trying to do all along?" She tried for eye contact but he looked away. "You've been trying to get me to leave you? So, what? So you can be alone with your drugs?"

"Sophie, you've always known me so well. How can you not understand me now?"

His pain was so raw that it triggered her years-long habit of wanting to be the one to fix him, even after just telling him she had been delusional to keep hanging on to this pattern. She reached out to touch him but he jerked away.

"Tell me," she said. "Talk to me."

"Don't you see?" he asked. "I don't deserve you. I don't."

She shook her head. "I don't believe that. I won't give up on you, baby."

There was relief in his eyes but it quickly gave way to something else. Something dark. She thought it was self-loathing, but what he said next deflected that hatred to her.

"You're so weak," he said softly, and her stomach dropped at the cruelty of his words. "I didn't marry this girl."

Her chin quivered, not from tears but from the burning rage that warmed her body from the inside out. Once again, he was twisting things to suit himself. He had spent months holding firm to her while at the same time pushing her away. It was an untenable dynamic he had created and she was finally ready to put an end to it.

"No, you didn't. You *made* me this way," she replied. "You made me just as weak and selfish as you because even though you pretend you want to be alone with your misery, you've always made sure I was right there with you. So don't you tell me it's anything else."

The truth of her words froze him.

She yanked opened the car door and paused. "Are you coming home?" she asked, the anger drained from her voice.

Nodding, he got in the car with her.

THEY EMBRACED SILENCE. Silence during the drive. Silence as they entered the house. Sophie went to their bedroom's en suite to take a shower without saying a word. Gavin mutely traded places with her as she was stepping out.

Dry and warm now under a layer of heavy bedding, she still couldn't stop trembling. Gavin soon joined her, wrapping his arm around her from behind. She felt the regret and fear in his body as he clung to her, the desperation in his mouth as he pressed his lips to her neck and shoulder. And when he pulled her over so that she lay on her back, she let him make love to her, even as she felt the tears he tried to hide by sinking his face into her hair.

She suspected it was a silent goodbye. And this was confirmed when in the morning she found him gone again. This time he left a note:

My sweet girl,
I've left for LA. Jackson's filming there and has offered to help me sort things out for good. You are all that I have ever wanted. But you deserve so much more. I'm going to get to a place where I can give you something other than my misery. Be patient.
I love you.
G

PART IV

83

Gavin had always asked a lot of her, and she had always sought to fulfill his needs. Being needed by him had been the defining aspect of her life. Then he took that away when he fell into depression and cocaine. And now he was in Los Angeles, just about as far away from her as he could be. He'd asked her in his note to be patient but what he really seemed to want was to live his life without her.

That was clear enough when he didn't answer her calls but instead replied with short, impersonal texts. It was also clear as the days went by, turning into weeks, and she could see through tabloid coverage that he was a healthier version of himself, with a little weight gain and a light tan. There were photos of him smiling —*smiling!*—while on set with Jackson. One of his texts let her know that he was clean and enjoying Venice Beach. He said nothing about returning home. It all added up to her certainty that their separation was bound to become permanent.

When she saw the headlines announcing that Conor had broken off his engagement with Colette, she wanted to reach out to him. She wanted to see his handsome face and engage in the mildly flirtatious banter they had perfected over the years. She wanted to hear what books he had been reading, what hikes he had done, what exotic food he had tried, and if he had seen any good art shows. She missed his friendship. Hurting him the way she had when he'd come to commiserate about Sammy-the-Stripper was something she deeply regretted.

She'd been no better than Gavin in the way she pushed Conor away so she could be alone in her own misery.

As she thought about him, she realized she didn't just miss his friendship. She missed *him*. Because as much as she had denied or rationalized her feelings for him over the years, she realized that they were more than friends. There was love there—and not just on his side. It was only now that she had real time with her own thoughts, removed from Gavin's angst, that she could be honest about her feelings.

Looking out at the expansive sea view from the deck, she focused on the way the sun was breaking through the clouds and shining down on the deep blue water, and thought about all the times Conor let her cry on his shoulder over Gavin. Now that he was dealing with a breakup, she thought she should at least offer him the same.

After a moment, she took her phone and typed, "Let me know if you want to talk." It seemed supportive without being provocative.

The nearly immediate response surprised her: "As a matter of fact, I do. I'm at your gate. Let me in."

They had a surveillance system that showed the gated driveway, so she rushed to the computer set up in a nook of the kitchen to be sure he wasn't joking.

He wasn't. He was sitting in his Aston Martin, waiting. She was unable to stop the smile from spreading across her face as she pressed the keys to allow him access.

It didn't take him long to drive through and she met him at the door with unbridled excitement. As he walked up the wide-set stair-case to meet her, she took in the sight of him. He wore form-fitting jeans along with his ever-present pocket chain and a thin black cashmere sweater. His hair was recently trimmed, his face clean-shaven, and his blue eyes unadorned by sunglasses. She could see then, as he met her eyes, that despite having hurting him the last time they saw each other, he still adored her.

Closing the short distance between them, she threw her arms around his neck and squeezed him tightly. He hesitated in returning her embrace for a moment, but then held her just as tightly, lowering his face into her neck.

Their hug lasted minutes rather than seconds, and when she finally pulled away, she could feel her heart thumping in her chest.

Being close to him, taking in his familiar scent, and feeling his strong embrace, she knew where this visit would go. Where she wanted it to go.

"Come inside," she said, pulling him by the hand.

He hadn't seen this house before and took his time looking around at the high ceilings, the cream L-shaped sofa positioned to take advantage of the sea views, and the sophisticated but cozy lit gas fireplace. "A bit of a step up from the other place, yeah?" he asked with a smile.

"How are you?"

He tilted his head noncommittally. "Fine. It's for the best. I see Gavin's off in Los Angeles, playing movie star."

She shrugged and shook her head, not wanting to talk about it. Instead, she said, "I'm so happy to see you, Connie." She playfully plucked at his ribs. "You look good."

"You too, honey."

She nodded. "Come, let me show you the rest of the house."

84

The tour ended in the master bedroom, where Sophie insisted Conor try the oversized chair in the sitting area of the room to enjoy the endless sea view.

As he looked out at the water, he wondered at her welcome of him. God, it felt good to be received like that. Her smile was more brilliant than the view spread out before him. And the feel of her body against his with that lingering hug, well, it had almost done him in.

"This is spectacular," he told her. "Well done."

She didn't reply but instead moved in front of him, blocking his view. The deep v-neck of her sweater allowed a tempting peek at the curves of her breasts, and he assumed she hadn't expected any company as she usually wore some sort of pretty layer under such things. But he wasn't complaining. Slouched in the chair, he smiled up at her in anticipation of some winsome remark she might make. Instead, she fell to her knees, her body pressed between his legs. That sweater was now pulled even lower at the neckline, and as he looked down at her he could tell she was wearing his favorite style of bra beneath it. The pale pink demi-cup bra gave her smooth breasts the look of an offering. And she was tantalizingly close to being at eye-level—or rather, *mouth*-level with his groin. This was not at all what he had anticipated when he came here. He had simply wanted to see her, to be sure she was all right.

"Em," he started, and moved to straighten up in the chair because his body was already responding to her. Jesus, what she could do to him.

But she grabbed his hips to stop him and he watched her. She reached out and touched his cheek, then let her fingers trail slowly down the side of his neck and along his chest, over his abdomen and across the waistband of his jeans. When her hand reached his crotch, he was hard.

"Sophie," he said, and put his hand over hers. But she didn't try to slip her hand away. Instead, she rubbed the length of him and he bit his lip, fighting to find the strength to stop her. And yet, he did nothing when she pulled open the buttons of his fly.

"This is what I want. Is it okay?" she asked.

He met her eyes and there was only desire for him. It was what he had wanted to see and feel from her for so long, and now there didn't seem to be any hesitation on her part. He didn't want to think about her motivations or what would happen beyond this moment. He didn't want to think about the fact that she was likely using him in some way or what the consequences would be. It was wrong, but he couldn't stop himself now that she was the one seducing him.

"You're fucking right it's okay," he said and leaned toward her, kissing her full and hard on the mouth.

85

As only the second lover she had ever had, Conor did not disappoint. He was confident and clearly knew how to touch a woman. After all their years of restraint, this could have been a feverish and quick initial experience, but he was deliberate in slowing it down, making sure he read her cues as he caressed every part of her body. She surrendered herself to the moment, thinking only of him: the way he smelled with the trace of cologne she suspected he wore so women would lean close to him; the strength and definition of his muscles; the mixture of heated desire and satisfaction on his face when she touched him with her hands and tongue. Their closely aligned orgasms had them dissolving into subdued laughter at the sweet pleasure of it.

Wrapping her arms around him and pressing her naked body to his, she kissed his temple. "Don't think I'm done with you," she whispered into his ear. "We are going to make this last."

"Christ, I hope so," he replied with a sigh.

She trailed her fingers over his chest and downward to the sculpted oblique muscles above his hips, and he flinched.

He was fighting off a smile when she looked at him.

"How did I not know you were ticklish?" she asked with wide eyes.

Taking her hand, he kissed her fingertips and smiled, relaxed and content. She pulled away and quickly straddled him, pushing his arms up above his head.

"What's this?" he asked, unable to hide his delight at her unexpected move.

"I want to see how much of me you can handle."

He raised his eyebrows. "A lifetime's worth, honey."

That response made her chest burn with a mixture of emotions she didn't want to confront. Instead, she leaned over him and began to kiss, bite, and lick the sensitive skin on the inside of his bicep, moving slowly upward. Beside a few twitches, he held his own. She should have known he could control himself if he wanted. The rest of his body responded to her positioning, however, and she soon took advantage of that. There was no fumbling with each other or second-guessing on rhythms and pressure, just pure chemistry.

It was beginning to get dark out when they finally settled into each other's arms again. He held her as he had in New York, facing her and with her head pulled against his neck and shoulder. Having enjoyed more than one orgasm in their uninhibited love making, she was now perfectly content to hold him and be held in return.

"This is everything," he told her quietly.

She smiled into his shoulder and he stroked her back lazily in return, and they were quiet. The crushing guilt and regret she knew she should feel wouldn't come. This was a connection years in the making that had finally culminated in one of the most exciting, intense, and satisfying experiences she had ever had. She had wanted to know this part of him, even though it was incredibly selfish. Selfish because this didn't change the fact that Gavin was who she wanted. He would always be the one she wanted, even if she was capable of loving someone else. Her guilt, therefore, was in having given Conor hope for them being something more.

"Will you stay the night?" she asked. She knew she shouldn't draw this out longer, but couldn't stop herself.

There was a long silence before he responded with, "I can't."

"No?" The idea of him getting up and walking out left her feeling empty.

He pulled away from her so that he could look into her eyes. "Sophie, I would love to stay. I would *love* it. But if I don't let you go now . . . I won't ever be able to let you go."

So he had known where her heart was all along. It was just another way in which it was clear that he was attuned to who she was and what she needed, and that realization was so bittersweet that she physically ached.

"And I do have to let you go, don't I?" he asked, stroking her cheek.

Tears filled her eyes and she managed the slightest nod. "It hurts," she whispered.

"It does."

"I'm sorry, Conor."

"Don't be. I'm not."

She searched his eyes and found he meant what he said. She kissed him anxiously, wanting him all over again, for the last time.

86

C onor stayed away for two and half days before returning unannounced with a bottle of wine and takeaway Italian food. His only expectation was friendship, though they shared the kind of emotional intimacy reserved for lovers.

Over the next couple of weeks, he made a habit of arriving at midday, and they would take long walks to explore the surrounding Dalkey area. They played tourist when they came upon the James Joyce Tower, a utilitarian stone structure built to withstand an invasion by Napoleon, and now a museum devoted to the life and works of its namesake. Joyce, they learned, had made the tower the setting for the first chapter of Ulysses. They walked along Colimore Road, delighting in finding both Cliff Castle, a mock castle built in the 1850s, and Elsinore, the house rented by U2 in 1991 where they completed *Achtung Baby*. In the park above the eight Victorian homes that made up Sorrento Terrace, they took in spectacular views of the whole of Dublin, along with the full sweep of Killiney Bay across to Bray Head and the Wicklow Mountains. They'd return to her house after these walks chilled from the fall weather, make a simple dinner, and eat in front of the fireplace.

Gavin hadn't contacted her in sixteen days by this time. Sophie and Conor's bubble could have stretched on uninterrupted had she not realized how late she was. A home test confirming her suspicion was followed by conclusive results at the doctor's office.

That afternoon, Sophie lay on the sofa, staring out at the sea while Conor sat on the floor close by, reading a Dave Grohl interview in *Rolling Stone*.

"Hey," she said.

"Hmm?" He turned the page, continuing to read.

"Do you ever wonder why certain things happen at certain times?"

"God works in mysterious ways and all that," he said with distraction.

"Conor?"

"Just a sec." He held up a finger while he read.

"Conor, I'm pregnant."

That got his attention. He dropped the magazine and turned to her. "You're—but, I thought you were on the pill," he stammered.

"You're in the clear," she said with a wry smile as she sat up. "I'm seven weeks."

"Oh, Soph," he said. "Congratulations?"

"It's such an amazing thing to think that there's a life growing in there," she said, touching her flat belly. "I want to be excited. I want to celebrate and make plans. But Conor, I'm pretty sure my husband left me and just hasn't gotten around to telling me."

"He's got his head up his arse. But once he knows about this everything will change."

"That could be true. But would it be for the right reason?"

"Isn't a baby the right reason?"

"I want him to want our marriage."

"He does. Of course he does. I can't say I've known him well these past months, but I know that much about him."

"What if you're wrong?"

"There's only one way you'll know, honey. You need to tell him face to face."

She nodded but her stomach was queasy with the thought of trying to force her husband to be present again in their marriage. This wasn't how it was supposed to be.

87

SOPHIE

Yellow haze obscured Sophie's view as the plane readied for landing in Los Angeles. She turned away from the window and closed her eyes. Her hometown had become a foreign place to her in the last few years. It was ironic that she felt more comfortable in Ireland than in America, while her Irish husband now seemed so at home in America.

After trading a series of messages with Gavin, she had decided to force the matter and simply fly into town. By the time the car service dropped her off at their Venice Beach home, the sun was setting with an unnatural purple-orange intensity aided by the thick layer of smog over the ocean.

The house was empty, but had obviously been lived in. Gavin hadn't kept up with his laundry or dishes. And there were beer and water bottles strewn around carelessly. From what she could tell, only he had used the bed in the master suite. But she couldn't be certain.

Their interior designer had agreed with Sophie's suggestion that they break up all the white space in the house with colorful rugs and pieces of furniture. It had all come together to form a bright, cheerful home. But that now stood in contrast to her conflicted emotions.

Grabbing a plastic bag from the kitchen, she began gathering the bottles. As she worked, she thought how she was once again chasing after Gavin. This dynamic had begun in their school days, when she'd lingered at Rogue's band practice hoping to get a chance to talk to him. It repeated itself when she tracked him down during their first tour, only to be blown off. The following year she had that momentous radio phone call with him and later showed up at his hotel room. And here she was again, running after him. After almost ten years of marriage, she was still the one doing the hard work in their relationship. She had excused so much in deference to the wound he wallowed in. It was time to break the pattern, no matter what that meant for their future family.

Sitting down on the burnt-orange-colored living room sofa, she sent him a simple text: "I'm here at the Venice house. Please come home."

As soon as Sophie heard the garage door open, she went downstairs to meet Gavin in the foyer. It felt like hours before he opened the door to let himself in, and in that time her anxiety built until her body trembled. She didn't know how it would feel to see him after all these weeks, not just because he had left their home to "get well" and hadn't returned once he was better, but because of what had happened with Conor. Would he somehow know she had been with another man? Then, of course, there was the baby. As well as she knew him, she couldn't envision his reaction to this unexpected pregnancy.

When he stepped into the foyer, all the conflicting thoughts melted away. She was relieved to see that he looked remarkably healthy, especially compared to the last time she saw him. His eyes were clear and he had his usual few days' worth of beard growth. The navy blue, long-sleeve O'Neil tee shirt and jeans he wore with flip-flops made him look like a handsome beach bum. Most of all, however, it was the broad smile on his face that made her feel at ease.

"Darlin," he said, "I'm so glad you came." He pulled her into his arms, kissed her cheek and lips, and held her for a long moment. "Let me look at you." Taking a step back, he looked her up and down.

"Do I look different?" she asked.

"You're gorgeous as always."

"You look really good, baby. Like your old self."

He nodded. "I feel good."

"So, I—"

"Are you hungry? You must be. We're walking over to Abbot Kinney to meet Jacks for dinner. He should be getting us the table now, so we'd better run."

She hadn't expected to have company on the night of their reunion. "Wait, Gavin. I don't want to go out to dinner with Jackson. I want—I need to talk to you."

"Well, it would be rude to cancel now. He drove all the way out here from the Hills. Let's talk as we walk, yeah?"

She was too dumbfounded to argue as he led her out of the house. To get to the restaurant, they would walk along the canal and down busy South Venice Boulevard until they reached boutique and restaurant-laden Abbot Kinney Boulevard. It was less than a mile away, which meant she had limited time to say anything of importance to him. She wondered if this was his aim, if he had wanted a buffer between them. If he really was ready to end their marriage, yet not eager to say the necessary words, this would be a good strategy.

While still on the canal, with the relative quiet, she took his hand and forced him to stop walking. The water was aglow in patches where nearby houses had their shades open and lights on. Colorful canoes and kayaks were tied up near some of the homes, but otherwise they were alone.

"Gavin, wait a second, okay?"

He turned to her expectantly.

"I, um, I came here, I came all the way here to see you—"

"And here I am," he said with a smile.

"Were you planning on coming home?"

"Yes, of course. I've just been in a good place here. You know that. I haven't done any coke in more than three weeks. I didn't want to ruin the streak."

She winced. "And coming home would do that?"

"Let's talk later, darlin'. I don't want to leave Jacks waiting. He's been great, by the way. Really helped me stay on the straight and narrow, if you can believe that."

"Can't you call him and say we're not up for dinner?"

He pulled on her hand. "We're almost there. Let's just have a nice meal."

"Gavin, I'm pregnant."

He stopped and turned to her, incredulous. "Say that again?"

She repeated the news, adding, "It's a total surprise, I know. I must have missed my pill, got off schedule, and, well, we're going to have a baby."

He looked away and took a deep breath. "A baby," he murmured on the exhale.

"I know the timing is terrible. And look, I get that you were moving in a completely different direction. I'm not trying to force anything here with this. I just thought you should know."

"You thought I should know?" he asked with confusion, turning back to her.

"It's obvious you're done with us, that you've been done. I finally get it." She tried to keep her voice steady and her eyes dry. "But this is still something good we made," she said, touching her belly, "and we can be parents even if we're not together."

Shaking his head, he said, "I don't get it. I don't get what you're saying. I'm not done with us, for fuck's sake. I've been out here working so hard to get clean so that there can be an us."

"How can you say that? How can you expect me to believe that when you've pulled so far away from me—even after you got clean?"

An older woman with two long gray braids was walking a terrier down the path, and Gavin kept quiet until she had passed.

"Sophie, I only stayed away because I didn't know how to face you again," he told her urgently. "I'm so fucking ashamed of what I became, of how I let you down. I've got your words burned into my heart about how I made you weak and selfish just so I could have you by my miserable fucking side. The fact that I did that kills me. And I've been trying to get my nerve up to earn your forgiveness, to be the man you deserve. I didn't want to go back until I was sure I could make things right."

Now tears filled her eyes and she didn't try to blink them back. "Why didn't you tell me that?" she asked in a whisper.

He smiled weakly. "I didn't think you'd believe me. I've broken your trust in so many ways. I've hurt you. I've hurt you so much. And I'm so sorry for that." He reached out and cupped her cheek, rubbing her tears dry with his thumb.

Though she deserved his apologies, it didn't seem fair to her that he was taking all the blame for wrongdoing. "Gavin, I'm not innocent. I—"

Before she could continue, he dropped to his knees and wrapped his arms around her waist. He pressed his face to her belly.

"I don't deserve it, but I'm asking to start again. Let me try to be what you need for once. I want to be a parent with you, a father to this child."

"Baby, get up. Please. You have to know that I have regrets too." All the guilt she should have had about Conor before came rushing to her now. She had her own apologies and requests for forgiveness to make, only he didn't know it.

He shook his head against her. "I just want to move forward, darlin'. Don't let's go backwards."

She tried to pull him up but he was holding fast to her, so she went to her knees with him and wrapped her arms around his neck, sinking heavily into him so that he faltered for a moment. Her relief at hearing him say this was so great that she discarded all the other issues they had. It was selective denial in favor of hope for a new, better future.

88

GAVIN

Gavin was vaguely aware that both he and Sophie were forging ahead in their relationship without looking back. It started at dinner where they banded together in opposition to Jackson's date for the night: Colette. The pairing was awkward, both because it felt wrong for her to be with someone other than Conor, and because she was in an especially combative mood, drinking too much and goading Gavin when she sensed his disapproval of her presence. He and Sophie instinctively used the drama of Colette's unexpected presence to pivot away from all the things they should have been talking about. He had told her he didn't want to go backwards, and that was true, but at the same time, he knew they had unfinished business. It was just easier to ignore it and focus on the fact that they finally had something positive to celebrate.

They spent the next several days cocooned together, not working through the past but envisioning their future. They talked baby nonstop, imagining life with a newborn girl or boy and wondering how soon they should try for a sibling. They debated the advantages of finding out the sex as opposed to letting it be a surprise. They spent hours brainstorming names, coming up with separate categories for traditional, contemporary, American, and Irish options. They agreed that the model Martin had set of having Celia and the kids travel with the band on tour until the kids were preschool age was a good one. Gavin went out to the stores on Abbot Kinney to pick up lunch and came back with the tiniest pair of Converse either had ever seen. They were fully immersed in planning for parenthood, gratefully latching onto it as a way to leave behind all the damage they had done to their relationship.

But all that came to an abrupt halt the morning Conor called. Gavin heard a phone buzzing and didn't know if it was his or Sophie's. He reached into the folds of a soft blanket on the sofa just as she did.

"I think it's mine," she said. As she pulled it free, he saw Conor's photo and name on the screen. "Oh." She turned away as she answered.

He sat stone-still as he listened to her side of the conversation.

"Hi," she said. "Yes, I'm okay. Everything's fine. Yes. He's really happy. We are happy. Making lots of plans for the little one. Uh-huh. Okay, I'll tell him. Bye."

Gavin waited a full thirty-seconds for her to explain, but she simply started folding the blanket they had cuddled under together that morning while having coffee and pastries.

"Conor, yeah?" he finally said.

"Yes."

"You told him about the baby?"

He saw her stiffen. She wouldn't look at him.

"Yeah."

"Why would you tell another man before me?" He tried to keep his voice level, though the urgency was difficult to mask.

"I, um, just because he was there. He's been there for me, Gavin."

"He has always been very concerned for your well-being."

Sophie sat with him now. "And he's the one who told me I should come out here to see you." She put her arm around his neck. "And now look," she said with a smile.

He accepted a kiss from her reluctantly, unable to keep images from flashing through his mind. The particular way Conor would gaze at Sophie in those rare moments when his usually controlled manner was undone, like in that famous tabloid photo. The time when the two of them shared a night out in New York, and then when he found them embracing in the lobby of the Four Seasons in Paris. The way he inserted himself into their relationship by standing up for

Sophie, like over that *SI* cover, and more recently when he declared he should have been the one to marry her.

Unable to help himself, he pulled away and examined his wife. His beautiful, long-suffering, pregnant wife who had just days ago admitted she was not innocent.

"Conor's in love with you."

Everything about her reaction—the slowly fading smile, the concern bordering on fear filling her eyes—told him he was right.

"Fucking hell." He leaned forward, elbows on knees and head in his hands. "And what are you guilty of?" he mumbled.

"What?"

He straightened up and looked at her. "You said you weren't innocent." Why was he asking this question? Why wasn't he letting it go, like she had let Sammy-the-Stripper go? Because he wasn't someone who let things go. Jesus, he'd been stuck on the unanswered questions of his mother's abandonment of him for over twenty years.

"I thought you wanted to move forward? Not look back?"

The physical reaction he had to her clear desire not to answer the question distracted him for a moment. It felt like a hundred pounds of sand slowly moving through his body and weighing him down. To combat it, he stood and pulled her with him, to better look at her in the pale winter light coming through the windows.

"Tell me," he said, feeling the blood drain from his face in anticipation.

She hesitated, obviously debating whether he would drop this or not. But she knew him better than anyone, so she finally said in a small voice, "It was just one time and it will never happen again."

"You slept with someone else?" he asked.

Tears filled her eyes as she ever so slightly inclined her head.

"Who?"

"Can't we leave it at that? You had your one time and I had mine?"

He shook his head. "Tell me who, Sophie."

"It's not even important, Gavin, because it doesn't change what I want. I want to be with you. I choose to be with you."

Her argument went unheard, as all he wanted to know was who she'd let touch her in a way only he ever had. And who she had touched in return.

"You tell me who!" he shouted. She flinched and crossed her arms over her chest, but this defensive reaction didn't move him either. He grabbed her firmly—too firmly—by her shoulders. "I need to know," he said.

"No, you don't. We can just move on and—"

"There's no moving on from this unless you tell me who it was."

She stared into his eyes for a long moment. "Conor," she whispered.

It was what he'd expected her to say. Of course that was who it would be. The answer was there all along and he had refused to entertain it. Yet it still hit him as a shocking blow. He released his grip on her and stepped back several feet, looking away.

"Don't," she said, going to him. "Please, baby, don't pull away from me now."

"Get away," he told her, brushing off her attempt to touch him.

"Talk to me. Please."

The betrayal took his breath away for a moment. "And it had to be Conor, why? It had to be my best fucking friend since I was seven years old?"

"I'm sorry," she said.

"Why? Wasn't it any good, Sophie?"

"Don't do that," she begged.

The regret and sadness was plain on her face but it did nothing to change things. All he wanted was to strike back against this treachery, to unload some of his pain onto her.

He moved to her aggressively, backing her up against the wall. "Tell me you didn't like it," he said, his face close to hers. "Tell me you didn't like the way he fucked you."

She turned her face away from him and shut her eyes as the tears fell down her cheeks.

"When was this, anyway?"

"What?"

"When was this wonderful union between you two? And exactly how pregnant are you, again?"

She looked at him with cold eyes now. "I would never lie to you about something like this. It's your baby."

"Convince me," he replied. "Tell me when you fucked him."

"Two weeks ago," she replied numbly.

He nodded and then turned away from her.

"And what of all the other times you two went off together?" he asked.

"It was just this one time," she said.

"And I'm supposed to trust you on that?" he asked with a weak laugh.

"The same way I trust you."

He looked at her sharply. "Nice try, darlin', but it is not the same. It's not equal. Whether you believe it or not, I did *not* fuck that stripper. So, don't you dare try to say we've done the same thing."

"I'm so sorry, Gavin. I felt alone, like you had given up on us, and I—"

"And so you decided fucking my best friend would make it all right?"

"Stop saying 'fuck.' It wasn't like that. It—"

"Good job destroying anything we ever had."

"You can't blame me for everything."

"No, not everything." He felt so weak, so ready to give into the temptations of cocaine he thought he had left behind. It would not only take the edge off his pain, but also give him an excuse to go off the fucking rails while he was at it.

"I've only ever wanted to be with you. My whole life," she said, and let out a sob, "my whole life has been about you."

Now he was the one who couldn't look at her. He wanted out of this place. Away from her. "I gotta go. I can't stay here with you," he said, shaking his head. "I need to figure this out. Alone. And don't go following me."

All he needed was to find his passport. He'd go straight to the airport to avoid the temptation of ingesting a snow bomb like he had on the way to LA. By wrapping the cocaine in a small wad of toilet paper and swallowing it, the high could be prolonged and there was no worry about carrying drugs on a plane. The resulting euphoria and pretense of control was exactly what he wanted at this moment, but he'd have to resist that easy way out.

He looked at his wife, saw his own devastation mirrored on her face, and he hesitated.

"Just—take care of the baby," he said, then turned and walked away.

89

GAVIN

Coffee seemed like a good idea after having spent the entire flight from Los Angeles to Dublin quietly drunk, so Gavin invited Shay to join him at Kaph on Drury Street. He placed an order on the first floor before heading up the stairs where he settled in at a large, desk-like table. This area didn't have the bright and open feel of the main level, but the aroma of fresh coffee and pastries wafted up and the strains of the Pixies could be heard, making the private area comfortable.

"Thanks for coming, mate," Gavin said when Shay joined him a few minutes later.

"Sure, Gav." Shay sat opposite him.

"I took the liberty of ordering you their specialty."

Shay looked down at the ceramic mug. It was filled with a milky green liquid, a decorative leaf drawn into the light foam.

"What the fuck is this?"

Gavin laughed. "They call it a Matcha green tea latte. Try it."

Shay eyed the drink suspiciously before taking a tentative sip. "Ah, it's not half bad." He took another drink. "And how are you getting on, then?"

"Listen, I want to apologize for all the shite I've put you through," Gavin started. He knew he had no right to start anywhere but with this. He owed his friend his honesty and contrition.

"What shite would that be?" Shay asked. "Not returning my calls or texts? Not showing up to half a dozen band meetings? Not following through on any fucking thing for months now?"

"You're right. You're exactly right. I've fucked up." Gavin didn't shy away from making eye contact. "I let you down. I'm sorry, Seamus."

Shay was silent.

Gavin knew his cocaine use had hit Shay hard. Seeing his friend, the person he revered and relied on, turn into a sketchy drug abuser had to be a huge blow. And even though Gavin was saying the right things now, it had to be hard for Shay to trust him. Shay had spent too many years being manipulated by his heroin-addicted brother to take Gavin's word at face value now.

"You can rest assured that all that is done with," Gavin continued.

"All that?"

Gavin could see that Shay wanted him to finally admit to him he had been doing drugs, to give him that honesty. He was ready. Doing so was a relief, actually.

"Coke. I'm done with it. I'm clean. Have been for about a month."

"Glad to hear that," Shay said, with only a hint of sarcasm.

As had been the case for as long as he could remember from almost everyone he knew, forgiveness was forming fast. He never understood what it was about him that solicited this benevolence, but he was especially grateful for it now.

"I know I've been a crap friend, Seamus. I'm aware of my short-comings. And I'm committed to actually dealing with them now instead of running away."

"Well, I know it's been tough what you've had to go through. I do understand to an extent."

Gavin smiled. "Thanks, man. Thing is, I can sort out the situation with my mother. I can deal with what a bastard I was to you and the others. But something else has happened. And I—"

He had to stop when he started to tear up. This display of emotion wasn't unusual. He had never hidden the fact that he felt things deeply. It had made him an incredible songwriter and singer. But Shay must have seen something more worrisome than strong emotions because he leaned forward in response. "What is it, Gav?"

Gavin opened his mouth, then stopped. "Fuck's sake, I don't want to even say it aloud." He took a deep breath and Shay waited. "Sophie told me she slept with Conor. Once. She says."

Shay looked away for a moment, then sat back.

"You don't actually look surprised by it."

"I don't know what to think, Gav."

"I think you do, though."

Shay was an observer, a watcher. He was the opposite of Gavin in that he preferred to sit back and enjoy the gregariousness of others rather than try to be the spectacle. Gavin suspected he had seen a connection between Conor and Sophie that Gavin had been willfully blind to.

But apparently Shay wouldn't twist that knife by admitting his insight. Instead, he asked, "Where do things stand now?"

"Thing of it is," Gavin said, shaking his head, "we had gotten together in LA and things were feeling good for the first time in so long. Then she tells me that a couple weeks ago they . . . ." He cleared his throat. "But she says it was a one-time thing, that she wants to be with me."

"You don't believe her?"

He twisted his wedding ring to the left, then to the right and back to the middle again, a tic of restlessness. "I think I do. Problem is, it feels like there's more to it. I feel like an idiot now that I think about it, but it's pretty obvious Conor's been in love with her for a long time. And I can't be sure that she didn't fall in love with him."

Shay took a sip of tea as he thought. "So the worst part is thinking that even though she wants to be with you, she may have had feelings for Conor?"

"It makes me sick to my stomach to think of it, Seamus. I mean, I know I fucked up with that stripper and she let it go, but for Christ's sake it was nothing like this. Nothing." Gavin picked up his mug and held it for a moment, staring down at the remnants before taking a drink. He had ordered himself a regular black coffee. "This is," he continued, "a betrayal of the heart from my two best friends."

"It is indeed," Shay agreed. "But you've got to decide what's most important, and what you're willing to do to keep whatever that is alive."

"What would you do?"

"I can't say, Gavin. I don't know how it really feels," Shay said.

Gavin got lost in thought. They sat together quietly.

Suddenly, Gavin pounded his fist on the table. His voice shook from a raw combination of hurt and anger. "Don't you know I could fucking kill him?"

Shay ran his hands over his closely buzzed strawberry-blond hair. "Is this going to make you disappear off into coke again, then?"

Gavin's eyes widened at the directness of the question. Then he laughed. "The thought has crossed my mind."

"Well, don't fucking do it," Shay told him urgently.

"I'm trying really hard, Seamus. It's no lie to say it's not easy, though."

Shay shook his head in frustration. The silence stretched out between them.

"For fuck's sake," Gavin finally said with a tortured moan, "we were writing love songs to the same woman. No wonder we were such a great songwriting team."

"You still are."

Gavin closed his eyes and let his head drop. After a moment, he looked up and stared at the small piece of colorful artwork on the wall. It wasn't clear whether a child had done it or if it had been made to look inexpert.

"She's pregnant," he said.

Shay met his eyes in surprise.

"Says it's mine," he said. "I can't imagine she'd ever lie about that. But it muddies things even more."

"Gavin, this makes a difference. If she's pregnant and she wants to be with you, then don't hesitate."

"That's what my mind tells me. But, fuck, Seamus, all of my heart aches with the thought that she loves him. There was love involved in this thing. How do I move forward?"

"Find a way. Find it."

Gavin nodded. That was his challenge. He had to somehow find a way to accept what had happened. He had asked so much of her over the years, couldn't he bury this episode and move on? Surely other couples had managed this or worse. He had to be a better man. He had to swallow his pride.

And for a moment, he believed he could. But then the vision of her giving herself to Conor came to him. It wasn't just fucking. She had been sure to tell him that. His wife had been in love with another man. With the worst possible other man. It hadn't just been sex, and that made it far harder to forgive and get past, no matter the ways in which he had pushed her away and likely driven her into Conor's arms.

So much for the vaunted "fearless" thing he had claimed they possessed in that famous line from "You're My One." Because the truth was that he was scared. Scared that he didn't have the strength to move forward and make things right.

90

Conor could have punched in the access code at the gate at Gavin's house, but he decided instead to buzz the intercom. It had been three days since the tabloids reported Gavin's return to Dublin. Conor hadn't been able to take the anticipation of the confrontation he expected any longer, and decided to force the issue himself.

After several fruitless tries at the intercom, he pulled his car to alongside the stone wall and got out. He leaned against the car door and dialed Gavin's cell.

The corresponding ring had a surround-sound to it, as he heard it in his own phone and in the air behind him. Turning, he saw that Gavin was returning from a run, clad in tracksuit bottoms, long-sleeve tee shirt, and trainers. The idea of Gavin purposefully exercising was almost as shocking as the haggard look on his face.

"What the fuck do you want?" Gavin asked. He said it without malice, though, as he brushed past him to punch in the access code to the gate. "Sophie's not here. She's in LA."

Conor knew that. She had called to warn him about Gavin finding out about them. He'd been dumbfounded, but hadn't pressed her to explain why she had confessed.

"I want to talk to you, Gav," he said.

Gavin didn't reply and instead walked up the drive. Conor

followed him, a step behind. They were halfway to the house when Gavin turned around to face him.

"Just have your say. Go ahead and be done with it," he said.

"Here's the thing," Conor started. "I took advantage of a bad situation. She was weak and lonely. It was just once and I'll always regret it."

Gavin examined him for a moment. "No, you won't."

"What?"

"You won't regret it. Not really. You love her. For years, yeah?"

Conor started to shake his head to protest, then gave up. He put his hands on his hips and looked away. The light rain that had been falling was growing heavier.

"Gavin, I'm sorry. I know that doesn't mean much to you, but I'm truly sorry."

Gavin took a deep breath and looked up at the sky as the rain came down. He washed his hands over his face, clearing away the sweat from his run.

Conor waited, the only noise the patter of raindrops. Then he was startled as Gavin let out a groan that turned into an anguished roar.

"Every one of those songs we wrote together about her—you were able to add your own special fucking touch, weren't you?"

"I, em, I don't know."

"Yeah, right," Gavin said with disgust, shaking his head slowly. "Christ, I let you two have at it, didn't I?"

"What?" Conor asked, thrown by Gavin's change in direction.

"I've been jealous and protective of her since we were kids. Except with you. I let you two go off god knows how many times. I saw the way you cared for her and I let it go on."

"I'm not sure—"

"I just about pushed her into your arms. I always told her I didn't deserve her. I couldn't be—I could never live up to the version of me she had in mind. I mean, what was she ever even doing with a fuckup like me?"

"You've got it wrong. The girl worships you. She made a mistake and that's it."

"Tell me something. She love you?" Gavin asked, again shifting from the topic Conor thought they had a handle on.

"No," Conor said without hesitation.

"No?"

"No. We got to be mates, really good friends. But I was the one who wanted more. Not her, Declan." He might lose his best friend over this. His band, too. But he would at least go out trying to help Sophie salvage what it was that she had always wanted—Gavin.

The rain had drenched them both and now Conor saw that Gavin was trembling from the wet and the cold. He had also retreated into his own thoughts. Conor was unnerved by Gavin's lack of any real malice. He was almost apathetic about it all, which was worse than if he had taken it out on him physically. Several minutes passed and Conor realized Gavin wasn't going to express anything else on the subject.

"You should go inside, dry off," Conor said.

Gavin looked at him with confusion for a moment, then seemed to realize that he was soaked and it was getting colder by the minute. With a half-hearted wave, he turned and walked the rest of the way to the house, disappearing inside.

91

GAVIN

"Gavin, I'm sorry to do this over the phone."

The anguish in the caller's words registered before he could sort out who it was. Even with her voice masked by emotion, there was something familiar in it. Why she was emotional, he couldn't say.

All he knew was that it was the middle of the night and the ringing of his mobile had startled him awake so that he reflexively answered the call.

"Are you there?"

Clearing his throat, he replied, "Yes. Sorry, who is this?"

"It's Maggie. Sophie's mother."

"Oh, yes, of course." Again, he'd responded as a reflex. It took the silence of her hesitation to raise the alarm in him. What was Sophie's mother doing calling at this hour?

"Listen, Sophie doesn't know I'm calling," she continued. "In fact, she forbade me to do so. But you're going to find out about this soon enough in the media, so I thought you should hear it from family first."

That sent a ripple of dread through his core and he sat up quickly.

"What's happened? Is she all right? Tell me she's all right."

"She ... will be. But, Gavin, I'm so sorry." She took a breath and let it out haltingly. "She lost the baby."

"Lost the ..." The words came out choked before he gave up. The baby. *Their* baby. All that promise of a new life, then it was overwhelmed by the hurt and anger over Conor, only to be left with this. This sudden emptiness.

"Wait," he said, "Sophie *forbade* you to tell me? Why?"

"Honestly, she's in a dark place right now. She blames herself."

"Surely, she can't do that."

"She shouldn't. There was nothing she did to bring this on, of course. It was just one of those awful things that happens."

"Well, I need to talk to her. She needs to know not to blame herself. She—"

"Give it some time. I don't think she's up to speaking."

"That's ridiculous, Maggie. I need to speak with her."

"I think you do, too. I'm just warning you that she may not be open to it yet."

"Okay, sure, yeah," he said dismissively. It seemed impossible that Sophie wouldn't speak to him at a time like this. "Thank you for letting me know. I, em, I'm going to try ringing her now."

Maggie apologized once more before letting him go. Sophie's cell went immediately to voicemail. Calling repeatedly didn't change the result and he fell back in bed in frustration.

Why wouldn't she want to speak to him now, at this most heartbreaking moment? His mind raced as he tried to sort out why she was blaming herself for this.

Take care of the baby.

Oh fuck. Those were the last words he'd spoken to her before leaving, before also telling her she'd destroyed anything they'd ever had.

That's why she couldn't bear to speak to him.

And *that's* why he should force the issue and go to her.

But, even though he knew that was the right thing to do, he didn't fling off the bedcovers and book a flight. Instead, he lay still because he knew that if he saw her in this state of brokenness, he'd be right back in their marriage. They'd pretend again like they did in those few days in Los Angeles that they could just brush past all the damage they'd done to each other. And that would just be repeating the ugly cycle they'd been stuck in for the last year.

Jesus, was that even important, though? Wasn't it more important to be there for her? For them to be together to grieve this loss?

Without thinking any more about it, he tried her number again and was relieved to hear it ring.

"I'm so sorry, Gavin," Sophie said as she answered, her voice croaky with tears and fatigue.

"Darlin'," he said, "all that matters is you're all right. Are you?"

"Will you come? Will you give us another chance?"

"Sophie, don't let's make it about us. I just want to know if you're physically all right."

There was a long silence and he worried she'd disconnected the call for a moment.

"I'm sorry. That's all I can say," came her whispered reply.

"Your Ma says you blame yourself. Please don't do that. Please, I'm begging you not to do that."

"It's all you asked of me, that I take care of—"

He squeezed his eyes shut as she cut herself off, his heart aching at her guilt. At the guilt he'd brought on.

"No," he said firmly. "Don't do that. You are *not* to blame for this. I have absolutely no doubt about that."

"I need you, Gavin. I need you to give us another chance."

Though he nodded, his eyes watery, he was glad she couldn't see him. Because he wouldn't go to her. He couldn't. Not like this. Not when he knew that doing so right now would only tear open the wound that was their marriage.

"I, em," he started, "I can't. Not yet."

Again, another long silence, followed by the sound of her trying to hold back tears.

"I'm sorry, darlin', but you understand that we're not in a place to just—"

"Okay, sure. Um, I have to go now." She said the words in between gulping deep breaths, racking sobs barely staved off.

"Wait—"

The call was disconnected. He tried her again and it was clear she'd shut off her mobile once more. He spent the next several hours calling her over and over, never getting through and never really knowing what he would say.

It wasn't fair to let her go through this on her own. But at the same time, he knew that her insistence that him being there would be a return to their marriage wasn't right either. Was he just supposed to forget about Conor? What was he supposed to do with all of those unresolved feelings?

When the sun rose, he was still in bed, still dialing Sophie with no response. He only stopped when his mobile died. Rather than plug it in to recharge, he took it as a sign that he should give up. For now. Just until he could sort out his heart.

———

IT WASN'T until later in the day when he charged his phone and received a slew of voicemails and texts that he realized the extent of Sophie's miscarriage. Yes, he knew she'd lost the baby, but he hadn't realized it was so serious. News reports detailed the story of her having felt unwell for a day, collapsing in the street, and being rushed to the hospital. The pregnancy was ectopic, causing internal bleeding and requiring surgery.

He took a beating in the tabloids once news got out that she'd been in the hospital and he hadn't been at her side.

Why hadn't she told him she'd had surgery? Maybe she suspected that would have been the thing to bring him running? And maybe she held off because she also knew that reconciling this way wasn't healthy?

The only thing he knew for sure was that she still wasn't answering his calls.

He took the easy way out after that, letting her dictate their continued separation, all the while knowing he should have been a stronger man than he was.

Instead, he kept quiet, kept out of sight, and stewed in his own grief, ignoring all phone calls, texts, and emails.

One day, Julia showed up at his house, leaning on the intercom at the gate for an obnoxiously long time while he willed her to go away. Though he knew Sophie had harbored suspicions, he hadn't crossed any lines with Julia. He hadn't thought of her as anything other than a friend since before he and Sophie were engaged. But her continued presence after all that had happened with the breakup of his marriage seemed wrong. He wanted to move on from the chaos he'd wrought with his bad choices—the cocaine, the running away from his problems, hurting the ones he loved.

Moving on meant cutting ties with Julia, too. If he was honest with himself, he could see that she had ached for them to slip into their old intimacy for years now. His current situation provided just the opening she'd want to exploit. That was the last complication he needed. He texted her to say their friendship wasn't a good idea anymore.

She replied with "selfish poncy southside bastard" as a confirmation that they were done. And he was relieved.

For weeks after that, he merely existed, numb and disconnected. It was the only way he could get through the days without falling back on the cocaine habit that he'd used before to keep from feeling.

At last, he started to emerge from this state. It came slowly at first, and then with urgency, as if he had sunk down to the deepest part of the pool and held his breath longer than he should, only to rise to the surface, desperately seeking the light, seeking oxygen.

It was the instinct to survive. To try to make something meaningful out of his life.

Seeing through the tabloids that Sophie was photographed taking long, solitary walks on the beach near her parents' Malibu home was bittersweet. She, too, was surviving, moving on. But it was without him.

He tried to write, to find the kind of catharsis in the act of exposing his tortured heart just as he had for years, but words failed him.

Instead of writing, he focused on the things he felt capable of doing, like running and weight lifting to sweat out the demons. One he got into a consistent routine with that physical exertion, he reached out to a respected voice coach to help him build up his long-neglected vocals. This eventually gave him both the confidence and inspiration to start writing again.

It wasn't everything, but it was a start.

92

GAVIN

The treadmill was at a six percent incline and the speed was at eight, pushing Gavin to the point where his legs burned. Even breaths were starting to slip away but he kept going, willing himself to get lost in Arctic Monkeys' brilliant album AM. Singer Alex Turner was a friend and hadn't taken the least offense to Gavin's dig at his voice on the Sean Reynolds chat show. Their friendship was based on playful slagging like that, though it was usually done privately.

As he swiped at the sweat dripping down his forehead and temples, a flash of the previous night's dream came to him. It was fleeting, though, and he struggled to grasp what it had been. But with each increasingly heavy footfall the image repeated in his mind. He finally pulled the emergency stop cord on the machine, took several gulps of water, and headed to his writing room.

He woke the MacBook Pro and opened a search engine. But his fingers hesitated over the keyboard. Suddenly, he felt ridiculous. This dream had sent him chasing after . . . what?

Something about the rose in his mother's hair. But what did it have to do with anything? He couldn't remember her ever having worn flowers in her hair, though she had loved to garden and bring fresh flowers inside.

He meditated on the particular connection between roses and his mother for several minutes. That soon led to another excavated memory, that of his normally non-demonstrative father calling his mother "my little rose" when he thought the children were out of earshot.

"Rose," Gavin said aloud.

He then typed "Rose McManus" into the search engine.

The results were nothing he connected with. He then typed in "Rose" with his mother's maiden name and found even fewer hits. He thought for a moment more and then typed in "my little rose" and "flowers."

When the screen refreshed, there was only one result that jumped out at him. It was a phone directory listing for "My Little Rose Flower Shop" in County Wexford. The exact town was called Rosslare Strand, a place he had never been. He remembered that she had often spoken about the garden she could have had if only they lived in sunnier southern Ireland. A town like Rosslare, in the southeastern part of the country, was exactly where she could grow those treasured flowers.

He knew this was where he would find his mother.

The mother who had abandoned her family after the car crash that had killed his baby sister. The mother who by running away had motivated him to funnel his anger and sadness and wounded sensitivity into becoming one of the most famous rock singers of his time.

93

GAVIN

The small village of Rosslare was a seaside resort, attracting local tourism to its swimming beaches and golf courses. Gavin drove through the town proper, noting the abundance of cheery yellow-painted buildings edging around the coast, before finding his way to the outskirts. It was late afternoon when he pulled the Mercedes to a stop in front of the address listed for the My Little Rose Flower Shop. It had only taken two hours to drive south to this spot. His mother had been an easy drive away all this time.

The flower shop was a private home with every bit of land surrounding it used for gardening, either in planters, in neat rows in the earth, or in a greenhouse. Though there was a small plaque noting that the home also housed the business of My Little Rose Flower Shop, it was clear that whatever was sold was secondary to the pleasure of gardening.

He took a deep breath and told himself to get out of the car and approach the front door. But he stayed quite still, comfortably ensconced in the rich leather of the driver's seat, his thoughts drifting.

He called to mind the way he had comforted himself as a child with the stories of other musicians who had lost, or been neglected by, their mothers. If those artists had had a stable upbringing, with their mothers present for them, it was doubtful that they would have been compelled to create the way they had. Or if they had ended up as musicians, perhaps their work would have lacked the fire that their childhood losses stoked.

It had been an escape, a fantasy, to identify with the list of talented artists that had turned their pain into something bigger to share with the world. And if he were honest, he'd admit that he had gone even further than identifying with them. At some point, he had twisted his own pain into an obsession for the exact purpose of having something to write about.

He and Conor had often talked of artists they admired, and how when they got to a certain age they became fat with success and complacent in their music. They became uninspired and repetitive, or just plain dull. At the corners of Gavin's mind, he had worried that if he had a resolution with his mother, he might lose the thing that had driven him to creative heights. Sophie had often urged him to seek out his mother and he had been stubborn in his refusal, claiming it was his mother's responsibility to make the first move. And while he did sincerely believe this, there was a part of him that feared he'd have nothing left to say if the wound he had so carefully cultivated over the years closed over. Three-quarters of an hour passed before Gavin found the courage to get out of the car and make his way up the cobblestone path toward the house.

The Kelly-green front door was partially open. Looking inside, he could see the afternoon sunlight pouring through the window, casting a warm golden glow over the small front room.

There was no one there to greet him, though he could hear noises at the outside rear of the house. Figuring there was nothing left to lose now, he stepped inside and took in in his surroundings .

The room was sparsely furnished with a loveseat, a single recliner, and a side table in between. There was a battered steamer trunk positioned as a coffee table of sorts in front of the sitting area. A long, narrow table sat under the large bay window. Two tall bookcases hugged the walls, and fine white lace curtains hung pulled back on either side of the window.

A large, scarred butcher-block counter, served as a bridge between the front room and a partially visible kitchen.

But his eyes lingered on the pale pink roses in small mismatched vases on every surface, even crammed into nooks on the bookcases. A quick estimate put the number of vases scattered throughout the room at near three dozen.

The mini arrangements, along with the well-worn but comfortable surroundings, complete with framed Georgia O'Keeffe prints, gave him a sense of familiarity.

The front door was pulled all the way open then, as a plump woman, her brown curls strewn with gray, entered the room. As she looked up and made eye contact with Gavin, she dropped the large bunch of long stem white tulips in her hands, each stem making a dull thud on the wood floor as they scattered.

Gavin felt a sudden rush of bravado.

"Hello . . . Ma," he said, nodding slightly.

Joy filled her face as her eyes welled with tears. She brought shaking fingers to her lips. Within a moment, she recovered herself.

"Gavin," she said brightly. "My Gavin."

She went to him without hesitation and wrapped her arms around him, locking his arms into an awkward embrace.

Gavin had waited so long, had hoped for this reception for so many years. But now that it was here, he saw clearly that nothing was ever resolved this simply. He looked down at the woman gripping him with familiarity, her face buried into his chest. He felt nothing.

Gently, he pulled away and looked at this stranger. Her face fell, but she shook it off with a small smile.

"Would you like a cuppa?" she asked.

"Sure, I'll take tea," he replied, glad for the delay this nicety would afford.

"I'll be back in a sec. Sit down, please."

After she left the room, he spotted several old-fashioned photo albums on the side table. Curious to see what she held dear, he flipped open a book at random.

A newspaper clipping pasted to black paper caught him off guard. It was a review of the last show Rogue had in Dublin, complete with a photo of him on stage, sweat dripping down his neck as he cradled the microphone in his hands. His eyes were closed in the shot, his face typically intense with the emotion of the song.

He quickly leafed through the other pages, finding one article after another that centered on him in some way. Then he came to the full-page shot of him and Sophie on their wedding day. It was the candid photo that most of the tabloids had featured. They had stolen away from the reception for what they thought was a private moment. They stood close together under the shade of a tree, he in his bespoke dark suit and she in her elegant wedding gown. Smiles lit up their faces as she grabbed his backside playfully.

"Oh, that's my favorite, too," Bernadette McManus said as she returned with a tray of tea and placed it on the steamer trunk. "Your Sophie seems like a wonderful girl. And so very beautiful, isn't she?"

Gavin nodded dumbly.

"Sit, sit," she said, full of nervous energy.

He gestured for her to take her seat first and then followed by sitting as well. They both reached for a cup of tea at the same moment, and Bernadette let out a giggle. It occurred to Gavin that she sounded childish and not at all how he remembered. Definitely not maternal. And then he caught the distinctive scent of whiskey, which triggered a sense memory he had long forgotten. Or buried. But now he clearly remembered that his mother had invariably taken not a splash of milk, but rather a shot of whiskey in her tea. It had been the accepted norm in their house, even when his father prepared her morning cup.

"Care to add a taste of whiskey to my cup as well?" Gavin asked with a conspiratorial wink.

She smiled eagerly. "Yes, of course. One more sec, then." She jumped up and took his cup with her.

He watched with distraction as she left the room, trying to decipher the memories rushing back to him. It wasn't exactly that his mother was a drunk, but there was suddenly too much familiarity about alcohol. How had that never come to the forefront of his consciousness before now? Had he really suppressed it in his desire to anoint her to some sort of sainthood rather than acknowledge such a major flaw? He had always excused her running away as her reaction to the traumatic loss of her daughter. He had romanticized her pain and convinced himself that with time she would return, healed and ready to be a mother to him again. But the awareness of her reliance on alcohol now lent a different angle to things. He sighed audibly and looked back at the scrapbook to distract himself.

He came upon a clipping of Rogue's sold-out Wembley show. It had taken place after their last tour and was recorded as a combination CD/DVD package to fulfill their obligations to the label to produce another album. Ninety thousand fans had joined them that evening for the performance of their career. They had brought the house down in a wide-ranging two-and-a-half-hour concert celebration. That level of success was what he had hungered after for so many years precisely so that his mother might understand who he'd come to be, and therefore want to seek him out. But that hadn't happened.

"I always knew you'd do something big, you know," she said as she returned. She handed him his spiked tea. "I knew you had it in you, just waiting to come out."

"That's grand and all, but can we go back a few steps here?" he said, unable to help himself.

"You're right, I know it." She nodded shortly and lowered her eyes deferentially as if accepting a scolding from a schoolmaster. "Where shall I start, then?"

"Tell me about the day you left and never came back."

94

GAVIN

After several false starts and draining half of her tea, Bernadette finally said, "What you have to know is that I wasn't right after the accident. I was healing on the outside but I was broken on the inside."

"Weren't we all?" Gavin replied, but not with anger.

"I know. I know what I did. But I didn't plan it. I left hospital that day because I had to see your sister. I had to see her for myself. And when I did, after I convinced the nurse to take me to that awful morgue for a viewing, I almost lost my mind."

Gavin looked at his mother, envisioning the trauma she had endured. The accident had flipped their car three times, leaving her with a broken collarbone and a concussion. It had also knocked his two-year-old sister out of her car seat restraints and killed her upon impact. Gavin had walked away without so much as a bruise. His father was home with his older brother, Ian, who had taken ill. Because it was raining hard that morning, Bernadette had decided to drive Gavin to school. She'd taken his little sister along for the ride, hoping to lessen her contact with the flu germs in the house.

"You don't have children yet," she continued. "But when you do, you'll know there is nothing that can drive you to madness like losing one of your babies."

He didn't correct her on the loss he had experienced, because though he knew his suffering was real, it still didn't compare to losing

385

a child of two years of age. Instead he said, "Okay, I get going away for a period. But you decided to lose all of your children."

"I wasn't rational. Lord knows I'm not claiming my thinking was on. It wasn't." She finished off her tea like a shot. "I had to be away from everything that reminded me of the pain—and the guilt. I would not have been able to live through your father's careful acceptance of what I had done."

"What you had done? What do you mean?"

"Well, I'm the reason Nora is dead, aren't I?"

"It was slick with rain that day," he said. "That lorry ran into us. I knew as much on the day and I was only seven."

"It got so twisted in my head, you see. I was convinced that I had somehow been to blame. And—"

"Because of your whiskey habit?"

She turned her face away as abruptly as if he had physically slapped her.

"Were you drunk that morning?" he asked when she didn't speak for a lengthy moment.

"No." She shook her head violently, with childlike gracelessness.

"I remember now." He twisted his wedding ring to the left, then to the right and back to the middle again. "I can't believe I blocked it out all these years. But now I remember your need for it throughout the day."

"It's medicinal." She looked at him with imploring eyes. "I have a nervous condition and a nip here and there is what helps me function. I'm not a drunk, Gavin. You have to believe me."

He not only didn't believe her, but her issues made him realize his own dependence problems had a hereditary basis. Still, it wasn't why he had come here.

"Just keep telling me what happened."

She nodded eagerly, clearly grateful to drop the topic of her drinking. "I, em, I think it's called 'survivor's guilt.' I couldn't fathom the part I had in losing your sister. And then it spiraled into a real breakdown as I was overcome with thinking that I'd do more harm than good to you boys if I came back. I know it makes no sense. I know that now. But back then, I feared somehow my other children would be next."

"This idea can't have lasted all these years. At some point you must have thought to return."

"Aye, I did. So many times. But I had abandoned you all. I didn't know what you'd do if I just showed up."

That logic struck Gavin as terribly cruel. "You should have fucking tried," he said.

"I did," she said quickly. "I did come back once."

95

GAVIN

Gavin was frozen still at the idea that his mother had come back at some point. And he had never known. He wondered if Brendan, his father, had turned her away before he and his brother had a chance to see her. His father had never said a negative word against her, but he had acted as if she was a chapter in their lives that had closed.

"When was this?" he asked.

"It was about four months later. I went to yours and Ian's school, thinking I'd walk you home and then have a talk with your Da. But seems Brendan had been called in to get you. I heard Ian teasing you about the school warning you'd have to repeat the year if you didn't pull yourself around. Then your Da, he did this lovely thing. Do you remember?"

Of course he remembered. It had been one of the few times his father had mentioned her after she had disappeared. The memory was clear for that reason, and also because of the rare instance of his father showing him some tenderness.

"He got down on one knee before us, to look us in the eye," Gavin said. "Then he said I had nothing to be ashamed of, because didn't I remember Mammy always said I'd do great things. And then he told Ian to give us a break, that it'd been rough on us all but we had to look at us three as being a team now."

"Exactly. I saw that and I knew you boys would be okay. It made me think God had it planned—"

"Fuck the god that would orchestrate the death of a child and the abandonment of two others," he said quickly, her invocation raising the incoherent rage he'd felt as an adolescent. "This kind of self-serving justification in God's name is why I lost faith long ago."

"It made me think God had it planned this way," she repeated, undeterred, "so your Da could be the kind of father he never would have been if I'd been around."

He wanted to shake her, to force her to see that her logic wasn't just flawed but hurtful. "What bullshit. Take responsibility for the fact that you fucking walked away. Twice."

"It was for the best," she said, ignoring him again. "I was in no position to be a mother, a wife. It's taken me so long to come to terms with myself. By the time I felt capable of returning, I knew it would have only made things worse for you all."

Her inability to acknowledge the damage of her actions was hard to bear. He took a deep breath and decided his only choice was to pursue a different direction. "What about later, then? We did grow up, you know?"

She met his stare with silence.

He stood up and paced the small room.

"Your absence, your abandoning me, has defined my life. Everything I am is a result of your decision to run away and not face your problems like a fucking adult."

"Ah, but look what you've made of yourself, Mr. Rock Star." She tried for a coquettish smile and he felt revulsion.

"Who are you, even?" he asked.

"I'm me. I did what I did and there's nothing I can do about it now." She retreated into herself then, staring at some middle distance. "I did what I did for Maria," she sang softly.

He shook his head in frustration and confusion. He vaguely recognized the song she had sung apropos of nothing as the cheesy 1970s hit "I Did What I Did For Maria" by Tony Christie, but for the life of him, he couldn't understand what she was getting at. Her explanations and moods were all over the map. Perhaps she really had gone mad with the accident and was left in this perpetual state of teetering on the edge ever since.

"Do you know that I was desperate to be a famous singer so you'd have an easy time of it when you decided to find me?" he asked, and then laughed softly at himself.

"I've always followed your news stories. I saw the way you played it off as if I were dead."

"And?"

"I decided to stay that way," she replied meekly.

He watched her for a long moment, slowly understanding that she enjoyed the solitary life she had established for herself. She hadn't wanted to be found.

He shook his head. "So once you had run away from your family, you found you quite liked the single life, aye? Is that it? Better off with no children, no husband?"

"No, not exactly. Gavin, I love you and your brother. I do. But I couldn't imagine that I'd ever be capable of giving the way you needed it. Something in me died when Nora died. I'm not who I used to be."

"You should have fucking tried," he said with disgust. Why did he have to repeat such a basic point to her? "You don't walk away. You don't do that to those you're supposed to love."

Bernadette nodded contritely but said nothing more. The look of sympathy on her face was so at odds with the rationalizations she had given him thus far that he found the attempt pointless. And then he realized she hadn't apologized for leaving.

He turned away from her and looked out the front window. The sky had gone pale as the sun began its descent. The disappointment of this encounter threatened to overwhelm him. But he soon found he shared something with his mother. He had done exactly what she had done. He had walked away from Sophie when things got tough.

"You know," he said softly, "it was a bleedin' miracle I was still able to learn what it feels like to be loved. I've been loved beyond all limits since I was sixteen." He turned to her. "I don't want to be like you. I don't want to reject those that love me."

Bernadette's eyes filled with tears. "I'm sorry, Gavin. I am so very sorry for the damage I've done."

There it finally was. The apology.

He waited for it to have the impact he'd thought it should. But it didn't heal him the way he had fantasized. It didn't make up for anything. Nor should it have, he realized. What had happened couldn't be undone.

He understood now that subconsciously, he had known this would be the case. He had nurtured his hurt and loss all these years with the buried understanding that the artistic benefit he reaped was more rewarding than any kind of resolution he might get by tracking down his mother. It wasn't his pride that kept him from seeking her out. It was the fear that he'd find it was all as simple as what Ian said: their mother couldn't be bothered.

And at this point, the life he had lived as a result of her leaving couldn't be altered. The truth was, he wouldn't want it to be. For all his faults, he was the passionate and brilliant singer-songwriter of one of the best bands in the world, and she had set that into motion by leaving.

He saw her then for what she was—an emotionally fragile, aging woman who had done the only thing she knew to ensure her own survival. But it was her selfishness that stuck with him. Wasn't the point of parenthood that you gave up being selfish in order to care for your children? He shook his head in frustration and was dizzy from the conflicting emotions she brought forth.

"I think I'll be going now," he said.

"Won't you stay the night? You can't drive back to Dublin now."

Prolonging this reunion like that was the last thing he wanted. Had she presented herself the way he had always hoped, as someone desperate to make amends and to care for him after all these years, he might have felt differently. But the will to dissect their history had left him. All he wanted now was out. He needed time and distance to process all of this.

His instinct was to let her down easy, though, to employ the charm he had become so well known for.

"I'll be fine to drive," he said, and she did not hide her disappointment. "Dublin's not far, after all. Perhaps we might be friends and have another visit sometime?" he asked gently.

She searched his eyes as if to see whether he was mocking her. When she saw he was serious, she smiled, sniffled, and nodded.

"Oh, Gavin, I'd love it. I'd simply love it," she told him.

96

GAVIN

The two-lane road felt exceptionally dark as Gavin drove toward home. Though his foot was pressed hard on the pedal and the Mercedes was going well over eighty miles an hour, he felt no motion. His gaze was fixed on the few feet ahead where the headlights shone on the road, and the rest of his body was just as paralyzed.

His thoughts kept leaving what had just happened and focusing instead on what he had done to Sophie. How he had abandoned her when she was vulnerable and in need. It felt like a sick replica of what his mother had done to him. He'd meant it when he told her he didn't want to be like her. Now that all the artifice was torn away from his imaginings of what had propelled his mother to run away, he had to face the facts as they were. He had to take responsibility for his life and his choices in a whole new way, without the safety net of his childhood hurt as an excuse.

Sophie was in California, suffering the traumatic effects of a miscarriage and the end of their marriage. While he knew she was staying with her parents in Malibu, they had never given her the care she craved. She had always said he was the only one who could do that. He wanted to go to her, to wrap her in his forgiveness and beg for hers in return. He wanted to push past this painful part of their lives.

The farther he drove, the more certain he was that he needed to take action and win back his wife. "It's okay. It's all going to be okay."

That was what she had told him once when he was reeling. She had suffered the weight of his burdens all these years, just as he had begged of her in "You're My One." He could do the same for her.

Besides, hadn't he told her long ago that he would always be the one to mend her heart?

Nodding to himself, he knew it was time to live up to his promises.

EPILOGUE

Dear Sophie,

Bereft.

It's an odd word. Old fashioned. No one uses it in speech, really. But in writing to you, it's the only word that I can conjure.

I am *missing* something. I am *deprived* of something.

That something, of course, is *you.*

I miss your scent, that mixture of your essence and the perfume you've worn for so many years now that it's become an essential part of your very chemistry. I miss the heat of your body near mine in bed, the way we'd linger together in the mornings, never wanting to leave the special warmth that only we could create. I miss watching for that exact moment when your hazel eyes would turn green, always making me catch my breath. I miss the delicate trail of your fingertips on the inside of my wrist in those times when you wanted to bring me to myself.

But it's more than your physical presence. It's the place you have had in my heart for as long as I can remember. You've left that spot and all that remains is an aching coldness that I can't shake off. I've turned numb without you.

You might call me on this and say I'm the one who left you. Not after finding out about Conor … but well before that. I left you when I couldn't cope with my life.

What self-pitying nonsense, right? It is. I see that now. But in the middle of it, when all the years of suppressed … *feelings*, for lack of a better word, about my mother came down on me like a weight I had no strength to lift, well, I let it drop. But instead of the barbell and weights bouncing down on the floor in front of me, I let it drop right on top of me. I let it push me down—*ground me down*, really—deep into a darkness I hadn't ever known. A kind of darkness that I didn't want to expose you to. Not you, my pure sweet girl who had only ever tried to walk with me in the light.

That's when I left you. That's when I stopped leaning on you and expecting you to suffer the weight of my troubles. You say that I forced you to my level, that I made you just as miserable as I was so that I wouldn't be alone with it. That's true. But it's never what I really *wanted*.

So … will I actually send this letter to you? Or should I give us both time and space for some kind of healing?

For now, I'll tuck it away and think about it.

But should you read this, the thing that I want you most to know is that I am sorry. I am sorry for letting you down. Not just once, but over and over until I did so at the most painful point in your life. I have no legitimate excuse. I have no hope of you forgiving me for not being there when you needed me most. Maybe … maybe that's why I'm inclined to keep this letter from reaching you. I can't possibly make amends for that last final act of withdrawal. That cowardice.

Maybe, though, if I give us time, we can each of us gain back some strength. I need this far more than you, darlin.' We both know that. And when I do get back to myself, when I am finally ready to fully live this life while accepting responsibility for all that I have done, there won't be a single thing that can stop me from coming for you. Because our love story isn't over. That is the truest thing I know.

I once told you that I love you with everything that I am—even when that isn't good enough. You told me that I am always enough. It isn't fair to you, but I'm banking on that still being true down the line. Because I will right myself. I will return to you. I just need time to figure out how to be worthy of you, my love.

XX Gavin

Sign up for my newsletter HERE and you'll receive an <u>EXCLUSIVE FREE BONUS</u> chapter titled *Conor's Folly*.

Gavin and Sophie's story continues in the next Rogue Series book. We know by now that their roller coaster love story won't be an insta-fix, but it will have an HEA!
You'll also get Conor's story when you read on in this next book. To find out more, download
<u>PLAYING AT LOVE</u>

EXCERPT FROM THE NEXT BOOK IN THE ROGUE SERIES

<u>PLAYING AT LOVE</u>

This moment was two months in the making. Sixty-three days, to be precise, in which Conor Quinn was mired in the wretched, sinking feeling that came with knowing he had hurt his friend as deeply as one could. And so now he greeted that friend, Gavin McManus, at the front door of his house, eager to ignore the fact that he was more than a half hour late.

Hope was plain on Conor's face as he watched Gavin, willing him to show some sign that all would be well. But it seemed they had exchanged personalities on this occasion. Gavin was self-contained, cool, and impassive, while Conor couldn't suppress his emotions, looking to the other man with uncharacteristic neediness.

With eyes averted and a barely perceptible nod, Gavin brushed past Conor to make his way straight through the house and out the back to the studio.

"Happy New Year, yeah?" Conor called after him.

They were headed into the third week of January and hadn't spent any of the holidays together as they had in years past. A recent falling-out meant their friendship had suffered, but so too had the band they started together over a dozen years ago. One couldn't exist without the other.

This reunion—such as it was—had been orchestrated by an unlikely source. Conor had just returned from a quick trip to New York City when he got a phone call from Shay, their drummer, to say Gavin was ready to get back with the band to work on new music. The news was a happy surprise, as his weekly calls to Gavin over the last couple months had been routinely ignored. Now Shay was playing the role of intermediary, which while helpful, was also completely foreign.

As the lead guitarist of the popular Irish rock band Rogue, Conor had used his striking good looks, natural talent, and confidence to create an iconic image that transcended the music industry. Respected by his peers, he was also a paparazzi favorite, garnering attention for his dating life rather the kind of scandals Gavin had generated. His charm and status meant others clamored for his attention, but his loner tendencies made him highly selective with friendships. He and Gavin had been the best of friends for over two decades until everything imploded.

Taking a deep, fortifying breath, Conor nodded to himself. Gavin was here now, which meant he was open to working with the band. If they could rekindle their writing partnership, there might be a way to also rebuild their friendship.

Conor headed out back to the detached studio in his garden. This space had been his salvation during the low times of the last two months. He had painstakingly pieced the studio together over the years so that the band had a place to experiment and record demos. Oriental rugs, the obligatory design accent in the rock world, were scattered over the rustic wood floors. The walls were adorned with a precise row of framed copies of each of Rogue's four studio albums, along with a copy of their live album recorded at Wembley. The row beneath these held gold record frames certifying the band's impressive sales. A set of well-worn sofas and a coffee table rounded out the setup.

Gavin was huddled with Shay and Martin, Rogue's bassist. The three were speaking softly but with warm smiles and the occasional slap on the arm or back. Conor wasn't used to being the one on the outside looking in. The vague jealousy that came with this wasn't exactly new however, because if he was honest, he had felt jealous of

Gavin before—jealous over Gavin's talent, jealous over Gavin's marriage.

Conor had always been drawn to those who possessed raw talent —both out of admiration and a tinge of envy. He was attracted to that intangible thing that elevated mere aptitude to something great, especially in music. By studying his favorite artists, he realized the key to their genius was an ability to channel the wounds of a damaged childhood into their art. Gavin, having lost his baby sister and mother when he was just seven, had that same wounded artist aura. And he had used it to impressive effect over the years.

With a stable home life, Conor had had the opposite experience. In fact, things had always come easily to him: academics, sports, girls, and especially music. He had shown exceptional ability with classical piano and violin, but he yearned for more. He wanted to lead from passion rather than proficiency but as a cautious, only child to older parents, he was inherently risk-averse. That all changed with the influence of Gavin's unguarded friendship. Alongside his fearless and outgoing friend, Conor found a way to explore his passions, eventually funneling them into Rogue. Thus, the defining—and ultimately trite—conflict of his childhood was that his parents felt he was wasting his intelligence and talent by turning to rock music.

Rogue offered Conor the outlet to develop his talent, but it wasn't until he fell for Sophie—Gavin's wife—that his abilities reached new heights. It would take years for him to understand that part of his initial attraction to her had been a subconscious attempt to manufacture his own wounds as a way to stoke the kind of musical inspiration he'd always been drawn to. The anguish came, of course, from the fact that Sophie would always be Gavin's, no matter how Conor might desire her. Or love her, as it turned out.

That unrequited emotion was a large part of what made Rogue's second album such a standout success. It had been written when, after several years apart, Gavin and Sophie were reunited, and the songwriting he and Gavin did together took on a new urgency. Conor's guitar playing on "You're My One" had so well conveyed ache and longing in the first half of the song, with a sense of soaring ecstasy driving it home, it was often called Rogue's "Little Wing." With Jimi Hendrix being one of Conor's guitar idols, he was hesitant to accept the comparison. But he did understand that he and Gavin had created something with that song that resonated with millions of people around the world. He also knew his part in the song wouldn't have happened without his own tortured feelings for Sophie.

As of two months ago, Gavin knew that as well.

"So, I've got something I want you to hear," Conor said as he pulled a Martin HD-28V acoustic guitar from its stand. The guitar felt like a natural extension of his hands. He had honed his skills so well over the years that he could manipulate the instrument like a toy.

The three men stopped talking and turned expectantly to him. The comfort he'd gained with picking up the guitar evaporated along with the riff he had in mind, and he stood frozen. His announcement had been born more out of a desire to insert himself into the group rather than true inspiration.

"Hang on," Shay said. "I've got to hit the jax." He removed his black flight jacket, tossed it on the sofa, and headed back to the main house to use the toilet.

"You gotta take a look at the pictures of Celia and the kids from our trip to Disney World," Martin said, pulling out his phone.

Conor nodded, sensing that Shay and Martin were colluding to alleviate the tension in the room. Their distraction techniques would only work so long. Eventually, he and Gavin would have to communicate. But he gladly looked at the photos of Martin's wife and their three boys. Conor was their godfather, after all, and seeing the kids' ear-to-ear smiles on the Tea Cups ride elicited his own grin.

Shay returned and threw himself down on one of the sofas. Martin soon joined him, leaving Gavin standing and Conor leaning against a stool, his guitar idle.

"Well? Let's have it, then," Gavin said.

Conor looked at Gavin, saw the challenge in his eyes. The hardness, too. Gavin was forcing himself to be here. There would be no "How have you been?" catch up session, no reassurance that they could begin anew. It was more of a straight in, no kissing situation, as the expression went.

With a small nod, Conor launched into a riff he concocted on the spot, a variation, it turned out, of something he should have known better than to get anywhere near.

"Enough," Gavin said sharply before too long and they all looked at him. "Fuck's sake, it's got the same vibe as 'You're My One.'"

Shit. He sure as hell hadn't meant to conjure that up. The last thing he wanted at this moment was to agitate the wound he had inflicted on Gavin when he slept with his wife.

Get your copy of <u>PLAYING AT LOVE</u> to keep reading

ABOUT THE AUTHOR

Lara Ward Cosio is the author of the Rogue Series - books that feature complex, flawed, and ultimately redeemable rockers, and the women they love. When not writing, Lara can be found chasing her daughters around the house or at the beach, always with music on in the background.

Sign up for my newsletter HERE and you'll receive an <u>EXCLUSIVE FREE BONUS</u> chapter titled *Conor's Folly*.

If you enjoyed this novel, please share your thoughts
in a review on Amazon or Goodreads

To learn more about the Rogue Series, visit:
LaraWardCosio.com

Join the **Rogue Rockers** Facebook Group for exclusive excerpts and
Rogue Series News

ALSO BY LARA WARD COSIO